TOTAL CWAC REPORT
COORDINATED WATERBIRD COUNTS
IN SOUTH AFRICA, 1992–97

P.B. Taylor, R.A. Navarro, M. Wren-Sargent,
J.A. Harrison and S.L. Kieswetter

AVIAN
DEMOGRAPHY
UNIT

Published by the Avian Demography Unit, University of Cape Town

Published by the Avian Demography Unit, University of Cape Town

Avian Demography Unit
University of Cape Town
Rondebosch, 7701
South Africa
Telephone (021) 650-2423; Fax (021) 650-3434
E-mail: adu@maths.uct.ac.za
Web page: www.uct.ac.za/depts/stats/adu

First published 1999

© Avian Demography Unit 1999

Cover photograph: Cattle Egret, photographed at Verlorenvlei, Elandsbaai, by R.A. Navarro

Title page line art: Yellowbilled Egret by S. MacLarty

Other line art: Lesser Moorhen by S. MacLarty; Common Sandpiper by P. Meakin; Cape Teal by D. Lewis.

Proof-reading: L.G. Underhill and D.M. Harebottle

Maps and graphics: R.A. Navarro

DTP: R.A. Navarro and F.A. Stoch

Printing: University Document Management Services, 11 St Michael's Road, Observatory, 7925, South Africa

ISBN: 0-620-24713-4

Recommended citation formats

Book: Taylor, P.B., Navarro, R.A., Wren-Sargent, M., Harrison, J.A. & Kieswetter, S.L. 1999. TOTAL CWAC Report:
Coordinated Waterbird Counts in South Africa, 1992–97. Avian Demography Unit, Cape Town.

Chapter: Allan, D.G. & Underhill, L.G. 1999. The significance of South Africa's wetlands for birds. In: TOTAL CWAC
Report: Coordinated Waterbird Counts in South Africa, 1992–97. Taylor, P.B., Navarro, R.A., Wren-Sargent, M., Harrison,
J.A. & Kieswetter, S.L. pp. 10–17. Avian Demography Unit, Cape Town.

Site: Taylor, P.B. & Navarro, R.A. 1999. Blesbokspruit, Nigel, Gauteng. In: TOTAL CWAC Report: Coordinated
Waterbird Counts in South Africa, 1992–97. Taylor, P.B., Navarro, R.A., Wren-Sargent, M., Harrison, J.A. & Kieswetter,
S.L. p. 44. Avian Demography Unit, Cape Town.

Species: Taylor, P.B. & Navarro, R.A. 1999. White Pelican *Pelecanus onocrotalus*. In: TOTAL CWAC Report:
Coordinated Waterbird Counts in South Africa, 1992–97. Taylor, P.B., Navarro, R.A., Wren-Sargent, M., Harrison, J.A.
& Kieswetter, S.L. p. 183. Avian Demography Unit, Cape Town.

Contents

Foreword

This report is published in the year in which the African–Eurasian Waterbird Agreement (AEWA) comes into force. The first Meeting of the Parties of AEWA takes place in Cape Town in November 1999. AEWA is an Agreement in terms of the Convention on the Conservation of Migratory Species of Wild Animals, and it aims to improve the conservation status of waterbird species which will benefit from a multilateral approach. Many of the waterbirds occurring at South African wetlands regularly move between countries – there are bird-ringing results demonstrating links with virtually all countries in Africa, Europe and western Asia. So the results contained in this report have an importance which transcends purely South African interests.

This report contains two conflicting messages. The Coordinated Waterbird Counts (CWAC) project has come a long way since it started in 1992. But the project is also a good distance away from its ultimate goal of monitoring trends in waterbird populations in South Africa.

On the positive side, there are currently 270 CWAC sites. These include all the South African Ramsar sites, except the 'Turtle beaches' of northern KwaZulu-Natal, and a large number of the wetlands within Important Bird Areas.

On the other hand, there are many wetlands at which waterbirds are not yet being monitored. We estimate that there are another 60 wetlands in South Africa which ought to be included in the project. Our short-term goal is to reach a total of 350 wetlands, at which point we believe that CWAC data will be able to generate useful population-trend data.

In the Avian Demography Unit (ADU), we are proud of this report. The entire pages of graphics are largely generated by computer programs. Behind the graphics lie the raw data, which are available to those who need more detailed information. Behind the data lie the observers, without whom there would be no report. At the ADU, we deeply appreciate and value their faithful and regular contributions.

The project's sponsors have enabled the ADU to maintain its coordination role. But their funding has been multiplied probably a hundredfold by the contributions of the observers' time, travel and commitment.

Professor Les Underhill
Director, Avian Demography Unit, University of Cape Town

Acknowledgements

The success of CWAC is due largely to the dedication and high level of expertise of CWAC compilers and counters, impressive qualities which deserve recognition. Counting wetland birds is frequently very time-consuming, and is often undertaken under adverse conditions. It can be less than pleasant to undertake an all-day count, by boat, of the birds at a large open water site in the heat and storms of summer or the cold and wind of winter. It is also often both difficult and frustrating to attempt counts of large, densely packed flocks of shorebirds and waterfowl (especially when trying to avoid scaring them into flight), and to identify and count birds on distant shorelines and choppy water, but CWAC counters appear to succeed remarkably well in these tasks.

The information presented in this report is the product of more than 10 000 person hours (approximately six person working-years) of observation time. The network of volunteers and participating organizations which supports CWAC is impressive and continually growing. We applaud all of them and trust that this report demonstrates the contribution they have made to the conservation of waterbirds and wetlands.

Participating governmental and non-governmental organizations

Addington Conservancy
William Quentin Karoo Wild Bird Society
Blythedale Conservancy
Cape Bird Club
Cape Nature Conservation
De Beers Consolidated Mines
Free State Department of Environmental Affairs
Hermanus Bird Club
Inkwazi Bird Club
KwaZulu-Natal Nature Conservation Service
McGregor Museum
Middelburg Bird Club
Mpumalanga Parks Board
Natal Bird Club
Natal Midlands Bird Club
Northern Cape Nature Conservation Service
Portnet, Richards Bay
Potchestroom University for CHE – School of Environmental Sciences
Pretoria Bird Club
Sappi – Stanger Mill
Somerset West Bird Club
South African National Parks
South Coast Trogons Bird Club
Southern African Crane Foundation
Tygerberg Bird Club
West Coast Bird Club
Western Districts Council (formerly Algoa Regional Services Council)
Wesvaal Bird Club
Wildlife and Environment Society of South Africa: Ladysmith Branch
Wildlife and Environment Society of South Africa: Springs–Nigel Branch
Witwatersrand Bird Club

Participating individuals

K Abraham, M Abraham, D Ackhurst, M Ackhurst, Dr RA Adam, D Ainsworth, PK Albertyn, DG Allan, M Allan, GM Allin, H Alting, M Andela, Dr PC Anderson, G Anderson, MD Anderson, P Anderson, K Andrews, G Aukamp, D Badenhorst, M Badenhorst, P Bailey, W Bailey, A Barkhuizen, H Barnard, W Barnard, EL Barnes, K Barnes, R Barnes, T Barnes, The late S Baron, J Basson, S Basson, L Bauwer, M Bauwer, R Bauwer, S Bennett, H Bentley, G Berda, B Bergman, C Bernard, W Bernard, A Berruti, P Besaans, S Beukes, M Bilstone, M Bilstrode, L Bingham, D Bishop, AC Blackmore, E Bloch, R Bloch, E Block, R Block, D Bloem, E Board, W Board, C Boix, E Bolding, E Bolliger, W Bolliger, R Boon, W Boon, LM Booth, S Booysen, M Borcheros, L Bornman, M Bosch, HL Bosman, T Botbijl, C Botha, L Botha, M Botha, J Boucher, T Boucher, C Bouwer, F Bouwer, H Bouwman, K Bowker, M Bowker, N Bowker, S Bowker, Dr D Bracey, K Bradshaw, M Bragg, M Brand, A Brash, D Bray, J Brenner, J Brett, R Brett, D Brews, M Brews, N Breytenbach, G Briede, P Brink, P Britz, B Bromfield, J Brooks, K Brown, E Brune, L Brune, G Bruyns, A Bryington, L Bryington, W Bryington, N Buchan, E Bucholz, T Bucholz, M Burger, S Burger, E Buric, R Buric, P Burke, L Burman, A Burne, C Burne, M Burningham, C Caldwell, P Caldwell, P Caldwell, M Cambell, A Campbell, Dr H Campbell, J Campbell, G Canning, R Capell, C Cardwell, P Cardwell, J Carey, S Cargill, J Carry, J Carter, L Cellier, J Ceronio, A Chalmers, L Chalmers, P Charlton, K Chegwidden, N Chegwidden, R Chegwidden, M J Chinner, H Chittenden, M Christian, J Claassen, R Claassen, G Clarence, K Clarence, R Clark, A Clarkson, R Clarkson, K Claxton, A Cleal, G Cleaver, J Clements, A Cloete, RAM Cloete, J Coats, C Coetzee, L Coetzee, K Coetzer, C Cohen, L Cohen, BD Colahan, G Coleman, T Coleman, A Collier, Dr P Collier, E Collier, I Collier, G Collins, JC Conradie, CA Cook, JF Cook, D Coombe-Davis, L Cooper, D Cope, N Copeland, P Copeland, R Cowgill, D Cowie, M Cox, P Cox, W Cox, V Craig, Y Craig, G Crawford, H Cripps, P Cripps, RC Crisford, M Cronje, P Cronje, R Crosbie, P Crouse, G Cuff, B Cullen, T Cullen, A Cunningham, C Dabner, D Dalton, J Daneel, The late Dr C Dare, D Davids, Dr JB Davies, J Davies, J Davies, R Davies, SB Davies, S Davis, S Davis, B Day, G de Beer, V de Bie, J de Boer, A de Bruyn, I de Bruyn, E de Goede, A de Jager, P de Jager, S de Jager, D de Klerk, W de Klerk, B de Kock, C de Kock, H de Kock, I de Kock, C de Meyer, D de Villiers, E de Villiers, H de Villiers, M de Villiers, P de Villiers, J de Wet, C de Wit, H de Witt, L Deacon, A Deenik, G Deiner, M Delport, JJ den Houting, EB Denman, B Dennis, W D'Hondt, N Dickens, NM Dickens, R Dicks, S Dickson, T Dijkzeul, J Disey, H Dittmer, B Dives, J Dives, R Dodds, K Dolpire, C Dorse, N Dos Santos, A du Bruyn, I du Bruyn, A du Plessis, C du Plessis, F du Plessis, J du Plessis, M du Plessis, NL du Plessis, S du Plessis, P du Preez, AF du Toit, E du Toit, JL du Toit, C Easton, S Edwards, G Egan, M Eigelaar, A Eksteen, C Eksteen, M Eksteen, A Elliott, C Elliott, B Ellis, R Ellis, J Ellison, J Ellison, F Ellmore, T Eloff, J Els, SJ Els, B Emberton, A Emburey, A Engelbrecht, G Engelbrecht, JA Engelbrecht, A Engels, L Enslin, DJ Erasmus, L Erasmus, R Erasmus, B Ernie, R Erntzen, A Erwee, H Espach, C Etty, J Etty, J Eva, S Evans, V Evans, P Falla, RJ Faria, P Farmer, I Felton, G Fenton, J Fenton, BM Ferguson, DE Ferguson, H Ferguson, S Ferguson, T Ferguson, A Ferreira, B Ferreira, H Ferreira, V Fick, D Field, N Field, FP Fihlo, B Findlay, J Findlay, J Fish, L Fish, J Fisher, P Fisher, K Foce, S Foggo, E Fokkens, F Fokkens, F Fokkens, L Fokkens, Y Folmer, T Forde, G Forrest, L Forrest, H Fotheringham, M Fouché, A Fourie, B Fourie, J Fourie, W Fourie, WB Fourie, C Fox, C Francis, M Fraser, The late E Friend, R Fromberg, R Frommurze, D Fuhri, G Fuhri, D Furlong, J Furlong, R Furlong, J Fyrlong, P Gallager, L Gardner, D Gaynor, H Gaynor, A Geiger, S Geils, H Geldenhuys, J Gerber, R Geves, W Geves, R Geyser, D Gibbs, A Gibson, D Gill, R Gill, C Gladwin, BS Glenday, DN Glenday, PA Glenday, D Goetz, B Gold, M Golding, Dr PS Goodman, RW Goodwin, D Goosen, LE Goosen, C Gordon, J Gordon, K Gordon, J Graham, I Grant, A Gray, K Gray, R Gray, J Greeff, A Green, R Grey, H Griggs, P Grimes, C Grobelar, E Grobbelaar, LM Grobler, P Grotsche, R Grotsche, J Gumede, M Gumede, R Gumede, I Guthrie, R Guy, H Haig, L Hains, R Hains, P Hall, J Hamman, C Hanekom, Dr N Hanekom, NW Hanekom, R Hanekom, R Hann, T Hardaker, JC Hardy, J Harding, DM Harebottle, D Harris, M Harris, JA Harrison, K Harrison, R Harrison, W Harrison, J Hartnick, B Harvey, P Harvey, A Hattingh, K Hattingh, R Hattingh, C Haw, T Hayes, B Hayter, DJ Hayter, G Hegter, K Hendricks, A Hendrikson, G Hendrikson, S Herbert, BD Herman, Dr M Herremans, D Herremans-Tonnoeyr, MS Hess, N Hess, C Heÿl, H Hibbett, H Hill, P Hill, K Hiscock, RE Hiseman, J Hobbs, D Hoddinott, N Hoets, H Hofmeyer, P Hofmeÿr, S Hogan, S Hogan, B Hogg, D Hogg, M Hoile, M Holcroft, G Holland, S Holland, R Holloway, G Holtshausen, M Hood, M Hopkins, R Horner, D Horning, I Horwood, S Hoseck, C Howell, C Huchzermeyer, P Huchzermeyer, E Hughes, P Hughes, S Hughes, E Hugo, J Hugo, L Hugo, S Hugo, V Hugo, J Huisamen, J Hundt, A Hunter, RC Hunter, J Ihlenfeldt, B Ingram, C Ingram, G Ingram, R Irons, A Irvine, J Irvine, J Irvine, G Jackson, N Jackson, T Jackson, W Jackson, A Jacobs, N Jacobs, R Jalving, B James, L James, R Jangle, JG Janse van Rensburg, A Janssen, S Jenkin, V Jenner, E Jewitt, S Jex, Dr D Johnson, G Johnson, J Johnson, R Johnson, S Johnson, V Johnson, W Johnstone, A Jones, C Jones, D Jones, E Jones, M Jones, P Jones, R Jones, S Jones, W Jones, E Jooste, GW Jooste, M Jooste, HL Jordaan, M Jordaan, R Jordan, J Josling, L Josling, F Joubert, J Joubert, JJ Joubert, B Kaighin, B Kakebeeke, Dr B Kaletja, G Karosky, D Kay, L Kay, J Kelly, L Kelty, L Kemery, O Kemp, E Kerr, I Kerr, M Kerr, S Keswa, E Khawula, S Kidson, GA Kieswetter, SL Kieswetter, A Kietzman, B Kihn, G Kihn, M Killeen, AB Kilpin, D Kilpin, B King, J King, S King, D Kingwell, D Kinross, A Kirk, S Kitlery, L Klopper, D Klöss, P Klöss, D Knobel, R Knoetze, D Knoetze, Y Knowles, S Kockett, J Koen, W Koen, IH Koker, H Kolberg, C Kolver, J Kolver, Y Koovadia, A Kotze, E Kotze, I Kotze, K Kotze, N Kraucamp, L Krause, R Kriel, K Krige, F Krome, E Kruger, H Kruger, J Kruger, R Kruger, M Kuipers, NA Kulubane, D Kyle, R Kyle, R Kyle (jnr), C Labuscagne, S Lake, Dr GT Lamont, S Langton, JG Lawrence, ML Lawrence, C Lawson, G Lawson, R Lawson, A le Roux, E le Roux, K le Roux, R le Roux, T le Seur, A Lecocq, S Ledgard, L Leigh, R Leigh, J Leinberger, P Leinberger, D Leitch, A Lendrum, C Lendrum, J Lendrum, K Lendrum, MJ Lesale, A Leslie, D Leslie, R Leslie, C Lewis, A Linström, S Livingstone, J Llewellyn, NG Lock, G Lock, PS Lockhart, N Loftus, K Logan, M Logan, M Lonce, DT Longrigg, A Lötter, J Lotter, L Lötter, M Lötter, RC Lotze, J Loubscher, M Louis, P Louis, J Louw, K Louw, W Louw, C Lovell, G Lowden, R Lubbe, E Lucchesi, B Ludorf, D Lundie, S Lundie, R Machin, J Mackay, M Mackay, A Mackenzie, C MacLarty, L Macnain, A Madden, D Madden, S Madden, T Madden, A Maddern, R Maddern, M Madonsela, J Magali, M Macgiver, PI Maine, L Mair, R Makathini, A Mak'Ochieng, M Mak'Ochieng, MS Makubo, C Malan, T Mallon, J Maltby, B Mann, W Mans, C Marais, F Marais, M Marais, N Marais, R Marais, R Marais, V Marais, Q Marcus, S Marcus, S Maré, BS Mariti, R Marriott, D Marshall, Dr AP Martin, A Martinuzzi, E Martiny, A Marx, J Marx, L Matthews, W Matthews, K Mauer, N Maxwell, N McCabe, M McCall, MP McCarthy, H McClaggen, A McClelland, R McCosh, D McCulloch, R McDonald, I McEwan, I McEwan, E McGill, G McGuinness,

DR McKenzie, G McKenzie, W McKenzie, M McKinsh, P McKinsh, Dr GR McLachlan, H McLaggan, I McLaggan, R McLaggan, A McLennan-Smith, C McLennan-Smith, S McLeod, TRA McLetchie, K McMahon, G McMillan, R McMillan, H Mead, L Mead, W Meanly, A Mearns, K Mearns, K Meiring, L Meiring, R Melville, N Menzies, D Meyer, I Meyer, MJ Meyer, R Meyer, N Meyers, C Middleton, L Middleton, M Middleton, O Middleton, A Mills, C Mills, L Mills, D Milstein, V Minnaar, M Mitchell, A Mocke, S Modise, S Moffat, Z Moffat, D Molelekoa, J Moll, F Moodie, N Moore, H Morris, L Morris, The late P Morris, D Morrison, J Mortimer, C Mossop, M Mostert, N Mostert, S Mostert, T Mostert, S Motaung, H Mthembu, A Mudge, N Mudge, KWA Muggleston, M Muggleston, H Mulder, A Muller, CM Mulqueeny, A Munn, J Munro, K Munro, C Murphy, A Murray, B Murray, NJ Myburgh, A Myeza, G Nanni, D Nash, R Naudé, E Naude, F Naude, R Navarro, B Neave, N Neave, A Nel, The late HJ Nel, N Nel, W Nel, K Newell, A Newell, P Ngubane, P Nicol, E Nielsen, V Nielsen, L Nielson, E Nielssen, A Niemand, A Nieuwoudt, FP Nieuwoudt, H Nieuwoudt, N Nieuwoudt, C Nisbet, A Nixon, TS Nkosi, J Norman, D Norris, P Nsidande, R Nuttall, H Nuttall, M Nxumalo, C Oberholzer, C Oberholzer, G Oberholzer, L O'Dell, B Odendaal, D Odendaal, Dr A Odendaal, K Odendaal, L Odendaal, M Odendaal, R Odendaal, VM Odendaal, WS Odendaal, J O'Donnell, J Oelofse, J Oliver, A Oosthuisen, L Oosthuisen, A Oosthuizen, B Oosthuizen, E Oosthuizen, G Oosthuizen, J Oosthuizen, M Oosthuizen, M Oosthuizen, E Oosthuysen, H Oram, D Oschadleus, P Outhwaite, N Palmer, P Palmer, A Parkhouse, F Pascoe, J Pascoe, D Pearson, J Pearson, G Peatling, J Peatling, W Peddie, C Pemberton, M Penning, E Penrith, L Perry, DD Persse, S Peter, M Peters, S Petersen, J Phelan, S Phelan, Daniel Philogene, Debbie Philogene, J Philogene, L Philogene, K Pickels, G Pienaar, R Pienaar, A Pierres, G Pieterse, S Pike, L Pillans, P Pluke, V Pluke, J Pocock, S Pocock, R Pohlman, T Pooley, D Porter, I Porter, E Potgieter, G Potgieter, K Potgieter, S Potgieter, S Potgieter, B Powell, K Pressly, G Preston, B Pretorius, C Pretorius, W Pretorius, G Priday, M Pringle, A Purves, M Quadling, W Raats, M Ralfe, B Randall, Dr RM Randall, J Randall, J Raubenheimer, T Rautenbach, C Redfern, W Redfern, E Reed, K Reed, K Rees, C Reid, E Reinecke, F Reinecke, A Rennie, L Rens, J Rens, E Reynolds, F Reynolds, M Reynolds, R Reynolds, JS Rheeder, K Richards, A Ricketts, C Rippon, D Ritson, A Roberts, J Roberts, C Robertson, G Robertson, P Robertson, T Robertson, K Robes, B Robinson, N Robinson, R Robinson, K Robos, Q Rochat, K Rodgers, J Roelofse, R Roets, M Roodt, A Rose, S Rose, R Rose, M Ross, R Ross, W Ross-Adams, G Ross-Adams, D Rossouw, J Rossouw, JJ Rousseau, P Rousseau, R Rousseau, D Rousseau, D Roussouw, L Rouwenhorst, R Rouwenhorst, M Roux, W Rudings, A Rudolf, J Rüger, IA Rushworth, IA Russell, LM Russel, L Ryan, B Sachse, E Sales, J Samuels, I Sanderson-Smith, C Sanford, C Satchel, R Satchel, A Saunders, K Saunders, P Saville, C Schlebach, AFJ Schlemmer, O Schmidt, R Schmidt, R Schoeman, M Schofield, A Scholtz, G Scholtz, GD Scholtz, MA Scholtz, S Scholtz, H Schouwink, G Schroeder, J Schroeder, A Schultz, E Schultz, M Schuwerack, K Schwane, O Sclander, HA Scott, D Scott, J Scott, J Scott, RM Scott, M Scott, S Scott, F Searle, G Searle, R Searle, L Selkirk, L Serra, P Severin, G Sharpe, G Shaw, KA Shaw, D Short, R Shuttleworth, S Sibaya, J Sibiya, M Simon, G Simpson, W Simpson, W Sinclair, C Skinner, D Slater, M Sleigh, M Slotar, A Smit, M Smit, B Smith, C Smith, E Smith, G Smith, I Smith, M Smith, N Smith, P Smith, RB Smith, Y Smith, N Smits, E Smuts, J Smythe, A Snaddon, A Snyman, C Snyman, T Snyman, R Spalding, I Spencer, T Spencer, M Spies, C Spottiswoode, WP Standford, L Standley, A Starkey, L Starkey, K Stead, S Steenkamp, A Stembull, S Stevenson, A Steyn, C Steyn, D Steyn, S Steyn, R Stokes, H Stoop, A Strauss, D String, W String, FSA Ströhfeldt, M Ströhfeldt, N Ströhfeldt, WP Ströhfeldt, H Stuart, R Stumpf, L Styles, T Styles, AC Sutherland, M Suttill, M Sutton, A Swanepoel, H Swanepoel, K Swanepoel, C Swingler, Sykes, D Sykes, P Sykes, R Symmonds, R Taking, F Taljaard, M Tarboton, W Tarboton, Dr B Taylor, J Taylor, P Taylor, R Taylor, J te Groen, Robyn Teifel, Robin E Teifel, P Terblanche, S Terblanche, PJ Thamaha, F Theunissen, C Thomas, J Thomas, M Thomas, D Thompson, R Thomson, K Thornberry, M Thornhill, S Thusi, G Tiera, DJ Tieras, J Tieras, E Tilanus, J Tindledale, W Titus, B Tong, C Tong, GB Tong, AJ Tree, M Tripp, P Trollip, A Tucker, P Tyler, Prof. LG Underhill, G van Aswegen, M van Breda, D van Choler, FP van den Berg, R van der Bijl, BK van der Lecq, EN van der Linde, M van der Linde, C van der Merwe, E van der Merwe, I van der Merwe, J van der Merwe, Dr J van der Merwe, Le Roux van der Merwe, M van der Merwe, M van der Merwe, N van der Merwe, R van der Merwe, S van der Merwe, W van der Merwe, J van der Schyff, N van der Vyver, AP van der Walt, B van der Walt, D van der Walt, E van der Walt, I van der Walt, P van der Walt, R van der Walt, S van der Walt, L van der Watt, S van der Watt, A van der Westhuizen, B van der Westhuizen, B van der Westhuizen, H van der Westhuizen, S van der Westhuizen, H van Dijk, JD van Dijk, G van Drimmelen, E van Eeden, I van Essen, L van Essen, L van Groeningen, L van Herck, W van Lelyveld, G van Niekerk Brink, H van Niekerk, J van Niekerk, K van Niekerk, M van Niekerk, P van Niekerk, S van Rensburg, I van Rooyen, PF van Rooyen, CR van Tonder, GS van Tonder, RC van Tonder, RL van Tonder, J van Veuren, J van Viegen, T van Viegen, T van Wyk, A van Wyk, G van Zijl, H van Zijl, J van Zyl, J Venter, M Venter, J Verloren van Themaat, R Verster, R Victor, A Viljoen, D Viljoen, D Visser, J Visser, W Vogt, J von Korff, G von Ullmenstein, I von Ullmenstein, S Vorster, A Vos, A Vosloo, P Waddell, SR Wakely-Smith, W Waldek, B Walker, JM Walker, SM Walker, T Walls, JT Walton, E Wandrag, GF Wandrag, S Wanlass, C Ward, M Ward, A Watermeyer, Dr G Watermeyer, JP Watson, JP Watson, L Watt, F Weakley, A Weaver, D Weaver, DC Weaver, D Webb, J Webber, J Webster, KM Webster, M Webster, YD Weiss, F Welch, NG Wessels, TB Wessels, C Wex, J Weyermans, J Wheeler, L Wheeler, M Wheeler, M Whillier, PA Whittington, L Wicks, T Wiehand, A Wienand, P Wilkes, A Willcocks, E Willcocks, Z Willemse, Ann Williams, Arrie Williams, L Williams, A Wilson, G Wilson, H Wilson, J Wilson, M Wilson, A Wimpie, D Winter, CW Winterbach, S Wishant, N Womack, B Wood, T Wood, Woods, I Woods, W Woubain, S Woudberg, P Wright, A Young, P Young, S Young, T Young, T Yule, B Zeiss, R Zeitsman, A Zellerhof, G Zellerhof, M Ziere, K Zillen, L Zillen, Tyberberg Bird Club, Hangklip Junior School, Cape Bird Club, Mtuba Bird Club, SA Crane Foundation, Harris family, members of the Pretoria Bird Club, WHNA, Members of the Wilger Veld and Youth Club, Junior members of the Witwatersrand Bird Club, Witwatersrand Bird Club, President Ridge Bird Club, Inkwazi Bird Club.

We are sure that there were other participants whose names were not listed on the returns.

Introduction and methods

INTRODUCTION

This report is the first comprehensive overview of the Coordinated Waterbird Counts (CWAC) since inception of the project in 1991. Thanks to the enthusiastic participation of hundreds of voluntary and professional ornithologists, CWAC has become an important event on South Africa's birding calendar and the biggest regular survey of waterbirds in the country's ornithological history.

OBJECTIVES

The original project documentation defines CWAC's primary objectives as:

❑ to monitor populations of waterbirds by carrying out regular summer and winter counts at as many of South Africa's major wetlands as possible, on an ongoing basis;
❑ to identify and document the threats to waterbird populations and wetlands;
❑ to coordinate the efforts of amateur volunteers and professional conservators in achieving (1) and (2);
❑ to collate and computerize the results of each count and maintain, manage and update a database on an ongoing basis;
❑ to develop computer-based approaches to the analysis of the data and the generation of easily interpretable indices and computer-generated reports, both for each count and for comparisons of counts between years;
❑ to communicate by means of a regular newsletter which informs and encourages participants and presents interim results;
❑ to liaise with and provide copies of data and reports to the South African Ramsar Working Group (convened by the South African Department of Environmental Affairs and Tourism), and to Wetlands International (Wageningen, Netherlands) as a contribution to their African Waterfowl Census programme, and to make data available to researchers working in South Africa;
❑ to use the data to generate reports and publications relevant to conservation planning and the management of South Africa's wetland systems.

Key questions which direct the collection of data are:

❑ Which species are to be found at a particular wetland and in what numbers?
❑ Are there significant and consistent differences between summer and winter counts of a species at a particular wetland?
❑ Do patterns of species abundance and seasonality vary in different parts of the country?
❑ What is the range of fluctuations in abundance at particular sites and in different regions of the country?
❑ Is there evidence for long-term trends in the abundance of particular waterbird species? If so, what are the features of the trend?
❑ How do the South African indices relate to those obtained for the same species in other parts of Africa and in Europe or Asia?

Further questions directing the application of the data to the solving of specific problems could be:

❑ Which wetland sites have special significance for the conservation of waterbirds?
❑ What are the implications of the findings for the setting of hunting seasons and quotas?
❑ How sensitive are waterbirds to various environmental factors such as water quality?
❑ What is the potential of the data in monitoring long-term environmental change resulting from changes in land use and/or climatic change?
❑ Does comparison of statistics from different wetlands suggest that a given phenomenon is the result of factors operating locally or factors operating on a regional, continental or even global level?
❑ Does a particular change in an index of abundance suggest a crisis in the environment which requires further investigation and action?
❑ How do CWAC results relate to the distributional and relative abundance information collected by the Southern African Bird Atlas Project?

CWAC is a monitoring project and therefore its findings will become more informative and valuable with each season's data that are added. Nevertheless, after six years of data collection, useful site- and species-specific information has emerged.

METHODS

Sites registered with CWAC have their waterbirds censused every six months, in midsummer and midwinter. The permissible periods are mid-January to mid-February, and July, respectively. While it is recognized that, ideally, all counts should be carried out on the same day, in practice it is necessary to provide a wider window of opportunity to accommodate the programmes of participating volunteers and organizations. Originally, summer counts were conducted in January; the slightly later period was instituted to avoid overlap with the disruptive summer-holidays. Monthly counts are carried out at a few sites and this is encouraged so that more details of patterns of seasonality can be obtained.

The method of counting is standardized for a particular site, that is, the area covered, and the manner in which counters are deployed is kept constant from count to count. Between sites such standardization is not feasible because of the great variation in size of sites and their logistical characteristics. This means that some sites are censused by observers on foot, while at others, boats and motor vehicles are employed. A sketch map indicating the areas covered, and the routes and methods used, is lodged with the project coordinator.

Counters are provided with information sheets which advise on how to count efficiently and avoid double-counting and misidentifications. In the case of sites affected by tidal fluctuations, it is recommended that counts be consistently carried out at low tide when mud flats are exposed and waders are feeding. Observers are also requested to monitor their sites by means of fixed-point photography at two-year intervals. This type of monitoring is considered valuable in providing information about long-term physical changes at wetlands, but has still to be firmly established as an integral part of the CWAC method.

Counts are submitted on standard forms which also ask for details of weather during the count, and threats currently having an impact on the wetland and its waterbirds. Data are keyed in directly from these forms. Computer-generated versions of the count data are returned to the observers for verification of the details.

Feedback on each seasonal count is provided by means of a newsletter which is distributed shortly before the next count, together with computer output for the previous count, and a blank report form.

SITES

Any wetland site which regularly holds at least a few hundred waterbirds is considered eligible for inclusion in the CWAC programme. New sites are registered with the project as new participants are recruited and they volunteer to monitor wetlands of their choice. Maps of sites are lodged with the project coordinator in the ADU.

Such ad hoc growth in coverage has been a practical and successful approach to expanding the programme in its early phases; however, as growth in participation has slowed and the scope of the project has become more comprehensive, it has become increasingly important to focus new growth on sites of relative importance in terms of numbers of birds. Efforts have been made to identify priority sites and to encourage the adoption of such sites by new recruits. This will need to be an ongoing effort as new information on unregistered sites becomes available.

For the purposes of CWAC, the concept 'wetland' includes pans, vleis, marshes, lakes, impoundments, sewage ponds, rivers, estuaries, lagoons and even stretches of coastline. Table 1 provides a list of all sites covered by this report. Statistics on the various wetland categories are presented in the *Overview of Results* chapter.

Table 1. *List of all sites covered in the TOTAL CWAC report, with page numbers.*

Name	Nearest Town	Grid Cell	Page	Name	Nearest Town	Grid Cell	Page
NORTHERN PROVINCE				**GAUTENG cont.**			
Pietersburg Bird Sanctuary	Pietersburg	2329CD	28	Rietvlei Dam	Pretoria	2528CD	53
Rust de Winter Dam	Pienaarsrivier	2528AB	28	Rolfe's Pan	Kempton Park	2628AA	54
				Rondebult Bird Sanctuary	Germiston	2628AC	55
MPUMALANGA				Rooiwal Sewage Works	Pretoria	2528CA	56
Blaauwater Pan	Lake Chrissie	2630AD	29	Rynfield Dam	Benoni	2628AB	57
Blinkpan (Lothair)	Lake Chrissie	2630AD	29	Springs Bird Sanctuary	Springs	2628AB	58
BP's Dam	Wakkerstroom	2730AA	30	Stan Madden Bird Sanctuary	Nigel	2628AD	59
Clarens' Pan	Wakkerstroom	2730AC	30	Steward's Pan	Benoni	2628AB	60
Cloete Pan	Lake Chrissie	2630AD	31	Vlakplaas Water			
Driefontein Pan	Lake Chrissie	2630AD	31	Treatment Works	Germiston	2628AC	61
Eilandsmeer South Pan	Lake Chrissie	2630AC	32				
Fickland Pan	Wakkerstroom	2730AA	32	**NORTH WEST**			
Goedehoop Pan	Lake Chrissie	2630AD	33	Barberspan	Delareyville	2625DA	62
Hamilton Pan	Lothair	2630AD	33	Hartbeespoort Dam	Hartbeespoort	2527DD	63
Heyshope Dam	Piet Retief	2730AB	34	Klipvoor Dam	Brits	2527BB	64
Lake Banagher West	Lake Chrissie	2630AD	34	Leeupan	Delareyville	2625DA	65
Lake Chrissie East Pan	Lake Chrissie	2630AC	35	Prozesky Bird Sanctuary	Potchefstroom	2627CC	66
Lake Chrissie Pan	Lake Chrissie	2630AC	35	Vaalkop Dam	Brits	2527DB	67
Lakenvlei Wetland	Belfast	2530CA	36				
Leeuwpan	Secunda	2628DB	37	**NORTHERN CAPE**			
Lusthof Pan	Lake Chrissie	2630AA	36	Benfontein Pan	Kimberley	2824DD	68
Lydenburg Fisheries	Lydenburg	2530AB	38	Bosduiwekop Dam	Petrusville	3024BB	68
Magdalenasmeer 2	Lake Chrissie	2630AD	38	Dampoort Dam	Warrenton	2824AB	69
Mkhombo Dam	Libangeni	2528BB	39	Daniëlskuil Dams	Daniëlskuil	2823BA	70
Mooigelegen Pan	Lake Chrissie	2630AD	40	Du Toit's Pan	Kimberley	2824DD	69
Tevrede se Pan	Lake Chrissie	2630AA	40	Espagsdrift Vlei	Jan Kempdorp	2724DC	70
Tweelingpan – East	Lake Chrissie	2630AC	42	Faugh A Ballagh	Hanover	3024DC	71
Tweelingpan – West	Lake Chrissie	2630AD	41	Ganspan Pans & Vlei	Jan Kempdorp	2724DD	72
Wim Rabe Pan	Wakkerstroom	2730AA	42	Grootdam (Rooipoort)	Schmidsdrif	2824CA	71
Witbank Dam	Witbank	2529CD	43	Kamfers Dam	Kimberley	2824DB	73
				Kriegerspoort Dam	Hanover	3124BC	72
GAUTENG				Nantwich Saltpan	Kimberley	2824BD	74
Blesbokspruit	Nigel	2628AD	44	Orange River Estuary	Alexander Bay	2816CB	74
Bronkhorstspruit Dam	Bronkhorstspruit	2528DC	45	Platfontein Pans	Kimberley	2824DA	75
Diepsloot Nature Reserve	Johannesburg	2528CC	46	Sakrivierspoort Wetlands	Loxton	3122CC	76
Grootvaly	Springs	2628BC	47	So Ver Myn Dam	Windsorton	2824BA	75
Homestead, Benoni &				Spitskop Dam	Spitskop	2824BA	77
Middle Lakes	Benoni	2628AB	48	Springbok Sewage Works	Springbok	2917DB	78
Korsman Bird Sanctuary	Benoni	2628AB	49	Strydenburg Pan	Strydenburg	2923DC	77
Leeupan	Benoni	2628AB	50	Vaalharts Weir	Warrenton	2824BB	78
Marievale Bird Sanctuary	Nigel	2628BC	51	Vanderkloof Dam	Vanderkloof	3024BB	79
Rietspruit (Rooikraal)	Boksburg	2628AD	52	Volstruis Pan	Schmidsdrif	2824CA	79

Table 1 cont.

Name	Nearest Town	Grid Cell	Page	Name	Nearest Town	Grid Cell	Page
FREE STATE				**KWAZULU-NATAL cont.**			
Allemanskraal Dam	Ventersburg	2827AC	80	Tshanetshe Pan	Mbazwane	2732CB	129
Benfontein Dam	Kimberley			Tugela River Mouth	Mandini	2931AB	130
	(N. Cape)	2824DD	86	Umgeni River Estuary	Durban	2931CC	131
Bloemhof Dam	Bloemhof	2725DA	81	Umhlanga Treatment Works	Umhlanga .	2931CA	132
Erfenis Dam	Winburg	2826DB	82	Umvoti River Estuary	Stanger	2931AD	133
Gariep Dam (West)	Gariep Dam	3025DA	83	Watermead Dam	Underberg	2929DC	134
Kalkfontein Dam	Koffiefontein	2925CB	84	Yengweni Lake	Mbazwane	2732CB	135
Knellpoort Dam	Wepener	2926DD	85				
Loch Athlone	Bethlehem	2828AD	86	**EASTERN CAPE**			
Rietpan	Brandfort	2826CB	86	Bar None Saltpans	Port Elizabeth	3325DC	136
Rusfontein Dam	Thaba Nchu	2926BC	87	Cape Recife Reclamation			
Seekoeivlei	Memel	2729DA	88	Works	Port Elizabeth	3425BA	137
Sterkfontein Dam	Harrismith	2829AC	89	Chatty Saltpans	Port Elizabeth	3325DC	138
Welbedacht Dam	Wepener	2926DD	90	Ghio Pans	Kenton-on-Sea	3326DA	139
				Great Fish River Estuary	Port Alfred	3327AC	140
				Kabeljous River Estuary	Jeffreys Bay	3424BB	141
KWAZULU-NATAL				Queenstown Sewage Works	Queenstown	3126DD	142
Albert Falls Dam	Pietermaritzburg	2930AD	91	Redhouse Saltpan	Port Elizabeth	3325DC	143
Banzi Pan (Ndumo)	Ingwavuma	2632CD	92	Seekoei River Estuary	Jeffreys Bay	3424BB	144
Blood River Vlei	Vryheid	2730DC	93	Swartkops River Estuary	Port Elizabeth	3325DC	145
Bushlands Pan	Hluhluwe	2832AB	93				
Chelmsford Dam	Newcastle	2729DD	94	**WESTERN CAPE**			
Collin's Lake	Mtubatuba	2832AC	95	Beaufort West Bird			
Durban Bayhead	Durban	2931CC	96	Sanctuary	Beaufort West	3222BC	146
Hlatikulu Vlei	Hlatikulu	2929BA	97	Berg River System	Velddrif	3218CA	147
Hlonhlela Pan	Mkuze	2732CA	98	Bitou River	Plettenberg Bay	3423AB	148
Hluhluwe River Vlei				Botriviervlei	Kleinmond	3419AC	149
& Floodplain	Hluhluwe	2832AB	99	De Hoop Vlei	Bredasdorp	3420AD	150
Klipfontein Bird Sanctuary	Vryheid	2730DD	99	De Mond Estuary	Bredasdorp	3420CA	151
Klipspruit Dam Complex	Vryheid	2730DC	97	Dick Dent Bird Sanctuary	Somerset West	3418BB	152
Kosi Bay Nature Reserve	Manguzi	2632DD	100	Droëvlei	Klipheuwel	3318DA	153
kuNdlebeni Pan	Mbazwane	2732DA	101	Eikenhof Dam	Grabouw	3419AA	154
Lake Eteza	Mtubatuba	2832AC	102	Groenvlei	Sedgefield	3422BB	154
Lake Mfutululu	Mtubatuba	2832AD	103	Jakkalsvlei	Lambert's Bay	3218AB	155
Lake Sibaya	Ubombo	2732BC	106	Keurbooms River Estuary	Plettenberg Bay	3423AB	156
Lake St Lucia	Hlabisa	2832AB	104	Klavervlei	Somerset West	3418BB	157
Malandeni Sewage Works	Ladysmith	2829DB	107	Kleinmond River Estuary	Kleinmond	3419AC	158
Mandini Sewage Works	Mandini	2931AB	105	Knysna Lagoon	Knysna	3423AA	159
Maputaland Coast	Kwangwanase	2632DD	108	Langebaan Lagoon	Langebaan	3318AA	160
Mavuya Pan	Mtubatuba	2832AC	109	Mossel Bay Sewage Works	Mossel Bay	3422AA	161
Mbozambo Waste Water				Olifants River Mouth (South)	Lutzville	3118CA	161
Lagoon	Stanger	2931AD	110	Paardevlei Dam	Somerset West	3418BB	162
Mfazana Pans	St Lucia	2832AD	108	Paarl Bird Sanctuary	Paarl	3318DB	163
Mfolozi Mouth Area	St Lucia	2832AD	111	Raapenberg Bird Sanctuary	Cape Town	3318CD	164
Mfula Pan	Mbazwane	2732DA	112	Radyn Dam	Malmesbury	3318BC	165
Mhlazi Pan	Mbazwane	2732DA	113	Rietvlei	Milnerton	3318CD	166
Midmar Dam	Howick	2930CA	114	Rocher Pan	Velddrif	3218CB	167
Mlalazi River Estuary	Mtunzini	2831DD	115	Rondevlei	Cape Flats	3418AB	168
Mtunzini Prawn Hatchery	Mtunzini	2831DD	116	Springfontein Dam	Beaufort West	3222BC	169
Muzi Lake (South)	Mbazwane	2732CB	111	Steenbras Dam	Gordon's Bay	3418BB	170
Neshe Pan	Mbazwane	2732CB	117	Strandfontein Sewage			
Northern Treatment Works	Durban	2930DD	118	Works	Muizenberg	3418BA	171
Nsumu Pan	Mkuze Game			Theewaterskloof Dam	Villiersdorp	3419AA	172
	Reserve	2732CB	119	Verlorenvlei	Elandsbaai	3218AD	173
Nyamithi Pan (Ndumo)	Ingwavuma	2632CD	120	Vermont Salt Pan	Hermanus	3419AC	174
Pongolapoort Dam	Mkuze	2731BD	121	Voëlvlei	Mossel Bay	3421BD	175
Reichenau Mission Dam	Underberg	2929DC	122	Voëlvlei Dam	Gouda	3319AC	176
Richards Bay	Richards Bay	2832CC	123	Wellington Waste Water			
Shokwe Pan (Ndumo)	Ingwavuma	2632CD	124	Works	Wellington	3318DB	176
Slangdraai Dam	Ladysmith	2829BA	125	Wilderness – Swartvlei			
Sodwana Bay to				System	Sedgefield	3422BB	177
Cape Vidal	St Lucia	2732DC	125	Wilderness – Touw River			
Spioenkop Dam	Winterton	2829CB	126	System	Sedgefield	3322DC	178
Sundumbili Sewage Works	Mandini	2931AB	127	Wildevoëlvlei	Kommetjie	3418AB	179
The Swamp	Underberg	2929DC	125	Zandvlei	Muizenberg	3418AB	180
Thulazihleka Pan	Richards Bay	2832CC	128				

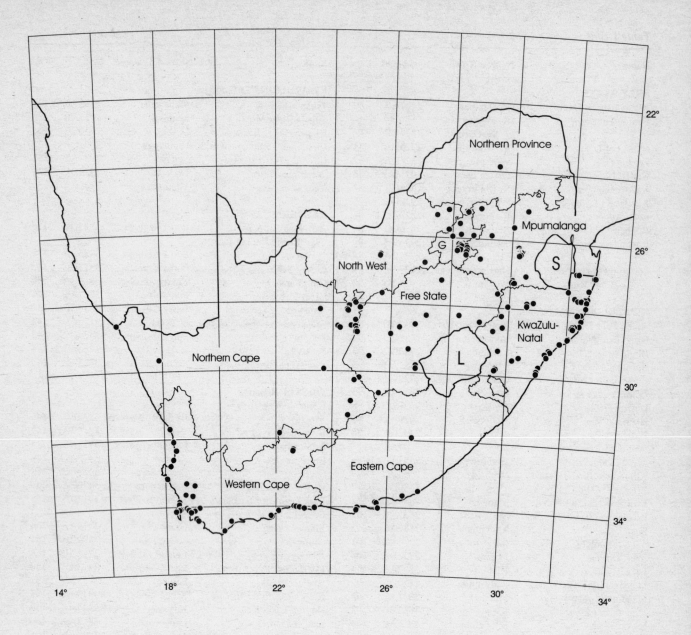

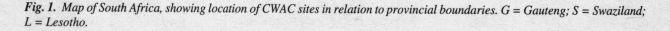

Fig. 1. *Map of South Africa, showing location of CWAC sites in relation to provincial boundaries. G = Gauteng; S = Swaziland; L = Lesotho.*

SPECIES

The birds covered by CWAC include all non-passerine species normally associated with wetland habitats. Passerine species typical of wetlands are recorded during counts as present only: that is, their presence is recorded but not their numbers. Passerines are not included in this report, except for wagtails which are counted at most sites.

The species identifications made by observers are essentially taken at face value, except in the case of obvious errors. There are several waterbird taxa which can provide difficulties with identification, however, particularly when viewed over large distances or in poor light conditions (ASAB1: liii–lvi). CWAC forms provide places to record counts of unidentified waders, ducks and terns, and these counts have not been included in the data presented in this report. Some of the data presented may be erroneous owing to misidentifications.

Table 2 lists the species covered in this report together with the population thresholds and average body masses used in the analyses.

DATABASE

The CWAC database consists of field data in ASCII-format files, one for each seasonal count. Processing of these files is done by means of custom-written FORTRAN programs written by R.A. Navarro of the ADU. The data also exists as summary files by site and by species.

Copies of CWAC data are lodged with Wetlands International as the South African contribution to the African Waterfowl Census programme.

Table 3 provides an overview of the size and scope of the database used in compiling this report.

ANALYSES

Only data from 1992–97 were used in the analyses, i.e. a maximum of six winter and six summer counts per site. Many sites have fewer than this maximum number of counts. There are two basic types of analysis, namely site and species analyses, which reflect the same data viewed from two distinct

Table 2. List of all species covered in the TOTAL CWAC Report, with page numbers.

Roberts No.	English	Scientific	Page	Roberts No.	English	Scientific	Page
006	Great Crested Grebe	*Podiceps cristatus*	182	223	Purple Gallinule	*Porphyrio porphyrio*	215
007	Blacknecked Grebe	*Podiceps nigricollis*	182	224	Lesser Gallinule	*Porphyrula alleni*	215
008	Dabchick	*Tachybaptus ruficollis*	183	226	Moorhen	*Gallinula chloropus*	216
049	White Pelican	*Pelecanus onocrotalus*	183	227	Lesser Moorhen	*Gallinula angulata*	216
050	Pinkbacked Pelican	*Pelecanus rufescens*	184	228	Redknobbed Coot	*Fulica cristata*	217
055	Whitebreasted Cormorant	*Phalacrocorax carbo*	184	229	African Finfoot	*Podica senegalensis*	217
056	Cape Cormorant	*Phalacrocorax capensis*	185	240	African Jacana	*Actophilornis africanus*	218
058	Reed Cormorant	*Phalacrocorax africanus*	185	241	Lesser Jacana	*Microparra capensis*	218
060	Darter	*Anhinga melanogaster*	186	242	Painted Snipe	*Rostratula benghalensis*	219
062	Grey Heron	*Ardea cinerea*	186	244	African Black Oystercatcher	*Haematopus moquini*	219
063	Blackheaded Heron	*Ardea melanocephala*	187	245	Ringed Plover	*Charadrius hiaticula*	220
064	Goliath Heron	*Ardea goliath*	187	246	Whitefronted Plover	*Charadrius marginatus*	220
065	Purple Heron	*Ardea purpurea*	188	247	Chestnutbanded Plover	*Charadrius pallidus*	221
066	Great White Heron	*Casmerodius albus*	188	248	Kittlitz's Plover	*Charadrius pecuarius*	221
067	Little Egret	*Egretta garzetta*	189	249	Threebanded Plover	*Charadrius tricollaris*	222
068	Yellowbilled Egret	*Egretta intermedia*	189	254	Grey Plover	*Pluvialis squatarola*	222
069	Black Egret	*Egretta ardesiaca*	190	258	Blacksmith Plover	*Vanellus armatus*	223
070	Slaty Egret	*Egretta vinaceigula*	190	259	Whitecrowned Plover	*Vanellus albiceps*	223
071	Cattle Egret	*Bubulcus ibis*	191	260	Wattled Plover	*Vanellus senegallus*	224
072	Squacco Heron	*Ardeola ralloides*	191	261	Longtoed Plover	*Vanellus crassirostris*	224
074	Greenbacked Heron	*Butorides striatus*	192	262	Turnstone	*Arenaria interpres*	225
075	Rufousbellied Heron	*Butorides rufiventris*	192	263	Terek Sandpiper	*Xenus cinereus*	225
076	Blackcrowned Night Heron	*Nycticorax nycticorax*	193	264	Common Sandpiper	*Actitis hypoleucos*	226
078	Little Bittern	*Ixobrychus minutus*	193	265	Green Sandpiper	*Tringa ochropus*	226
079	Dwarf Bittern	*Ixobrychus sturmii*	194	266	Wood Sandpiper	*Tringa glareola*	227
080	Bittern	*Botaurus stellaris*	194	269	Marsh Sandpiper	*Tringa stagnatilis*	227
081	Hamerkop	*Scopus umbretta*	195	270	Greenshank	*Tringa nebularia*	228
084	Black Stork	*Ciconia nigra*	195	271	Knot	*Calidris canutus*	228
086	Woollynecked Stork	*Ciconia episcopus*	196	272	Curlew Sandpiper	*Calidris ferruginea*	229
087	Openbilled Stork	*Anastomus lamelligerus*	196	274	Little Stint	*Calidris minuta*	229
088	Saddlebilled Stork	*Ephippiorhynchus senegalensis*	197	281	Sanderling	*Calidris alba*	230
090	Yellowbilled Stork	*Mycteria ibis*	197	284	Ruff	*Philomachus pugnax*	230
091	Sacred Ibis	*Threskiornis aethiopicus*	198	286	Ethiopian Snipe	*Gallinago nigripennis*	231
093	Glossy Ibis	*Plegadis falcinellus*	198	288	Bartailed Godwit	*Limosa lapponica*	231
094	Hadeda Ibis	*Bostrychia hagedash*	199	289	Curlew	*Numenius arquata*	232
095	African Spoonbill	*Platalea alba*	199	290	Whimbrel	*Numenius phaeopus*	232
096	Greater Flamingo	*Phoenicopterus ruber*	200	294	Avocet	*Recurvirostra avosetta*	233
097	Lesser Flamingo	*Phoeniconaias minor*	200	295	Blackwinged Stilt	*Himantopus himantopus*	233
099	Whitefaced Duck	*Dendrocygna viduata*	201	298	Water Dikkop	*Burhinus vermiculatus*	234
100	Fulvous Duck	*Dendrocygna bicolor*	201	304	Redwinged Pratincole	*Glareola pratincola*	234
101	Whitebacked Duck	*Thalassornis leuconotus*	202	305	Blackwinged Pratincole	*Glareola nordmanni*	235
102	Egyptian Goose	*Alopochen aegyptiacus*	202	312	Kelp Gull	*Larus dominicanus*	235
103	South African Shelduck	*Tadorna cana*	203	315	Greyheaded Gull	*Larus cirrocephalus*	236
104	Yellowbilled Duck	*Anas undulata*	203	316	Hartlaub's Gull	*Larus hartlaubii*	236
105	African Black Duck	*Anas sparsa*	204	322	Caspian Tern	*Hydroprogne caspia*	237
106	Cape Teal	*Anas capensis*	204	324	Swift Tern	*Sterna bergii*	237
107	Hottentot Teal	*Anas hottentota*	205	325	Lesser Crested Tern	*Sterna bengalensis*	238
108	Redbilled Teal	*Anas erythrorhyncha*	205	326	Sandwich Tern	*Sterna sandvicensis*	238
112	Cape Shoveller	*Anas smithii*	206	327	Common Tern	*Sterna hirundo*	239
113	Southern Pochard	*Netta erythrophthalma*	206	328	Arctic Tern	*Sterna paradisaea*	239
114	Pygmy Goose	*Nettapus auritus*	207	329	Antarctic Tern	*Sterna vittata*	240
115	Knobbilled Duck	*Sarkidiornis melanotos*	207	330	Roseate Tern	*Sterna dougallii*	240
116	Spurwinged Goose	*Plectropterus gambensis*	208	334	Damara Tern	*Sterna balaenarum*	241
117	Maccoa Duck	*Oxyura maccoa*	208	335	Little Tern	*Sterna albifrons*	241
–	Mallard	*Anas platyrhynchos*	209	338	Whiskered Tern	*Chlidonias hybrida*	242
148	African Fish Eagle	*Haliaeetus vocifer*	209	339	Whitewinged Tern	*Chlidonias leucopterus*	242
164	European Marsh Harrier	*Circus aeruginosus*	211	393	Grass Owl	*Tyto capensis*	243
165	African Marsh Harrier	*Circus ranivorus*	210	395	Marsh Owl	*Asio capensis*	243
170	Osprey	*Pandion haliaetus*	210	403	Pel's Fishing Owl	*Scotopelia peli*	244
207	Wattled Crane	*Bugeranus carunculatus*	211	428	Pied Kingfisher	*Ceryle rudis*	244
209	Crowned Crane	*Balearica regulorum*	211	429	Giant Kingfisher	*Ceryle maxima*	245
210	African Rail	*Rallus caerulescens*	212	430	Halfcollared Kingfisher	*Alcedo semitorquata*	245
212	African Crake	*Crex egregia*	212	431	Malachite Kingfisher	*Alcedo cristata*	246
213	Black Crake	*Amaurornis flavirostris*	213	434	Mangrove Kingfisher	*Halcyon senegaloides*	246
215	Baillon's Crake	*Porzana pusilla*	213	711	African Pied Wagtail	*Motacilla aguimp*	247
217	Redchested Flufftail	*Sarothrura rufa*	214	712	Longtailed Wagtail	*Motacilla clara*	246
222	Whitewinged Flufftail	*Sarothrura ayresi*	214	713	Cape Wagtail	*Motacilla capensis*	247
				714	Yellow Wagtail	*Motacilla flava*	248

Table 3. Totals for 12 counts (6 summer and 6 winter).

	No. of wetlands counted	No. of birds
Summer 1992	45	159 246
Winter 1992	48	139 337
Summer 1993	74	229 493
Winter 1993	88	130 406
Summer 1994	96	200 768
Winter 1994	100	166 244
Summer 1995	112	251 447
Winter 1995	103	157 958
Summer 1996	130	204 722
Winter 1996	130	130 026
Summer 1997	136	192 118
Winter 1997	154	171 769
TOTAL	1216	2 133 535

perspectives. Other perspectives, using different units of analysis, are possible, for example: regional groupings of sites, groupings of sites according to their biophysical characteristics, various groupings of species, groupings of sites and species according to categories of threat to wetlands, etc. Such analyses may be attempted in future reports, but at this stage in the development of CWAC, we believe that the site and species analyses presented provide a useful summary of the data available to date.

Site analyses

For each site a full list of all counted species (see 'Species' above) is presented. For each species the mean and maximum counts are given for both summer and winter; the number of counts on which the data are based is given in brackets at the top of the columns. Dashes opposite species indicate seasons for which no counts are available; zeros indicate actual counts of zero. At the bottom of the columns a species total is given, which is the number of different waterbird species which have been observed and counted during the counts (other species may have been observed on other occasions, but are not included here). Also given are a 'total mean count' and a 'total maximum count', for both summer and winter. The total mean counts are the sum of the means for all the individual species in the columns above. The total maximum count is the highest number of birds actually recorded during one seasonal count, *not* the sum of the species' maxima.

Mean and maximum counts for species are marked with asterisks where they reach certain thresholds: 1% of the estimated global population (two asterisks), and 0.5% of the estimated global population (one asterisk). These thresholds (see Table 1) represent levels which are deemed to be globally and nationally important, respectively, and as such are useful yardsticks for assessing the importance and conservation worthiness of a site (Barnes 1998; Fishpool 1997). Nevertheless, these thresholds are by no means the only criteria relevant to measuring the importance of a site. A site has to be viewed in its regional context and in the light of the role it may play in conjunction with other neighbouring sites; this is particularly relevant in the case of clusters of relatively small wetlands, a situation typical of panveld, dams in farming districts, and vleis in the slacks of dune fields. Small, ephemeral wetlands also often provide breeding habitat for waterbirds and are important in that regard, despite the fact that they may never hold large aggregations of birds.

Where three or more counts are available for a site, graphs are provided for a selection of species. The selection includes the species with the highest mean count from each of the following six groups: (1) grebes and coot; (2) herons, egrets, storks and cranes, (3) ducks and geese, (4) African waders, including flamingos, Avocet and Blackwinged Stilt, (5) Palearctic waders, and (6) gulls and terns. For each of these six species, plots show the fluctuations in the summer and winter counts (solid and broken lines, closed and open circles, respectively). Where the sequence of counts is broken by a season in which a count did not take place, the successive points are not joined by a line.

The purpose of these plots is to give an indication of possible trends or patterns of occurrence. A comparison of summer and winter counts will suggest residency or possible seasonal movements. Consistent upward or downward trends in numbers may indicate trends in the population of the species, and/or changes in conditions at the wetland.

In addition to the six species-specific graphs, three graphs depict the summer and winter trends in (a) species total, (b) total count, and (c) total biomass. Species total is the number of counted species (see 'Species' above); total count is the sum of all counted species; and total biomass is the number of individuals per species multiplied, respectively, by the average mass of an individual of each species (see Table 2), summed across all species. These three graphs can be used as indicators of the quality of the wetland as a whole. Species total is an indication of the diversity and quality of habitats available. Total count and total biomass indicate the quantity of useable habitat and the carrying capacity of that habitat. Total count and total biomass should be viewed in conjunction because fluctuations in numbers may not necessarily indicate changes in carrying capacity if biomass is relatively constant, and vice versa. An example would be of species of different size predominating at a wetland in different seasons, and in markedly different numbers, but without greatly changing the total biomass.

The timing of the counts in the middle of their respective seasons has the advantage of avoiding periods of passage by migrants and measurement of populations during intervals of relative stability. This has the corollary that CWAC counts for some sites – particularly those used for 'staging' – will not reflect maximum numbers of migratory birds because such maxima are reached outside the count periods.

Despite the mid-season timing of counts, unpredictability of rainfall in large parts of South Africa means that large-scale fluctuations in waterbird populations at sites are commonly observed. This underlines the importance of long-term monitoring if actual population trends, rather than temporary local fluctuations, are to be detected and understood.

Each site analysis is accompanied by a textual account which generally covers the following topics: (i) the biophysical nature of the site, (ii) the important features of the waterbird assemblage, (iii) apparent patterns of seasonal fluctuation and temporal trends in the counts, and (iv) the threats to the wetland and its birds. Alongside the text is a map of South Africa in which the position of the site is indicated.

Threats

In addition to information gathered on standard CWAC report forms, a specially designed form was sent to all CWAC compilers in June 1998, to obtain up-to-date information on threats to sites. Information was received for sufficient sites to give a good general picture of the major threats facing CWAC wetlands, the relative impact of different types of threat, and the number and type of wetlands most significantly affected.

For the purpose of this enquiry, the levels of threat were defined as follows:

- ❑ **Critical:** likely to have dramatic negative impacts on birdlife presently, or in the near future.
- ❑ **Severe:** likely to cause declines in birdlife in the short to medium term.
- ❑ **Important:** likely to cause long-term declines in birdlife if the threat is not ameliorated.
- ❑ **Mild:** likely to have only slight negative impacts on birdlife.

In addition to the relevant details given in each site account, an analysis of the results of this threats survey are presented in this report in the overview chapter by Dr Barry Taylor.

Species analyses

For each species counted, a list of the most 'important' sites is presented. The list comprises the fifteen sites with the highest mean counts, in rank order. For each site the summer and winter mean and maximum counts for the species are shown. Means and maxima, which exceed the thresholds of 0.5% and 1% of the estimated global population of the species in question, are indicated with one and two asterisks respectively (see 'Site analyses' above).

This list should not be interpreted simplistically and the following salient points should be taken into account: Firstly, CWAC does not cover all of the potentially important sites for a particular species; this is a fundamental limitation to the data which should not be overlooked. Secondly, amongst sites that are covered, the only criterion which can easily be used to attribute importance is total numbers. Other factors not addressed by CWAC, e.g. importance for breeding or moulting, importance as a seasonal staging or fuelling point, outside of the count months, etc., cannot be factored in and may be essential to a definitive list of important sites for a particular species. Thirdly, CWAC counts are less than reliable and comprehensive for species which are (a) secretive and inconspicuous, particularly several rallids, and (b) for species which are difficult to identify and count, e.g. some of the small migratory waders. Lastly, an arbitrary limit of 15 sites was applied because of space constraints; 15 may be more or (more likely) less than the true number of important sites in any particular case. In some cases fewer than 15 sites are listed because the species was recorded at fewer sites.

Nevertheless, with these caveats in mind, the list of sites presented for each species should provide useful pointers to some of the wetlands that are significant in supporting South African populations of particular waterbirds. Furthermore, one can confidently claim that sites which repeatedly appear in the lists for a range of different species are likely to be wetlands of national and, in some cases, global importance.

In addition to the table of 15 sites, the four sites with the most complete and longest series of counts are plotted in four graphs. For each site, both summer and winter counts are plotted (solid lines with filled circles, and broken lines with empty circles, respectively). Individually these plots give an indication of seasonal patterns of occurrence, and of trends in numbers over the study period, at these sites. Collectively they suggest whether seasonal patterns are widespread or local, and whether trends in numbers are specific to particular wetlands or possibly indicative of a trend in the population as a whole.

Each species analysis is accompanied by a textual account which generally covers the following topics: (i) the status and distribution of the South African population, (ii) patterns in the seasonality of occurrence, (iii) spatial and temporal features of breeding, and (iv) counts and sites of special significance. A few species have only texts, sometimes very brief, because there is insufficient CWAC data – if any – to justify the presentation of quantitative data.

Alongside the text is a map in which the distribution of the species, according to the SABAP database, is indicated by means of shaded quarter-degree grid cells, and the positions of the 15 listed sites is shown with black dots. The positions of the dots, relative to the whole of the species' distribution, provide some insights into the degree of evenness or concentration of a population across its range.

Comparison of CWAC and atlas data for species

Most species analyses do not give a complete picture, because most species occur at more than 15 sites and space does not allow details from additional sites to be included. However, each site account has a species table which summarizes all counts of all species which occur, so that all the relevant summary information for each species does appear in the report. The species analyses, together with this additional information, provide a good indication of the overall distribution and status of all species for which adequate data are available. They are often sufficiently detailed and comprehensive to provide a meaningful comparison with the information in ASAB.

In many cases the CWAC results confirm ASAB findings, and often they also provide new information on such topics as distribution, status and seasonal occurrence patterns. In this context it must be borne in mind that the ASAB reporting period largely spanned a period of below-average rainfall, and that bird distribution and abundance data in the atlas are therefore likely to be biased against the arid and drought-prone western areas (Allan *et al.* 1997). The unpredictability of rainfall in these drier areas, and the consequent erratic occurrence of wetland habitats, should also be considered when attempting to interpret CWAC results with regard to the occurrence, distribution and status of wetland bird species, and when making comparisons with ASAB.

When comparing results from the atlas and CWAC, it must be borne in mind that the projects differ in basic respects. The atlas recorded the presence or absence of species in grid cells but numerical abundance was not measured by counting, and the temporal resolution was a calendar month. Geographical and temporal variations in occurrence and relative abundance were described using an index, namely the reporting rate which is the proportion of checklists on which a species is recorded; differences in reporting rate were interpreted as indicating changes in abundance or density. The potential for variation in conspicuousness and identifiability between bird species makes it impractical to use reporting rates for between-species comparisons (Harrison & Underhill 1997).

The CWAC scheme, on the other hand, records the actual number of birds of each species seen at a specific site during each count, providing an absolute measure of numerical abundance which allows comparisons between species (given that relative conspicuousness and ease of identification may also introduce some bias here), as well as comparisons of seasonal and geographical variations in abundance for a given species.

The fact that the two schemes do not use the same recording units and methods of analysis must be taken into account when attempting to make direct comparisons. For example, temporal or regional variations in atlas reporting rates may not necessarily mirror variations in CWAC count figures. CWAC sites tend to be permanent waterbodies rather than ephemeral ones, and thus one may expect CWAC counts, for nomadic or regionally migratory wetland birds, to rise at times when such species concentrate at permanent waterbodies and forsake ephemeral ones. At such times, atlas reporting rates for the same species might fall because the birds are less widespread, being more concentrated at fewer and larger sites, and thus tend to be recorded less often and from fewer grid cells. However, if one takes factors such as this into account, it is usually possible to make meaningful comparisons between results from the two schemes.

THE HISTORY OF CWAC

November 1991–December 1992

CWAC was initiated in November 1991 by the Avian Demography Unit (ADU) at the University of Cape Town. This was done in response to a request from the state Department of Environmental Affairs and Tourism (DEAT) through the Ramsar Working Group, a committee of DEAT, coordinated at that time by Dr Mike Cohen and Dr Geoff Cowan.

DEAT's initiative arose from the department's decision for South Africa to rejoin Wetlands International (WI) (then the International Waterfowl and Wetlands Research Bureau, IWRB). One implication of this step was that South Africa would participate in WI's African Waterfowl Census (AfWC).

1992 was the first year of CWAC and its participation in the African Waterfowl Census. Prof. Les Underhill, Mr James Harrison and Mrs Sue Kieswetter, all of the ADU, were appointed Project Leader, Project Manager and Project Coordinator, respectively. The work was supported in part by a grant from DEAT. CWAC was initiated by means of a December 1991 letter to a wide range of potential participants in conservation agencies and bird clubs, inviting participation in the January 1992 count. There was a good response and 43 sites were counted.

Early in 1992, the ADU's computer programmer, Mr René Navarro, gave attention to the development of computer programs for the entry and processing of the data. The programs provided for presentation of the results of particular site counts and for summaries of results across all sites. A new CWAC Report Form was designed with a more appropriate list of species and with a layout which permitted direct data capture from the form. The new form also solicited a wider range of information about the count itself and the condition of the wetland. Seven information sheets and a circular were prepared and distributed to participants. These covered a variety of topics related to techniques and the organization of counts.

In September 1992, the Project Manager, Mr James Harrison, visited the headquarters of WI in Slimbridge, UK, and had useful discussions with the Director, Dr Mike Moser, and with the Coordinator of the African Waterfowl Census (AfWC), Dr Christian Perennou. He also participated in a workshop on the AfWC during the 8th Pan-African Ornithological Congress in Burundi in October. The most important issue discussed at the workshop was the question of suitable dates for the AfWC counts. It was agreed that the January count should be maintained across the whole continent, but that the timing of the second count would be flexible to allow countries the option of censusing their wetlands at a time when populations were likely to be at their peak. South Africa decided to adhere to the original July count as this was considered to be appropriate for contrasting the winter- and summer-rainfall areas of the country.

Second report: January 1993–December 1993

In 1993, the Council of BirdLife South Africa (BLSA) (then the Southern African Ornithological Society, SAOS) formally adopted CWAC as a society project and gave it full support.

The number of sites registered with CWAC doubled during 1993. BLSA involvement at the level of the bird clubs was a major factor in this growth and underlined the important contribution which amateur birdwatchers make to the programme. The involvement and commitment of the nature conservation agencies continued with 13 new sites being added by this sector.

During 1993 CWAC acquired an official sponsor. An application for funding was submitted to WWF-SA and, through Dr Ian Macdonald and Carine van der Merwe of that organization, a relationship between CWAC and Teal's Whisky of Stellenbosch Farmer's Winery was fostered.

Some of this money was put towards the salary of Dr Bozena Kalejta-Summers who conducted research and wrote scientific papers using analyses of CWAC data. The ADU was contracted by WWF-SA to produce a report on the birds of Rietvlei, the site of a newly established nature reserve near Milnerton. Bozena Kalejta-Summers and David Allan produced the report in which they integrated recent CWAC counts with historical data collected by the late Jack Winterbottom in the 1950s. Analysis of this time-series of count figures enabled them to document the changes in the avifauna of Rietvlei which have resulted from alterations to the hydrology of the vlei. They were also able to place the site in a context of national priority wetlands and make recommendations for the future management of Rietvlei for the maintenance of species diversity and population sizes. This report served as a model for one of the important uses to which CWAC data can be put, one which has a direct bearing on the conservation of birds and the management of wetlands.

Third report: January 1994–March 1994

Dr Bozena Kalejta-Summers wrote up the report on Rietvlei (see above) as a scientific paper entitled 'Long term trends, seasonal abundance and energy consumption of waterbirds at Rietvlei, southwestern Cape Province, South Africa, 1950–1993'. This paper was submitted to the journal *Ostrich*. Dr Kalejta-Summers also prepared a number of articles for popular publications (see references below). These served to highlight the importance of southern Africa for migratory waterbirds.

Dr Kalejta-Summers was responsible for organizing the first Berg River count in January 1994. Members of the ADU continued to organize Berg River counts subsequent to her resignation from the unit in May 1994.

Mr René Navarro developed a routine to convert CWAC data into the species codes and format which WI use. The ADU is able to present WI with data in a convenient format for incorporation into the African Waterfowl Census database.

In January 1994 the number of registered sites grew from 114 to 127. Important additions were the Berg River, Redhouse Saltpan and Tugela River Mouth.

Fourth report: April 1994–March 1995

A CWAC Workshop was held in Wakkerstroom in February 1995. It was felt that, despite CWAC's good progress over the past three years, the need existed to redefine its objectives and set targets for the next five years. Priority wetlands needed to be identified, as were institutions and individuals who could help expand the scope of the project. Shortly after the CWAC Workshop, Dr Mike Moser, Director of WI, visited the ADU.

Mr René Navarro developed and improved the computer program to summarize CWAC results for species in map form. These maps were featured in a report: 'Coordinated Waterbird Counts: Preliminary Results 1992–1994'.

Fifth report: April 1995–March 1996

The Winter 1995 census took place in July; 103 count forms were submitted and 157 958 birds were recorded. In the forms submitted in winter, 11 new CWAC sites were registered.

In late January the Summer 1996 count took place; 130 forms were received. Mr Mark Anderson of the Northern Cape Nature Conservation Service added 17 new Northern Cape sites; of these, Spitskop Dam yielded the highest number of birds, 7616.

It was decided to alter the timing of the midsummer counts from January to a four-week period from mid-January to mid-February, thus avoiding the disruptive holiday period. Participants were also encouraged to try to do quarterly counts, but this was not made mandatory.

Participants were asked to provide fixed-point photographs of their wetlands. It is hoped that such photography will provide a method of monitoring wetlands and thus be an aid in explaining trends in bird numbers. It intended that such sets of photographs be submitted every two years.

CWAC participants have also been requested to furnish the ADU with historical data for sites registered with the current project. The ADU has historical data for, *inter alia*, Langebaan Lagoon, Paarl Sewage Works, Rietpan, Rondevlei and Strandfontein Sewage Works. Datasets spanning long periods of time will be useful in shedding light on changes and trends in waterbird populations over time. René Navarro of the ADU, together with Prof. Les Underhill and Manfred Waltner, presented a paper at a conference, *Trends in Numbers of Waders (Charadrii) and Other Waterbirds at Langebaan Lagoon, South Africa, 1975–1995.*

Dr Barry Taylor was employed to conduct a countrywide survey of palustrine wetlands. At the CWAC workshop in February 1995 it was decided that there was a need to include surveys of palustrine wetlands which are important for secretive and poorly known bird species, including most members of the family Rallidae. Existing surveys provide very little data on these birds and it is accepted that surveying them requires special expertise. The objective was to survey all South African palustrine wetlands likely to be of significance in terms of the occurrence, numbers or breeding of secretive rallid species. Total project time was calculated as five months, over the period mid-September 1995 to mid-April 1996. Seven major, and one short, field trips were planned, with intervening and concluding periods for documentation.

Sixth report: April 1996–March 1997

130 count forms were submitted for the winter 1996 census. In total 130 026 birds were recorded. Six sites were registered with CWAC for the first time. Counts for 136 wetlands were submitted for summer 1997 with more new sites added to the CWAC list. Ten new sites were registered bringing the number of sites registered to 184.

The results of the countrywide survey of palustrine wetlands by Dr Barry Taylor were presented in two comprehensive reports, namely *South African Palustrine Wetlands: The Results of a Survey in Summer 1995/96* and *The Status and Conservation of Rallids in South Africa: Results of a Wetland Survey in 1995/96.* These reports covered (a) wetlands relevant to rallid species, assessing their habitats, importance and population sizes supported by them and (b) rallid species, their distribution, status and preferred wetlands. These reports represented a major advance in the documentation of palustrine wetlands and rallids in South Africa.

In a circular to participants, the question of ownership was raised in an effort to establish who CWAC data belongs to and, secondly, who may use it. Compilers were asked to choose one of the following options to specify ownership of and copyrights to CWAC data:

- ❑ *Option 1:* All data are ceded to the ADU.
- ❑ *Option 2:* Data may be used by the ADU for its own research, reports, and publications, but not by anyone outside the ADU without prior permission.
- ❑ *Option 3:* No data may be used for any purpose without prior permission.
- ❑ *Option 4* (relevant only to institutions): In the case of institutions participating in CWAC, particularly nature conservation agencies, reports and papers on specific relevant wetlands shall not be published in the open literature without prior invitation to compilers, and their institution, to co-author and to vet the contents of the publications.

Of the forms returned to the ADU, the vast majority of compilers selected Option 1 as their preference. This means that in most cases the ADU will be free to release data without obtaining prior permission. The ADU follows a policy of making data available on request; data-extraction charges are levied, commensurate with the academic, commercial or private nature of the use to which data are to be put.

CWAC acquired a new sponsor – TOTAL SOUTH AFRICA. WWF-SA was instrumental in forging a relationship between CWAC and TOTAL. The support of TOTAL SOUTH AFRICA has made the production of this report possible.

Seventh report: April 1997–March 1998

Winter 1997 and Summer 1998 counts were carried out.

In response to an appeal from the British Trust for Ornithology, a special effort was made to include as many new sites as possible in the Summer 1998 count. This count was referred to as 'TOTAL CWAC' in honour of our sponsor. The objective was to count the shorebirds along the coasts and estuaries as well as the birds at inland wetlands, countrywide.

The response to the TOTAL CWAC appeal could be described as moderately good, with data for 50 new sites being submitted. Some of these are small pans with only a few birds; others, such as Soutvlei (Eastern Cape) with 2991 birds, Lemoenfontein Dam (Mpumalanga) with 1233, Modder River Mouth (Western Cape) with 3978 and Wadrif Saltpan (Western Cape) with 7507, clearly warrant ongoing monitoring.

The two reports on the Rallid Survey prepared by Dr Barry Taylor (see Sixth Report, above) were published, printed and distributed. An initial printing of 50 copies was followed by a further printing of 30 copies to satisfy demand. Free copies were distributed to all conservation agencies and relevant NGOs. The Mazda Wildlife Fund generously donated R6000 towards the costs of printing and postage.

Progress was made with the preparation of this report. René Navarro wrote software to analyse the accumulated count data and to present it in the form of tables and graphs which summarize the data for sites.

ACKNOWLEDGEMENTS

Barry Taylor, Les Underhill and René Navarro commented on a draft of this chapter. Marja Wren-Sargent, Doug Harebottle and René Navarro assisted in preparation of the tables and map.

J.A. Harrison

The significance of South Africa's wetlands for birds

This chapter provides an introduction to the importance of wetlands in South Africa to waterbirds. It does not review the extensive literature covering other aspects of wetland ecology. Davies & Day (1998) provided an overview of wetland issues in South Africa and this book is compulsory reading for all interested in the conservation of wetlands in the region. They provided 'reading lists' at the end of each chapter, many of which are comprehensive bibliographies.

This chapter is an expanded version of the wetlands section in an introductory chapter (Allan *et al.* 1997) of volume one of *The Atlas of Southern African Birds* (Harrison *et al.* 1997a). Its focus, however, is confined to South Africa, with some mention of Lesotho and Swaziland. We classify the wetlands into broad types, and discuss each in turn: rivers; estuaries, lagoons and coastal lakes; the coastline; vleis and marshes; pans; anthropogenic wetlands, such as impoundments, sewage works and saltworks. We also consider these wetlands in relation to a recent initiative in the avian conservation arena in South Africa, the Important Bird Areas (IBAs) project (Barnes 1998). Whereas the next chapter in this report discusses wetlands in relation to the results of the Coordinated Waterbird Counts (CWAC) project, this chapter aims to provide background to this project, and to set it in a broader context.

RIVERS

Noble & Hemens (1978) provided a map showing the major drainage catchments in South Africa and the contribution of each to the total mean annual run-off. Most rivers are in the higher-rainfall east and south. Not surprisingly, there is a gradient of increasingly intermittent river flow with increasing aridity.

The major river drainage systems of South Africa can be summarized as follows. Along the moist southern and eastern coasts there are numerous river courses draining south and east, usually with relatively small catchments owing to the proximity of the Great Escarpment inland of the coast. Most of the arid western and central interior of South Africa is drained westwards by the extensive Orange–Vaal system. The Orange River is the longest in South Africa (1950 km), has a catchment size of 852 000 km^2 (covering 47% of the area of South Africa), but receives only 22% of the total mean annual run-off (Noble & Hemens 1978; van Zyl 1991). By comparison, the run-off from northeastern South Africa (mainly from north of the Witwatersrand), draining into Mozambique through the Limpopo and Komati rivers and their tributaries, is 17% of the total; rivers in the winter-rainfall region in the southwest receive 13%, and the remaining 48% of annual run-off flows through rivers east of the Escarpment to the Indian Ocean (calculated from Noble & Hemens 1978).

Reviews of the ecology, classification and conservation status of rivers in South Africa have been undertaken by Noble & Hemens (1978), O'Keeffe *et al.* (1989), Davies *et al.* (1993), Rogers (1995), Eekhout *et al.* (1997), Cowan & van Riet (1998) and Davies & Day (1998). They stressed that virtually all rivers have been highly modified by anthropogenic influences and that many have been transformed from perennial to intermittent systems, e.g. the Letaba and Luvuvhu rivers in the Kruger National Park. They listed the major threats to rivers as impoundments, pollution, land-use changes in catchment areas, interbasin transfers, which result in the loss of biogeographic barriers, and alien biota, both plants and animals. Invasive aliens impose several threats: floating weeds, such as water hyacinth *Eichhornia crassipes,* cover and smother slow-flowing rivers; trees, such as black wattle *Acacia mearnsii* and *Sesbania punicea*, choke riverbeds and reduce run-off; trout *Salmo* spp. and *Oncorhynchus* spp., and bass *Micropterus* spp. are predators which pose a major threat to indigenous fish communities. O'Keeffe (undated) provided a particularly valuable map of South Africa showing the major river courses and the conservation status of each.

The waterbird communities of South African rivers have received little attention compared with several other aquatic habitats, although selected species have been investigated, e.g. Ball *et al.* (1978) for the African Black Duck *Anas sparsa* and Arkell (1979) for the Giant Kingfisher *Megaceryle maxima*. The most comprehensive survey covers rivers in the Lesotho highlands (343 km of rivers sampled), the headwaters of the Orange River, where 13 waterbird species (excluding wagtails) were counted (one of which was a vagrant) at a mean linear density of 1.5 birds/km of river (Allan 1999). The three most abundant species were African Black Duck, Yellow-billed Duck *A. undulata* and Whitebreasted Cormorant *Phalacrocorax carbo*. A single survey counted waterbirds along a 160-km section of the lower Orange River between Kotzeshoop and Sendelingsdrif, and recorded 23 waterbird species (excluding wagtails) at a mean linear density of 4.6 birds/km of river (Allan & Jenkins 1993). The three most abundant species were Darter *Anhinga melanogaster*, Egyptian Goose *Alopochen aegyptiacus* and Grey Heron *Ardea cinerea*. A series of counts along the middle Komati River in Swaziland (62 km of river sampled) found 18 species (excluding wagtails) at a mean linear density of 2.4 birds/km of river (Allan & Davies 1999). The three most abundant species were Pied Kingfisher *Ceryle rudis*, African Black Duck and Common Sandpiper *Actitis hypoleucos*. The Lesotho and Komati River counts, which included a seasonal range, suggested that waterbird densities along these rivers were highest during the low-water late-summer to spring periods.

There are also connections between rivers and bird species which are usually characterized as being purely terrestrial. River courses are often characterized by tall, fringing riverine forest and well-developed woodland, quite distinct from the surrounding dryland vegetation. These well-vegetated areas usually support a diverse and distinct forest and woodland avifauna, often comprising more species (and individual birds) than the waterbirds associated with the actual aquatic habitat. For example, along the Sabie River in Mpumalanga, Monadjem (1996) found that five bird species were associated with the river channel itself, 18 with the reed fringe, 24 with the unvegetated river banks and no less than 70 with the riparian thickets. Of these 70 species, 22 were entirely restricted in the region to this habitat. Allan & Davies (1999) similarly found that, in their study area along the middle Komati River in Swaziland, of the 178 terrestrial species present, 29 were either restricted to, or showed markedly higher abundance in, the riverine strip. Winterbottom (1972, p. 49) and Brooke (1992) discussed the bird communities associated with seasonal rivers and drainage courses in the Karoo in the arid west of South Africa. In this region, these last two authors listed 32 terrestrial bird species which are largely dependent on the riverine thickets dominated by *Acacia karroo* or *Tamarix usneoides*. A species worthy of particular mention in this regard is the Namaqua Warbler *Phragmacia substriata*. This dryland bird is essentially restricted to riverine woodland within its arid range and has perhaps its main stronghold centred on the riparian thickets of the Orange River (ASAB2 328–329).

The courses of some major rivers can be discerned from atlas distribution maps. Many species, including some dryland species, have linear distributions following the routes of these rivers (Harrison *et al.* 1997a,b). This is most apparent for the Orange River as it passes through an otherwise arid landscape. Note especially the atlas maps for Darter, Goliath Heron *A. goliath*, Hamerkop *Scopus umbretta*, African Black Duck, African Fish Eagle *Haliaeetus vocifer*, Pied, Giant and Malachite *Alcedo cristata* Kingfishers, Cape Robin *Cossypha caffra* and African Pied Wagtail *Motacilla aguimp* (ASAB1 40–41, 46–47, 80–81, 128–129, 205–207, 640–643, 646–647; ASAB2 200–201, 374–375).

Although many waterbirds typical of various wetland types also occur along rivers, there are several species that are exclusively, or largely, restricted to riverine habitats. These species are badly affected by the construction of impoundments and associated water extraction, either through direct inundation of their habitats or downstream impacts on river flow. These 'river specialists' include Whitebacked Night Heron *Gorsachius leuconotus*, Greenbacked Heron *Butorides striatus*, Black Stork *Ciconia nigra*, Saddlebilled Stork *Ephippiorhynchus senegalensis*, African Black Duck, African Finfoot *Podica senegalensis*, Whitecrowned Plover *Vanellus albiceps*, Pel's Fishing Owl *Scotopelia peli*, Halfcollared Kingfisher *Alcedo semitorquata* and Longtailed Wagtail *Motacilla clara* (although the Black and Saddlebilled Storks, and Pel's Fishing Owl are also regular on some floodplain and estuary habitats, and the Whitebacked Night Heron is fairly frequently recorded at impoundments). Considering the beleaguered position of southern Africa's river ecosystems, it is no surprise that seven of these 10 river-associated species are included in the newly revised South African Red Data Book (Barnes 1999).

The criteria for the selection of Important Bird Areas did not apply particularly well to rivers, because they seldom hold large numbers of birds and are also difficult to split into sections (Barnes 1998). The most significant river section to qualify as an IBA was a 100-km stretch of the middle Vaal River between Orkney and Vanderbijlpark (IBA SA038). It has a high concentration of one threatened bird species, the Whitebacked Night Heron.

Many other IBAs contain river sections which reinforce their importance for birds; for example, the rivers and gorges within the Blyde River Canyon (IBA SA010) support breeding Black Storks and Pel's Fishing Owl. Although individual rivers did not qualify as IBAs in their own right, many large catchment areas are contained within sites which qualified as IBAs, as did several areas with substantial river sections. In particular, portions of the lowveld rivers such as the Limpopo in Vhembe Nature Reserve (SA001) and the Sabie, Letaba,

Olifants, Luvuvhu and Limpopo Rivers in the Kruger National Park (SA002) are included within IBAs. Many highveld rivers fall within the Waterberg System (SA007), Grassland Biosphere Reserve (SA020), Pilanesberg (SA023), and the Magaliesberg and Witwatersberg (SA025). The Auob and Nossob rivers are in the Kalahari-Gemsbok National Park (SA027); sections of the middle and lower Orange River fall within the Augrabies Falls National Park (SA029) and Orange River Mouth Wetlands (SA030), and the rivers of the Lesotho highlands in the upper Orange River catchment are associated with the six IBAs in that country (L001, L002, L003, L004, L005, L006) respectively. Part of the Pongola River and its floodplain lie within the Ndumo Game Reserve (SA052); the Mkuze River lies in the Mkuzi Game Reserve (SA057), and in Lake St Lucia and Mkuze Swamps (SA058); and the Hluhluwe and Umfolozi rivers in Hluhluwe–Umfolozi Park (SA060). The headwaters of many of KwaZulu-Natal's rivers fall within the Natal Drakensberg Park (SA064). The Umzimkulwana River falls within Oribi Gorge Nature Reserve (SA085).

The cliffs carved by the Umtamvuna (IBA SA086), Mzikaba and Mtenu (SA087) and Mbashe (SA088 and SA089) rivers are important for breeding Cape Vultures *Gyps coprotheres* and the riparian vegetation is important for threatened riverine bird species. The Cedarberg Koue-Bokkeveld Complex (SA101) holds most of the catchment of the Olifants River. Other rivers within IBAs in the Fynbos Biome include the lower Berg (SA104) and Heuningnes (SA121) rivers, and the catchment areas of the Swartberg (SA106), Eastern False Bay Mountains (SA107) and Southern Langeberg Mountains (SA113) contain many rivers and streams.

ESTUARIES, LAGOONS AND COASTAL LAKES

Estuaries and lagoons are coastal wetlands typically, but not invariably, associated with the mouths of rivers. They are most abundant along the higher-rainfall east and south coasts of South Africa, although the west coast supports several large and ornithologically important coastal wetlands, e.g. Orange River mouth, Olifants River mouth, Berg River estuary and Langebaan Lagoon.

Estuaries and lagoons form the interface between inland freshwater ecosystems and the marine environment, and are characterized by a direct connection to the ocean, which plays a major role in their ecological functioning and in the species composition and abundance of their avifauna. Estuaries (e.g. Berg River estuary) are permanently subject to tidal influences, while lagoons typically have closed river mouths that are only intermittently breached by extensive flooding, wave action or man-made activities, e.g. Verlorenvlei) and Bot River Lagoon (Begg 1978). Most of the other large, natural and static waterbodies in the interior fall within the definition of pan ecosystems (see below). Virtually all natural freshwater lakes of South Africa occur along the coast, where they can be differentiated from estuaries and lagoons by being permanently isolated from any seawater influences, which is again important in determining their waterbird communities. Similar to the situation with estuaries and lagoons, the vast majority of coastal lakes are found along the eastern and southern coasts of South Africa (Hart 1995).

The literature dealing with the location, extent and basic ecology of South African estuaries, lagoons and coastal lakes is extensive. This literature has been reviewed and made accessible by Davies & Day (1998) and Cowan & van Riet (1998). Noble & Hemens (1978) listed 196 estuaries along the South African coast and classified 32 of these as 'major'. They also discussed 16 'coastal and estuarine lakes'. Hart (1995) listed 39 coastal freshwater lakes and provided a discussion of the ecology of these systems. Begg (1978) presented ecological information on 73 estuarine systems along the KwaZulu-Natal coast. Heydorn & Tinley (1980) provided an overview of the estuaries on the coastline of the former Cape Province; this was followed up by a series of 43 detailed ecological reports on individual estuaries of this province. Day (1981) presented information for each of 43 large estuaries along the South African coast. Heydorn (1989) listed 73 estuaries, lagoons and coastal lakes in KwaZulu-Natal, 56 in the former Transkei and 167 in the former Cape Province, and estimated the total extent of these habitats to be 500–600 km².

The aquatic avifauna of estuaries has received considerable attention, especially with regard to species composition and counts of the numbers of birds present. Underhill & Cooper (1984a) compiled a comprehensive set of counts of waterbird populations at estuaries and other coastal wetlands. This was based on a series of surveys between 1975 and 1984, most of which produced reports and papers for the regions covered (Table 1). Key examples of publications on waterbird populations at important individual sites include Williams (1986) for the Orange River mouth, Velásquez et al. (1991) for the Berg River estuary, Summers (1977) and Underhill (1987) for Langebaan Lagoon, Kalejta-Summers et al. (in press a) for Rietvlei, Guillet & Crowe (1987) for Rondevlei, Heyl & Currie (1985) for the Bot River estuary, Boshoff et al. (1991a,b,c) for the Wilderness Lakes, Shewell (1950) for the Gamtoos estuary, Martin & Baird (1987) for Swartkops estuary, Allan et al. (1999) for Durban Bay, and Whitfield & Blaber (1978, 1979a,b) and Berruti (1980a,b, 1983) for Lake St Lucia. The most detailed discussion of the waterbirds of these habitats is that of Siegfried (1981), which covers 59 southern African coastal wetlands. Turpie (1995) compared alternative methods of prioritizing the conservation status of 42 of South Africa's largest estuaries using waterbird data.

Many of the distribution maps for non-passerine waterbirds in Harrison et al. (1997a) show concentrations of records, often at high reporting rates, along the coastal strip of eastern and southern South Africa. Many, if not most, of these records came from the numerous estuaries, lagoons and coastal lakes scattered along the coastline. Similarly, along the west coast of South Africa, many of the isolated concentrations of waterbird records are associated with the relatively fewer, but in many cases extensive, coastal wetlands in these arid regions.

Siegfried (1981) listed 127 waterbird species as having been recorded at the 45 major coastal wetlands covered in his review. The most common waterbird families are Pelicaniformes (pelicans, cormorants and darters), Ciconiiformes (herons, egrets, storks, ibises and spoonbills), Phoenicopteriformes (flamingos), and Charadriiformes (plovers, sandpipers, gulls and terns). He reported Anatidae (ducks and geese) as being relatively uncommon at coastal wetlands in southern Africa. Although Palearctic migrants (mainly waders and terns) seasonally outnumber resident species by a wide margin at these sites, the large-bodied resident species (mainly pelicans, cormorants and flamingos) overwhelming dominate in terms of biomass throughout the year. The waterbirds of these wetlands are also dominated by fish and invertebrate feeders, rather than herbivorous species, the latter being more prevalent at inland waterbodies (e.g. Redknobbed Coot *Fulica cristata*). Coastal wetlands are especially important sites for immature Palearctic waders which remain in South Africa during the southern winter and as drought refuges for some inland waterbird populations (Summers et al. 1995; this report).

Siegfried (1981) also discussed the differences between the aquatic avifauna of the more tropical east coast wetlands, compared with the more temperate west coast wetlands; the south coast (Transkei to Cape Agulhas) being intermediate in this regard. There is a greater species diversity at east coast wetlands, largely due to a greater diversity of ciconiiform birds. East coast wetlands tend also to be dominated by typically sedentary, fish-eating species, compared with a dominance of usually migratory, invertebrate feeders on the west coast. Brown & Jarman (1978) divided the estuaries into two categories: east coast examples characterized by the presence of mangroves, and south and west coast wetlands without mangroves. Mangroves occur along the east coast as far south as the Nahoon estuary in the Eastern Cape (see Steinke 1995 for a map of the location and extent of mangroves in South Africa). South Africa, however, has only a single mangrove specialist waterbird, the Mangrove Kingfisher *Halcyon senegaloides*, although several waterbirds, such as Terek Sandpiper *Xenus cinereus* and Whimbrel *Numenius phaeopus*, find mangrove areas highly suitable foraging areas (Siegfried 1981; Hockey & Douie 1995).

The difference between tidally influenced estuaries and lagoons, and freshwater coastal lakes, in terms of their aquatic avifauna, is profound. For example, most Palearctic charadriid waders are common at either tidal sites or freshwater lakes, but rarely at both. Little Stints *Calidris minuta*, Ruffs *Philomachus pugnax*, Wood Sandpiper *Tringa glareola* and Marsh Sandpiper *T. stagnatilis* prefer the freshwater conditions of coastal lakes, and are therefore also common at inland waterbodies, whereas Sand Plover *Charadrius leschenaultii*, Grey Plover *Pluvialis squatarola*, Turnstone *Arenaria interpres*, Terek Sandpiper, Sanderling *Calidris alba*, Knot *C. canutus*, Curlew *Numenius arquata*, Whimbrel and Bartailed Godwit *Limosa lapponica* are uncommon at freshwater wetlands and occur mainly on tidal habitats (Harrison et al. 1997a). Only Ringed Plovers *Charadrius hiaticula*, Common Sandpipers, Curlew Sandpipers *Calidris ferruginea* and Greenshanks *T. nebularia* appear equally at home in both saltwater and freshwater environments. Another pattern evident from the atlas maps (and confirmed by count data) is that most of the Palearctic waders restricted to tidal habitats are more common along the west coast, becoming less common along the south coast and, especially, the east coast. The only exceptions are the Sand Plover and Terek Sandpiper (Summers et al. 1987; Harrison et al. 1997a).

The proximity of these lakes to tidal wetlands and the marine environment, however, results in many of the 'saltwater specialists' visiting the lakes to roost, sometimes in large numbers, occasionally to forage, and sometimes even to breed. Examples are the marine cormorants, terns and gulls, African Black Oystercatcher *Haematopus moquini* and the saltwater Palearctic migrant waders.

South African coastal wetlands support significant numbers of many waterbird species, including several threatened species. Species included in the South African Red Data Book (Barnes 1999) which fall into this category are White Pelican *Pelecanus onocrotalus* (with two major breeding colonies in South Africa, at Dassen Island off the Western Cape coast and at St Lucia) and Pinkbacked Pelican *P. rufescens* (with a major breeding colony close to St Lucia); Bittern *Botaurus stellaris* (with Richards Bay as one of the few South African coastal localities where it has occurred recently); Black Stork (large concentrations can gather at Eastern Cape estuaries) and Saddlebilled Stork (several pairs breed at St Lucia); Greater Flamingo *Phoenicopterus ruber* (which has bred successfully at De Hoop and St Lucia) and Lesser Flamingo *Phoeniconaias minor*; Redwinged Pratincole *Glareola pratincola* (breeding at St Lucia); Caspian Tern *Hydroprogne caspia* (with the largest southern African breeding colony at St Lucia and several other breeding sites at coastal wetlands (Cooper *et al.* 1992); and Mangrove Kingfisher. The African Skimmer *Rynchops flavirostris*, one of only two birds to have become extinct as a breeding species in South Africa during the 20th century (Barnes 1999), previously bred at St Lucia. The Chestnut-banded Plover *Charadrius pallidus*, although typically associated with inland pan habitats, also occurs in large numbers at some coastal wetlands, especially where these support commercial saltworks, e.g. Berg River estuary. The isolated population of Painted Snipes *Rostratula benghalensis* in the Western Cape is now believed to be highly threatened and a large proportion of this population is associated with coastal wetlands, such as Rietvlei, in this region (Hockey & Douie 1995; ASAB1 372–373).

Coastal wetlands are important for African Fish Eagles, for example at Lake St Lucia, for Ospreys *Pandion haliaetus*, for example in the Wilderness Lakes region (Boshoff & Palmer 1983), and probably also for the threatened African Marsh Harrier *Circus ranivorus*. The only two breeding populations of Palmnut Vultures *Gypohierax angolensis* in South Africa, although centred on stands of raffia palms *Raphia australis* (which grow in standing water), are also associated with coastal wetlands (Kosi Bay and Umlalazi estuary near Mtunzini), where these birds also forage on aquatic foods (Mundy *et al.* 1992). Many records of rare and vagrant scolacipid waders in South Africa come from coastal wetlands (Hockey *et al.* 1986; Hockey & Douie 1995).

Being situated along the coast, and concentrated on the south and east coasts, South Africa's natural wetlands are threatened by high human pressures. For example, Allan (1996) presented a detailed discussion of the ecological problems faced by a major coastal lake (Rietvlei) situated in an urban environment (Cape Town). The principle threats can be summarized as excessive water abstraction and agricultural practices in their catchments, and sometimes within the bounds of these wetlands themselves; residential and industrial developments; road, rail and port construction; interference with the dynamics of the river mouths; pollution in many forms; and the development of saltworks (Connor 1980; Heydorn 1989; this report). On the positive side, some major estuaries enjoy formal protection, e.g. Langebaan Lagoon and St Lucia, but the level of protection of many others is woefully inadequate, e.g. Berg River estuary (Barnes 1998), and even the best protected sites are often negatively impacted by surrounding and upstream developments. The example presented by the decrease in waterbird abundance and habitat at Durban Bay with burgeoning harbour and industrial development is an insightful worst-case scenario (Allan *et al.* 1999).

Nine of 16 wetlands listed by South Africa under the Ramsar Convention as 'Wetlands of International Importance' are coastal (Cowan 1995; Dodman & Taylor 1996). All of these sites met the criteria to qualify as Important Bird Areas (Barnes 1998). These wetlands are Orange River mouth (SA030), Verlorenvlei (SA102), Langebaan Lagoon (SA105), De Hoop Vlei (SA119), De Mond (Heuningnes estuary) (SA121), Wilderness–Sedgefield Lakes (SA114), St Lucia (SA058), Lake Sibaya (SA054) and Kosi Bay (SA053). In addition, the following estuaries and natural coastal wetlands were classified as Important Bird Areas (Barnes 1998): Olifants River estuary (SA099), Berg River estuary (SA104), Rietvlei (SA111), Botriviervlei and Kleinmond estuary (SA118), Swartkops River estuary (SA096), Umvoti River estuary (SA073), Umlalazi River lagoon (SA063), southern Richards Bay estuary (SA079) and Lake Eteza (SA061). The mouths of the Dwesa and Cwebe rivers occur within an IBA (SA089); these are important sites for the Mangrove King-

fisher, near the southern limit of its range (ASAB1: 652–653). Results presented in this report suggest that other coastal sites may qualify as IBAs (see following chapter).

COASTLINE

South Africa has about 3000 km of coastline. The most comprehensive dataset covering the waterbird populations of the coastline is that of Underhill & Cooper (1984b), which detailed the numbers of waterbirds counted during censuses along almost the entire length of coast. A total of 190 000 individual waterbirds were counted during these censuses, covering 74 aquatic species. A series of papers and reports have summarized the results of these counts for various regions along the South African coastline (Summers *et al.* 1976, 1977; Underhill *et al.* 1980; Ryan & Cooper 1985; Ryan *et al.* 1986, 1988). Hockey *et al.* (1983) undertook an analysis of the spatial distribution of waterbirds on the sandy shores of South Africa and Namibia, and concluded that there were two distinct biogeographical zones on the South African coastline: a temperate southwestern zone from the Orange River estuary to Cape Agulhas, and a subtropical east coast zone from the Kei River estuary eastwards, with a transition zone between Cape Agulhas and the Kei River.

Seasonality of occurrence of waterbirds on the coastline has been reported by Pringle & Cooper (1977) for two sections of the Cape Peninsula, by Spearpoint *et al.* (1988) at Cape Recife, Algoa Bay, and by McLachlan *et al.* (1980) on the shore between the Gamtoos and Maitland river estuaries, and on the shore between the Sundays River estuary and Woody Cape. Both these last sections were subsequently selected as IBAs (IBA SA097 Maitland–Gamtoos Coast and SA094 Alexandria Coastal Belt) (Barnes 1998) .

Other IBAs with coastal components within them include West Coast National Park (SA105), Boulders Bay (IBA SA117), De Hoop Nature Reserve (SA119), Wilderness–Sedgefield Lakes Complex (SA114), Tsitsikamma National Park (SA098), Dwesa and Cwebe Nature Reserves (SA089), Mkambati Nature Reserve (SA087), the Kosi Bay System (SA053) and Lake St Lucia and Mkuze Swamps (SA058) (Barnes 1998).

VLEIS, MARSHES, SPONGES, FLOODPLAINS AND INLAND LAKES

The inland regions of South Africa are virtually devoid of natural freshwater lakes. One of the few true lakes in South Africa is Lake Fundudzi in the Northern Province (Noble & Hemens 1978). This lake, about 5 km by 1.2 km, was created five centuries ago by a landslide across the Mutale River, a tributary of the Limpopo River.

Vleis and marshes are palustrine wetlands, characterized by slow-flowing and even static water, and are frequently covered with tall emergent wetland vegetation. Sponges are marshes associated with the upper catchments of watercourses and usually occur at high altitudes (Schwabe 1995). Floodplains are typically associated with the middle and lower reaches of larger rivers, where these enter level terrain and waterflow becomes slow, and the rivers break their banks during flooding to inundate adjacent level ground. Floodplains are therefore typical of coastal flats but can also arise under suitable conditions far inland, e.g. Nylsvlei, which is one of the most important subtropical vleis in South Africa. As with most other wetlands in South Africa, these aquatic habitats are mostly in the higher-rainfall east and extreme south.

Noble & Hemens (1978) mapped the broad distribution of

'vleis and floodplains' in South Africa, and identified 21 of these as being particularly important systems, although three of these, in the central Karoo (Vanwyksvlei, Grootvloer and Verneukpan) are better classified as pan systems, described in the next section. Begg (1989) comprehensively documented these wetland types in KwaZulu-Natal, detailing 24 'priority' wetlands that fall within this category in this province. Rogers (1995) provided an inventory of 37 major 'riparian wetlands' in South Africa; most of these are floodplains and vleis.

Despite the great significance of these types of wetlands for waterbird populations, little has been published on the bird communities present at individual sites. Among the few examples are Tarboton (1987) for Nylsvlei (in addition Higgins *et al.* (1996) provided a detailed review of the ecology of this system) and Kok & Roos (1979) for Seekoeivlei. A paper by Heyl (1988) revealed that there is a large body of unpublished waterbird count data, starting in 1968, for Rocherpan, a vlei in the Western Cape, with surveys having been made mostly monthly.

The list of waterbirds for which vleis and floodplains provide significant habitat is too extensive to review here. The patterns of distribution and abundance of many of these species are dictated by the location and extent of marsh and floodplain habitats. For example, the Wattled Crane *Bugeranus carunculatus*, a globally threatened species (Collar *et al.* 1994; Barnes 1999) is restricted in South Africa to the relatively high-altitude sponges and marshes of the eastern grassland regions (Tarboton *et al.* 1987b). The Crowned Crane *Balearica regulorum*, another crane of conservation concern (Meine & Archibald 1996; Barnes 1999), shares many of the same wetlands with the Wattled Crane in South Africa (e.g. Johnson 1992; Tarboton 1992). The globally threatened Whitewinged Flufftail *Sarothrura ayresi* (Collar *et al.* 1994) is restricted in the region to nine high-altitude sponges in South Africa; the three most important are Middelpunt, Wakkerstroom and Franklin vleis (Taylor 1994; ASAB1 334; Barnes 1999).

As well as being important habitats for a wide range of waterbird species, vleis and floodplains, with their well-vegetated nature, are major strongholds of the skulking Rallidae (crakes and rails). Taylor (1997a,b) surveyed many of South Africa's palustrine wetlands for rallids. Birds impacted specifically by vlei degradation include Bittern, Wattled Crane and Whitewinged Flufftail, three of the five species considered to be critically threatened in South Africa (Barnes 1999).

The threats to these wetlands are similar to those faced by other wetland types in the country: water extraction for irrigation and other uses, impoundments, drainage, erosion, burning, overgrazing, stock trampling, crop-farming practices, direct disturbance, pollution, and reduced inflows owing to commercial afforestation in catchments, which provides an example of how management in regions distant to a wetland can have profound negative influence on it. Although some of these wetlands have at least some formal protection (e.g. Mkuzi floodplain, Seekoeivlei, Mvoti and Mgeni Vleis), most are unprotected. The conservation status of Nylsvlei, the Pongolo River floodplain and the unprotected large marshes and sponges of the eastern grassland regions are probably of the most concern. Formal protection of individual sites, however, is meaningless if management practices in their catchment regions sabotage such efforts. The only South African wetlands in this category listed as 'Wetlands of International Importance' under the Ramsar Convention are Nylsvley (IBA SA008), Blesbokspruit (SA021) and Seekoeivlei (SA020). Blesbokspruit, however, is adversely impacted by large volumes of polluted water from neighbouring mines and industries, and is consequently on the Montreux Record of degraded Ramsar sites (Dodman & Taylor 1996).

Even within the context of wetland degradation in South Africa, floodplains, vleis and marsh ecosystems are particularly severely impacted (e.g. Kotze *et al.* 1995; Rogers 1995; Davies & Day 1998). Vlei degradation alone, particularly within the high-altitude grassland biome, is threatening several bird species with local extinction in South Africa. Vleis within the Grassland Biome are one of the most important habitats for bird conservation in South Africa (Barnes 1998).

Many wetlands in this category are included in IBAs (Barnes 1998). Upland vleis within Important Bird Areas include Alexpan (IBA SA042), Bedford/Chatsworth (SA043), Murphy's Rust (SA045), Chelmsford (SA059), Umvoti Vlei (SA069), Blinkwater Nature Reserve (SA070), Hlatikulu Sanctuary (SA072), Umgeni Vlei Nature Reserve (SA075), Midmar Nature Reserve (SA 076), Impendle Nature Reserve (SA077), Greater Ingwangwana River (SA080), Franklin Vlei (SA081), Penny Park (SA083), Mount Currie Nature Reserve (SA084), and there are numerous small vleis in the Natal-Drakensberg Park (SA064). The proposed Grassland Biosphere Reserve (SA020) holds several major upland vleis with Wakkerstroom Vlei, Seekoeivlei and Blood River Vlei being the most significant. The Steenkampsberg IBA (SA016) contains two particularly significant areas of wetland systems, both of which provide habitat for threatened waterbird species: Lakensvleispruit and Verloren Valei. The vleis in these areas are threatened by drainage, canalization and the building of trout dams. The following are examples of IBAs which contain floodplain habitat: the Pafuri floodplain lies in the northern Kruger National Park (SA002), Nyl River floodplain (SA008), part of the Pongolo River floodplain lies in the Ndumo Game Reserve (SA052), and the Mkuze River floodplain lies in the Mkuzi Game Reserve (SA057) and Lake St Lucia and Mkuze Swamps (SA058). Coastal vleis are found within the following IBAs: Verlorenvlei (SA103), West Coast National Park (SA105), Rietvlei (SA111), Wilderness–Sedgefield Lakes Complex (SA114), Botriviervlei and Kleinmond Estuary (SA118), De Hoop Vlei (SA119) and the Heuningnes River and Estuary System (SA121). There are extensive vlei and floodplain systems on the Agulhas Plain within the Overberg Wheatbelt IBA (SA115).

PANS

Pans are endorheic wetlands, defined as having closed-drainage systems, with water flowing in from usually fairly small catchments but with no outflow from the pan basins themselves (Allan *et al.* 1995). They are typical of poorly drained and fairly dry regions. Water loss is mainly through evaporation, resulting in saline conditions, especially in the more arid regions. Their shape is usually circular to oval. Water depth is shallow (<3 m), and flooding is characteristically seasonal to erratic.

The typical 'panveld' of South Africa lies on the central plateau (e.g. Noble & Hemens 1978), especially in the Nama Karoo, where Verneukpan, Grootvloer and Vanwyksvlei close to Brandvlei are perhaps the best known, in the southern Kalahari (Parris 1984), and in the grassland region (e.g. Geldenhuys 1982; Allan *et al.* 1995). Pan ecosystems, however, can also be found along the coastline in places, e.g. Yzerfontein Pan north of Cape Town (Hockey *et al.* 1989). The pans in grassland are the most frequently inundated (usually annually), owing to the high-rainfall regime, while those in the drier west (Karoo and Kalahari) are only intermittently flooded in occasional years of high rainfall only. In the eastern parts of the grassland, e.g. in the Lake Chrissie region, rainfall is sufficient to ensure that some pans are essentially permanent and more similar to lakes in their ecological functioning. These pans have a greater diversity and biomass of aquatic vegetation than the highly ephemeral (and saline) western pans and therefore tend to support a greater diversity of waterbirds. However, the western pans, on the rare occasions when they have water, can support vast numbers of birds. When they are dry, they sometimes provide habitat for large concentrations of Kittlitz's Plover.

In the grassland biome, the best-known and ornithologically most important example is Barberspan (e.g. Milstein 1975). The pans in the Welkom area, and extending southwest into the Free State, are also especially significant for waterbirds (e.g. Brooke 1960; Geldenhuys 1982). In the central and eastern grasslands, the East Rand pans (e.g. Tarboton 1977; Allan *et al.* 1995) and the Lake Chrissie system (Allan *et al.* 1995) support an abundant and diverse aquatic avifauna.

A striking feature of a high proportion of the distribution maps for non-passerine waterbirds in ASAB1 is the concentration of records, at high reporting rates, on the eastern plateau of South Africa. This region corresponds with the major grassland panveld (although there are also high densities of artificial impoundments, e.g. farm dams, in this region). The distribution maps in ASAB1 therefore emphasize the critical importance of this region, and its pans, for South Africa's waterbird populations to an extent not previously fully appreciated. It should be borne in mind, however, that most fieldwork for the Southern African Bird Atlas Project took place during a period of drought in southern Africa (Allan *et al.* 1997), when in most years the pan ecosystems in the west did not receive adequate rainfall for sustained inundation. During a higher-rainfall period, waterbirds may be spread more evenly across western South Africa and also into Botswana and Namibia. During drought periods it is likely that the eastern panveld serves as an important refuge.

Many waterbird species have been demonstrated to show two centres of abundance in South Africa: one in the winter-rainfall area of the Western Cape and another on the highveld plateau, e.g. Yellowbilled Egret *Egretta intermedia* and Cape Shoveller *Anas smithii* (ASAB1 52–53, 136–137). It can be speculated that some species may migrate annually between these two regions to exploit the winter-rainfall inundation in the former region and the summer-rainfall inundation in the latter. This is a potentially fruitful field for future research.

No southern African waterbird is so specialized that it can be classed as being exclusive to pan habitats. The avifauna of pans is fairly typical of inland static waterbodies generally, although pans undoubtably provide prime habitat for several species, especially those associated with brackish water conditions. The ephemeral nature of pans results in particularly rich nutrient cycling and these habitats can carry high densities of waterbirds, unlike the situation with more permanent and often artificial waterbodies, although this requires empirical confirmation. The frequent desiccation of pans and their closed drainages, however, are prejudicial to the survival of fish, and mainly piscivorous waterbirds are uncommon at most pans, at least as a feeding habitat, unless they are connected at least occasionally to major drainage systems, or have their water levels artificially maintained and support introduced fish stocks. Typical pan waterbirds include grebes, cormorants, herons and egrets, ibises, spoonbills, flamingos, ducks and geese, coots and waders. Pans may be particularly noteworthy for their ducks and geese, particularly as breeding sites for some of these species, many of which are relatively scarce at estuarine and floodplain habitats (e.g. Geldenhuys 1980 for the South African Shelduck *Tadorna cana*). Inland pans are also important habitats for Palearctic

migrant waders, especially Ringed Plover, Common Sandpiper, Wood Sandpiper, Marsh Sandpiper, Greenshank, Curlew Sandpiper, Little Stint and Ruff (Underhill 1995).

The Chestnutbanded Plover, a Red Data species in South Africa (Barnes 1999), probably comes closest to 'pan specialization' and the vast bulk of the southern African population is found at saline pans. This species benefits from commercial saltworks in pan basins (Allan *et al.* 1995; Hockey 1995). Other waterbirds apparently preferring brackish waters and typical of pan ecosystems are Blacknecked Grebe *Podiceps nigricollis*, South African Shelduck, Cape Teal *Anas capensis*, Greater Flamingo, Lesser Flamingo and Avocet *Recurvirostra avosetta*. Most breeding by Whiskered Terns *Chlidonius hybridus* on the highveld takes place at pans (e.g. Allan 1988) and the breeding sites of the large Greyheaded Gull *Larus cirrocephalus* population centred on the East Rand are at pans, albeit highly modified ones. Pans also serve as roosting sites for some dryland species, e.g. the globally threatened Blue Crane *Anthropoides paradiseus* (Collar *et al.* 1994; Allan 1995). Reedbeds associated with some pans provide roosting sites for species such as European Swallow *Hirundo rustica* and for many weavers, bishops and widows (Allan *et al.* 1995). The Cape Wagtail *Motacilla capensis* is known to congregate along pan shorelines in the central highveld during winter (Tarboton *et al.* 1987a).

The conservation status of pans in the drier regions is relatively sound but those in the higher-rainfall areas are under severe threat from many factors (Allan *et al.* 1995). These include infilling, transformation to artificially permanent waterbodies, pollution, eutrophication, agriculture, mining and industrial development, urbanization, commercial afforestation, road building and invasion of alien biota. Relatively few pans are formally protected. An anthropogenic modification characteristic of the more saline pans is the transformation of their basins brought about by commercial saltworks (Connor 1980).

Barberspan is listed as a 'Wetland of International Importance' under the Ramsar Convention, one of two South African wetlands to be so designated when the convention came into force in 1975 (Cowan 1995). Barberspan and adjacent Leeupan are IBAs (IBA SA026); other pans to qualify were the Lake Chrissie Pans (SA019) and Kamfers Dam (SA032), although water supply to the latter is supplemented by effluent from a sewage works and it is a very modified habitat (Barnes 1998).

IMPOUNDMENTS, SEWAGE WORKS AND SALTWORKS

The river systems of southern Africa are characterized by large numbers of man-made dams, ranging in size from large state impoundments many kilometres in length to small farm dams of only a few hectares in extent. Most are in the higher-rainfall east and extreme south of South Africa; 517 major reservoirs had been constructed by July 1986 (Macdonald 1989). The most comprehensive inventory of South African dams is provided by Department of Water Affairs (1986). There are 44 major dams in the Orange–Vaal catchment (van Zyl 1991). The Vanderkloof and Gariep Dams on the Orange River, the Vaal and Bloemhof Dams on the Vaal River, and the Pongolapoort Dam on the Pongola River have capacities exceeding one billion cubic metres (m^3) and inundate areas exceeding 100 km^2 (Noble & Hemens 1978; Davies & Day 1998). The total annual run-off into South African rivers has been estimated to be 52 billion m^3 (Noble & Hemens 1978); the total capacity of the impoundments is approximately 27 billion m^3 (Davies & Day 1998, Fig 2.13). Total capacity of

South African impoundments is therefore about 52% of the annual run-off.

The total number of small dams on private land in South Africa is unknown but must number many tens of thousands (e.g. Benade & Gaigher 1987 for the former Cape Province). The number of farm dams in KwaZulu-Natal doubled during the period 1956–1986 (Macdonald 1989). Despite the ubiquity of farm dams in the South African landscape, the significance of these habitats to waterbirds has attracted little research attention.

Dams frequently inundate riverine and wetland ecosystems. However, the major ecological impact of these impoundments is on the downstream sections of the rivers affected, e.g. through reducing river flow and removing much of its variability, and altering the seasonality and temperature of flow, sediment loads, channel morphology and water chemistry (Macdonald 1989; O'Keeffe et al. 1989; Davies & Day 1998). However, poor management of dam capacities during major floods often leads to a dam filling to wall-threatening levels, and emergency decisions are taken to release water from a dam faster than the rate of inflow. In consequence, the river downstream of the dam is subjected to unprecedented flood levels after years or even decades of no flood activity.

The aquatic avifauna of large dams in South Africa has been poorly researched; some of the few examples are for the following impoundments, although several of these studies only examine a selection of the waterbird species present: Lake Mentz (3325AA) (Broekhuysen & Taylor 1942; Taylor 1945, 1947), Vogelvlei (3319AC) (Siegfried 1967) and Gariep (Farkas 1981). Liversidge (1958, 1962) reported on the waterbirds associated with mine dams of the Free State Goldfields, and Geldenhuys (1975) covered the ducks and geese on dams in the Free State. Some waterbirds, usually those favouring deep, open-water conditions, have undoubtedly benefited from the construction of dams (e.g. Siegfried 1970) but this has been at the cost of a larger guild of waterbird species, including many threatened species, which have lost habitat through the inundation of marshy and riverine habitats, and through the deleterious downstream impacts on riverine, floodplain and estuarine environments.

Allan (1999) is the only study in the region to examine waterbird populations present in a section of river (the Malibamatso River, a major tributary of the Orange River, in the Lesotho highlands) before and after its inundation by a major dam (Katse Dam). Of the 13 waterbird species present originally, two disappeared after inundation (Black Stork – a Red Data species, and Malachite Kingfisher), two decreased in abundance (Threebanded Plover Charadrius tricollaris and Giant Kingfisher), the status of seven was largely unchanged (Whitebreasted Cormorant, Grey Heron, Hamerkop, Hadeda Ibis Bostrychia hagedash, African Black Duck, Common Sandpiper and Cape Wagtail), and two species increased in abundance (Reed Cormorant Phalacrocorax africanus and Yellowbilled Duck). A further two species colonized the area with inundation (Dabchick Tachybaptus ruficollis and Redknobbed Coot). Although African Black Duck numbers remained stable, a startling finding, considering the 'river specialist' status of this bird, was that a significantly lower proportion of the post-inundation population comprised breeding pairs. This study, however, covered the period immediately after inundation and before the dam had stabilized, and further changes were expected to occur in the waterbird populations with time.

An example of a waterbird benefiting from dams is the African Fish Eagle in the former Transvaal, where an estimated 25% of the total breeding population occurs at impoundments (Tarboton & Allan 1984). In the Free State, the occurrence of African Fish Eagles is largely limited to impoundments exceeding 200 ha and only one of 36 nest sites was natural; the remainder were either in trees that had drowned as a result of dam construction or in exotic trees on islands and shores of dams (Geldenhuys 1984). Williams & Randall (1995) provided examples of the beneficial effects of dams for the pelecaniforms (pelicans, darters and cormorants). Two particularly important functions of large dams are as moulting sites for waterfowl (e.g. Geldenhuys 1975) and dry-season/drought refuges for waterbirds generally (Junor & Marshall 1987 provided an example from Zimbabwe). For example, at least 70% of the global population of the South African Shelduck gathers to moult at only 23 localities in South Africa; all but two of these are large dams (Geldenhuys 1981). They also serve as important breeding sites for some species, e.g. waterfowl (Geldenhuys 1976). These habitats therefore are known to support significant populations of many waterbird species and these include a few species of conservation concern (Brooke 1984). For example, the Pink-backed Pelican have nested at Jozini Dam on the Pongolo River (Tarboton et al. 1987a) and Caspian Tern have bred at the Vaal and Kalkfontein Dams (Cooper et al. 1992).

The saltworks that have the most impact on waterbirds are those within a few kilometres of the shoreline. The saltworks in the interior are mainly based on natural pans and lie in a broad arc encompassing Vryberg, Hopetown and Brandvlei; these operations have limited impact on waterbirds, which use them mainly when they are flooded and salt production generally ceases (Geldenhuys 1976; Connor 1980). Most of the coastal saltworks are on the west coast, with the Berg River estuary area having the largest area of evaporation pans, and in the Swartkops River valley in the Eastern Cape. Martin & Randall (1987) undertook an intensive study of the aquatic avifauna of one of these commercial saltworks, and made recommendations for management strategies that would increase their value for waterbirds.

Another class of artificial wetlands which is important for waterbirds is wastewater treatment (sewage) works. These wetlands can support particularly high densities of aquatic birds owing to the rich nutrient cycling in these systems. Improvements in the technology of processing sewage, however, have reduced waterbird numbers at many wastewater treatments works in recent years. Virtually every town in South Africa has an associated sewage works, and large cities often have several. The total number of such sites is likely to be in the thousands. Well-known examples of sewage works are Strandfontein in Cape Town, and Diepsloot in Johannesburg. Some recent accounts describing the waterbirds of various sewage works include Allan (1990) and Kalejta-Summers et al. (in press b) for Strandfontein, Claassen & Claassen (1991) for the Beaufort West sewage works, Mulder et al. (1993) for O.P.M. Prozesky Nature Reserve, Potchefstroom, and Weiss (1997) for Paarl Sewage Works. The number and diversity of aquatic birds at the Strandfontein sewage works rivals that at many of the major natural wetlands in southern Africa (Kalejta-Summers et al. in press b). These man-made wetlands also provide habitat and drought refuges for some threatened waterbirds (Brooke 1984), e.g. Strandfontein for White Pelican, Greater Flamingo and Caspian Tern, and Paarl Sewage Works for Lesser Flamingo.

Artificial wetlands are included in many IBAs, frequently because the surrounding areas are protected areas (Barnes 1998). Several impoundments within IBAs hold large concentrations of waterbirds: Loskop (IBA SA015), Heyshope (SA020), Spitskop (SA028), Bloemhof (SA039), Allemanskraal (SA044), Sterkfontein (SA046), Gariep (SA048), Krugersdrif (SA049), Kalkfontein (SA050), Pongolapoort

(SA055), Chelmsford (SA059) and Midmar (SA076) Dams. Saltworks in the lower reaches of the Swartkops and Berg Rivers are key components of their respective IBAs (SA096 and SA104). The Strandfontein Sewage Works is the main component of the False Bay Park IBA (SA116). Results presented in this report suggest that several other impoundments may qualify for IBA status.

OVERVIEW

In spite of being a generally arid country, South Africa has an impressive variety of wetland types. Many of these wetlands have satisfied objective criteria that make them globally important for the conservation of just one component of their biodiversity, namely birds. Their value for other components of biodiversity, and the critical importance of maintaining the ecological functioning of wetlands to meet human water demand, has been highlighted by Davies & Day (1998).

ACKNOWLEDGEMENTS

Keith Barnes, John Cooper, Doug Harebottle and James Harrison commented on a draft of this paper. Keith Barnes examined it from the perspective of Important Bird Areas, and made many suggestions for incorporating information from that project into this chapter.

D.G. Allan and L.G. Underhill

An overview of results, 1992–97

THE SITE ANALYSES

There is great variation between CWAC sites in the total number of bird species recorded and the size of the total counts, and it is interesting to compare the results obtained from different wetland types. However, because they concentrate on waterfowl, shorebirds and other relatively obvious species, CWAC counts do not necessarily give an accurate estimate of the number and variety of wetland birds which all types of site may support. At open lagoons, estuaries, saltpans, dams and pans where birds are usually easily visible, counts could theoretically include all the birds present, but at sites with dense emergent and fringing vegetation (e.g. marshes, sewage works, and some pans, lakes and dams) some species which inhabit such vegetation may not be counted, and it is often difficult to estimate total bird numbers. There is also some variation in the completeness of the counts and the total number of counts made, while counts often do not differentiate between those birds which roost (often in large numbers) at the site and those which are dependent on its resources on a more permanent basis, e.g. for foraging or breeding.

Despite these caveats, CWAC data are still very useful aids in assessing the value of CWAC sites in terms of their bird species (overall species richness and the occurrence of threatened species) and of their total bird populations. To provide some indication of relative species richness, Table 1 shows that coastal lakes, estuaries and lagoons yield the largest number of recorded species, with dams and coastal pans also having high totals. The least diverse avifaunas are those of coastal beaches, where only open shoreline habitat exists, and of endorheic pans, which are sometimes relatively small and which often provide relatively few habitat types (for examples, see individual site descriptions).

The total counts recorded from CWAC sites vary greatly between sites and between seasons. Although large wetlands might be expected to hold more birds than smaller ones, factors such as the relative diversity and suitability of habitats greatly affect the number and variety of birds counted. For example, a small sewage works with much habitat diversity may contain as many bird species as a large dam, while a large dam with much open water and a relatively featureless barren shoreline will probably hold fewer birds than a smaller dam which has bays, inlets, and fringing and emergent vegetation.

The individual site analyses show that the wetlands with the highest overall counts are coastal lakes, lagoons and estuaries, at which large numbers of birds congregate to feed and/or roost, and some large inland waterbodies (dams and pans) which hold concentrations of nonbreeding waterfowl (and Redknobbed Coot *Fulica cristata*) and some of which are important moulting sites for ducks and geese. Some sites hold large numbers of birds in both summer and winter, good examples being Spitskop Dam (Northern Cape), Lake St Lucia (KwaZulu-Natal) and the Berg River system (Western Cape). Others, which are often important for Palearctic migrants, hold the largest numbers in summer; examples are Richards Bay (KwaZulu-Natal) and Voëlvlei (Western Cape). Large inland impoundments which hold good numbers of moulting waterfowl include Barberspan (North West), Chelmsford Dam

(KwaZulu-Natal), and the Bloemhof and Gariep Dams (Free State).

It must also be borne in mind that the distribution and abundance of wetland birds can be profoundly affected by rainfall. Much of South Africa is semi-arid to arid and such environments are characterized by rainfall which is not only low but also highly unpredictable. Waterbodies in such regions are often seasonal or ephemeral and individual sites may be dry for several years in succession. When flooded they may hold large concentrations of wetland birds but, as flood events are often not annual, mean count figures for the whole CWAC period may not reflect the periodic significance of the sites for wetland birds. Good examples of erratically flooded sites are the Platfontein and Benfontein pans in the Northern Cape. Furthermore, rainfall may be irregular even in mesic areas, and periods of very low or very high rainfall may result in large fluctuations in the water level of permanent wetlands with consequent great variations in the amount of habitat suitable for some wetland birds, particularly those requiring shallow water, emergent vegetation, or exposed muddy or sandy shorelines. In the case of impoundments, artificial manipulation of the water level may result in the erratic occurrence of such habitats, with similar effects on bird numbers. The effects of such water-level fluctuations on the bird numbers of permanent waterbodies may be seen at sites such as Krugersdrift Dam (Free State) and Albert Falls and Pongola Poort Dams (KwaZulu-Natal).

An important result of the survey is the identification of sites which hold significant concentrations of wetland bird species. One of the criteria for designating a site as an Important Bird Area (IBA) (Barnes 1998) is the regular occurrence of 20 000+ waterbirds (Global IBA) or 10 000+ waterbirds (Sub-regional IBA). In view of the ephemeral nature of many waterbodies it is difficult to define the term 'regularity', and the occurrence of the requisite number of birds may qualify a wetland for inclusion even if the site is flooded only every 4–5 years (Barnes 1998). For many sites the total count figures are shown on a graph; it is clear that at least 13 sites have the potential to hold 10 000+ birds at least in some years, that three of these (Spitskop Dam, the Berg River system and Strandfontein Sewage Works) regularly hold 10 000+ birds, and that two sites (Lake St Lucia and the Wilderness/ Swartvlei system) can sometimes hold over 20 000 birds. Langebaan has the highest counts, regularly holding *c.* 30 000 birds in summer.

A site may also be designated as a Global IBA (Barnes 1998) if it regularly supports any globally critically threatened/endangered species, or significant numbers of globally vulnerable/near-threatened species, or 1% or more of the biogeographic population of a congregatory species (indicated on the analyses by two asterisks; see comments on 'regularity' in the preceding paragraph). It may be designated a Sub-regional IBA if it regularly holds significant numbers of a nationally threatened species, or 0.5% or more of the biogeographic population of a congregatory species (indicated on the analyses by one asterisk). CWAC data show that at least 12 sites which have not been identified as IBAs do, in fact, meet the IBA criteria for biogeographic populations of one or more

Table 1. Number of bird species recorded at different CWAC site types.

Site type	No. of sites	No. of spp.: range	No. of spp.: mean (SD)
Small to large dams	63	3–65	39.9 (16.8)
Sewage works/ponds	20	5–72	42.4 (17.3)
Endorheic pans	34	7–74	28.9 (16.6)
Coastal pans	19	24–79	46.7 (15.8)
Saltworks/saltpans	5	10–50	38.0 (16.6)
Marshes/vleis	14	9–66	50.7 (14.3)
Coastal lakes	10	23–90	56.0 (19.9)
Coastal estuaries/lagoons	24	26–86	55.1 (16.0)
Coastal beaches	2	12	12.0 –

congregatory species, and thus could be considered for IBA status. They include six sites which meet the Global IBA criteria: Krugersdrift Dam, Rocher Pan, Radyn Dam, Paarl Bird Sanctuary, the Keurbooms Estuary, and Knysna Lagoon. The six sites which meet the Sub-regional IBA criteria are Klipvoor Dam, Allemanskraal Dam, the Umgeni Estuary, Theewaterskloof Dam, Wildevoëlvlei and Voëlvlei. Furthermore, counts show that at least 14 other non-IBA sites sometimes hold globally endangered species, or globally or nationally significant numbers of congregatory species, and are thus important and worthy of regular monitoring. While there are probably good reasons for not designating all of the above-mentioned impoundments as IBAs, it is clear that CWAC provides valuable information supplementary to that in Barnes (1998), and the data should certainly be used in a future update of the directory, especially in the case of natural systems like Knysna Lagoon. Furthermore, CWAC provides information which can be used nationally and provincially to prioritize and plan conservation measures for wetland birds.

Table 1 shows that, of 191 sites surveyed, 88 (46%) are artificial habitats (dams, sewage works, sewage ponds, saltworks and saltpans). Many birds have benefited from the construction of such sites, as is clearly shown in the species texts of the recently published Southern African Bird Atlas (Harrison *et al.* 1997a,b; hereafter referred to as ASAB), and the CWAC data from the 88 sites underline the importance of artificial habitats. For example, CWAC data show that Great Crested Grebe *Podiceps cristatus*, Blacknecked Grebe *Podiceps nigricollis* and Dabchick *Tachybaptus ruficollis* all make use of artificial impoundments, especially in winter when some dams hold globally significant numbers of one or more of these species. Some coastal sewage works and saltpans also provide important refuges for nonbreeding Blacknecked Grebes.

The wide use made of artificial impoundments by Whitebreasted Cormorant *Phalacrocorax carbo*, Reed Cormorant *P. africanus* and Darter *Anhinga melanogaster* is clearly shown by the CWAC data; the largest counts of all three species come from dams, some of which hold significant breeding colonies. Dams are also important for Grey Heron *Ardea cinerea* and Blackheaded Heron *A. melanocephala*, and there are good winter counts of the latter species at several dams. Of 72 CWAC sites for the Goliath Heron *A. goliath*, 30 (42%) are dams, and most high counts of this species come from large dams, which also provide breeding sites. Large impoundments are also important as moulting sites for several species of waterfowl (see the Species Analysis summary below). Although the African Marsh Harrier *Circus ranivorus* is normally considered a breeding species of extensive marshes, it also occurs at many other types of wetland, often when foraging; of the 63 CWAC sites at which it was recorded, 24 (38%) are dams and sewage works.

Among the rails, the secretive and poorly known Baillon's Crake *Porzana pusilla* is not entirely confined to inaccessible natural marshes, and often occurs in artificially created habitats, sometimes small and accessible, such as flooded grass and sedges at the margins of dams and sewage ponds. This species undoubtedly occurs at significantly more CWAC sites than the few available records suggest. There are some good counts of the much larger and more easily visible Purple Gallinule *Porphyrio porphyrio* from dams and sewage works, which also often hold good numbers of the Black Crake *Amaurornis flavirostris*, another species which is greatly under-recorded by CWAC. The presence of significant populations of the more aquatic Moorhen *Gallinula chloropus* and Redknobbed Coot at artificially created wetlands is amply demonstrated by CWAC data.

Some African plovers, such as Kittlitz's Plover *Charadrius pecuarius*, Threebanded Plover *C. tricollaris* and Blacksmith Plover *Vanellus armatus*, make extensive use of the shorelines of artificial impoundments, while the last two species are also often numerous at sewage ponds. Palearctic migrant waders also make extensive use of open muddy or sandy shorelines at dams, while sewage works and saltpans may hold good numbers of Marsh Sandpipers *Tringa stagnatilis*, Wood Sandpipers *T. glareola*, Little Stints *Calidris minuta* and Ruff *Philomachus pugnax*. Dams and sewage works also often hold large numbers of the Palearctic Whitewinged Tern *Chlidonias leucopterus*.

The site analyses highlight one group of wetlands which is not yet adequately covered by CWAC: palustrine wetlands. These are characterized by emergent vegetation, usually herbaceous but sometimes also woody, are seasonally to permanently flooded and, although often including areas of open water, open shoreline or mud, are predominantly densely vegetated. Their vegetation may be dominated by reeds, sedges, restios or grass, and they comprise floodplains, swamps and marshes (including vleis); many of their characteristic birds are secretive and poorly known. Only 14 (7%) of 191 CWAC sites fall into this category, designated 'marshes/vleis' in Table 1, and most are significant sites for secretive wetland bird species. However, there are also extensive and significant palustrine wetland habitats at some other sites, including the pans and estuaries of northern coastal KwaZulu-Natal, the sedge pans and reed pans in the Lake Chrissie area, and coastal lakes and estuaries in the Western Cape such as the Wilderness Lakes, Groenvlei, Verlorenvlei and the Bitou River. Sewage works also often have good habitat of this type, and Malandeni Sewage Works, Ladysmith, is one of the most important palustrine wetland sites in interior KwaZulu-Natal. Other inland sites also have good marshy habitat, examples being Prozesky Bird Sanctuary (North West), the Lakenvlei system (Mpumalanga), Rietspruit (Gauteng) and the Klip-

Table 2. Numbers of CWAC sites affected by different levels of threat.

Site type	Total no. of sites	No. of sites with top threat-level				Total (%) sites threatened	
		Critical	Severe	Important	Mild	Any threat	Critical/severe
Small to large dams	63	4	8	14	24	50 (79%)	12 (19%)
Sewage works/ponds	20	2	3	4	5	14 (70%)	5 (25%)
Endorheic pans	34	1	3	4	9	17 (50%)	4 (12%)
Coastal pans	19	3	6	1	4	14 (74%)	9 (47%)
Saltworks/saltpans	5	0	1	0	4	5 (100%)	1 (20%)
Marshes/vleis	14	0	8	4	2	14 (100%)	8 (57%)
Coastal lakes	10	1	3	1	5	10 (100%)	4 (40%)
Coastal estuaries/lagoons	24	8	6	6	4	24 (100%)	14 (58%)
Coastal beaches	2	0	0	1	0	1 (50%)	0
Grand Total	191	19	38	35	57	149 (78%)	57 (30%)

fontein Birds Sanctuary (KwaZulu-Natal). Some dams also have patches of fringing reedbeds or marshy habitat, especially where streams flow into them or in seepage areas below dam walls; even small patches of such habitat may support Little Bittern and rails, crakes and flufftails.

Considering the importance of palustrine wetlands, the lack of current knowledge of these habitats in South Africa, the destruction and degradation which they have already suffered, and the threats which they face (e.g. Begg 1989; Breen & Begg 1989; Kotze & Breen 1994; Kotze *et al.* 1995; Breen *et al.* 1997; Taylor 1997a, 1997b; Cowan & van Riet 1998), it is essential that more attention be paid to these habitats and their birds. Further comments on this subject appear in the 'Whither CWAC?' section of this chapter.

THREATS

The types of threat noted as affecting CWAC sites fall into the following 15 broad categories (not listed in order of frequency or importance):

❑ pollution and poisoning by agrochemicals (e.g. fertilizers, pesticides, herbicides), industrial and domestic liquid waste (including oil), and effluent from sewage treatment works;

❑ eutrophication as a result of agrochemical pollution (this may lead to algal blooms, deoxygenation of the water, and the excessive spread of certain types of vegetation);

❑ reed encroachment, often a result of eutrophication following nutrient enrichment by agrochemicals etc.;

❑ invasion by alien vegetation, largely water plants (e.g. *Eichhornia crassipes, Myriophyllum aquaticum, Salvinia molesta, Paspalum vaginatum*); also commercial afforestation in the immediate catchment of wetlands;

❑ large, erratic or otherwise unnatural fluctuations in water level, and also prolonged very high or very low water levels (such effects may be caused by modification or manipulation of the normal inflow, or by water abstraction, dam-wall building, and stormwater run-off);

❑ siltation caused by increased sediment deposits from erosion in the catchment or from industrial or urban development;

❑ residential or industrial development which encroaches on the wetland;

❑ pollution by solid waste and rubbish from industrial or residential sources;

❑ landfill, mining, severe bank or channel erosion, and the dumping of tailings from adjacent mines;

❑ excessive grazing or trampling by livestock; also excessive vegetation cutting or clearance, and cultivation along wetland margins;

❑ human disturbance, particularly boating and especially power boats and jetskis, and water-skiing, microlight aircraft, and the use of four-wheel-drive vehicles on beaches;

❑ hunting or poaching;

❑ fishing and/or the introduction of alien fish species;

❑ predation or disturbance by domestic animals such as dogs and cats;

❑ overhead power lines across or adjacent to wetlands.

The details from the threats forms, together with information from the standard CWAC site forms (completed by compilers at each six-monthly count), are summarized in Tables 2 and 3. Table 2 shows that 149 (78%) of the 191 wetlands included in the analysis are affected by at least one known threat. Of these 149 wetlands, 19 sites (10%) suffer at least one critical threat (seven sites have two critical threats and five have both critical and severe threats), while a further 38 sites (20%) suffer one to three severe threats. Thus the wetland bird populations at 57 (30%) of the CWAC sites are critically or severely threatened, and almost all of these also suffer lower levels of threat (important or mild). Including the additional 35 sites at which important threats represent the highest level, 92 (48%) of CWAC sites are threatened by short-term to long-term declines in their bird populations.

The commonest threat to CWAC sites is pollution or poisoning by substances which are either pumped directly into the wetlands or their inflow rivers or streams or, more commonly, which enter the systems via runoff from the immediate catchment (Table 3). This threat is listed for 57 (30%) of the 190 sites, but probably affects more sites than this, at least to a limited extent. It should also be noted that, although eutrophication is listed as a threat to only 32 (17%) of the sites, it could potentially affect all those sites which have an inflow of agrochemicals, sewage effluent and other nutrient-rich pollutants. Other threats which affect more than 25% of the sites are damage to plant communities and wetland margins by livestock pressure, vegetation cutting, and cultivation, and the various types of human activity (boating, aircraft, vehicles) which come under the broad heading of disturbance. 'Disturbance' assumes more significance if one includes with

Overview of results

Table 3. *Types and levels of threat affecting CWAC sites* (n = 191 sites). (See text for full description of threat types.)

| Type of threat | No. of sites affected by threat level | | | | Total & (%) |
	Critical	Severe	Important	Mild	Sites affected
Pollution/poisoning	3	10	16	28	57 (30%)
Eutrophication	1	4	9	18	32 (17%)
Reed encroachment	1	4	9	4	18 (9%)
Alien vegetation	2	5	6	10	23 (12%)
Water-level fluctuations	2	12	12	13	39 (20%)
Siltation	3	2	6	22	33 (17%)
Residential/industrial development	4	3	9	7	23 (12%)
Solid waste/rubbish	0	0	5	5	10 (5%)
Landfill/mining/erosion/mine tailings	1	5	4	6	16 (8%)
Livestock grazing/trampling; vegetation cutting; cultivation	2	5	13	29	49 (26%)
Human disturbance	4	4	15	26	49 (26%)
Hunting/poaching	1	2	5	21	29 (15%)
Fishing/alien fish introduction	0	3	6	18	27 (14%)
Domestic animals	0	0	7	6	13 (7%)
Overhead power lines	0	0	5	12	17 (9%)

it other human activities, such as hunting, poaching and fishing, which also have a direct disturbance effect. Other important threats include the adverse effects of unnatural fluctuations in water levels (and the prolonged maintenance of unnaturally high or low water levels) and the effects of increased sediment deposits.

Table 2 highlights the disturbing fact that the bird populations of all CWAC saltworks, saltpans, marshes, vleis (including floodplains), coastal lakes, and coastal estuaries and lagoons suffer from some level of threat. The situation is obviously most serious at coastal estuaries and lagoons, 14 (58%) of which are severely threatened (eight critically), but 47% of coastal pans and 40% of coastal lakes are also critically or severely threatened. It has already been noted that these wetland types hold some of the largest concentrations of birds recorded during the survey, and have the greatest species richness. The only other sites with a comparably high incidence of serious threats are palustrine wetlands, eight out of 14 (57%) of which have critical/severe threats; these wetlands also have a high species richness. Endorheic pans have the lowest overall incidence of threat, only half of the 34 sites being threatened, and few sites are seriously affected. With the exception of coastal shorelines (only two CWAC sites), at least 70% of wetlands of all other types are threatened. However, in the case of dams, more than one third of the affected sites currently suffer only mild threats.

Tables 2 and 3 do not show the relative importance of different threats at different wetland types, and these may be summarized as follows. Dams are subjected to a wide variety of threats, often not of a serious nature, and commonly including the expected threats of pollution, human disturbance (especially boating), hunting, fishing, and grazing pressure at dam margins. Sewage works, as may be expected, appear to be most commonly affected by threats related to nutrient enrichment, pollution, rubbish accumulation, the growth of reeds and alien vegetation, and human disturbance factors such as hunting, fishing, livestock grazing, and adjacent residential development. Endorheic pans are mainly affected, at relatively low levels, by grazing, adverse water-level fluctuations, human disturbance, domestic animals, and the impact of alien plants; coastal pans appear to suffer mostly from water-level fluctuations, cattle grazing/trampling, siltation,

and various forms of human activity including hunting and fishing. Palustrine wetland sites are most affected by chemical pollution and the associated effects of nutrient enrichment, and also by siltation, grazing pressure and unnatural water-level fluctuations.

Coastal lakes are mostly threatened, often at a low level, by eutrophication, siltation, alien plants, reed encroachment, and human disturbance/hunting/fishing; they may also be threatened by variations in water level, and by residential development. Estuaries and lagoons suffer a wide range of threats, the commonest and most serious being human disturbance (including hunting and fishing), pollution and adverse water-level fluctuations; other frequent threats include siltation and grazing pressure. Two saltworks/saltpan sites are potentially threatened by reclamation, while all coastal sites with beaches are potentially threatened by disturbance from four-wheel-drive vehicles.

Very few, if any, CWAC sites can be regarded as being completely free of any threat. The absence of listed threats does not necessarily mean that a site is safe, and in some cases reflects only that specific information is not available. At some sites threats may not yet be obvious, but the nature and position of the wetlands suggest that threats probably exist. For example, any waterbody with agricultural land in its immediate catchment must suffer to some extent from nutrient enrichment caused by fertilizer run-off, and must therefore be threatened, if only in the long term, by eutrophication and thus possibly also by reed encroachment, deoxygenation, vegetation death, algal blooms, and other severe effects. All types of wetland in agricultural catchments are also potentially threatened by pollution from pesticides and herbicides which may have serious effects on the wetland biota.

Although not specifically listed, other forms of pollution can also affect wetlands. For example, relatively few of the pans in the Lake Chrissie area have listed threats (some are affected by eutrophication and increased vegetation growth as a result of agrochemical pollution), but all may be threatened to some extent by atmospheric pollution, which gives rise to acid rain (J. de Villiers *in litt.*).

My personal impression, from observations made during a nation-wide survey of palustrine wetlands (Taylor 1997a,b), is that the threats have not been overstated by CWAC compilers and, indeed, that the levels of threat may sometimes be more serious than has been recorded. This applies especially to threats such as eutrophication, and disturbance by power-boats (including jetskis) and four-wheel-drive vehicles, and also to threats affecting sites with significant palustrine wetland habitat, which is often in relatively poor condition as a result of a variety of factors. Such factors not only include those listed (especially herbicide pollution, siltation, excessive penetration of dense vegetation by large herbivores, and increased dominance of marsh vegetation by single species such as *Phragmites* or *Typha*) but also some which are less immediately obvious. These include: too infrequent burning (which allows an excessive build-up of moribund vegetation); too frequent (e.g. annual) burning; the reduction of vegetation height and cover by excessive grazing pressure (especially by spring grazing after annual burning); erosion due to distur-bance of wetland soil by trampling, grazing and cultivation; the effects of commercial afforestation in the immediate catch-ment; and the permanent lowering of the water table by ditches and drains (often a long-established problem).

South Africa is subject to a high occurrence of wetland loss and degradation (e.g. Breen *et al.* 1997) and, given the ever-increasing pressure from an expanding human population, threats to wetlands in South Africa will continue to increase. According to a summary provided by Kotze *et al.* (1995), threats appear to be greatest in:

❑ the coastal belt (high human population, high agricultural and urban development), including the degradation of estuaries (a serious problem),
❑ the high-rainfall areas of the marginal zone between the coast and the escarpment (high agricultural potential),
❑ semi-arid areas of the inland marginal zone (high erod-ibility of wetland soils).

Some examples of these high levels of threat are given by the CWAC analysis, which highlights the severe threats to estuaries and coastal lagoons, and records the adverse effects of agriculture at many sites. In general, in the arid and semi-arid areas of the interior plateau, such as the panveld regions of the western Free State, threats to wetlands tend to be less severe because of a low human population, reduced erosional degradation, and soils which are unsuitable for agriculture (Gueldenhuys 1981; Allan *et al.* 1995; Breen *et al.* 1997), and in the CWAC analysis the lowest incidence and levels of threat are recorded for the endorheic pans. However, in the former Transvaal, threats to endorheic pans may be severe and can include agricultural development, mining, industrial development, road building, urbanization and commercial afforestation (Allan *et al.* 1995).

Of major concern is that in South Africa there is no national wetland conservation policy or strategy (Breen *et al.* 1997), and there is also a lack of basic information on individual wetlands, a poor understanding of wetland functions and values, and a lack of management guidelines to promote the wise use of wetland resources. These are serious problems to overcome, but the CWAC scheme can help by providing information on the conservation significance of many wet-lands for bird species, and on the incidence and severity of threats to different wetland types and their birds. It is encour-aging that legislation specifically designed to protect wetlands was formulated recently, within the Environment Conserva-tion Act of 1998, but it remains to be seen whether it will be implemented effectively, especially as this task will probably devolve predominantly upon overstretched provincial depart-ments of environmental affairs.

Some of the threats currently affecting CWAC sites and other wetlands important for birds could be alleviated by good management practices. Much mismanagement of palustrine wetlands results from ignorance, on the part of both landown-ers and managers, of the value of the wetland resources under their control and of the correct management procedures nec-essary to safeguard these resources (pers. obs.). The adoption of such procedures need not be prohibitively expensive or time-consuming, with significant improvements achievable through education and advice.

THE SPECIES ANALYSES

Afrotropical and subtropical species

One of the most valuable results to emerge from the CWAC analysis is the provision of evidence for seasonal variations in the occurrence patterns of species for which regular movements are unknown or poorly understood. No regular movements are described for the Whitebreasted and Reed Cormorants, but the analyses indicate that, in both species, winter peaks are commoner at coastal localities and summer peaks at inland sites (e.g. the Free State and the former Trans-vaal). The Blackcrowned Night Heron *Nycticorax nycticorax* is suggested to be nomadic and also a partial migrant, com-monest in the breeding season (ASAB1); in support of this theory, CWAC counts are higher, and isolated occurrences more frequent, over much of its range in summer, and often in July in the Western Cape, where it breeds immediately after the winter rains. In the Glossy Ibis *Plegadis falcinellus*, winter movement to the tropics are suspected, and there is a marked decrease in winter numbers at most CWAC sites.

The Hadeda Ibis *Bostrychia hagedash* is regarded as mainly sedentary but as possibly having some regional move-ments in response to localized rainfall (ASAB1). The CWAC analysis shows winter peaks at many permanent wetlands, reflecting the widespread occurrence of nonbreeding flocks at such sites; whether these birds are of local or remote origin is not clear. There is apparently no evidence that the African Spoonbill *Platalea alba* has any regular migration and it is regarded only as nomadic in response to habitat changes and rain. CWAC gives an indication of seasonal movements in that the species is more widespread and numerous in the breeding season in coastal KwaZulu-Natal (winter) and the Western Cape (summer), and is locally commoner in summer in the northeast interior, possibly because habitat there is more extensive then.

The analysis shows seasonal concentrations, at permanent waters, of three heron species which are assumed to be largely resident. There are marked summer peaks of the Grey Heron at some CWAC sites, possibly associated with breeding, and winter peaks (postbreeding dispersal?) at others; the propor-tion of summer peaks is highest at dams. The Blackheaded Heron is thought to have some seasonal local movements associated with changes in food availability, and CWAC data show marked winter peaks at numerous sites (dams, vleis, pans, sewage works, etc.). Although the Goliath Heron is acknowledged to be perhaps only dispersive and nomadic, moving when water levels change, CWAC data show marked summer peaks at many sites of regular occurrence, especially in the interior.

Most members of the family Rallidae are generally under-recorded by CWAC, but fairly good data exist for the rela-tively conspicuous Moorhen. The African race *meridionalis* is normally regarded as sedentary, but seasonal local move-ments are widely reported. Although known to breed at sea-sonal and temporary wetlands in southern Africa, movements are not shown by ASAB1, and it is resident at many CWAC sites. However, CWAC counts at 14 permanent waterbodies, from the Western Cape to the Free State, Mpumalanga and KwaZulu-Natal, show a great winter increase in numbers, suggesting regular winter influxes of birds which have bred elsewhere in seasonal habitat. For the more secretive African Rail *Rallus caerulescens*, Black Crake and Purple Gallinule, the survey shows that apparent winter peaks can be due to increased visibility rather than increased abundance.

The highlighting of under-recorded species is another valuable outcome of the analysis, which thus indicates which species need extra attention. As well as the secretive rails, crakes and gallinules, other species which fall into this category include Painted Snipe *Rostratula benghalensis*, Ethiopian Snipe *Gallinago nigripennis*, Purple Heron *Ardea purpurea*, Blackcrowned Night Heron and Grass Owl *Tyto capensis*. Some other species are rarely recorded because their preferred habitats are not well covered by CWAC, examples being African Finfoot *Podica senegalensis* and Halfcollared Kingfisher *Alcedo semitorquata*.

The analyses are particularly interesting for waterfowl. They highlight the occurrence of moult migrations in several species, such as South African Shelduck *Tadorna cana*, Egyptian Goose *Alopochen aegyptiacus*, Southern Pochard *Netta erythrophthalma* and Spurwinged Goose *Plectropterus gambensis*, and also provide new information on seasonal fluctuations in numbers of some species. For example, ASAB1 suggests that the Whitefaced Duck *Dendrocygna viduata* has nonbreeding-season (winter) movements northwards out of southern Africa, but at 41 of 56 CWAC sites throughout its main South African range, peak numbers of nonbreeders (including many large counts) were recorded in winter. These birds may have come from ephemeral breeding sites in the region, and such movements and nonbreeding concentrations may not be apparent from atlas data (see Introduction). The Redbilled Teal *Anas erythrorhyncha* is also known to exploit temporary waters, and when these disappear in the dry season large flocks gather at permanent sites. CWAC counts show that Western and Eastern Cape sites together have approximately equal number of summer peaks and winter peaks, but 46 sites elsewhere have a definite winter peak and only 12 a summer peak.

The Cape Shoveller *A. smithii* is regarded as largely resident, although some movement takes place between the Western Cape and the highveld, where large numbers occur after good rains. The analysis shows large summer (postbreeding) peaks at most major Western Cape sites; winter peaks predominate on the highveld and in the KwaZulu-Natal coastal region where counts are small; some Free State dams have summer peaks. It is suggested that large-scale movements of the Knobbilled Duck *Sarkidiornis melanotos* occur out of southern Africa in winter (ASAB1), but CWAC data show that, at sites where 3+ birds are recorded, almost all occurrences are in July, and that there are no January records from KwaZulu-Natal, which has 12 of 31 CWAC sites and the majority of birds.

For a few migrant species the analysis also highlights years in which birds were particularly abundant, or when local movements were particularly widespread. Counts of Cape Cormorant *Phalacrocorax capensis* peak in summer on the west coast, where breeding occurs, and in winter to the east, from the Wilderness Lakes to KwaZulu-Natal, where counts are normally small and irregular. However, in winter 1994 large counts were recorded in KwaZulu-Natal at Kosi Bay and Lake St Lucia, and isolated records also came from six sites from Verlorenvlei (Western Cape) to Richards Bay (KwaZulu-Natal). Counts confirm that Pygmy Geese *Nettapus auritus* are more numerous and widespread in winter, and also show

that particularly good numbers occurred in the 1992 and 1995 winters. In winter 1994, CWAC recorded unusually high numbers of Curlew *Numenius arquata*, a Palearctic migrant, at three freshwater-pan and floodplain sites in northern coastal KwaZulu-Natal.

The analyses also provide interesting information on the movements of some African waders for which migrations are poorly understood. The Blacksmith Plover, for example, is not known to have regular migrations although postbreeding dispersal occurs and there are irregular movements in response to flooding and drying of habitats. CWAC data for this species indicate regular seasonal variations in numbers, showing a preponderance of summer peaks in all regions, most consistently in the Western Cape. Habitat changes may cause much movement of Wattled Plovers *Vanellus senegallus* in the nonbreeding season, and CWAC data show fewer birds in winter at high-altitude sites (possibly owing to reduced prey availability), and at some sites where habitat may dry out; seasonal movements may be local, as sites with winter and summer peaks occur in the same areas. In the Blackwinged Stilt *Himantopus himantopus*, for which movements are poorly known, the analysis shows winter peaks at KwaZulu-Natal sites, where good breeding habitat may occur, summer peaks at Northern Cape sites (possibly representing influxes of birds from the north, as suggested by ASAB1), and both winter and summer peaks at Western Cape sites.

The data for the Kelp Gull *Larus dominicanus* confirm the bird's eastward coastal movement to KwaZulu-Natal in the winter, while the data for the Greyheaded Gull *L. cirrocephalus* show the expected winter peaks at breeding sites and summer peaks at many other inland and coastal sites, including sewage works, saltpans, dams, estuaries, and permanent and ephemeral pans. The Swift Tern *Sterna bergii* is known to disperse widely after breeding, and the analysis shows winter peaks at some Eastern Cape and KwaZulu-Natal sites which are consistent with the suggestion that southwestern Cape birds move east after breeding (ASAB1). CWAC data also show summer peaks at several Western Cape sites, just before the breeding season.

The Site Analysis section of this chapter briefly discusses some sites which hold large numbers of wetland birds or globally and nationally significant concentrations of one or more species. The CWAC data also give a good indication of which *regions* hold the greatest concentrations of individual wetland bird species, useful information to have whether or not such numbers are of global or national significance. For example, CWAC data show that Western Cape sites hold globally significant numbers of Dabchick (in winter), Cape Shoveller (in summer), Kelp Gull, Hartlaub's Gull *Larus hartlaubii* and Swift Tern. Globally significant numbers of Darter occur in the Western Cape and the North West Province, of African Spoonbill in the Western Cape, North West, Free State and KwaZulu-Natal provinces, and of Egyptian Goose and Yellowbilled Duck *Anas undulata* at dams in the Free State where birds congregate to moult. Globally significant numbers of moulting South African Shelduck also occur at these Free State dams in the summer, as well as in the North West and the Western Cape, while moulting Spurwinged Geese concentrate mainly at sites in KwaZulu-Natal and the Free State.

For the Greater Flamingo *Phoenicopterus ruber*, globally significant counts are recorded in the Northern Cape (Kimberley area) and western North West, at Western Cape coastal sites, and at Lake St Lucia. Large concentrations of Redknobbed Coot, again involving globally significant numbers, are recorded from seven large waterbodies in the North West, Free State, Northern Cape and Western Cape. The largest concentrations of Southern Pochard and Blacksmith Plover are recorded on the highveld and at sites in the Western Cape, while significant winter concentrations of Blacknecked Grebe occur along Cape coasts and in the panveld region of the highveld.

Wetlands of interior KwaZulu-Natal hold good numbers of Hottentot Teal *Anas hottentota*, as well as many large winter concentrations of Hadeda Ibis, while coastal CWAC sites in that province are important for a wide variety of species. For example, they provided the only records of Woollynecked Stork *Ciconia episcopus* and Openbilled Stork Stork *Anastomus lamelligerus*, almost all records of Pygmy Goose and Lesser Jacana *Microparra capensis*, most large counts of African Jacana *Actophilornis africanus*, and many records of African Pied Wagtail *Motacilla aguimp* during the survey period. The largest colony of Caspian Tern *Sterna caspia* is also on this coast, at St Lucia.

A review of the sites at which a particular wetland bird species occurs gives much information on the habitat preferences of that species. Comparing such information with the details available in ASAB and other publications (e.g. Cramp *et al*. 1977, 1980, 1983, 1985; Del Hoyo *et al*. 1992, 1994, 1996; Urban *et al* 1986; Fry *et al*. 1988; Keith *et al*. 1992) shows that some species are recorded in habitats which are not mentioned in these standard references. In most cases such habitats are artificial, but they may be important for some species; for example, CWAC data for the African Fish Eagle show that 46% of 97 CWAC sites are dams and sewage works, and that this eagle breeds at some dams. (For each species, any otherwise undocumented habitat types are mentioned in the species analysis text, with a summary of the published information on habitat preferences.)

Palearctic migrants

The survey data generally provide relatively little new or surprising information for Palearctic migrants, but they confirm the known distribution and status of the regularly occurring species. Good examples include the occurrence of Ringed Plover *Charadrius hiaticula* predominantly in coastal regions of the Eastern and Western Cape and KwaZulu-Natal, the concentrations of Knot *Calidris canutus* on the Western Cape coast, the large numbers of Ruff in the panveld region of the highveld, and the concentrations of Little Terns *Sterna albifrons* in northern coastal KwaZulu-Natal. They also indicate that the most significant concentrations of Greenshank *Tringa nebularis* occur at Western and Eastern Cape coastal sites, and of Curlew Sandpiper *Calidris ferruginea* at coastal sites in the Western Cape, Eastern Cape and KwaZulu-Natal. The counts also give a useful indication of the most important sites for individual species; for example, see species such as the Grey Plover *Pluvialis squatarola*, Turnstone *Arenaria interpres*, Terek Sandpiper *Xenus cinereus*, Curlew, Whimbrel *Numenius phaeopus*, Sandwich Tern *Sterna sandvicensis* and Common Tern *S. hirundo*. The regular records, from at least one site, of the infrequently recorded Yellow Wagtail *Motacilla flava* are of particular interest.

The survey also highlights sites at which globally and nationally significant numbers of Palearctic migrants occur. While important sites for all these species coincide largely with the information given in existing publications (e.g. Underhill 1995), the survey results often add to the details available in such publications. For the Grey Plover, CWAC data indicate a decrease in numbers at Langebaan Lagoon which is worthy of note. In other cases, apparently increasing numbers are highlighted, such as those of Terek Sandpiper, Greenshank and Knot at the Swartkops Estuary.

The survey results effectively highlight the relative extent to which individuals (usually first-year birds) of different species remain in South Africa during the austral winter, and provide an indication of the most important localities for overwintering birds and of population sizes at these sites: see, for example, the analyses for Grey Plover, Turnstone, Curlew Sandpiper, Sanderling *Calidris alba*, Curlew, Whimbrel and Common Tern. The Little Stint data provide interesting evidence for widespread winter occurrences, occasionally in good numbers, which is not mentioned in ASAB1. The Common Sandpiper *Actitis hypoleucos* data show good winter numbers at one coastal and two inland sites, which may reflect concentrations of early arrivals at waters in largely dry areas.

For the Squacco Heron *Ardeola ralloides* and Little Bittern *Ixobrychus minutus*, local populations of which are augmented by unknown numbers of Palearctic migrants during the summer months, the CWAC data do not indicate the relative numbers of Palearctic and African birds present in the summer, but do support the suggestions (ASAB1) that local birds are also migratory to some extent, many leaving South Africa in the dry season.

Regarding the habitat preferences of Palearctic migrants, the CWAC data also give information additional to that provided by ASAB and other sources. For example, CWAC highlights the occurrence of Turnstones at some coastal saltpans, and the large concentrations of Wood Sandpipers which can occur at sewage works, a good habitat for this species.

WHITHER CWAC?

This report shows that CWAC is producing important and meaningful results which are not available through any other wetland monitoring project; this fact should be emphasized to all organizations and individuals involved. This is particularly important today, when tight budgets and reduced resources tend to restrict the amount of fieldwork undertaken by professionals. Although many sites are counted by enthusiastic amateurs, counts of others, especially of large waterbodies and extensive wetland systems, are organized and run by professional ornithologists working for national and provincial conservation organizations. If long-term and potentially costly projects such as waterbird counts are not shown to produce valuable results, there is the danger that they may be discontinued, with consequent loss of valuable information. Not only is it important to establish the numbers and variety of birds which occur at CWAC sites; it is equally important to measure changes in the bird populations and species diversity of these sites, which may function as indicators of regional, national, and even international trends in bird population levels. It is to be hoped that the CWAC scheme will not only continue at its present level, but will increase in scope.

Considering the data currently collected, and the comments already made on the results obtained, it is possible to suggest ways of improving the value of the data:

❑ For each count, provide information on which species are breeding at the site, and in approximately what numbers. Monitor to see if breeding numbers are stable, increasing or decreasing.

❑ Monitor threats regularly and provide more information on threats to sites. Indicate if threats may affect certain species more than others.

❑ If counts are unusually high or low at a site, give details of the habitat and weather conditions which may have contributed. If possible, mention whether the observed trends are also apparent at other local sites.

❑ In periodic reports such as this, provide an index of

change in status for all species, at each site. Comparisons between neighbouring sites would be useful.

❏ In periodic reports such as this, provide regional and/or national indices of change in status for all species.

The above additions would improve the quality of existing information without significantly increasing the scope of the scheme. Considering possible enhancements to the scheme, based on the experiences of census work in other parts of the world (see, for example, Dodman 1997; Dodman & Rose 1997; Rose 1997), the following ideas are advanced:

❏ Continue to encourage the inclusion of new sites, with priority given according to (1) size and numbers of waterbirds, (2) wetland status as part of an IBA or potential IBA, and (3) the need to obtain a representative sample of wetlands, both regionally and by wetland type. Include more palustrine and riverine wetlands, to improve coverage of these important wetland types.

❏ The scope of CWAC should be expanded to include the collection of data on the roosting and breeding sites of waterbirds at wetlands.

❏ Surveys of shorebirds, gulls and terns along the entire coastline of South Africa should be repeated. Apart from a 1995/96 survey between the Orange and Olifants River estuaries, population size estimates are still based on surveys done in the late 1970s and early 1980s.

❏ Include samples of small farm dams from selected areas in order to estimate the contribution to the maintenance of waterbird populations made by this very numerous class of wetland, and to assess how their contribution could be enhanced.

❏ For wetlands with no CWAC data, make provision for inclusion into the database of occasional counts made at any time of the year. Register all sites which have any data.

❏ Historical datasets of waterbird counts should be captured and curated as part of the CWAC scheme. Examples are the duck counts of the African Waterfowl Enquiry, and the surveys of the nature conservation departments of the former Transvaal, the former Orange Free State and the former Cape Province.

❏ Encourage the counting of secretive waterbird species (especially members of the family Rallidae) at all potentially suitable sites. Provide tape-recordings to assist in the identification of calls and to allow limited playback for the purpose of establishing which species occur, and provide instructions on the safe usage of this technique. Even presence/absence data for such species would considerably enhance our knowledge of these birds' distribution and status.

❏ Carry out more frequent monitoring of particularly important sites (e.g. monthly or every three months) to investigate fluctuations in numbers, to allow more accurate timing of migratory and nomadic movements, and to help establish geographical boundaries for discrete populations. For species which may congregate at times other than January and July, establish counts at times which will enable peak numbers to be counted.

❏ Try to identify the factors governing bird numbers at CWAC sites. This will involve the monitoring not only of threats but of other environmental factors; fixed-point photography is a useful technique in this regard.

❏ Initiate special surveys for monitoring priority regions, habitats, sites and species, as and when necessary, e.g. use simultaneous coordinated counts at key sites to develop more accurate population estimates for selected priority species. Investigate the international implementation of such surveys.

❏ Develop systems to use bird population trends and threats information to predict wetland deterioration, and to disseminate such information to landowners and managers. Adopt an advocacy programme which actively encourages wise management practices. Actively support the adoption of a national wetland policy.

The future of wetlands and their birds in South Africa depends heavily on the education of landowners, managers, local communities, and government decision-makers, in the values of wetlands and on the need to establish policies to ensure sustainable utilization of wetland resources through wise management. The CWAC scheme can make a significant contribution by improving the scope and depth of its coverage to provide more information on which to base conservation-related decisions, and by highlighting threats to wetlands and actively encouraging wise management. It can also help by involving local communities in wetland monitoring and encouraging community involvement in wetland management issues. CWAC workers have the knowledge, and can create the opportunity, to provide training and education programmes to promote the involvement of local people in these activities. The widespread promotion of education, public awareness and training at all levels of society is an essential first step towards achieving any meaningful fulfilment of wetland conservation objectives in Africa.

ACKNOWLEDGEMENTS

James Harrison and Les Underhill commented on a draft of this chapter.

P.B. Taylor

Site accounts

Texts by P.B. Taylor

Graphics by R.A. Navarro

Pietersburg Bird Sanctuary, Pietersburg, Northern Province
23° 51' S 29° 27' E (2329CD)

A reserve with dams and a seasonal marsh. The count for summer 1997 shows some notable concentrations of waterbirds, including a good count of Knobbilled Duck (the only high summer count from any site during the survey period) and the highest summer count of Sacred Ibis from any site. The count of Southern Pochard is good for an area where this duck is not widespread; there were also reasonable counts of Redbilled Teal, Hottentot Teal, Maccoa Duck and Wattled Plover for the region. Halfcollared Kingfisher also occurs. A threat is the presence of overhead power lines.

		Summer (1) Mean	Max.	Winter (1) Mean	Max.			Summer (1) Mean	Max.	Winter (1) Mean	Max.
008	Dabchick	21	21	5	5	115	Knobbilled Duck	18	18	0	0
055	Whitebreasted Cormorant	50	50	14	14	117	Maccoa Duck	5	5	0	0
058	Reed Cormorant	19	19	2	2	148	African Fish Eagle	2	2	0	0
060	Darter	6	6	0	0	213	Black Crake	6	6	6	6
063	Blackheaded Heron	6	6	0	0	226	Moorhen	17	17	26	26
067	Little Egret	4	4	0	0	228	Redknobbed Coot	31	31	31	31
071	Cattle Egret	26	26	23	23	249	Threebanded Plover	2	2	0	0
072	Squacco Heron	2	2	0	0	258	Blacksmith Plover	22	22	20	20
074	Greenbacked Heron	6	6	5	5	260	Wattled Plover	12	12	0	0
076	Blackcrowned Night Heron	2	2	0	0	264	Common Sandpiper	14	14	4	4
091	Sacred Ibis	420	420	7	7	266	Wood Sandpiper	45	45	0	0
093	Glossy Ibis	2	2	0	0	269	Marsh Sandpiper	12	12	0	0
094	Hadeda Ibis	6	6	3	3	270	Greenshank	8	8	0	0
095	African Spoonbill	2	2	0	0	284	Ruff	81	81	15	15
099	Whitefaced Duck	28	28	0	0	295	Blackwinged Stilt	14	14	8	8
102	Egyptian Goose	0	0	29	29	428	Pied Kingfisher	3	3	0	0
104	Yellowbilled Duck	8	8	0	0	429	Giant Kingfisher	0	0	2	2
107	Hottentot Teal	16	16	4	4	431	Malachite Kingfisher	2	2	0	0
108	Redbilled Teal	33	33	12	12	713	Cape Wagtail	4	4	3	3
112	Cape Shoveller	2	2	6	6		Total	977	977	225	225
113	Southern Pochard	20	20	0	0		No. of species		40		

Rust de Winter Dam, Pienaarsrivier, Northern Province
25° 13' S 28° 30' E (2528AB)

Only two summer and two winter counts are available for this dam, and these have recorded a good selection of the commoner wetland bird species. Numbers of Dabchick, Whitebreasted Cormorant, Darter, Egyptian and Spurwinged Geese, all ducks (except Whitefaced), Redknobbed Coot, and Blacksmith Plover, have peaked in winter. Great Crested Grebe, Knobbilled Duck, African Jacana and African Fish Eagle are recorded. Very few shorebirds occur. Mild threats are posed by fishing and pollution.

		Summer (2) Mean	Max.	Winter (2) Mean	Max.			Summer (2) Mean	Max.	Winter (2) Mean	Max.
006	Great Crested Grebe	0	0	2	4	113	Southern Pochard	0	0	1	2
008	Dabchick	1	2	66	70	115	Knobbilled Duck	0	0	2	3
055	Whitebreasted Cormorant	2	3	15	17	116	Spurwinged Goose	0	0	11	11
058	Reed Cormorant	11	22	23	25	148	African Fish Eagle	1	1	2	2
060	Darter	6	12	27	28	228	Redknobbed Coot	1	1	74	139
062	Grey Heron	2	4	0	0	240	African Jacana	2	3	3	5
066	Great White Heron	4	8	8	15	249	Threebanded Plover	0	0	3	5
067	Little Egret	0	0	1	1	258	Blacksmith Plover	6	12	36	57
068	Yellowbilled Egret	1	2	2	3	260	Wattled Plover	0	0	3	5
069	Black Egret	1	1	0	0	264	Common Sandpiper	1	1	0	0
071	Cattle Egret	17	34	3	6	266	Wood Sandpiper	1	2	0	0
072	Squacco Heron	0	0	1	1	269	Marsh Sandpiper	0	0	1	1
074	Greenbacked Heron	0	0	1	1	270	Greenshank	0	0	2	2
091	Sacred Ibis	2	4	0	0	284	Ruff	0	0	2	3
093	Glossy Ibis	0	0	1	1	295	Blackwinged Stilt	0	0	7	13
094	Hadeda Ibis	0	0	6	11	338	Whiskered Tern	15	30	2	4
099	Whitefaced Duck	6	11	0	0	339	Whitewinged Tern	0	0	6	12
102	Egyptian Goose	2	3	53	100	428	Pied Kingfisher	1	2	5	8
104	Yellowbilled Duck	0	0	9	13	431	Malachite Kingfisher	0	0	1	2
108	Redbilled Teal	0	0	24	47		Total	79	158	398	561
112	Cape Shoveller	0	0	5	10		No. of species		40		

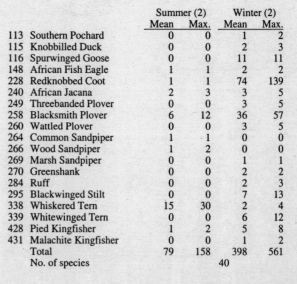

Blaauwwater Pan, Lake Chrissie, Mpumalanga
26° 17' S 30° 16' E (2630AD)

A large (>300 ha), semi-permanent open water pan, with predominantly rocky shoreline ((eastern shore more sandy), shallow water (has islands when water level low) and some submergent vegetation. One summer and two winter counts show small numbers of 18 species, mainly waterfowl and shorebirds, with 10 species recorded in summer and 14 in winter, the high winter mean being due largely to the presence of 55 individuals of four Palearctic shorebird species during one winter count. Kittlitz's Plover breeds. No significant threats have been identified.

		Summer (1)		Winter (2)					Summer (1)		Winter (2)	
		Mean	Max.	Mean	Max.				Mean	Max.	Mean	Max.
095	African Spoonbill	0	0	2	3		258	Blacksmith Plover	4	4	0	0
102	Egyptian Goose	14	14	2	3		266	Wood Sandpiper	1	1	0	0
104	Yellowbilled Duck	16	16	16	17		269	Marsh Sandpiper	1	1	0	0
108	Redbilled Teal	1	1	7	8		270	Greenshank	0	0	1	2
112	Cape Shoveller	4	4	4	5		272	Curlew Sandpiper	0	0	16	31
113	Southern Pochard	2	2	0	0		274	Little Stint	0	0	1	2
116	Spurwinged Goose	0	0	2	4		284	Ruff	0	0	10	20
228	Redknobbed Coot	8	8	6	12		713	Cape Wagtail	0	0	1	1
248	Kittlitz's Plover	0	0	5	7			Total	53	53	71	105
249	Threebanded Plover	2	2	1	2			No. of species			18	

Blinkpan (Lothair), Lake Chrissie, Mpumalanga
26° 20' S 30° 20' E (2630AD)

A salt pan of 95 ha, with a basin and shoreline of bare rock and sand; maximum recorded water depth 10–15 cm; surrounded by grassland, with one low sedge bed on the eastern shore. After one count in February 1992, there were counts from winter 1996 to winter 1997. Summer counts have yielded higher numbers and biomass of birds, but the total number of species recorded is similar in both seasons. Numbers of Greater Flamingo, and Egyptian and Spurwinged Geese, are higher in summer, when small numbers of Palearctic shorebirds occur; summer 1992 also produced a good count of Whitewinged Tern. Good winter counts of Curlew Sandpiper are recorded. The site is noteworthy for its small population of Chestnutbanded Plover. A count in September 1986 (D.G. Allan) included 25 Chestnutbanded and 4 Kittlitz's Plover (both species breeding), and 55 Crowned Crane roosting in the pan. Minor threats are livestock trampling, and fertilizer ingress after storms.

		Summer (2)		Winter (2)					Summer (2)		Winter (2)	
		Mean	Max.	Mean	Max.				Mean	Max.	Mean	Max.
006	Great Crested Grebe	0	0	1	1		249	Threebanded Plover	0	0	4	5
096	Greater Flamingo	6	11	3	5		258	Blacksmith Plover	5	8	4	5
097	Lesser Flamingo	22	43	25	50		266	Wood Sandpiper	0	0	2	3
100	Fulvous Duck	0	0	1	2		272	Curlew Sandpiper	1	1	18	22
102	Egyptian Goose	161	175	25	38		274	Little Stint	15	16	0	0
104	Yellowbilled Duck	1	2	3	5		284	Ruff	1	1	1	2
106	Cape Teal	7	9	2	2		289	Curlew	1	2	0	0
108	Redbilled Teal	2	3	1	2		315	Greyheaded Gull	3	4	2	4
112	Cape Shoveller	0	0	2	4		338	Whiskered Tern	0	0	1	2
116	Spurwinged Goose	27	53	1	1		339	Whitewinged Tern	62	123	0	0
228	Redknobbed Coot	0	0	3	6		713	Cape Wagtail	1	1	0	0
245	Ringed Plover	1	1	1	1			Total	315	363	101	120
247	Chestnutbanded Plover	3	4	4	6			No. of species			25	
248	Kittlitz's Plover	2	2	2	2							

BP's Dam, Wakkerstroom, Mpumalanga
27° 14' S 30° 09' E (2730AA)

A farm dam surrounded by grassland and maize cultivation. Only one count, in Feb. 1992, when the dam was 70% full and yielded good numbers of Dabchick, Yellowbilled Duck, Redknobbed Coot and Blacksmith Plover, with small numbers of other waterbirds and Palaearctic shorebirds. May hold 600+ Redknobbed Coot. When water is low, extensive shallowly sloping beaches provide good habitat for shorebirds (W.R. Tarboton). Used for irrigation, but no threats have been identified.

		Summer (1) Mean	Summer (1) Max.	Winter (0) Mean	Winter (0) Max.			Summer (1) Mean	Summer (1) Max.	Winter (0) Mean	Winter (0) Max.
008	Dabchick	68	68	–	–	249	Threebanded Plover	1	1	–	–
055	Whitebreasted Cormorant	1	1	–	–	258	Blacksmith Plover	31	31	–	–
058	Reed Cormorant	5	5	–	–	266	Wood Sandpiper	8	8	–	–
062	Grey Heron	1	1	–	–	270	Greenshank	4	4	–	–
063	Blackheaded Heron	1	1	–	–	272	Curlew Sandpiper	26	26	–	–
102	Egyptian Goose	13	13	–	–	274	Little Stint	7	7	–	–
104	Yellowbilled Duck	208	208	–	–	284	Ruff	17	17	–	–
112	Cape Shoveller	2	2	–	–	295	Blackwinged Stilt	1	1	–	–
113	Southern Pochard	5	5	–	–		Total	530	530	–	–
117	Maccoa Duck	3	3	–	–		No. of species		19		
228	Redknobbed Coot	128	128	–	–						

Clarens' Pan, Wakkerstroom, Mpumalanga
27° 15' S 30° 07' E (2730AC)

This partly vegetated pan was counted only once, in summer 1992, when it held good numbers of Yellowbilled Egret, Glossy Ibis, Yellowbilled Duck, Redbilled Teal, Cape Shoveller, Redknobbed Coot, Ruff, Blackwinged Stilt and Redwinged Pratincole. In view of this good count, regular surveys should be reinstated. No threats have been identified.

		Summer (1) Mean	Summer (1) Max.	Winter (0) Mean	Winter (0) Max.			Summer (1) Mean	Summer (1) Max.	Winter (0) Mean	Winter (0) Max.
008	Dabchick	1	1	–	–	249	Threebanded Plover	1	1	–	–
058	Reed Cormorant	19	19	–	–	254	Grey Plover	1	1	–	–
062	Grey Heron	1	1	–	–	258	Blacksmith Plover	9	9	–	–
063	Blackheaded Heron	1	1	–	–	266	Wood Sandpiper	10	10	–	–
066	Great White Heron	1	1	–	–	269	Marsh Sandpiper	6	6	–	–
067	Little Egret	1	1	–	–	270	Greenshank	22	22	–	–
068	Yellowbilled Egret	23	23	–	–	272	Curlew Sandpiper	31	31	–	–
081	Hamerkop	1	1	–	–	274	Little Stint	17	17	–	–
091	Sacred Ibis	5	5	–	–	284	Ruff	539	539	–	–
093	Glossy Ibis	104	104	–	–	294	Avocet	9	9	–	–
095	African Spoonbill	4	4	–	–	295	Blackwinged Stilt	122	122	–	–
104	Yellowbilled Duck	63	63	–	–	304	Redwinged Pratincole	191	191	–	–
107	Hottentot Teal	10	10	–	–	338	Whiskered Tern	1	1	–	–
108	Redbilled Teal	77	77	–	–	713	Cape Wagtail	3	3	–	–
112	Cape Shoveller	73	73	–	–		Total	1793	1793	–	–
213	Black Crake	1	1	–	–		No. of species		31		
228	Redknobbed Coot	446	446	–	–						

Cloete Pan, Lake Chrissie, Mpumalanga
26° 25' S 30° 15' E (2630AD)

A reed pan, not permanently flooded, with central *Phragmites* reedbed fringed by emergent sedges on northern side and seasonally flooded grass on eastern side; shoreline grassy. One summer and two winter counts yielded small to moderate numbers of a relatively good selection of species, with higher total numbers and species diversity in summer (136 birds of 21 species) than in winter ((mean: 66 birds; total: 18 species). The most noteworthy counts were of 38 Southern Pochard in winter (up to 1000 have been recorded here by J. de Villiers) and 15 African Spoonbills in summer ((up to 100 recorded by J. de Villiers). Counts are too few to indicate seasonal patterns in waterbird numbers, but ibises and Redknobbed Coot were commoner in summer, when more waterfowl species were also recorded. African plovers are recorded only in winter, when water level lower and fringing grass short (sheep-grazed). Purple Heron, Greenbacked Heron and African Marsh Harrier recorded; Blackcrowned Night Heron and Purple Gallinule occur (J. de Villiers); occurrence of Fulvous Duck exceptional in the area. Redknobbed Coot and Yellowbilled Duck breed. No significant threats have been identified.

		Summer (1)		Winter (2)				Summer (1)		Winter (2)	
		Mean	Max.	Mean	Max.			Mean	Max.	Mean	Max.
055	Whitebreasted Cormorant	0	0	1	1	112	Cape Shoveller	7	7	1	2
058	Reed Cormorant	15	15	0	0	113	Southern Pochard	4	4	19	38
062	Grey Heron	0	0	1	1	116	Spurwinged Goose	3	3	0	0
065	Purple Heron	1	1	0	0	165	African Marsh Harrier	0	0	1	1
066	Great White Heron	0	0	3	5	226	Moorhen	0	0	1	1
074	Greenbacked Heron	2	2	0	0	228	Redknobbed Coot	48	48	9	18
091	Sacred Ibis	11	11	0	0	248	Kittlitz's Plover	0	0	5	9
093	Glossy Ibis	3	3	1	1	249	Threebanded Plover	0	0	2	4
095	African Spoonbill	15	15	2	3	258	Blacksmith Plover	0	0	5	9
096	Greater Flamingo	5	5	0	0	266	Wood Sandpiper	1	1	0	0
100	Fulvous Duck	6	6	0	0	315	Greyheaded Gull	0	0	1	2
101	Whitebacked Duck	1	1	0	0	338	Whiskered Tern	1	1	0	0
102	Egyptian Goose	2	2	5	9	631	African Marsh Warbler	1	1	0	0
104	Yellowbilled Duck	4	4	8	10	713	Cape Wagtail	1	1	4	7
107	Hottentot Teal	1	1	0	0		Total	136	136	66	81
108	Redbilled Teal	4	4	3	5		No. of species		30		

Driefontein Pan, Lake Chrissie, Mpumalanga
26° 24' S 30° 15' E (2630AD)

A permanent sedge pan with a predominantly grassy shoreline. Only two winter counts are available; these show mainly small numbers of a reasonable selection of waterbird species, with good counts of Spurwinged Goose. No Palearctic migrants are recorded. Great Crested Grebe and Squacco Heron occur. No significant threats have been identified.

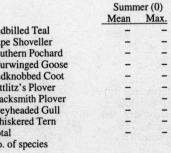

		Summer (0)		Winter (2)				Summer (0)		Winter (2)	
		Mean	Max.	Mean	Max.			Mean	Max.	Mean	Max.
006	Great Crested Grebe	–	–	1	2	108	Redbilled Teal	–	–	1	1
008	Dabchick	–	–	11	21	112	Cape Shoveller	–	–	6	11
058	Reed Cormorant	–	–	2	2	113	Southern Pochard	–	–	1	2
062	Grey Heron	–	–	2	3	116	Spurwinged Goose	–	–	103	168
068	Yellowbilled Egret	–	–	1	2	228	Redknobbed Coot	–	–	44	53
072	Squacco Heron	–	–	1	2	248	Kittlitz's Plover	–	–	3	5
093	Glossy Ibis	–	–	2	3	258	Blacksmith Plover	–	–	2	3
095	African Spoonbill	–	–	3	4	315	Greyheaded Gull	–	–	1	2
102	Egyptian Goose	–	–	13	18	338	Whiskered Tern	–	–	6	11
104	Yellowbilled Duck	–	–	11	13		Total	–	–	211	297
107	Hottentot Teal	–	–	1	2		No. of species		20		

Eilandsmeer South Pan, Lake Chrissie, Mpumalanga
26° 21' S 30° 19' E (2630AC)

A large, permanent open water (>500 ha); a lake rather than a pan because it has inflow and out-flow points. Shorelines range from rocky to short-grassed; western shore has some fringing reeds and sedges, hence occurrence of Squacco Heron. Much submergent vegetation (type unknown), apparently increasing in extent and beginning to attract Whitebacked Duck. Redknobbed Coot and Great Crested Grebe breed (J. de Villiers). One summer and two winter counts available, showing almost no birds in summer (reason unclear, as flooding is permanent) and small to high numbers of 22 species in winter, including good counts of Great Crested Grebe, Yellowbilled Duck, Redbilled Teal, Cape Shoveller, Spurwinged Goose (breeds in adjoining lands) and Redknobbed Coot. A winter count of 15 Whitewinged Tern is noteworthy. Southern Pochard also occurs (J. de Villiers). No significant threats have been identified.

		Summer (1)		Winter (2)				Summer (1)		Winter (2)	
		Mean	Max.	Mean	Max.			Mean	Max.	Mean	Max.
006	Great Crested Grebe	0	0	6	12	112	Cape Shoveller	0	0	8	15
058	Reed Cormorant	0	0	3	5	116	Spurwinged Goose	0	0	101	202
066	Great White Heron	0	0	2	3	228	Redknobbed Coot	0	0	46	86
068	Yellowbilled Egret	0	0	2	4	248	Kittlitz's Plover	0	0	2	3
072	Squacco Heron	0	0	1	2	258	Blacksmith Plover	0	0	6	6
091	Sacred Ibis	2	2	6	12	270	Greenshank	0	0	1	1
093	Glossy Ibis	0	0	7	13	295	Blackwinged Stilt	0	0	3	5
095	African Spoonbill	0	0	1	1	315	Greyheaded Gull	0	0	1	1
101	Whitebacked Duck	0	0	3	6	339	Whitewinged Tern	0	0	8	15
102	Egyptian Goose	2	2	2	4	713	Cape Wagtail	0	0	1	2
104	Yellowbilled Duck	0	0	75	150		Total	4	4	307	492
108	Redbilled Teal	0	0	27	53		No. of species		22		

Fickland Pan, Wakkerstroom, Mpumalanga
27° 14' S 30° 02' E (2730AA)

This 25 ha seasonal pan was counted only in summer 1992 and winter 1997. The most significant observation was the large number of Redknobbed Coot counted on both visits. Reasonable numbers of Dabchick, Blackheaded Heron and Maccoa Duck were recorded during the winter count, and of Glossy Ibis, Yellowbilled Duck and Redbilled Teal in summer. No threats have been identified.

		Summer (1)		Winter (1)				Summer (1)		Winter (1)	
		Mean	Max.	Mean	Max.			Mean	Max.	Mean	Max.
006	Great Crested Grebe	0	0	10	10	112	Cape Shoveller	1	1	0	0
007	Blacknecked Grebe	0	0	2	2	113	Southern Pochard	0	0	3	3
008	Dabchick	3	3	60	60	116	Spurwinged Goose	0	0	1	1
055	Whitebreasted Cormorant	1	1	0	0	117	Maccoa Duck	0	0	14	14
058	Reed Cormorant	3	3	1	1	209	Crowned Crane	2	2	1	1
062	Grey Heron	5	5	1	1	228	Redknobbed Coot	628	628	489	489
063	Blackheaded Heron	1	1	20	20	258	Blacksmith Plover	13	13	4	4
068	Yellowbilled Egret	4	4	0	0	266	Wood Sandpiper	5	5	1	1
081	Hamerkop	0	0	1	1	270	Greenshank	1	1	0	0
091	Sacred Ibis	7	7	2	2	274	Little Stint	3	3	0	0
093	Glossy Ibis	25	25	0	0	284	Ruff	34	34	0	0
095	African Spoonbill	4	4	2	2	286	Ethiopian Snipe	1	1	0	0
102	Egyptian Goose	7	7	4	4	295	Blackwinged Stilt	2	2	0	0
104	Yellowbilled Duck	43	43	7	7	713	Cape Wagtail	0	0	4	4
107	Hottentot Teal	6	6	0	0		Total	861	861	627	627
108	Redbilled Teal	62	62	0	0		No. of species		30		

Goedehoop Pan, Lake Chrissie, Mpumalanga
26° 19' S 30° 17' E (2630AD)

A small pan, probably ephemeral and with emergent grass/sedges; surrounded by several smaller pans. Counts were made in February 1992 and from winter 1996 to winter 1997. In February 1992 there were good numbers of Purple Gallinule, and also 80 Cattle Egret, 3 Purple Heron, 10 Glossy Ibis and 3 Hottentot Teal: the teal is infrequently recorded in counts from pans in this region. Good numbers of Spurwinged Goose and Redknobbed Coot occurred in summer 1997; numbers of Dabchick and Southern Pochard have peaked in winter. No threats have been identified.

		Summer (2)		Winter (2)				Summer (2)		Winter (2)	
		Mean	Max.	Mean	Max.			Mean	Max.	Mean	Max.
006	Great Crested Grebe	0	0	1	1	108	Redbilled Teal	1	2	2	3
007	Blacknecked Grebe	1	2	1	1	112	Cape Shoveller	0	0	1	2
008	Dabchick	3	5	14	17	113	Southern Pochard	3	6	10	20
058	Reed Cormorant	6	9	3	6	116	Spurwinged Goose	22	34	4	8
062	Grey Heron	1	1	1	1	117	Maccoa Duck	0	0	2	3
065	Purple Heron	2	3	1	1	223	Purple Gallinule	5	10	1	1
066	Great White Heron	1	1	2	3	228	Redknobbed Coot	108	170	67	78
068	Yellowbilled Egret	0	0	1	2	258	Blacksmith Plover	5	6	6	8
071	Cattle Egret	40	80	0	0	260	Wattled Plover	0	0	1	2
093	Glossy Ibis	5	10	2	3	286	Ethiopian Snipe	0	0	1	1
094	Hadeda Ibis	1	2	0	0	295	Blackwinged Stilt	2	4	1	1
095	African Spoonbill	1	2	0	0	338	Whiskered Tern	3	6	0	0
102	Egyptian Goose	0	0	1	2	339	Whitewinged Tern	0	0	1	2
104	Yellowbilled Duck	8	8	3	6	713	Cape Wagtail	0	0	3	3
106	Cape Teal	0	0	1	1		Total	215	236	126	127
107	Hottentot Teal	2	3	2	3		No. of species		30		

Hamilton Pan, Lothair, Mpumalanga
26° 19' S 30° 23' E (2630AD)

A reed pan of 25 ha, more than 95% of its area covered by dense, emergent *Phragmites*; it has a narrow peripheral ring of open water with dense submergents. Only one count available ((February 1992), recording few birds of 14 species. A count in August 1985 (D.G. Allan) totalled 111 birds of 15 species, including 12 Purple Gallinule, 18 Moorhen, 21 Redknobbed Coot and 2 African Marsh Harrier. The reedbed has held hundreds of roosting Eastern Redfooted Kestrels. This site should be counted regularly. A small stream arises close to the northeast edge of the pan; if this erodes back it could drain the entire basin. No other threats have been identified.

		Summer (1)		Winter (0)				Summer (1)		Winter (0)	
		Mean	Max.	Mean	Max.			Mean	Max.	Mean	Max.
063	Blackheaded Heron	2	2	–	–	223	Purple Gallinule	1	1	–	–
068	Yellowbilled Egret	1	1	–	–	226	Moorhen	1	1	–	–
072	Squacco Heron	1	1	–	–	228	Redknobbed Coot	2	2	–	–
076	Blackcrowned Night Heron	5	5	–	–	258	Blacksmith Plover	5	5	–	–
091	Sacred Ibis	1	1	–	–	260	Wattled Plover	2	2	–	–
093	Glossy Ibis	1	1	–	–	266	Wood Sandpiper	1	1	–	–
104	Yellowbilled Duck	2	2	–	–	713	Cape Wagtail	2	2	–	–
113	Southern Pochard	2	2	–	–		Total	30	30	–	–
213	Black Crake	1	1	–	–		No. of species		16		

Heyshope Dam, Piet Retief, Mpumalanga
27° 02' S 30° 30' E (2730AB)

A large, state-owned storage dam in the Assegaai River catchment, surrounded by agricultural land (beef and maize production). Shoreline gently sloping; either heavily grazed or with rank grass and weeds. A proposed Ramsar site which holds extremely large numbers of at least 52 waterbird species, concentrated in the 17 bays where rivers enter the dam. Small areas which are regularly counted hold up to 45 000 waterbirds; the entire system may hold 100 000. In drought years the dam provides a refuge for birds from surrounding pans, including Lake Chrissie. Only one CWAC count available, for winter 1992, when only small sections of the dam were visited but nationally significant numbers of Yellowbilled Duck and Cape Shoveller were recorded, plus high counts of Dabchick, cormorants, ducks, geese, and shorebirds (including some Palaearctic species). Eutrophication, resulting from inflow of agricultural fertilisers, is a potential problem. This important site should be monitored on a regular basis.

		Summer (0)		Winter (1)				Summer (0)		Winter (1)	
		Mean	Max.	Mean	Max.			Mean	Max.	Mean	Max.
008	Dabchick	–	–	159	159	116	Spurwinged Goose	–	–	22	22
055	Whitebreasted Cormorant	–	–	99	99	209	Crowned Crane	–	–	2	2
058	Reed Cormorant	–	–	159	159	240	African Jacana	–	–	1	1
060	Darter	–	–	13	13	248	Kittlitz's Plover	–	–	57	57
062	Grey Heron	–	–	5	5	249	Threebanded Plover	–	–	9	9
063	Blackheaded Heron	–	–	1	1	258	Blacksmith Plover	–	–	45	45
065	Purple Heron	–	–	1	1	269	Marsh Sandpiper	–	–	2	2
091	Sacred Ibis	–	–	1	1	272	Curlew Sandpiper	–	–	142	142
094	Hadeda Ibis	–	–	2	2	274	Little Stint	–	–	4	4
095	African Spoonbill	–	–	6	6	286	Ethiopian Snipe	–	–	24	24
096	Greater Flamingo	–	–	23	23	295	Blackwinged Stilt	–	–	94	94
099	Whitefaced Duck	–	–	162	162	315	Greyheaded Gull	–	–	23	23
101	Whitebacked Duck	–	–	33	33	322	Caspian Tern	–	–	1	1
102	Egyptian Goose	–	–	496	496	338	Whiskered Tern	–	–	8	8
104	Yellowbilled Duck	–	–	1571*	1571*	429	Giant Kingfisher	–	–	1	1
108	Redbilled Teal	–	–	625	625	713	Cape Wagtail	–	–	14	14
112	Cape Shoveller	–	–	272*	272*		Total	–	–	4243	4243
113	Southern Pochard	–	–	166	166		No. of species		34		

Lake Banagher West, Lake Chrissie, Mpumalanga
26° 20' S 30° 21' E (2630AD)

A 20 ha sedge pan; open water with dense submergents; dense fringing emergent *Schoenoplectus* sedges, with other sedges and *Leersia* grass on the waterlogged shore. Counts were made in February 1992, and from winter 1996 to winter 1997. These show small to good numbers of a reasonable variety of species. Counts of Southern Pochard are good in both seasons; numbers of all other waterfowl have peaked in winter (note the good count of Whitebacked Duck), when Dabchick and Redknobbed Coot are also more numerous; Purple Gallinule is recorded only in winter. Earlier counts (D.G. Allan) recorded 650–1400+ birds of 42 species, including 13 Great Crested Grebe, 31 Whitebacked Duck, 600 Redknobbed Coot (breeding) and 20 Ethiopian Snipe (August 1985), 107 Dabchick, 350 Southern Pochard and 332 Redknobbed Coot (February 1986), and 31 Cape Teal, 49 Blackwinged Stilt, c. 1000 Ruff and many other shorebirds (September 1986). Threats include severe damage to vegetation by cattle, water abstraction, introduction of alien fish, and waterfowl hunting; there are some alien plantations in the catchment.

		Summer (2)		Winter (2)				Summer (2)		Winter (2)	
		Mean	Max.	Mean	Max.			Mean	Max.	Mean	Max.
006	Great Crested Grebe	2	4	3	6	106	Cape Teal	0	0	1	2
007	Blacknecked Grebe	0	0	1	1	108	Redbilled Teal	0	0	5	8
008	Dabchick	2	3	12	19	112	Cape Shoveller	3	6	8	11
055	Whitebreasted Cormorant	0	0	1	2	113	Southern Pochard	35	70	30	60
058	Reed Cormorant	16	31	15	29	116	Spurwinged Goose	7	10	17	24
062	Grey Heron	2	4	1	1	117	Maccoa Duck	2	4	9	17
063	Blackheaded Heron	1	2	0	0	209	Crowned Crane	1	1	0	0
071	Cattle Egret	6	11	0	0	223	Purple Gallinule	0	0	7	14
081	Hamerkop	1	2	0	0	228	Redknobbed Coot	9	18	100	196
091	Sacred Ibis	3	4	1	1	258	Blacksmith Plover	12	15	5	6
093	Glossy Ibis	1	1	0	0	315	Greyheaded Gull	0	0	2	4
095	African Spoonbill	0	0	1	1	338	Whiskered Tern	2	4	0	0
097	Lesser Flamingo	3	5	0	0	339	Whitewinged Tern	12	24	0	0
101	Whitebacked Duck	3	5	16	31	713	Cape Wagtail	0	0	5	9
102	Egyptian Goose	2	4	56	110		Total	130	191	307	485
104	Yellowbilled Duck	9	12	15	15		No. of species		30		

Lake Chrissie East Pan, Lake Chrissie, Mpumalanga
26° 19' S 30° 15' E (2630AC)

A 10 ha sedge pan; open water with much submerged vegetation and fringed with tall, dense, emergent sedges and grasses; the upper shore has *Juncus*. Two counts are available ((summer and winter 1992), showing much greater bird species numbers and diversity in summer, when the commonest species were Redknobbed Coot (35) and Greenshank (76); the winter count yielded only 6 species and included 30 Little Stint. Counts in Feb. 1986 and 1987 (D.G. Allan) yielded 88 and 129 birds respectively (total 23 species), with maxima of 45 Redknobbed Coot, 60 Marsh Sandpiper, 10 Blackwinged Stilt and only 2 Greenshank. Cattle trampling and grazing affected half of the pan in 1986–87. No threats have been identified.

		Summer (1)		Winter (1)				Summer (1)		Winter (1)	
		Mean	Max.	Mean	Max.			Mean	Max.	Mean	Max.
008	Dabchick	7	7	0	0	249	Threebanded Plover	0	0	6	6
058	Reed Cormorant	3	3	0	0	258	Blacksmith Plover	9	9	15	15
071	Cattle Egret	11	11	0	0	266	Wood Sandpiper	21	21	0	0
091	Sacred Ibis	2	2	0	0	269	Marsh Sandpiper	3	3	0	0
093	Glossy Ibis	3	3	0	0	270	Greenshank	76	76	0	0
094	Hadeda Ibis	9	9	9	9	274	Little Stint	0	0	30	30
104	Yellowbilled Duck	3	3	0	0	284	Ruff	5	5	0	0
108	Redbilled Teal	9	9	0	0	286	Ethiopian Snipe	0	0	1	1
113	Southern Pochard	2	2	0	0	713	Cape Wagtail	0	0	5	5
223	Purple Gallinule	3	3	0	0		Total	201	201	66	66
228	Redknobbed Coot	35	35	0	0		No. of species		20		

Lake Chrissie Pan, Lake Chrissie, Mpumalanga
26° 19' S 30° 13' E (2630AC)

A large open pan (1045 ha) with a clay/silt basin and predominantly sandy shoreline; it dries out periodically. Counts in February 1992, and from winter 1996 to winter 1997, show mainly small numbers of a good selection of waterbirds, but noteworthy totals in February 1992 were 50 Greater Flamingo, 700 Lesser Flamingo and 200 Egyptian Goose. Of the nine waterfowl species recorded, numbers of six peak in winter, as do numbers of Redknobbed Coot. Incomplete counts in January–February 1986 (D.G. Allan) included hundreds of Greater Flamingo, thousands of Lesser Flamingo, 630 Curlew Sandpiper, 3000 Ruff, 153 Little Stint and 131 Avocet. Alien fish have been introduced for angling; no other threats have been identified.

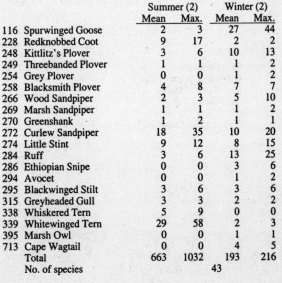

		Summer (2)		Winter (2)				Summer (2)		Winter (2)	
		Mean	Max.	Mean	Max.			Mean	Max.	Mean	Max.
006	Great Crested Grebe	2	3	2	3	116	Spurwinged Goose	2	3	27	44
008	Dabchick	3	6	8	10	228	Redknobbed Coot	9	17	2	2
055	Whitebreasted Cormorant	2	3	1	2	248	Kittlitz's Plover	3	6	10	13
058	Reed Cormorant	2	3	0	0	249	Threebanded Plover	1	1	1	2
062	Grey Heron	1	1	1	1	254	Grey Plover	0	0	1	2
066	Great White Heron	0	0	1	1	258	Blacksmith Plover	4	8	7	7
067	Little Egret	2	3	0	0	266	Wood Sandpiper	2	3	5	10
068	Yellowbilled Egret	1	2	0	0	269	Marsh Sandpiper	1	1	1	2
071	Cattle Egret	5	9	0	0	270	Greenshank	1	2	1	1
091	Sacred Ibis	1	1	1	2	272	Curlew Sandpiper	18	35	10	20
093	Glossy Ibis	0	0	3	6	274	Little Stint	9	12	8	15
094	Hadeda Ibis	1	2	0	0	284	Ruff	3	6	13	25
095	African Spoonbill	3	6	4	6	286	Ethiopian Snipe	0	0	3	6
096	Greater Flamingo	35	50	11	17	294	Avocet	0	0	1	2
097	Lesser Flamingo	350	700	0	0	295	Blackwinged Stilt	3	6	3	6
101	Whitebacked Duck	0	0	1	1	315	Greyheaded Gull	3	3	2	2
102	Egyptian Goose	146	200	6	11	338	Whiskered Tern	5	9	0	0
104	Yellowbilled Duck	3	5	13	20	339	Whitewinged Tern	29	58	2	3
106	Cape Teal	0	0	5	9	395	Marsh Owl	0	0	1	1
107	Hottentot Teal	0	0	3	5	713	Cape Wagtail	0	0	4	5
108	Redbilled Teal	1	2	15	16		Total	663	1032	193	216
112	Cape Shoveller	15	30	20	23		No. of species		43		
113	Southern Pochard	5	10	6	11						

Lakenvlei Wetland, Belfast, Mpumalanga
25° 37' S 30° 02' E (2530CA)

A reserve in an area of commercial afforestation; three dams, and a palustrine wetland dominated by dense reedbeds which make counting difficult. The winter 1997 count produced a reasonable selection of the commoner waterbird species, including good numbers of Dabchick and Red-knobbed Coot. The July 1998 count was excellent: 2174 birds, including 270 Whitebacked Duck and 1525 coot. Moorhen is widespread and Purple Heron and Redchested Flufftail occur. African Rail and Purple Gallinule occur locally in the area, but Black Crake is infrequent and localised at this altitude. Grass and Marsh Owls, and Wattled Crane, also occur in the area, and Ethiopian Snipe is locally common. Reed encroachment is a major threat; fishing and human disturbance are mild threats. The marshes of this region have been severely modified, and many have been destroyed, by the building of trout dams.

		Summer (0)		Winter (1)					Summer (0)		Winter (1)	
		Mean	Max.	Mean	Max.				Mean	Max.	Mean	Max.
008	Dabchick	–	–	133	133		213	Black Crake	–	–	1	1
055	Whitebreasted Cormorant	–	–	5	5		217	Redchested Flufftail	–	–	1	1
058	Reed Cormorant	–	–	20	20		226	Moorhen	–	–	23	23
062	Grey Heron	–	–	2	2		228	Redknobbed Coot	–	–	487	487
063	Blackheaded Heron	–	–	5	5		249	Threebanded Plover	–	–	12	12
065	Purple Heron	–	–	2	2		260	Wattled Plover	–	–	2	2
094	Hadeda Ibis	–	–	3	3		286	Ethiopian Snipe	–	–	3	3
101	Whitebacked Duck	–	–	2	2		428	Pied Kingfisher	–	–	2	2
102	Egyptian Goose	–	–	4	4		713	Cape Wagtail	–	–	9	9
104	Yellowbilled Duck	–	–	65	65			Total	–	–	818	818
113	Southern Pochard	–	–	7	7			No. of species		21		
116	Spurwinged Goose	–	–	30	30							

Lusthof Pan, Lake Chrissie, Mpumalanga
26° 13' S 30° 14' E (2630AA)

A fairly small (18 ha) sedge pan, with emergent sedges and grasses, and fringing sedges, grasses and rushes. Only one count is available (June 1992), recording 41 birds of 9 species. Earlier counts (D.G. Allan) listed 22 waterbird species, with 106 Spurwinged Goose (Sep. 1985) and 20–25 Purple Gallinule (Jan. 1986 and Jan. 1987, breeding on both occasions). Crowned Crane also recorded in the past. No threats have been identified.

		Summer (0)		Winter (1)					Summer (0)		Winter (1)	
		Mean	Max.	Mean	Max.				Mean	Max.	Mean	Max.
062	Grey Heron	–	–	1	1		116	Spurwinged Goose	–	–	6	6
066	Great White Heron	–	–	4	4		223	Purple Gallinule	–	–	8	8
072	Squacco Heron	–	–	1	1		258	Blacksmith Plover	–	–	3	3
091	Sacred Ibis	–	–	16	16			Total	–	–	41	41
093	Glossy Ibis	–	–	1	1			No. of species		9		
095	African Spoonbill	–	–	1	1							

Leeuwpan, Secunda, Mpumalanga
26° 35' S 28° 57' E (2628DB)

A large dam with fringing reeds and sedges, and open shoreline. Herons and spoonbills nest in nearby eucalyptus trees and on islands. Numbers of most waterfowl species are higher in winter; this trend is enhanced by exceptional counts in winter 1995, especially of Blacknecked Grebe, Hadeda Ibis, Whitefaced Duck, Egyptian and Spurwinged Geese, Yellowbilled Duck and Redbilled Teal. Good numbers of Redknobbed Coot occur all year (nationally significant numbers in winter); Southern Pochard were numerous from winter 1995 to summer 1996; Greater Flamingos occurred from winter 1994 to winter 1995. Cormorant and Darter numbers peak in summer. 23 Great Crested Grebe in summer 1997; good summer counts of Glossy Ibis in 1995 and Cape Teal in 1995–96. Threats include disturbance from boating, water-skiing and angling.

		Summer (3)		Winter (4)				Summer (3)		Winter (4)	
		Mean	Max.	Mean	Max.			Mean	Max.	Mean	Max.
006	Great Crested Grebe	14	23	5	10	108	Redbilled Teal	3	9	237	903
007	Blacknecked Grebe	11	33	23	45	112	Cape Shoveller	4	10	11	32
008	Dabchick	39	115	34	60	113	Southern Pochard	61	136	60	133
055	Whitebreasted Cormorant	145	181	23	32	116	Spurwinged Goose	3	4	40	127
058	Reed Cormorant	42	85	27	60	117	Maccoa Duck	1	3	4	17
060	Darter	10	26	3	4	165	African Marsh Harrier	0	0	1	2
062	Grey Heron	7	12	5	14	223	Purple Gallinule	0	0	0	1
063	Blackheaded Heron	1	2	8	22	226	Moorhen	1	3	2	4
064	Goliath Heron	2	3	1	4	228	Redknobbed Coot	1158	1694	1507	2975*
065	Purple Heron	1	2	1	1	245	Ringed Plover	1	2	0	0
067	Little Egret	0	1	0	0	248	Kittlitz's Plover	0	0	1	3
068	Yellowbilled Egret	0	0	0	1	249	Threebanded Plover	1	3	3	7
071	Cattle Egret	2	4	0	0	258	Blacksmith Plover	14	29	25	69
072	Squacco Heron	0	1	1	2	266	Wood Sandpiper	1	1	0	0
090	Yellowbilled Stork	0	1	0	0	269	Marsh Sandpiper	2	5	1	2
091	Sacred Ibis	1	4	0	0	270	Greenshank	1	4	1	2
093	Glossy Ibis	25	71	0	0	274	Little Stint	11	30	0	0
094	Hadeda Ibis	4	12	20	69	284	Ruff	84	250	0	0
095	African Spoonbill	1	2	1	2	294	Avocet	3	9	1	5
096	Greater Flamingo	30	90	105	247	295	Blackwinged Stilt	7	22	5	12
097	Lesser Flamingo	2	5	24	94	312	Kelp Gull	0	0	0	1
099	Whitefaced Duck	0	0	43	100	315	Greyheaded Gull	21	45	30	110
100	Fulvous Duck	6	14	0	0	338	Whiskered Tern	0	1	0	0
102	Egyptian Goose	66	132	527	1360	339	Whitewinged Tern	71	204	0	1
104	Yellowbilled Duck	4	10	89	310	395	Marsh Owl	2	2	2	4
105	African Black Duck	1	2	1	2	713	Cape Wagtail	2	3	10	18
106	Cape Teal	10	17	1	2		Total	1874	2635	2878	5223
107	Hottentot Teal	0	0	1	2		No. of species			54	

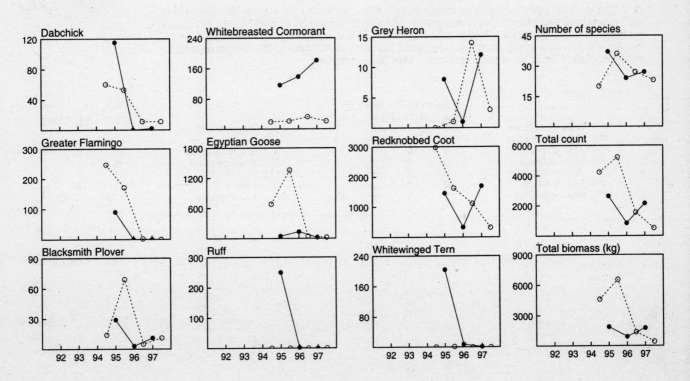

Lydenburg Fisheries, Lydenburg, Mpumalanga
25° 07' S 30° 28' E (2530AB)

Trout dams on the Sterkspruit River, with open water and some fringing reedy vegetation. Counts are available only for summer and winter 1997, when 19 species were recorded in summer and 16 in winter, with a very similar total count in each season. The commonest species, Sacred Ibis, was more numerous in winter, while Blacksmith Plover was common in both seasons; Reed Cormorant, Cattle Egret and Hadeda Ibis were commoner in summer. Purple Heron and African Black Duck are noteworthy. Important threats are the closing down of the fisheries station, which will affect the water supply to the dams, and suspected poisoning of birds, particularly Sacred Ibis, at a nearby rubbish dump. Other threats include livestock grazing/trampling, and overhead powerlines.

		Summer (1) Mean	Max.	Winter (1) Mean	Max.			Summer (1) Mean	Max.	Winter (1) Mean	Max.
008	Dabchick	2	2	1	1	105	African Black Duck	2	2	2	2
058	Reed Cormorant	13	13	3	3	249	Threebanded Plover	3	3	2	2
063	Blackheaded Heron	2	2	1	1	258	Blacksmith Plover	20	20	21	21
065	Purple Heron	0	0	2	2	266	Wood Sandpiper	4	4	0	0
071	Cattle Egret	25	25	2	2	428	Pied Kingfisher	1	1	0	0
081	Hamerkop	6	6	8	8	429	Giant Kingfisher	3	3	0	0
091	Sacred Ibis	4	4	54	54	431	Malachite Kingfisher	3	3	1	1
094	Hadeda Ibis	14	14	2	2	711	African Pied Wagtail	0	0	2	2
095	African Spoonbill	1	1	0	0	713	Cape Wagtail	12	12	18	18
099	Whitefaced Duck	9	9	11	11		Total	133	133	136	136
102	Egyptian Goose	2	2	6	6		No. of species		21		
104	Yellowbilled Duck	7	7	0	0						

Magdalenasmeer 2, Lake Chrissie, Mpumalanga
26° 24' S 30° 17' E (2630AD)

A large (>600 ha) open pan with no fringing vegetation; northern and western shorelines are rocky, southern and eastern shorelines grassy. Not rich in birds: one summer count gave small numbers of only two species, Yellowbilled Egret and Whiskered Tern (the latter breeds at nearby waters); two winter counts yielded small numbers of 10 species, the commonest bird being Redbilled Teal. No significant threats have been identified.

		Summer (1) Mean	Max.	Winter (2) Mean	Max.			Summer (1) Mean	Max.	Winter (2) Mean	Max.
066	Great White Heron	0	0	5	7	258	Blacksmith Plover	0	0	1	2
068	Yellowbilled Egret	4	4	0	0	286	Ethiopian Snipe	0	0	1	1
095	African Spoonbill	0	0	1	1	315	Greyheaded Gull	0	0	3	3
102	Egyptian Goose	0	0	3	5	338	Whiskered Tern	15	15	0	0
104	Yellowbilled Duck	0	0	3	5	713	Cape Wagtail	0	0	1	2
108	Redbilled Teal	0	0	8	15		Total	19	19	50	76
116	Spurwinged Goose	0	0	28	47		No. of species		12		

Mkhombo Dam, Libangeni, Mpumalanga
25° 06' S 28° 55' E (2528BB)

In summer this dam was counted in 1995 and 1996, while winter counts were made from 1995 to 1997. Summer counts recorded reasonable numbers of only Cattle Egret, Whitefaced Duck, Blacksmith Plover and Ruff, all in 1995. In winter, good numbers of cormorants, Darter, herons, African Spoonbill, Whitefaced Duck, Egyptian Goose, Redbilled Teal and Southern Pochard were recorded. Moderate numbers of Knobbilled Duck, Redknobbed Coot and African Jacana occur in winter, and of Blacksmith Plover in both seasons. Several large heronries were reported in winter 1997, when the dam was full and many acacia trees were standing in water. A severe threat to the habitat is livestock grazing and trampling, while hunting/poaching is an important threat and boating and fishing are mild threats.

		Summer (3) Mean	Summer (3) Max.	Winter (3) Mean	Winter (3) Max.			Summer (3) Mean	Summer (3) Max.	Winter (3) Mean	Winter (3) Max.
006	Great Crested Grebe	1	2	2	5	115	Knobbilled Duck	2	7	10	20
008	Dabchick	1	2	18	40	116	Spurwinged Goose	1	2	9	24
055	Whitebreasted Cormorant	32	94	122	250	148	African Fish Eagle	1	2	1	1
058	Reed Cormorant	26	75	24	40	170	Osprey	1	2	0	0
060	Darter	3	9	66	150	213	Black Crake	0	0	0	1
062	Grey Heron	4	10	38	84	226	Moorhen	0	0	1	2
063	Blackheaded Heron	1	3	23	64	228	Redknobbed Coot	7	20	42	46
064	Goliath Heron	1	1	1	2	240	African Jacana	1	2	20	52
066	Great White Heron	4	7	1	3	248	Kittlitz's Plover	0	0	0	1
067	Little Egret	1	2	1	2	249	Threebanded Plover	0	0	3	5
068	Yellowbilled Egret	1	2	0	1	258	Blacksmith Plover	17	36	28	60
069	Black Egret	1	2	1	2	260	Wattled Plover	1	2	2	3
071	Cattle Egret	160	449	24	43	264	Common Sandpiper	3	7	0	0
072	Squacco Heron	1	2	0	1	266	Wood Sandpiper	3	7	1	2
074	Greenbacked Heron	0	0	0	1	269	Marsh Sandpiper	0	0	0	1
076	Blackcrowned Night Heron	0	1	0	0	270	Greenshank	0	0	0	1
090	Yellowbilled Stork	5	13	0	0	284	Ruff	8	24	0	0
091	Sacred Ibis	0	0	2	4	295	Blackwinged Stilt	0	0	8	19
093	Glossy Ibis	2	6	4	8	315	Greyheaded Gull	0	0	0	1
094	Hadeda Ibis	2	5	5	7	322	Caspian Tern	0	0	1	2
095	African Spoonbill	4	13	19	40	338	Whiskered Tern	9	20	0	0
099	Whitefaced Duck	17	50	353	761	339	Whitewinged Tern	0	0	3	9
102	Egyptian Goose	19	49	82	215	428	Pied Kingfisher	0	1	2	2
104	Yellowbilled Duck	4	8	10	20	431	Malachite Kingfisher	0	0	1	3
108	Redbilled Teal	0	0	50	114	713	Cape Wagtail	1	2	1	2
112	Cape Shoveller	0	0	7	14		Total	343	824	1013	1375
113	Southern Pochard	0	1	27	75		No. of species			53	
114	Pygmy Goose	0	0	1	3						

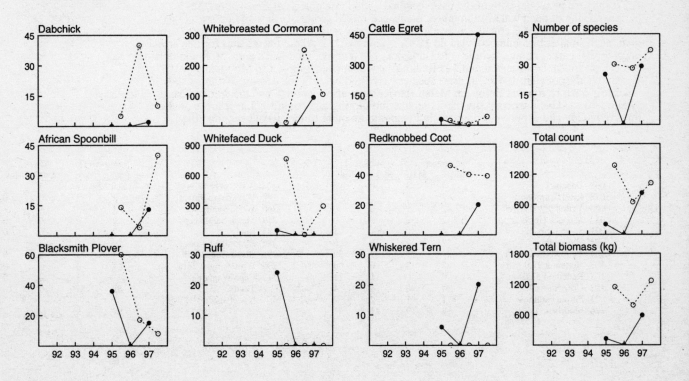

Mooigelegen Pan, Lake Chrissie, Mpumalanga
26° 25' S 30° 18' E (2630AD)

A relatively small (c. 150 ha) but excellent freshwater pan with grassy margins, some sedges at the southern end (note the occurrence of Squacco and Greenbacked Herons; Purple Heron is also recorded), and much submerged vegetation which attracts good numbers of Whitebacked Duck and Redknobbed Coot, as is shown by the one winter count; up to 900 coot have been recorded here (J. de Villiers). The one summer count yielded a good total of 61 Southern Pochard; up to 600 have been counted here ((J. de Villiers). Grebes, cormorants and herons were more numerous in summer. Blacknecked Grebe occurs; Fulvous Duck is noteworthy; the African Jacana (winter count) is a vagrant to this area. Great Crested Grebe, Dabchick, Redknobbed Coot and Whiskered Tern breed. No significant threats have been identified.

		Summer (1)		Winter (1)				Summer (1)		Winter (1)	
		Mean	Max.	Mean	Max.			Mean	Max.	Mean	Max.
006	Great Crested Grebe	4	4	2	2	117	Maccoa Duck	0	0	2	2
007	Blacknecked Grebe	1	1	1	1	228	Redknobbed Coot	99	99	610	610
008	Dabchick	10	10	2	2	240	African Jacana	0	0	1	1
058	Reed Cormorant	33	33	0	0	248	Kittlitz's Plover	0	0	5	5
062	Grey Heron	1	1	1	1	258	Blacksmith Plover	4	4	7	7
068	Yellowbilled Egret	1	1	0	0	266	Wood Sandpiper	4	4	0	0
072	Squacco Heron	2	2	0	0	270	Greenshank	2	2	0	0
074	Greenbacked Heron	2	2	0	0	272	Curlew Sandpiper	1	1	0	0
100	Fulvous Duck	0	0	9	9	274	Little Stint	1	1	0	0
101	Whitebacked Duck	0	0	19	19	713	Cape Wagtail	0	0	7	7
104	Yellowbilled Duck	10	10	2	2		Total	236	236	676	676
108	Redbilled Teal	0	0	8	8		No. of species			23	
113	Southern Pochard	61	61	0	0						

Tevrede se Pan, Lake Chrissie, Mpumalanga
26° 12' S 30° 12' E (2630AA)

A 270-ha reed pan, over 95% of the basin covered with dense emergent *Phragmites*; has a peripheral ring of open water, submergent plants and mixed sedges, rushes and grasses. Only summer and winter 1992 counts are available: these show reasonable numbers of Moorhen, but give much smaller bird numbers than do 1980s counts by D.G. Allan; the reasons for this are unclear. The earlier counts include: 170 Dabchick, 144 Yellowbilled Duck and 750 Redknobbed Coot (Sep. 1985), 84 Moorhen and 232 Redknobbed Coot (Jan. 1986); 136 Moorhen and 101 Redknobbed Coot (Jan. 1987); all these species have bred here. Purple Heron, Whitebacked Duck, Squacco Heron and European Marsh Harrier were also recorded, and the reedbed has a swallow roost. This important site merits regular monitoring and counting. Large areas of shore-line are muddy and exposed through cattle trampling; no other threats have been identified.

		Summer (1)		Winter (1)				Summer (1)		Winter (1)	
		Mean	Max.	Mean	Max.			Mean	Max.	Mean	Max.
008	Dabchick	3	3	0	0	228	Redknobbed Coot	18	18	7	7
058	Reed Cormorant	2	2	2	2	258	Blacksmith Plover	1	1	0	0
068	Yellowbilled Egret	2	2	0	0	266	Wood Sandpiper	1	1	0	0
072	Squacco Heron	2	2	0	0	269	Marsh Sandpiper	2	2	0	0
091	Sacred Ibis	0	0	1	1	284	Ruff	2	2	0	0
093	Glossy Ibis	2	2	0	0	286	Ethiopian Snipe	0	0	3	3
104	Yellowbilled Duck	29	29	39	39	295	Blackwinged Stilt	1	1	0	0
107	Hottentot Teal	2	2	0	0	339	Whitewinged Tern	1	1	0	0
108	Redbilled Teal	0	0	11	11	713	Cape Wagtail	1	1	0	0
112	Cape Shoveller	0	0	4	4		Total	89	89	110	110
223	Purple Gallinule	1	1	2	2		No. of species			21	
226	Moorhen	19	19	41	41						

Tweelingpan – West, Lake Chrissie, Mpumalanga
26° 22' S 30° 15' E (2630AD)

A 40 ha open pan with sandy and rocky shoreline, and sedges/grasses along the shore. Three winter counts and one summer count available: the winter counts yielded 12 species, with good numbers only of Whitebreasted Cormorant (winter 1997), while the summer count was very low, indicating that the pan was almost dry at the time. Four earlier counts by D.G. Allan gave the following highlights: August 1985, 77 birds of 10 species, including 33 Redbilled Teal and 10 Chestnutbanded Plover; September 1985 (incomplete count), 350 Ruff; February 1986, 60+ birds of 13 species, including 30 Whitewinged Tern; February 1987 (incomplete count), 23 birds of 8 species. Threats include introduction of alien carp for fishing, and presence of wattle plantation along northern shore.

		Summer (1)		Winter (3)					Summer (1)		Winter (3)	
		Mean	Max.	Mean	Max.				Mean	Max.	Mean	Max.
006	Great Crested Grebe	0	0	1	2		116	Spurwinged Goose	3	3	0	0
008	Dabchick	0	0	3	8		228	Redknobbed Coot	0	0	2	7
055	Whitebreasted Cormorant	0	0	25	63		258	Blacksmith Plover	0	0	1	4
058	Reed Cormorant	0	0	0	1		295	Blackwinged Stilt	0	0	1	2
062	Grey Heron	0	0	1	4		315	Greyheaded Gull	0	0	1	2
096	Greater Flamingo	0	0	4	11			Total	5	5	45	82
097	Lesser Flamingo	0	0	5	14			No. of species			13	
102	Egyptian Goose	2	2	1	2							

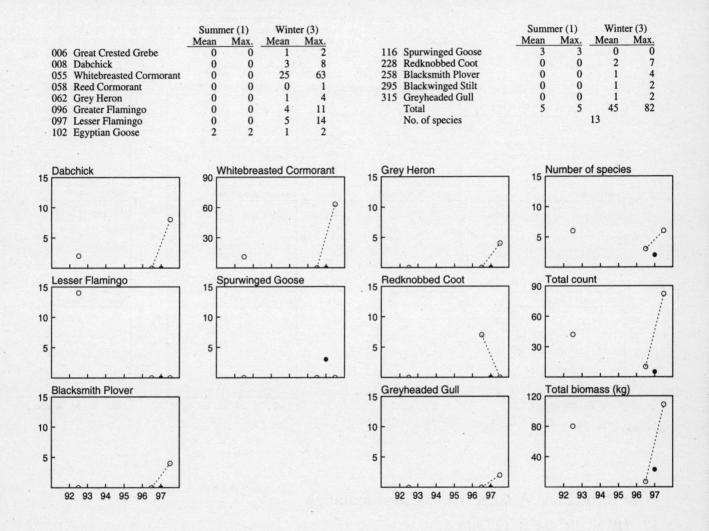

Tweelingpan – East, Lake Chrissie, Mpumalanga
26° 21' S 30° 15' E (2630AC)

A 35 ha open pan, with a sandy and rocky shoreline; variably lush shore vegetation of grasses and sedges. Three winter counts and one summer count are available, recording the occurrence of 14 bird species. Six species were recorded in summer 1997, including a good count of 15 Southern Pochard, while the winter counts produced 10 species, including 15 Egyptian Geese in winter 1992. A count in January 1985 (D.G. Allan) yielded 41+ birds of 10 species. Threats include water abstraction, and the presence of alien fish.

		Summer (1)		Winter (3)				Summer (1)		Winter (3)	
		Mean	Max.	Mean	Max.			Mean	Max.	Mean	Max.
055	Whitebreasted Cormorant	5	5	1	2	104	Yellowbilled Duck	0	0	2	3
058	Reed Cormorant	0	0	3	6	113	Southern Pochard	15	15	0	0
060	Darter	0	0	0	1	116	Spurwinged Goose	0	0	1	3
062	Grey Heron	4	4	1	1	228	Redknobbed Coot	0	0	3	5
074	Greenbacked Heron	1	1	0	0	258	Blacksmith Plover	0	0	0	1
091	Sacred Ibis	2	2	0	0	315	Greyheaded Gull	2	2	0	0
097	Lesser Flamingo	0	0	0	1		Total	29	29	16	25
102	Egyptian Goose	0	0	5	15		No. of species			14	

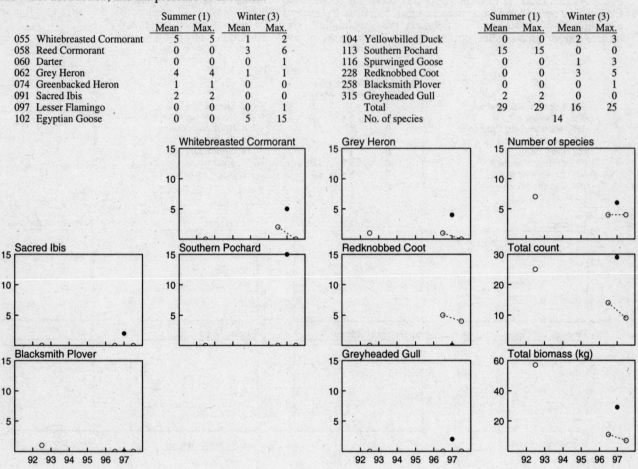

Wim Rabe Pan, Wakkerstroom, Mpumalanga
27° 10' S 30° 04' E (2730AA)

Only one count is available for this pan, from summer 1992, when 22 waterbird species were recorded, including good numbers of Dabchick, Yellowbilled Duck, Redknobbed Coot and Little Stint. On the basis of species richness and the overall number of birds counted, regular monitoring should be reinstated unless the habitat is only occasionally suitable for waterbirds. No threats have been identified.

		Summer (1)		Winter (0)				Summer (1)		Winter (0)	
		Mean	Max.	Mean	Max.			Mean	Max.	Mean	Max.
008	Dabchick	42	42	–	–	258	Blacksmith Plover	5	5	–	–
060	Darter	1	1	–	–	264	Common Sandpiper	2	2	–	–
063	Blackheaded Heron	1	1	–	–	266	Wood Sandpiper	6	6	–	–
101	Whitebacked Duck	10	10	–	–	269	Marsh Sandpiper	17	17	–	–
102	Egyptian Goose	13	13	–	–	270	Greenshank	5	5	–	–
104	Yellowbilled Duck	86	86	–	–	274	Little Stint	48	48	–	–
108	Redbilled Teal	2	2	–	–	284	Ruff	16	16	–	–
112	Cape Shoveller	2	2	–	–	338	Whiskered Tern	1	1	–	–
113	Southern Pochard	4	4	–	–	339	Whitewinged Tern	2	2	–	–
117	Maccoa Duck	9	9	–	–	713	Cape Wagtail	2	2	–	–
228	Redknobbed Coot	213	213	–	–		Total	490	490	–	–
249	Threebanded Plover	3	3	–	–		No. of species			22	

Witbank Dam, Witbank, Mpumalanga
25° 53' S 29° 18' E (2529CD)

A dam on the Olifants River. Numbers of cormorants, herons, egrets and Blacksmith Plover peak in summer, and of waterfowl, Kittlitz's and Threebanded Plovers, in winter. Redknobbed Coot is common, especially in winter, but a large count in summer 1995 contributed to the high total count and biomass figures for that survey, which also produced maximum counts of Whitebreasted Cormorant, Common Sandpiper, Little Stint and Greyheaded Gull. A high count of Whiskered Tern was made in summer 1994 and of Whitewinged Tern in summer 1995. Summer counts of Sacred Ibis and Reed Cormorant are declining; those of Blacksmith Plover are increasing. A serious threat is pollution by industrial waste, sewage and fertilisers; important threats are siltation, landfill, boating, water-skiing and fishing.

		Summer (4) Mean	Summer (4) Max.	Winter (5) Mean	Winter (5) Max.			Summer (4) Mean	Summer (4) Max.	Winter (5) Mean	Winter (5) Max.
006	Great Crested Grebe	5	9	7	18	148	African Fish Eagle	1	1	0	2
008	Dabchick	7	21	90	145	170	Osprey	2	4	1	1
055	Whitebreasted Cormorant	106	324	42	73	213	Black Crake	0	0	0	2
058	Reed Cormorant	101	157	52	89	223	Purple Gallinule	0	0	1	4
060	Darter	38	66	38	101	226	Moorhen	2	6	6	24
062	Grey Heron	19	41	6	10	228	Redknobbed Coot	464	1392	994	1839
063	Blackheaded Heron	4	5	2	4	240	African Jacana	2	7	1	2
064	Goliath Heron	8	10	6	10	248	Kittlitz's Plover	10	41	57	140
065	Purple Heron	5	8	1	2	249	Threebanded Plover	25	95	67	193
066	Great White Heron	10	11	1	3	258	Blacksmith Plover	121	153	73	147
067	Little Egret	10	19	1	3	260	Wattled Plover	5	10	1	3
068	Yellowbilled Egret	4	8	1	4	264	Common Sandpiper	44	149	1	2
069	Black Egret	1	1	0	1	266	Wood Sandpiper	6	11	0	0
071	Cattle Egret	44	62	2	6	269	Marsh Sandpiper	12	43	0	0
072	Squacco Heron	5	7	0	2	270	Greenshank	5	20	0	0
076	Blackcrowned Night Heron	1	1	0	0	272	Curlew Sandpiper	25	98	0	1
090	Yellowbilled Stork	1	2	0	0	274	Little Stint	108	392	3	13
091	Sacred Ibis	17	34	14	22	284	Ruff	3	10	0	0
093	Glossy Ibis	4	11	1	5	286	Ethiopian Snipe	6	23	1	4
094	Hadeda Ibis	5	7	15	21	294	Avocet	2	6	2	11
095	African Spoonbill	2	7	1	3	295	Blackwinged Stilt	8	30	7	15
096	Greater Flamingo	6	14	0	1	315	Greyheaded Gull	79	164	39	104
099	Whitefaced Duck	1	2	12	58	322	Caspian Tern	1	4	6	20
102	Egyptian Goose	54	100	139	246	338	Whiskered Tern	86	217	1	3
104	Yellowbilled Duck	74	172	186	402	339	Whitewinged Tern	115	409	0	0
105	African Black Duck	3	10	1	4	395	Marsh Owl	1	3	2	6
106	Cape Teal	1	3	5	18	428	Pied Kingfisher	8	11	2	7
108	Redbilled Teal	9	27	30	48	429	Giant Kingfisher	1	2	2	5
112	Cape Shoveller	7	25	13	23	431	Malachite Kingfisher	1	3	2	5
113	Southern Pochard	2	5	1	4	713	Cape Wagtail	26	47	187	325
115	Knobbilled Duck	0	0	1	3		Total	1717	3769	2174	2885
116	Spurwinged Goose	4	8	50	158		No. of species		62		

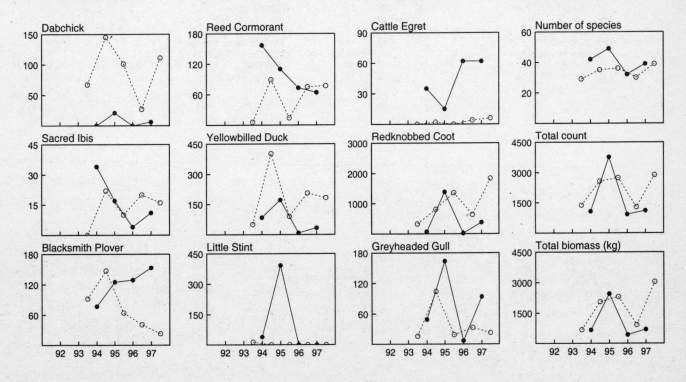

Blesbokspruit, Nigel, Gauteng
26° 29' S 28° 28' E (2628AD)

A Ramsar site and an important component of the Vaal River system; it purifies industrial effluent and is an important waterbird refuge. Permanent and seasonal marshes, pans, and dams. Parts of the site are protected within the Marievale and Stan Madden Bird sanctuaries (see accounts). Blesbokspruit formerly supported significant numbers of waterfowl, including thousands of Yellowbilled Duck, Redbilled Teal and Spurwinged Goose, but numbers have been drastically reduced in the last 15 years because of changes in the water regime and vegetation. Flamingos were formerly regular; Greater is now virtually absent. Squacco Heron and Black Egret are now regular. Goliath and Purple Herons, ibises and cormorants breed. Good numbers of African Rail, Black Crake, Purple Gallinule and Moorhen occur; African, Baillon's and Spotted Crakes are also recorded. The two counts available (1992) do not reflect recent avifaunal changes. Severe threats include greatly increased inflow of water from Grootvlei gold mine and other sources, with no winter drying out of the formerly seasonal wetland, and with a subsequent increase in reedbed cover; also siltation, pollution and eutrophication. Other threats include the presence of overhead power lines.

		Summer (1)		Winter (1)					Summer (1)		Winter (1)	
		Mean	Max.	Mean	Max.				Mean	Max.	Mean	Max.
006	Great Crested Grebe	16	16	0	0		117	Maccoa Duck	5	5	1	1
007	Blacknecked Grebe	0	0	51	51		148	African Fish Eagle	0	0	1	1
008	Dabchick	12	12	152	152		164	Euro. Marsh Harrier	1	1	0	0
055	Whitebreasted Cormorant	12	12	12	12		165	African Marsh Harrier	2	2	0	0
058	Reed Cormorant	75	75	44	44		210	African Rail	9	9	22	22
060	Darter	15	15	10	10		213	Black Crake	9	9	22	22
062	Grey Heron	4	4	6	6		217	Redchested Flufftail	3	3	0	0
063	Blackheaded Heron	13	13	8	8		223	Purple Gallinule	16	16	36	36
064	Goliath Heron	9	9	3	3		226	Moorhen	40	40	105	105
065	Purple Heron	12	12	8	8		228	Redknobbed Coot	397	397	508	508
067	Little Egret	3	3	0	0		240	African Jacana	1	1	0	0
068	Yellowbilled Egret	9	9	1	1		249	Threebanded Plover	4	4	24	24
069	Black Egret	5	5	0	0		258	Blacksmith Plover	79	79	95	95
071	Cattle Egret	143	143	19	19		260	Wattled Plover	12	12	7	7
072	Squacco Heron	18	18	0	0		264	Common Sandpiper	6	6	0	0
074	Greenbacked Heron	1	1	1	1		266	Wood Sandpiper	30	30	2	2
076	Blackcrowned Night Heron	4	4	0	0		269	Marsh Sandpiper	11	11	1	1
078	Little Bittern	4	4	0	0		270	Greenshank	6	6	0	0
091	Sacred Ibis	10	10	101	101		272	Curlew Sandpiper	3	3	1	1
093	Glossy Ibis	134	134	0	0		274	Little Stint	10	10	13	13
094	Hadeda Ibis	0	0	46	46		284	Ruff	114	114	2	2
095	African Spoonbill	3	3	0	0		286	Ethiopian Snipe	34	34	65	65
096	Greater Flamingo	78	78	341	341		287	Blacktailed Godwit	0	0	1	1
097	Lesser Flamingo	18	18	130	130		294	Avocet	36	36	9	9
099	Whitefaced Duck	41	41	4	4		295	Blackwinged Stilt	37	37	11	11
100	Fulvous Duck	96	96	0	0		315	Greyheaded Gull	80	80	8	8
102	Egyptian Goose	18	18	113	113		339	Whitewinged Tern	400	400	0	0
104	Yellowbilled Duck	81	81	279	279		393	Grass Owl	0	0	1	1
106	Cape Teal	6	6	19	19		395	Marsh Owl	4	4	3	3
107	Hottentot Teal	61	61	97	97		428	Pied Kingfisher	2	2	1	1
108	Redbilled Teal	54	54	483	483		431	Malachite Kingfisher	2	2	0	0
112	Cape Shoveller	22	22	40	40		713	Cape Wagtail	1	1	56	56
113	Southern Pochard	8	8	29	29			Total	2343	2343	3110	3110
116	Spurwinged Goose	4	4	118	118			No. of species			66	

Bronkhorstspruit Dam, Bronkhorstspruit, Gauteng
25° 54' S 28° 42' E (2528DC)

A dam on the Bronkhorstspruit River, with some fringing reedbeds, and sometimes (e.g. summer 1995) with good foraging substrates for shorebirds. A good variety of bird species recorded. Small numbers of Great Crested Grebe regular all year, and of Caspian Tern in winter; high count of Cape Wagtail in winter 1993. Greater Flamingo occurred only in summer 1995. Numbers of Dabchick, cormorants and most waterfowl peak in winter, when good counts of Redbilled Teal and Southern Pochard are noteworthy. Number of species, and total counts, declined during the survey period, possibly related to dam water levels. Important threats are residential development, boating and water-skiing; pollution is a mild threat.

		Summer (4)		Winter (4)	
		Mean	Max.	Mean	Max.
006	Great Crested Grebe	6	22	6	15
008	Dabchick	0	1	20	38
055	Whitebreasted Cormorant	10	17	19	30
058	Reed Cormorant	11	15	16	32
060	Darter	1	2	2	4
062	Grey Heron	4	6	3	7
063	Blackheaded Heron	1	1	1	2
064	Goliath Heron	0	1	0	0
065	Purple Heron	2	3	2	6
066	Great White Heron	2	4	2	6
067	Little Egret	2	5	2	6
069	Black Egret	3	6	0	0
071	Cattle Egret	25	48	0	0
072	Squacco Heron	1	2	0	0
076	Blackcrowned Night Heron	0	1	0	0
078	Little Bittern	1	3	1	1
090	Yellowbilled Stork	1	2	0	0
091	Sacred Ibis	1	2	1	5
093	Glossy Ibis	2	7	4	15
094	Hadeda Ibis	2	6	5	12
095	African Spoonbill	4	11	0	1
096	Greater Flamingo	12	48	1	4
099	Whitefaced Duck	0	0	5	18
100	Fulvous Duck	0	1	1	2
102	Egyptian Goose	14	18	22	67
103	South African Shelduck	3	9	1	4
104	Yellowbilled Duck	44	155	77	237
105	African Black Duck	1	2	0	0
108	Redbilled Teal	2	6	62	177
112	Cape Shoveller	0	0	4	12
113	Southern Pochard	0	0	28	112
116	Spurwinged Goose	0	0	3	8

		Summer (4)		Winter (4)	
		Mean	Max.	Mean	Max.
170	Osprey	0	1	0	0
213	Black Crake	0	1	0	1
223	Purple Gallinule	1	2	1	1
226	Moorhen	1	2	2	9
228	Redknobbed Coot	259	592	257	292
245	Ringed Plover	5	11	0	0
248	Kittlitz's Plover	23	56	32	63
249	Threebanded Plover	7	14	23	53
258	Blacksmith Plover	34	70	19	40
260	Wattled Plover	7	18	4	11
264	Common Sandpiper	5	15	0	0
266	Wood Sandpiper	1	1	1	3
269	Marsh Sandpiper	2	3	0	0
270	Greenshank	1	2	1	3
272	Curlew Sandpiper	70	142	1	3
274	Little Stint	104	281	0	0
281	Sanderling	0	1	0	0
284	Ruff	7	18	0	0
286	Ethiopian Snipe	0	1	8	17
294	Avocet	9	37	3	13
295	Blackwinged Stilt	1	3	0	1
315	Greyheaded Gull	16	38	12	36
322	Caspian Tern	0	0	8	17
338	Whiskered Tern	5	13	0	0
339	Whitewinged Tern	24	53	0	0
395	Marsh Owl	0	0	1	1
428	Pied Kingfisher	2	3	1	4
431	Malachite Kingfisher	1	2	0	0
713	Cape Wagtail	8	11	55	114
714	Yellow Wagtail	2	4	0	0
	Total	745	1329	713	963
	No. of species		62		

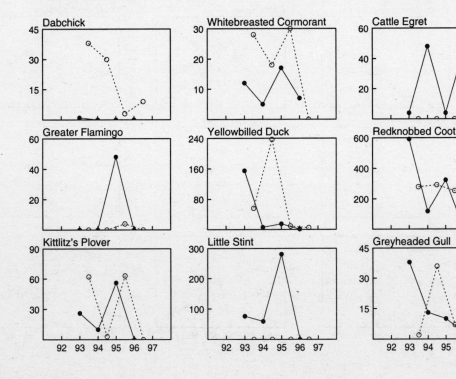

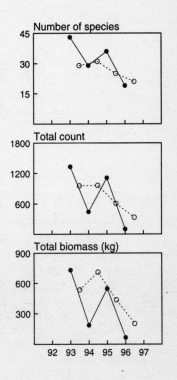

Diepsloot Nature Reserve, Johannesburg, Gauteng
25° 57' S 28° 00' E (2528CC)

Includes small dams, and pans of Johannesburg Northern Sewage Works. Diepsloot is a sewage farm with cattle pastures, maize and large reedbeds. Waterbirds are numerous and varied, with peak numbers of cormorants, Darter, egrets, Sacred and Glossy Ibises, and most shorebirds, occurring in summer, and of Dabchick, Hadeda, Southern Pochard, Spurwinged Goose, Red-knobbed Coot and Wattled Plover in winter; Egyptian Goose is common all year. There were exceptionally high winter counts of Whitefaced Duck in 1994 and of Yellowbilled Duck in 1996 and 1997. Little Bittern, Redchested Flufftail, Black Crake and Purple Gallinule occur. There appears to be an overall decline in species numbers and winter count totals. Threats include cattle grazing/trampling, informal housing, and poaching.

		Summer (4) Mean	Summer (4) Max.	Winter (5) Mean	Winter (5) Max.			Summer (4) Mean	Summer (4) Max.	Winter (5) Mean	Winter (5) Max.
006	Great Crested Grebe	1	1	0	1	112	Cape Shoveller	0	0	7	18
007	Blacknecked Grebe	0	0	0	1	113	Southern Pochard	6	23	21	45
008	Dabchick	7	18	53	61	115	Knobbilled Duck	0	0	2	10
055	Whitebreasted Cormorant	11	14	8	16	116	Spurwinged Goose	3	8	46	81
058	Reed Cormorant	25	61	11	19	148	African Fish Eagle	1	2	1	2
060	Darter	10	16	2	4	165	African Marsh Harrier	0	0	0	1
062	Grey Heron	1	3	1	2	213	Black Crake	6	10	9	12
063	Blackheaded Heron	2	3	2	7	217	Redchested Flufftail	0	0	0	1
064	Goliath Heron	3	3	3	5	223	Purple Gallinule	6	17	7	11
065	Purple Heron	0	0	0	1	226	Moorhen	14	25	22	32
066	Great White Heron	0	1	0	1	228	Redknobbed Coot	47	92	87	152
067	Little Egret	2	6	0	0	240	African Jacana	1	2	1	2
069	Black Egret	0	1	0	0	249	Threebanded Plover	6	13	5	9
071	Cattle Egret	83	102	16	24	258	Blacksmith Plover	89	191	63	127
074	Greenbacked Heron	0	0	0	1	260	Wattled Plover	23	50	43	65
078	Little Bittern	2	4	1	4	266	Wood Sandpiper	3	7	0	1
081	Hamerkop	1	2	2	4	269	Marsh Sandpiper	1	2	0	0
091	Sacred Ibis	136	322	10	16	284	Ruff	7	27	0	0
093	Glossy Ibis	29	101	1	1	286	Ethiopian Snipe	2	3	3	6
094	Hadeda Ibis	104	237	302	432	295	Blackwinged Stilt	0	0	0	2
095	African Spoonbill	0	0	0	1	315	Greyheaded Gull	0	0	3	7
099	Whitefaced Duck	23	48	170	672	339	Whitewinged Tern	21	83	0	1
100	Fulvous Duck	0	0	0	1	395	Marsh Owl	0	0	0	1
102	Egyptian Goose	190	299	169	207	428	Pied Kingfisher	1	1	1	1
103	South African Shelduck	0	0	1	2	429	Giant Kingfisher	0	0	0	2
104	Yellowbilled Duck	56	69	122	215	713	Cape Wagtail	5	9	5	7
105	African Black Duck	3	7	4	10	714	Yellow Wagtail	0	1	0	0
106	Cape Teal	0	0	0	2		Total	926	1000	1210	1707
107	Hottentot Teal	0	0	2	4		No. of species		57		
108	Redbilled Teal	1	2	1	4						

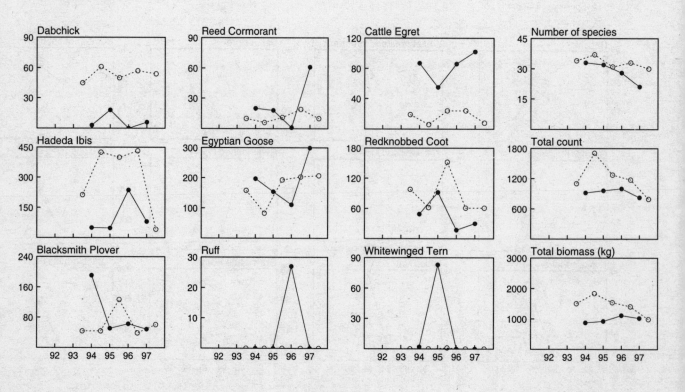

Grootvaly, Springs, Gauteng
26° 16' S 28° 30' E (2628BC)

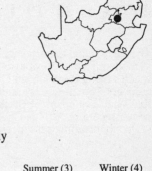

Part of the Blesbokspruit system, with open water, reedbeds and marshy habitat. Supports a wide variety of waterbirds, usually in small to moderate numbers, but the winter 1994 count was relatively high, with maximum counts of Glossy Ibis, Egyptian and Spurwinged Geese, Yellowbilled Duck and Redbilled Teal. Number of species, total count and total biomass all show a decline during the survey period; winter counts of Greyheaded Gull, Purple Gallinule and several waterfowl are declining, while winter Glossy Ibis numbers crashed after 1994. In contrast, winter numbers of Sacred Ibis are increasing. Egrets, Squacco Heron and Blackcrowned Night Heron occur predominantly in summer. Blesbokspruit is severely threatened by discharge of mine water which drastically increases total water volume, maintains artificially high water levels in the dry season, and contains many pollutants, including salt.

		Summer (3)		Winter (4)					Summer (3)		Winter (4)	
		Mean	Max.	Mean	Max.				Mean	Max.	Mean	Max.
006	Great Crested Grebe	0	1	0	0		113	Southern Pochard	1	2	2	3
008	Dabchick	4	12	10	17		115	Knobbilled Duck	1	3	0	0
055	Whitebreasted Cormorant	1	2	3	6		116	Spurwinged Goose	2	3	60	154
058	Reed Cormorant	32	52	20	48		117	Maccoa Duck	1	2	0	0
060	Darter	4	8	3	13		165	African Marsh Harrier	0	1	1	2
062	Grey Heron	3	6	2	4		210	African Rail	1	2	3	8
063	Blackheaded Heron	1	2	5	10		213	Black Crake	5	10	11	24
064	Goliath Heron	4	6	4	6		223	Purple Gallinule	4	10	9	14
065	Purple Heron	3	4	5	12		226	Moorhen	15	16	18	28
066	Great White Heron	1	2	0	0		228	Redknobbed Coot	86	119	61	80
067	Little Egret	2	7	0	0		240	African Jacana	0	1	0	0
068	Yellowbilled Egret	0	1	0	1		249	Threebanded Plover	0	0	1	4
069	Black Egret	6	13	0	0		258	Blacksmith Plover	23	24	13	16
071	Cattle Egret	84	151	1	2		264	Common Sandpiper	3	6	0	1
072	Squacco Heron	14	18	2	7		266	Wood Sandpiper	4	5	0	0
074	Greenbacked Heron	1	3	0	0		269	Marsh Sandpiper	0	1	0	0
076	Blackcrowned Night Heron	10	28	1	3		270	Greenshank	1	2	0	0
078	Little Bittern	0	1	1	2		272	Curlew Sandpiper	0	1	0	0
091	Sacred Ibis	32	40	25	58		284	Ruff	6	16	0	0
093	Glossy Ibis	185	332	125	481		286	Ethiopian Snipe	0	1	0	0
094	Hadeda Ibis	15	26	10	21		294	Avocet	0	0	0	1
095	African Spoonbill	1	2	1	4		295	Blackwinged Stilt	1	2	1	2
096	Greater Flamingo	0	0	2	9		315	Greyheaded Gull	2	6	14	19
099	Whitefaced Duck	7	18	17	57		338	Whiskered Tern	1	3	0	0
100	Fulvous Duck	42	88	1	5		339	Whitewinged Tern	1	2	0	0
102	Egyptian Goose	38	40	48	118		428	Pied Kingfisher	6	7	1	2
103	South African Shelduck	0	1	0	0		429	Giant Kingfisher	0	1	0	0
104	Yellowbilled Duck	14	29	95	141		431	Malachite Kingfisher	2	3	0	0
105	African Black Duck	1	2	0	0		713	Cape Wagtail	7	9	12	17
106	Cape Teal	0	0	1	3		891	Mallard	0	0	0	1
107	Hottentot Teal	23	38	26	36			Total	711	890	667	1403
108	Redbilled Teal	6	18	52	180			No. of species			63	
112	Cape Shoveller	3	8	5	8							

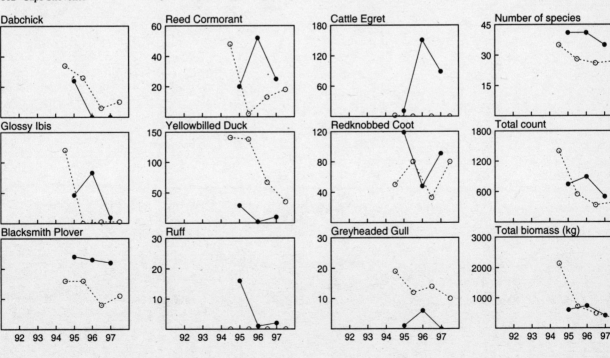

Homestead, Benoni & Middle Lakes, Benoni, Gauteng
26° 11' S 28° 19' E (2628AB)

These lakes and dams were counted only in summer 1992 and 1994 and in winter 1993. Small to moderate numbers of a good variety of waterbird species were recorded, the commonest species being Redknobbed Coot, which was much more numerous in winter. Sacred Ibis numbers were higher in summer, and Blackheaded Heron numbers were higher in winter. Reasonable numbers of Black Crake, Purple Gallinule and Moorhen are recorded, while the winter record of African Crake is indicative of the persistence of good habitat for this species in the nonbreeding season. No threats have been identified.

		Summer (2) Mean	Summer (2) Max.	Winter (2) Mean	Winter (2) Max.			Summer (2) Mean	Summer (2) Max.	Winter (2) Mean	Winter (2) Max.
006	Great Crested Grebe	6	12	6	7	103	South African Shelduck	1	2	0	0
007	Blacknecked Grebe	4	7	0	0	104	Yellowbilled Duck	2	3	4	8
008	Dabchick	12	20	16	20	108	Redbilled Teal	4	7	4	7
055	Whitebreasted Cormorant	10	19	16	28	115	Knobbilled Duck	2	3	0	0
058	Reed Cormorant	9	17	4	7	116	Spurwinged Goose	10	14	9	18
060	Darter	7	13	10	11	212	African Crake	0	0	3	5
062	Grey Heron	9	11	5	9	213	Black Crake	7	12	6	11
063	Blackheaded Heron	6	7	9	15	223	Purple Gallinule	9	14	9	18
065	Purple Heron	1	1	0	0	226	Moorhen	10	18	15	17
066	Great White Heron	1	2	1	1	228	Redknobbed Coot	54	62	203	208
068	Yellowbilled Egret	1	2	0	0	240	African Jacana	1	2	1	1
069	Black Egret	2	4	0	0	248	Kittlitz's Plover	0	0	6	11
071	Cattle Egret	28	31	24	29	249	Threebanded Plover	7	14	4	7
072	Squacco Heron	0	0	4	7	258	Blacksmith Plover	18	23	24	29
074	Greenbacked Heron	1	1	2	4	260	Wattled Plover	1	1	0	0
076	Blackcrowned Night Heron	2	3	2	3	286	Ethiopian Snipe	3	6	0	0
084	Black Stork	1	1	0	0	298	Water Dikkop	7	13	2	3
091	Sacred Ibis	48	54	21	27	315	Greyheaded Gull	16	31	24	27
093	Glossy Ibis	13	17	12	12	395	Marsh Owl	6	9	5	9
094	Hadeda Ibis	6	12	12	18	428	Pied Kingfisher	1	2	1	2
095	African Spoonbill	10	19	8	9	429	Giant Kingfisher	0	0	2	4
099	Whitefaced Duck	11	14	4	7	431	Malachite Kingfisher	2	4	0	0
100	Fulvous Duck	2	3	0	0	713	Cape Wagtail	39	60	32	43
101	Whitebacked Duck	0	0	2	4		Total	401	520	510	617
102	Egyptian Goose	24	34	7	13		No. of species		48		

Korsman Bird Sanctuary, Benoni, Gauteng
26° 11' S 28° 18' E (2628AB)

A small pan with open water and fringing vegetation. Has an impressive variety of waterbirds, with good counts of herons, African Spoonbill, flamingos and Greyheaded Gull. Available counts are not enough to give a good picture of seasonal variations, but some herons, Greater Flamingo and Hadeda seem to be commoner in winter, while Whitefronted, Threebanded, Blacksmith and Wattled Plovers, Avocet and Water Dikkop are commoner in summer. Greater Flamingo numbers have decreased; Greyheaded Gull numbers are rising. Numbers of Little Bittern, Purple Gallinule, and Grass and Marsh Owls, are reasonable. Occasional raw sewage overflow and wandering domestic dogs are potential threats.

		Summer (3)		Winter (3)				Summer (3)		Winter (3)	
		Mean	Max.	Mean	Max.			Mean	Max.	Mean	Max.
006	Great Crested Grebe	10	12	4	12	117	Maccoa Duck	4	5	0	0
008	Dabchick	9	14	11	13	210	African Rail	1	4	0	0
055	Whitebreasted Cormorant	16	20	53	125	213	Black Crake	6	11	2	7
056	Cape Cormorant	5	14	0	0	223	Purple Gallinule	11	19	13	22
058	Reed Cormorant	16	31	12	27	226	Moorhen	5	14	5	13
060	Darter	4	7	8	18	228	Redknobbed Coot	40	56	45	79
062	Grey Heron	4	6	27	76	229	African Finfoot	0	1	0	0
063	Blackheaded Heron	10	14	20	44	240	African Jacana	2	5	0	0
064	Goliath Heron	2	4	0	1	246	Whitefronted Plover	6	19	0	0
065	Purple Heron	2	3	0	0	248	Kittlitz's Plover	2	7	3	9
066	Great White Heron	1	2	0	0	249	Threebanded Plover	6	17	4	11
067	Little Egret	3	7	0	0	258	Blacksmith Plover	22	44	20	35
068	Yellowbilled Egret	2	6	0	0	260	Wattled Plover	5	13	3	9
069	Black Egret	7	12	5	13	264	Common Sandpiper	6	12	0	0
071	Cattle Egret	42	62	17	36	266	Wood Sandpiper	4	7	4	11
072	Squacco Heron	12	23	7	21	269	Marsh Sandpiper	4	10	3	10
074	Greenbacked Heron	1	2	0	1	270	Greenshank	0	0	3	9
076	Blackcrowned Night Heron	8	17	4	13	271	Knot	0	0	2	6
078	Little Bittern	6	10	2	5	272	Curlew Sandpiper	1	2	1	3
081	Hamerkop	1	3	0	0	274	Little Stint	16	28	2	7
091	Sacred Ibis	93	115	36	87	284	Ruff	5	7	3	10
093	Glossy Ibis	31	50	27	56	286	Ethiopian Snipe	2	5	2	6
094	Hadeda Ibis	13	31	12	19	294	Avocet	12	32	2	6
095	African Spoonbill	31	50	39	63	295	Blackwinged Stilt	6	15	7	21
096	Greater Flamingo	85	209	235	368	298	Water Dikkop	4	12	2	7
097	Lesser Flamingo	61	170	35	43	315	Greyheaded Gull	135	300	107	174
099	Whitefaced Duck	8	17	7	11	338	Whiskered Tern	6	18	0	0
100	Fulvous Duck	8	9	8	12	339	Whitewinged Tern	4	9	0	0
102	Egyptian Goose	35	54	26	49	393	Grass Owl	4	7	1	3
104	Yellowbilled Duck	7	9	11	14	395	Marsh Owl	4	10	5	15
105	African Black Duck	1	3	0	0	428	Pied Kingfisher	3	7	2	5
106	Cape Teal	3	6	3	6	429	Giant Kingfisher	3	7	2	7
107	Hottentot Teal	4	11	3	10	431	Malachite Kingfisher	3	9	0	0
108	Redbilled Teal	9	14	2	6	713	Cape Wagtail	19	27	19	41
112	Cape Shoveller	9	17	20	52	891	Mallard	1	2	0	0
113	Southern Pochard	2	4	1	4		Total	930	1339	1040	1362
116	Spurwinged Goose	14	29	141	179		No. of species		72		

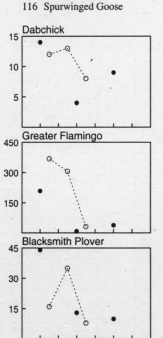

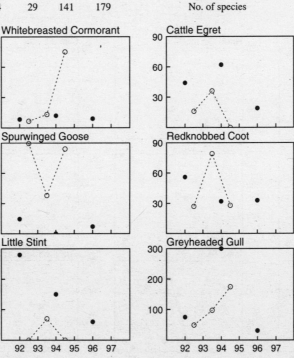

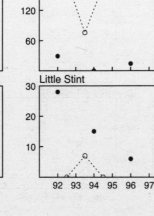

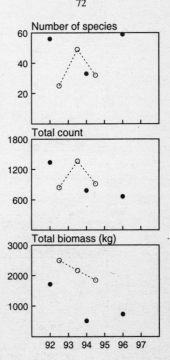

Leeupan, Benoni, Gauteng
26° 14' S 28° 19' E (2628AB)

A 40 ha open-water pan; shoreline grass/sedge, and *Phragmites* on an island. Whitebreasted Cormorant, African Spoonbill and Blackheaded Heron breed. Important for Great Crested Grebe in summer; good numbers of Whitebacked Duck (summer peak), flamingoes (most in winter), Redknobbed Coot, Greyheaded Gull (summer peak) and Cape Wagtail (winter peak). Sacred Ibis counts show a severe decline since 1992–1993, as do winter counts of Greater Flamingo and Redknobbed Coot. The high biomass in winter 1993 reflects an exceptional count of Spurwinged Goose. Sewage overflow enters the closed pan system, while squatter encroachment has been a critical threat since 1996, resulting in a dramatic decline in bird numbers.

		Summer (5)		Winter (6)				Summer (5)		Winter (6)	
		Mean	Max.	Mean	Max.			Mean	Max.	Mean	Max.
006	Great Crested Grebe	19	42*	2	8	112	Cape Shoveller	5	7	12	25
007	Blacknecked Grebe	1	7	1	4	113	Southern Pochard	2	6	0	0
008	Dabchick	9	26	22	35	115	Knobbilled Duck	0	1	0	0
049	White Pelican	1	5	0	0	116	Spurwinged Goose	5	27	62	255
050	Pinkbacked Pelican	0	1	0	0	117	Maccoa Duck	0	1	0	0
055	Whitebreasted Cormorant	7	22	6	20	223	Purple Gallinule	1	7	0	0
058	Reed Cormorant	15	22	5	17	226	Moorhen	1	5	1	7
060	Darter	7	27	2	11	228	Redknobbed Coot	376	669	445	730
062	Grey Heron	3	5	1	4	240	African Jacana	1	4	1	4
063	Blackheaded Heron	6	24	3	6	242	Painted Snipe	0	1	0	0
064	Goliath Heron	0	2	1	3	245	Ringed Plover	1	4	0	0
065	Purple Heron	0	1	0	0	246	Whitefronted Plover	0	1	0	0
066	Great White Heron	0	1	0	0	248	Kittlitz's Plover	4	8	11	30
067	Little Egret	2	6	0	1	249	Threebanded Plover	8	17	19	42
068	Yellowbilled Egret	1	2	0	0	258	Blacksmith Plover	40	82	34	81
069	Black Egret	1	6	0	0	260	Wattled Plover	5	21	1	7
071	Cattle Egret	27	75	11	23	264	Common Sandpiper	1	4	0	0
072	Squacco Heron	1	4	0	0	266	Wood Sandpiper	2	5	1	2
076	Blackcrowned Night Heron	0	2	0	0	269	Marsh Sandpiper	7	20	1	4
078	Little Bittern	0	1	0	0	270	Greenshank	1	3	0	0
081	Hamerkop	0	1	0	0	272	Curlew Sandpiper	11	45	0	0
090	Yellowbilled Stork	0	2	0	0	274	Little Stint	22	36	2	7
091	Sacred Ibis	24	55	10	47	284	Ruff	5	21	1	5
093	Glossy Ibis	45	98	12	42	286	Ethiopian Snipe	1	5	3	8
094	Hadeda Ibis	3	8	6	30	294	Avocet	0	2	0	0
095	African Spoonbill	6	23	5	25	295	Blackwinged Stilt	18	39	24	65
096	Greater Flamingo	37	94	96	241	298	Water Dikkop	2	12	0	2
097	Lesser Flamingo	9	45	53	202	315	Greyheaded Gull	249	653*	149	461
099	Whitefaced Duck	12	25	31	105	322	Caspian Tern	0	2	0	0
100	Fulvous Duck	6	19	3	15	338	Whiskered Tern	14	61	0	0
101	Whitebacked Duck	27	132	1	8	339	Whitewinged Tern	272	1300*	0	0
102	Egyptian Goose	81	275	42	98	393	Grass Owl	1	4	0	0
103	South African Shelduck	0	1	0	0	395	Marsh Owl	1	6	0	0
104	Yellowbilled Duck	4	11	10	29	428	Pied Kingfisher	0	1	0	0
105	African Black Duck	1	2	0	0	713	Cape Wagtail	39	107	80	125
106	Cape Teal	3	9	13	41	714	Yellow Wagtail	4	20	0	0
107	Hottentot Teal	0	2	4	12		Total	1468	2798	1199	2373
108	Redbilled Teal	3	9	17	33		No. of species		74		

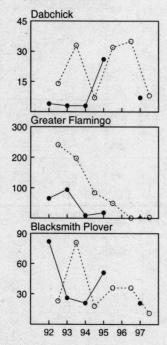
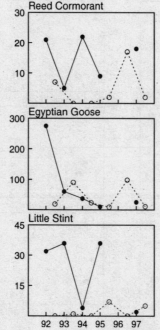
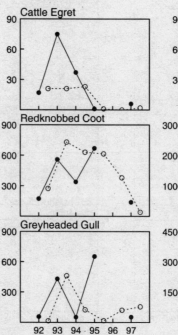
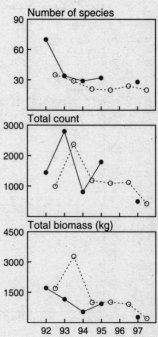

Marievale Bird Sanctuary, Nigel, Gauteng
26° 21' S 28° 30' E (2628BC)

An IBA and part of the Blesbokspruit Ramsar site. Has extensive *Phragmites* and *Typha* reedbeds, also sedgebeds, wet grass, and open water with floating-leaved vegetation. Good numbers of Glossy Ibis, Yellowbilled Duck and Redknobbed Coot occur all year; Squacco Heron may be quite common in summer. Hottentot Teal and Spurwinged Goose numbers peak in winter. A good selection of rails occurs, and Spotted Crake is also recorded. Purple Heron, Little Bittern, Grass Owl and Marsh Owl also occur. Increases are apparent in the number of species (summer and winter) and total count (summer). Blesbokspruit is severely threatened by discharge of mine water which drastically increases total water volume, maintains artificially high water levels in the dry season, and contains many pollutants, including salt.

		Summer (5)		Winter (5)				Summer (5)		Winter (5)	
		Mean	Max.	Mean	Max.			Mean	Max.	Mean	Max.
006	Great Crested Grebe	3	6	0	1	116	Spurwinged Goose	3	11	62	128
008	Dabchick	2	6	11	30	165	African Marsh Harrier	0	0	1	5
055	Whitebreasted Cormorant	1	4	5	14	210	African Rail	5	8	7	15
058	Reed Cormorant	30	54	21	61	213	Black Crake	13	20	10	19
060	Darter	1	4	0	1	217	Redchested Flufftail	0	1	0	0
062	Grey Heron	1	3	1	4	223	Purple Gallinule	9	21	13	32
063	Blackheaded Heron	3	7	6	24	226	Moorhen	41	93	31	54
064	Goliath Heron	3	5	3	4	228	Redknobbed Coot	310	650	302	645
065	Purple Heron	3	7	1	3	245	Ringed Plover	0	1	0	0
067	Little Egret	2	4	0	0	248	Kittlitz's Plover	0	0	1	4
068	Yellowbilled Egret	1	2	0	0	249	Threebanded Plover	1	4	1	3
069	Black Egret	2	7	0	0	258	Blacksmith Plover	24	77	11	14
071	Cattle Egret	80	237	6	31	260	Wattled Plover	4	14	1	5
072	Squacco Heron	11	33	1	4	264	Common Sandpiper	1	3	0	0
076	Blackcrowned Night Heron	2	6	0	0	266	Wood Sandpiper	5	21	0	0
078	Little Bittern	2	4	0	1	269	Marsh Sandpiper	1	2	0	0
091	Sacred Ibis	1	3	0	0	270	Greenshank	0	1	0	0
093	Glossy Ibis	40	173	23	109	272	Curlew Sandpiper	1	4	0	0
094	Hadeda Ibis	6	12	8	14	274	Little Stint	6	28	0	0
095	African Spoonbill	2	6	0	1	284	Ruff	6	26	0	0
096	Greater Flamingo	0	0	7	21	286	Ethiopian Snipe	7	17	24	81
097	Lesser Flamingo	0	0	2	12	295	Blackwinged Stilt	1	6	1	5
099	Whitefaced Duck	0	1	0	1	315	Greyheaded Gull	0	1	3	15
100	Fulvous Duck	13	47	0	0	322	Caspian Tern	0	0	0	2
102	Egyptian Goose	7	13	7	10	338	Whiskered Tern	0	2	3	15
103	South African Shelduck	0	0	0	2	339	Whitewinged Tern	3	6	0	0
104	Yellowbilled Duck	56	163	72	114	393	Grass Owl	0	0	0	1
105	African Black Duck	0	2	0	0	395	Marsh Owl	0	1	1	4
106	Cape Teal	0	0	0	2	428	Pied Kingfisher	1	5	0	1
107	Hottentot Teal	15	37	35	62	431	Malachite Kingfisher	1	2	0	0
108	Redbilled Teal	3	10	6	14	713	Cape Wagtail	4	8	7	11
112	Cape Shoveller	1	2	5	7	714	Yellow Wagtail	0	0	0	2
113	Southern Pochard	4	11	2	11		Total	744	966	707	964
115	Knobbilled Duck	1	3	0	0		No. of species			66	

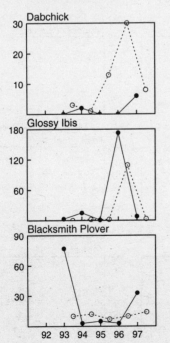

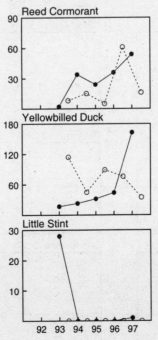

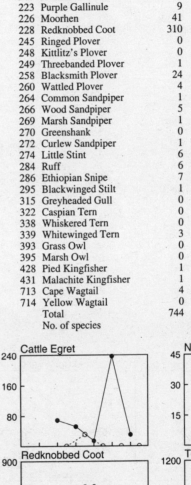

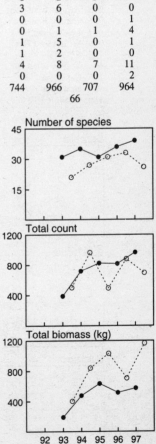

Rietspruit (Rooikraal), Boksburg, Gauteng
26° 20' S 28° 17' E (2628AD)

A dam on the Rietspruit, with an adjacent permanent marsh. Cattle Egret and Glossy Ibis are common in summer; flamingos are more numerous in winter. No Palearctic waders are consistently common, but a large count of Ruff was made in summer 1997, when Greyheaded Gulls were also numerous. A good variety of rails occurs. A high number of species is recorded, but there is a decline in species diversity and in the total number of birds in winter. Species showing a strong decline in winter numbers include Dabchick, Yellowbilled Duck, Redbilled Teal and Greater Flamingo. The dumping of tailings from a nearby mine is a critical problem, while siltation and reed encroachment are severe threats. Industrial pollution, and the recent appearance of squatters, are important threats.

		Summer (3) Mean	Summer (3) Max.	Winter (4) Mean	Winter (4) Max.			Summer (3) Mean	Summer (3) Max.	Winter (4) Mean	Winter (4) Max.
006	Great Crested Grebe	4	5	1	2	112	Cape Shoveller	2	6	1	2
008	Dabchick	5	13	7	14	113	Southern Pochard	1	3	1	4
055	Whitebreasted Cormorant	1	3	1	3	116	Spurwinged Goose	5	6	2	6
058	Reed Cormorant	9	18	7	17	165	African Marsh Harrier	0	1	1	2
060	Darter	7	11	1	1	210	African Rail	1	3	1	3
062	Grey Heron	2	6	0	0	213	Black Crake	2	6	3	5
063	Blackheaded Heron	2	2	10	17	217	Redchested Flufftail	0	0	0	1
064	Goliath Heron	0	1	1	2	223	Purple Gallinule	2	4	3	6
065	Purple Heron	0	0	1	1	226	Moorhen	3	3	5	10
066	Great White Heron	0	1	0	1	228	Redknobbed Coot	80	125	61	109
067	Little Egret	1	1	0	0	249	Threebanded Plover	1	2	2	3
068	Yellowbilled Egret	1	2	0	0	258	Blacksmith Plover	8	12	7	9
069	Black Egret	1	1	0	0	260	Wattled Plover	0	0	1	3
071	Cattle Egret	432	908	52	202	266	Wood Sandpiper	1	2	0	0
072	Squacco Heron	1	2	0	0	269	Marsh Sandpiper	0	1	0	0
076	Blackcrowned Night Heron	1	2	0	0	270	Greenshank	0	0	1	3
078	Little Bittern	0	1	0	0	274	Little Stint	2	6	0	0
090	Yellowbilled Stork	1	3	0	0	284	Ruff	46	132	0	0
091	Sacred Ibis	3	3	3	10	286	Ethiopian Snipe	1	1	1	2
093	Glossy Ibis	87	155	3	11	294	Avocet	2	6	3	8
094	Hadeda Ibis	2	4	0	1	295	Blackwinged Stilt	0	0	1	2
095	African Spoonbill	0	0	1	1	315	Greyheaded Gull	34	101	2	3
096	Greater Flamingo	0	1	51	118	338	Whiskered Tern	0	1	0	0
097	Lesser Flamingo	0	1	12	46	339	Whitewinged Tern	0	1	0	0
099	Whitefaced Duck	3	7	2	6	395	Marsh Owl	2	4	5	8
102	Egyptian Goose	7	12	8	29	428	Pied Kingfisher	1	2	1	2
104	Yellowbilled Duck	4	8	19	38	431	Malachite Kingfisher	0	0	0	1
106	Cape Teal	0	0	2	3	713	Cape Wagtail	1	2	3	7
107	Hottentot Teal	2	4	3	6		Total	774	1242	293	583
108	Redbilled Teal	1	3	10	27		No. of species		58		

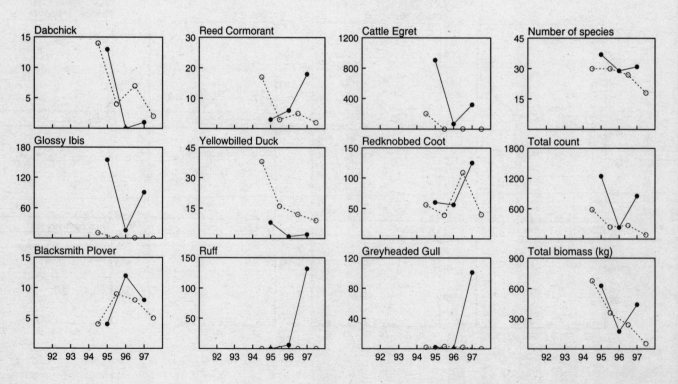

Rietvlei Dam, Pretoria, Gauteng
25° 53' S 28° 17' E (2528CD)

Two dams in a 3200 ha nature reserve. This site was counted only in 1997, when 29 waterbird species were recorded, 22 in summer and 23 in winter. The summer count yielded good numbers of Cattle Egret and reasonable numbers of Darter and Sacred Ibis, while the winter count yielded good numbers of Dabchick, Whitebreasted Cormorant and Egyptian Goose. Redknobbed Coot is numerous, especially in winter. The spread of Black Wattle is a potential threat.

		Summer (1)		Winter (1)	
		Mean	Max.	Mean	Max.
006	Great Crested Grebe	17	17	9	9
008	Dabchick	24	24	131	131
055	Whitebreasted Cormorant	21	21	45	45
058	Reed Cormorant	30	30	30	30
060	Darter	14	14	3	3
062	Grey Heron	1	1	4	4
063	Blackheaded Heron	1	1	5	5
066	Great White Heron	1	1	0	0
067	Little Egret	4	4	0	0
071	Cattle Egret	228	228	0	0
072	Squacco Heron	1	1	0	0
074	Greenbacked Heron	2	2	3	3
091	Sacred Ibis	23	23	10	10
094	Hadeda Ibis	4	4	2	2
095	African Spoonbill	0	0	1	1
102	Egyptian Goose	21	21	49	49
104	Yellowbilled Duck	2	2	19	19
108	Redbilled Teal	0	0	2	2
112	Cape Shoveller	0	0	3	3
148	African Fish Eagle	1	1	1	1
213	Black Crake	2	2	0	0
223	Purple Gallinule	0	0	2	2
226	Moorhen	2	2	32	32
228	Redknobbed Coot	214	214	461	461
249	Threebanded Plover	0	0	27	27
258	Blacksmith Plover	4	4	7	7
315	Greyheaded Gull	9	9	0	0
429	Giant Kingfisher	0	0	3	3
891	Mallard	0	0	3	3
	Total	626	626	852	852
	No. of species		29		

Rolfe's Pan, Kempton Park, Gauteng
26° 10' S 28° 13' E (2628AA)

A semi-permanent freshwater pan with dense submergents, emergent grasses and sedges, and beds of *Typha* and *Phragmites*. Greyheaded Gulls breed on an island; during the survey period very few were recorded in summer, and winter numbers were very low in 1993 and 1996. The only other species recorded in large numbers is Sacred Ibis, from winter 1994 through to winter 1995. Spurwinged Goose is almost exclusively of winter occurrence, numbers having apparently declined greatly since 1995. Recorded numbers of Purple Gallinule are consistently higher in winter; Moorhen and Redknobbed Coot counts are decreasing. Important threats include continuing industrial development encroaching on the shoreline, landfill on the pan perimeter, severe pollution from industrial effluent and solid waste, and unrestricted access.

		Summer (3)		Winter (5)				Summer (3)		Winter (5)	
		Mean	Max.	Mean	Max.			Mean	Max.	Mean	Max.
006	Great Crested Grebe	4	10	1	2	104	Yellowbilled Duck	3	5	4	11
008	Dabchick	1	1	5	12	105	African Black Duck	0	0	0	2
055	Whitebreasted Cormorant	0	0	3	5	106	Cape Teal	0	0	0	1
058	Reed Cormorant	7	10	7	10	107	Hottentot Teal	0	0	1	3
060	Darter	8	11	2	4	108	Redbilled Teal	0	0	2	8
062	Grey Heron	1	4	4	10	112	Cape Shoveller	0	0	2	7
063	Blackheaded Heron	3	5	7	12	113	Southern Pochard	0	0	2	7
065	Purple Heron	0	1	1	2	116	Spurwinged Goose	0	1	22	55
066	Great White Heron	0	0	0	1	223	Purple Gallinule	2	4	8	14
067	Little Egret	5	15	0	0	226	Moorhen	4	7	8	16
069	Black Egret	1	1	0	0	228	Redknobbed Coot	29	62	21	30
071	Cattle Egret	60	85	9	45	240	African Jacana	1	4	0	0
072	Squacco Heron	0	0	1	3	249	Threebanded Plover	2	4	4	10
074	Greenbacked Heron	0	0	0	1	258	Blacksmith Plover	13	16	9	18
076	Blackcrowned Night Heron	1	2	1	3	260	Wattled Plover	0	0	1	4
091	Sacred Ibis	81	222	169	511	266	Wood Sandpiper	1	2	0	0
093	Glossy Ibis	5	8	0	0	269	Marsh Sandpiper	1	2	0	0
094	Hadeda Ibis	1	2	1	3	274	Little Stint	2	6	0	0
095	African Spoonbill	1	3	1	5	315	Greyheaded Gull	10	16	112	265
096	Greater Flamingo	0	0	3	16	428	Pied Kingfisher	0	1	1	2
099	Whitefaced Duck	1	2	4	14	713	Cape Wagtail	1	2	6	14
100	Fulvous Duck	1	2	0	0		Total	262	436	436	827
101	Whitebacked Duck	0	0	0	1		No. of species		45		
102	Egyptian Goose	13	21	13	19						

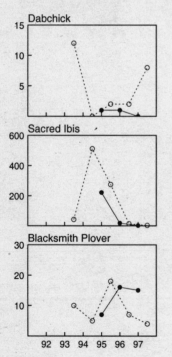

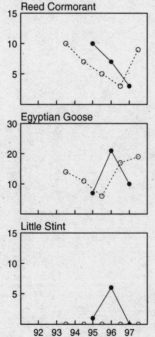

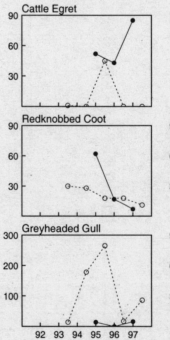

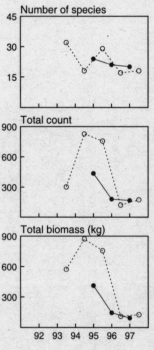

Rondebult Bird Sanctuary, Germiston, Gauteng
26° 18' S 28° 12' E (2628AC)

Permanent marsh with open water dams, reedbeds and sedgebeds; water comes from the adjacent sewage treatment plant. A good variety of waterfowl is recorded, some species being commoner in summer and others in winter; none occurs in very large numbers. Greater Flamingo numbers fluctuate widely, and Lesser Flamingo is recorded only in winter. Good numbers of Blacksmith Plover occur in summer and reasonable numbers of Avocet and Blackwinged Stilt in summer and winter. Relatively large counts of Dabchick, Sacred Ibis, Cape Teal, Redknobbed Coot, Avocet, Blackwinged Stilt and Greyheaded Gull were recorded in winter 1997. The overall number of species appears to be declining. Important threats are reed encroachment and the irregular water supply to some dams; sedimentation is a mild threat.

		Summer (4)		Winter (4)				Summer (4)		Winter (4)	
		Mean	Max.	Mean	Max.			Mean	Max.	Mean	Max.
006	Great Crested Grebe	1	2	0	0	113	Southern Pochard	1	5	0	0
007	Blacknecked Grebe	0	0	1	4	116	Spurwinged Goose	3	7	1	2
008	Dabchick	7	13	21	76	117	Maccoa Duck	3	7	0	0
058	Reed Cormorant	1	2	3	4	213	Black Crake	2	3	3	9
062	Grey Heron	1	3	4	10	223	Purple Gallinule	3	6	3	6
063	Blackheaded Heron	4	8	6	10	226	Moorhen	9	17	14	21
064	Goliath Heron	0	0	0	1	228	Redknobbed Coot	24	29	25	57
065	Purple Heron	0	0	1	2	249	Threebanded Plover	2	3	1	2
066	Great White Heron	0	1	0	0	258	Blacksmith Plover	79	110	8	19
067	Little Egret	0	1	0	1	264	Common Sandpiper	2	8	0	0
071	Cattle Egret	9	12	3	9	266	Wood Sandpiper	1	3	0	0
076	Blackcrowned Night Heron	1	2	1	1	269	Marsh Sandpiper	2	6	0	0
091	Sacred Ibis	1	4	9	26	272	Curlew Sandpiper	2	9	0	0
093	Glossy Ibis	4	5	0	1	274	Little Stint	26	85	0	0
094	Hadeda Ibis	14	25	2	4	284	Ruff	84	179	0	0
095	African Spoonbill	0	0	0	1	286	Ethiopian Snipe	0	1	0	0
096	Greater Flamingo	18	45	9	23	287	Blacktailed Godwit	0	1	0	0
097	Lesser Flamingo	0	0	18	68	294	Avocet	10	24	12	34
099	Whitefaced Duck	33	80	3	13	295	Blackwinged Stilt	15	28	14	35
100	Fulvous Duck	0	1	0	0	315	Greyheaded Gull	8	25	37	128
102	Egyptian Goose	6	17	12	28	338	Whiskered Tern	29	56	0	0
104	Yellowbilled Duck	22	28	17	41	339	Whitewinged Tern	0	1	0	0
106	Cape Teal	1	1	7	20	395	Marsh Owl	1	2	1	1
107	Hottentot Teal	13	25	5	14	713	Cape Wagtail	6	18	4	8
108	Redbilled Teal	7	11	12	36		Total	482	660	267	422
112	Cape Shoveller	32	69	12	27		No. of species		50		

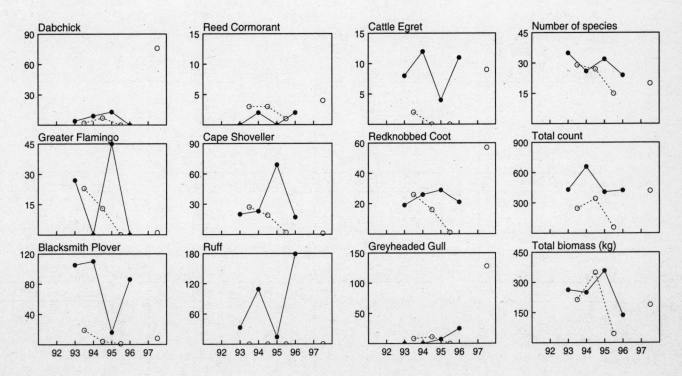

Rooiwal Sewage Works, Pretoria, Gauteng
25° 34' S 28° 14' E (2528CA)

Open sewage tanks and several shallow sedimentation ponds, with fringing reedbeds and some floating vegetation. Holds a good variety of waterbirds; counts usually total c. 500 birds but were high in summer 1993 (large numbers of Cattle Egret, Sacred Ibis, Redknobbed Coot, Ruff and Whitewinged Tern), winter 1996 (1215 Whitefaced Duck) and summer 1997 (Cattle Egret, Wood Sandpiper, Ruff and Whitewinged Tern were numerous). Exceptional concentrations of large waterbirds are reflected in relatively high biomass totals for summer 1993 and winter 1996. High counts of Yellow Wagtails in four of six summers. Mild threats are posed by the periodic invasion of alien waterplants, the periodic drainage and scraping of sedimentation dams, and human disturbance during working hours.

		Summer (4)		Winter (5)				Summer (4)		Winter (5)	
		Mean	Max.	Mean	Max.			Mean	Max.	Mean	Max.
006	Great Crested Grebe	1	1	0	0	116	Spurwinged Goose	0	0	3	17
008	Dabchick	4	13	33	47	148	African Fish Eagle	0	0	0	1
055	Whitebreasted Cormorant	25	37	4	8	165	African Marsh Harrier	1	2	0	0
058	Reed Cormorant	30	65	24	59	170	Osprey	0	1	0	0
060	Darter	7	15	8	17	213	Black Crake	0	1	1	1
062	Grey Heron	2	5	5	12	226	Moorhen	1	3	4	9
063	Blackheaded Heron	3	9	5	12	228	Redknobbed Coot	105	326	47	104
064	Goliath Heron	0	0	0	2	240	African Jacana	1	4	2	8
065	Purple Heron	2	4	1	2	248	Kittlitz's Plover	0	0	0	2
066	Great White Heron	0	0	0	2	249	Threebanded Plover	5	8	3	9
067	Little Egret	4	8	2	5	258	Blacksmith Plover	73	97	39	64
068	Yellowbilled Egret	0	0	1	2	260	Wattled Plover	0	0	1	6
071	Cattle Egret	112	228	53	114	264	Common Sandpiper	15	31	0	1
072	Squacco Heron	7	8	2	4	266	Wood Sandpiper	82	288	1	3
074	Greenbacked Heron	1	2	2	4	269	Marsh Sandpiper	7	21	0	0
078	Little Bittern	0	1	0	1	270	Greenshank	7	13	0	0
081	Hamerkop	3	6	1	3	272	Curlew Sandpiper	21	50	0	0
091	Sacred Ibis	47	151	43	106	274	Little Stint	15	31	0	0
093	Glossy Ibis	10	23	0	1	284	Ruff	217	470	0	0
094	Hadeda Ibis	3	5	20	41	295	Blackwinged Stilt	18	35	7	22
095	African Spoonbill	0	0	0	1	315	Greyheaded Gull	0	0	0	2
099	Whitefaced Duck	32	57	354	1215	339	Whitewinged Tern	227	467	0	1
102	Egyptian Goose	4	17	6	11	428	Pied Kingfisher	2	3	5	10
104	Yellowbilled Duck	13	38	4	16	429	Giant Kingfisher	1	2	1	3
105	African Black Duck	3	8	0	0	431	Malachite Kingfisher	1	1	0	1
106	Cape Teal	1	2	1	3	711	African Pied Wagtail	5	10	6	12
107	Hottentot Teal	1	3	0	1	713	Cape Wagtail	27	35	41	62
108	Redbilled Teal	7	21	15	39	714	Yellow Wagtail	25	47	0	0
113	Southern Pochard	6	13	18	52		Total	1177	1998	775	1688
115	Knobbilled Duck	0	0	7	31		No. of species		58		

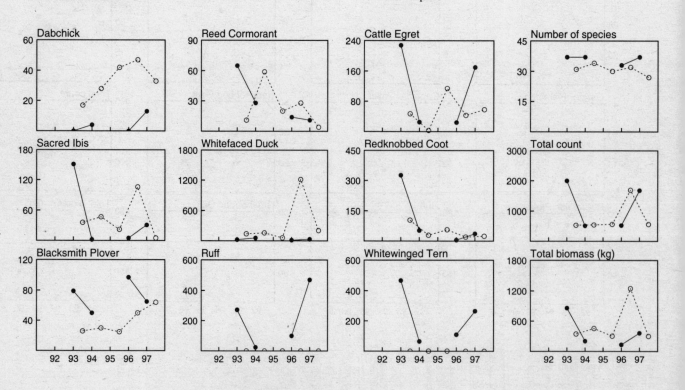

Rynfield Dam, Benoni, Gauteng
26° 09' S   28° 21' E (2628AB)

Two dams, the smaller holding treated effluent from an adjacent sewage works; also some marshy areas along streams. A good variety of waterbirds occurs, including Great Crested Grebe, Goliath and Purple Herons, Little Bittern, Glossy Ibis, Black Crake and Wattled Plover, and good numbers of Purple Gallinule. Numbers of cormorants and Cattle Egret peak in summer, but Dabchick, Blackheaded Heron, Hadeda Ibis, Egyptian Goose, Moorhen, Redknobbed Coot and Greyheaded Gull are more numerous in winter. Exceptionally good counts of Reed Cormorant and Cattle Egret were recorded in summer 1997. A critical threat on the larger dam is jetski boating in the shallow headwaters, which were formerly excellent for waders but now rarely hold any birds; power boats keep to deep water at the lower end of the dam.

		Summer (4)		Winter (5)				Summer (4)		Winter (5)	
		Mean	Max.	Mean	Max.			Mean	Max.	Mean	Max.
006	Great Crested Grebe	3	5	0	1	112	Cape Shoveller	1	2	3	10
008	Dabchick	3	4	8	11	113	Southern Pochard	1	2	4	14
055	Whitebreasted Cormorant	8	18	6	14	116	Spurwinged Goose	0	1	0	0
058	Reed Cormorant	58	183	38	70	213	Black Crake	2	4	0	2
060	Darter	8	13	4	10	223	Purple Gallinule	15	30	11	28
062	Grey Heron	1	2	1	3	226	Moorhen	15	25	26	38
063	Blackheaded Heron	19	36	34	66	228	Redknobbed Coot	59	120	158	332
064	Goliath Heron	2	3	2	4	248	Kittlitz's Plover	0	0	0	2
065	Purple Heron	1	2	1	1	249	Threebanded Plover	3	12	2	5
067	Little Egret	6	19	3	15	258	Blacksmith Plover	16	18	14	25
068	Yellowbilled Egret	0	0	1	3	260	Wattled Plover	2	3	2	7
069	Black Egret	1	2	0	1	264	Common Sandpiper	1	4	0	0
071	Cattle Egret	308	967	15	58	266	Wood Sandpiper	2	7	0	0
072	Squacco Heron	2	3	2	3	269	Marsh Sandpiper	2	5	0	0
076	Blackcrowned Night Heron	1	2	0	0	272	Curlew Sandpiper	2	5	0	0
078	Little Bittern	0	1	0	0	274	Little Stint	4	14	0	0
091	Sacred Ibis	8	14	13	25	284	Ruff	6	13	0	0
093	Glossy Ibis	6	10	3	15	286	Ethiopian Snipe	3	9	3	16
094	Hadeda Ibis	10	30	24	67	294	Avocet	1	2	2	6
095	African Spoonbill	0	1	2	5	295	Blackwinged Stilt	2	6	2	4
099	Whitefaced Duck	3	7	2	8	315	Greyheaded Gull	7	16	15	46
100	Fulvous Duck	3	10	0	0	338	Whiskered Tern	8	33	0	0
101	Whitebacked Duck	1	2	0	0	339	Whitewinged Tern	25	79	0	0
102	Egyptian Goose	6	9	12	20	428	Pied Kingfisher	0	1	0	0
104	Yellowbilled Duck	7	12	9	23	713	Cape Wagtail	15	45	16	27
105	African Black Duck	0	0	0	1		Total	660	1400	452	586
107	Hottentot Teal	3	11	5	10		No. of species		53		
108	Redbilled Teal	3	8	9	25						

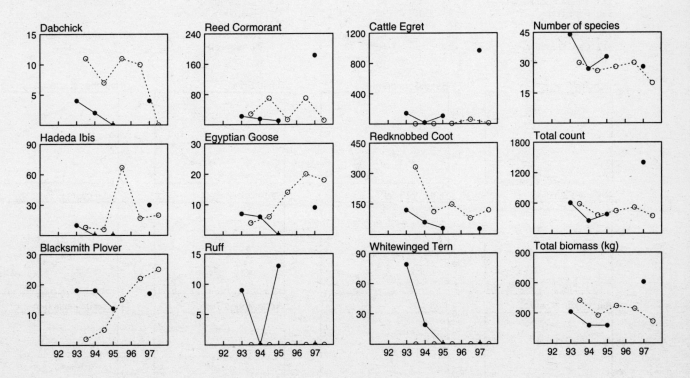

Springs Bird Sanctuary, Springs, Gauteng
26° 13' S 28° 28' E (2628AB)

Part of the Blesbokspruit Ramsar site; a dam, reedbeds, and marsh. With the exception of Southern Pochard and Fulvous Duck (high counts in summer 1994), waterfowl are more numerous in winter. In summer 1993 there were exceptional numbers of Ruff, Greyheaded Gull and White-winged Tern; the winter 1993 count shows large numbers of Dabchick, Sacred Ibis, Yellowbilled Duck, Redbilled Teal and Cape Shoveller; Moorhen were especially numerous in summer 1995, when the high summer biomass reflects the presence of 325 Greater Flamingo; flamingos are otherwise commoner in winter. Formerly an excellent site, but total counts and number of species are declining. In 1997 a large informal settlement was established on the eastern boundary; hunting and fishing are a severe threat; domestic dogs and cats an important threat.

		Summer (5)		Winter (5)				Summer (5)		Winter (5)	
		Mean	Max.	Mean	Max.			Mean	Max.	Mean	Max.
006	Great Crested Grebe	10	15	0	0	113	Southern Pochard	74	287*	14	29
007	Blacknecked Grebe	0	1	5	15	115	Knobbilled Duck	1	3	0	0
008	Dabchick	6	24	56	203	116	Spurwinged Goose	1	3	1	2
055	Whitebreasted Cormorant	6	17	2	3	117	Maccoa Duck	3	12	6	13
058	Reed Cormorant	20	37	3	6	165	African Marsh Harrier	0	1	1	2
060	Darter	2	3	0	1	210	African Rail	1	2	6	9
062	Grey Heron	0	1	2	5	213	Black Crake	2	4	11	17
063	Blackheaded Heron	2	6	11	25	215	Baillon's Crake	0	1	0	0
064	Goliath Heron	1	1	0	0	223	Purple Gallinule	6	14	16	36
065	Purple Heron	1	2	3	4	226	Moorhen	16	27	57	119
067	Little Egret	1	3	0	0	228	Redknobbed Coot	71	118	122	197
068	Yellowbilled Egret	3	11	0	0	245	Ringed Plover	0	2	0	0
069	Black Egret	1	3	0	0	249	Threebanded Plover	2	3	6	10
071	Cattle Egret	20	38	1	5	258	Blacksmith Plover	38	63	27	66
072	Squacco Heron	4	8	0	0	260	Wattled Plover	3	4	3	6
076	Blackcrowned Night Heron	5	12	2	11	264	Common Sandpiper	1	3	0	0
078	Little Bittern	2	7	0	1	266	Wood Sandpiper	11	20	1	2
081	Hamerkop	0	0	0	1	269	Marsh Sandpiper	4	10	1	7
091	Sacred Ibis	4	17	38	132	270	Greenshank	1	2	0	0
093	Glossy Ibis	38	62	11	30	272	Curlew Sandpiper	0	2	0	0
094	Hadeda Ibis	3	5	10	19	274	Little Stint	6	10	0	0
095	African Spoonbill	0	0	1	2	284	Ruff	151	707	0	2
096	Greater Flamingo	74	325	91	209	286	Ethiopian Snipe	7	16	13	31
097	Lesser Flamingo	8	40	52	127	294	Avocet	6	18	6	10
099	Whitefaced Duck	5	10	34	79	295	Blackwinged Stilt	13	39	12	32
100	Fulvous Duck	56	222	0	0	315	Greyheaded Gull	39	168	6	16
101	Whitebacked Duck	0	0	4	19	339	Whitewinged Tern	63	240	0	0
102	Egyptian Goose	6	14	53	156	395	Marsh Owl	0	0	1	2
104	Yellowbilled Duck	24	43	81	259	428	Pied Kingfisher	0	1	0	1
106	Cape Teal	8	19	12	20	431	Malachite Kingfisher	1	2	1	2
107	Hottentot Teal	53	83	59	86	713	Cape Wagtail	5	9	13	20
108	Redbilled Teal	20	53	61	150		Total	927	1874	980	1616
112	Cape Shoveller	19	32	66	122		No. of species			64	

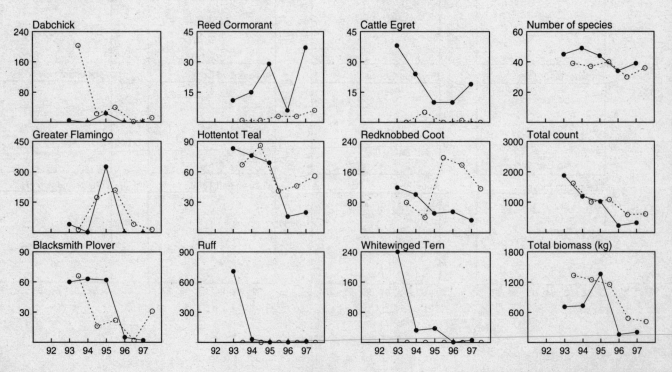

Stan Madden Bird Sanctuary, Nigel, Gauteng
26° 24' S 28° 28' E (2628AD)

A small dam and pan, and some permanent marsh; located just west of the Blesbokspruit wetland. A nationally significant number of Great Crested Grebe was counted in summer 1993, when maximum cormorant counts and maximum counts of the common Palearctic waders, were made. Good numbers of flamingos sometimes occur, especially in winter. A good variety of waterfowl is recorded, with notable numbers of Cape Teal in summer 1995 and of Redbilled Teal and Southern Pochard in winter 1996. A count of 200 Avocet in summer 1994 is also noteworthy. Numbers of Dabchick and Redknobbed Coot are increasing. The graphs show a sharp decline in total count and biomass during the survey period. No threats have been identified.

		Summer (5)		Winter (5)				Summer (5)		Winter (5)	
		Mean	Max.	Mean	Max.			Mean	Max.	Mean	Max.
006	Great Crested Grebe	17	49*	2	6	112	Cape Shoveller	8	19	5	6
007	Blacknecked Grebe	4	14	5	17	113	Southern Pochard	8	12	20	93
008	Dabchick	21	70	34	81	116	Spurwinged Goose	0	0	1	6
055	Whitebreasted Cormorant	21	68	2	5	117	Maccoa Duck	3	7	2	8
058	Reed Cormorant	18	45	8	20	213	Black Crake	0	0	0	2
060	Darter	4	10	8	20	223	Purple Gallinule	0	1	1	6
062	Grey Heron	2	5	1	3	226	Moorhen	3	7	4	11
063	Blackheaded Heron	1	3	0	1	228	Redknobbed Coot	237	450	292	638
064	Goliath Heron	0	1	1	1	245	Ringed Plover	1	6	0	0
065	Purple Heron	2	4	2	5	248	Kittlitz's Plover	22	63	3	10
067	Little Egret	3	10	0	1	249	Threebanded Plover	8	18	13	23
068	Yellowbilled Egret	1	2	0	0	258	Blacksmith Plover	32	54	17	26
071	Cattle Egret	5	9	0	2	264	Common Sandpiper	1	6	0	0
072	Squacco Heron	1	3	2	7	266	Wood Sandpiper	4	7	0	0
076	Blackcrowned Night Heron	2	6	2	7	269	Marsh Sandpiper	16	66	0	0
091	Sacred Ibis	2	6	0	2	270	Greenshank	4	16	0	0
093	Glossy Ibis	4	14	1	2	272	Curlew Sandpiper	25	65	1	7
094	Hadeda Ibis	5	16	3	10	274	Little Stint	27	53	0	0
095	African Spoonbill	0	0	0	2	284	Ruff	119	576	1	3
096	Greater Flamingo	207	388	179	480	286	Ethiopian Snipe	3	10	2	8
097	Lesser Flamingo	69	283	338	1625	294	Avocet	46	200	4	10
099	Whitefaced Duck	4	13	23	117	295	Blackwinged Stilt	34	66	4	13
100	Fulvous Duck	6	26	0	1	315	Greyheaded Gull	13	35	4	13
101	Whitebacked Duck	1	2	1	6	338	Whiskered Tern	3	12	0	0
102	Egyptian Goose	4	5	6	13	339	Whitewinged Tern	291	600	0	2
104	Yellowbilled Duck	7	26	5	11	428	Pied Kingfisher	1	2	0	2
106	Cape Teal	28	45	9	19	713	Cape Wagtail	6	11	19	31
107	Hottentot Teal	5	20	5	14		Total	1370	2263	1048	1887
108	Redbilled Teal	11	28	13	45		No. of species		56		

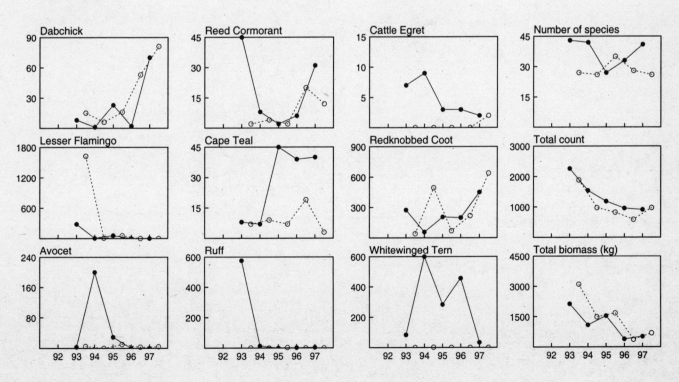

Steward's Pan, Benoni, Gauteng
26° 12' S 28° 17' E (2628AB)

A 12 ha permanent open water pan with fringing tall, dense *Typha* beds which probably result from the constant water level (there is an artificial embankment at the west end of the pan), and nutrient enrichment from a sewage outlet. Greyheaded Gulls breed: 400 nests in June 1985 but only 300 birds were counted in 1992–1994; live gull chicks and injured adults were harvested by local children in 1985 (D.G. Allan). Counts show a winter peak of ibises, African Spoonbill, flamingos (none in summer) and some waterfowl; grebes, cormorants and herons are recorded only in summer. The June 1985 count recorded about 20 Purple Gallinule and 20 Moorhen. No threats have been identified.

		Summer (2) Mean	Summer (2) Max.	Winter (1) Mean	Winter (1) Max.			Summer (2) Mean	Summer (2) Max.	Winter (1) Mean	Winter (1) Max.
006	Great Crested Grebe	2	3	0	0	108	Redbilled Teal	2	4	3	3
008	Dabchick	1	2	0	0	116	Spurwinged Goose	0	0	17	17
055	Whitebreasted Cormorant	3	6	0	0	213	Black Crake	1	1	3	3
058	Reed Cormorant	4	8	0	0	223	Purple Gallinule	2	3	11	11
060	Darter	1	2	0	0	226	Moorhen	1	2	9	9
062	Grey Heron	2	4	0	0	228	Redknobbed Coot	30	40	100	100
063	Blackheaded Heron	3	6	0	0	249	Threebanded Plover	9	18	0	0
067	Little Egret	1	1	0	0	258	Blacksmith Plover	17	25	23	23
071	Cattle Egret	33	50	50	50	274	Little Stint	1	2	0	0
072	Squacco Heron	1	2	0	0	298	Water Dikkop	3	6	4	4
091	Sacred Ibis	63	120	201	201	315	Greyheaded Gull	151	300	301	301
093	Glossy Ibis	5	6	23	23	393	Grass Owl	0	0	7	7
094	Hadeda Ibis	4	8	17	17	395	Marsh Owl	1	2	11	11
095	African Spoonbill	12	22	20	20	428	Pied Kingfisher	0	0	8	8
096	Greater Flamingo	0	0	90	90	429	Giant Kingfisher	0	0	3	3
097	Lesser Flamingo	0	0	17	17	713	Cape Wagtail	6	6	23	23
102	Egyptian Goose	1	1	5	5		Total	357	609	949	949
104	Yellowbilled Duck	2	3	3	3		No. of species		34		

Vlakplaas Water Treatment Works, Germiston, Gauteng
26° 22' S 28° 10' E (2628AC)

A sewage treatment works, with some reedy vegetation. Holds a wide variety of waterbirds, and has produced nationally significant counts of Great Crested Grebe (winter) and Southern Pochard, Greyheaded Gull and Whiskered Tern (summer). The 1995 summer count produced peak numbers of Blacknecked Grebe, Dabchick, Greater Flamingo, Cape Shoveller and Southern Pochard. Peak numbers of most waterfowl, and of Redknobbed Coot, occur in winter, while good numbers of Glossy Ibis, Maccoa Duck, Blacksmith Plover, Ruff and Avocet are recorded in summer. However, Ruff numbers show a sharp decline, as do summer counts of Reed Cormorant. The high biomass total for winter 1993 reflects the presence of peak numbers of Greater Flamingo, Spurwinged Goose and Whitefaced Duck; a good number of Cape Teal was also recorded. Hunting/poaching is a serious threat, but a fence is being installed.

		Summer (4)		Winter (4)					Summer (4)		Winter (4)	
		Mean	Max.	Mean	Max.				Mean	Max.	Mean	Max.
006	Great Crested Grebe	5	11	13	28*		112	Cape Shoveller	22	70	10	12
007	Blacknecked Grebe	21	68	21	36		113	Southern Pochard	185	476*	79	133
008	Dabchick	41	126	71	119		115	Knobbilled Duck	1	2	0	0
055	Whitebreasted Cormorant	5	6	3	5		116	Spurwinged Goose	3	7	94	215
058	Reed Cormorant	19	26	3	6		117	Maccoa Duck	10	34	1	4
062	Grey Heron	2	5	2	3		213	Black Crake	1	2	0	0
063	Blackheaded Heron	5	7	4	8		223	Purple Gallinule	0	1	0	1
064	Goliath Heron	0	1	0	0		226	Moorhen	5	11	14	22
066	Great White Heron	2	7	0	0		228	Redknobbed Coot	146	309	329	480
067	Little Egret	1	1	0	1		249	Threebanded Plover	2	3	1	3
071	Cattle Egret	33	55	6	10		258	Blacksmith Plover	71	167	15	22
072	Squacco Heron	5	16	0	0		264	Common Sandpiper	7	23	0	0
076	Blackcrowned Night Heron	0	0	1	4		266	Wood Sandpiper	1	4	0	0
078	Little Bittern	3	11	0	0		270	Greenshank	1	2	0	0
091	Sacred Ibis	55	93	46	82		274	Little Stint	26	93	0	0
093	Glossy Ibis	97	131	0	0		284	Ruff	384	700	0	0
094	Hadeda Ibis	2	3	3	6		286	Ethiopian Snipe	0	1	0	0
096	Greater Flamingo	121	377	135	323		294	Avocet	20	81	1	3
097	Lesser Flamingo	0	0	8	19		295	Blackwinged Stilt	9	28	6	10
099	Whitefaced Duck	18	59	210	473		315	Greyheaded Gull	329	539*	4	12
100	Fulvous Duck	19	41	22	63		338	Whiskered Tern	241	570*	0	0
102	Egyptian Goose	5	7	19	22		339	Whitewinged Tern	22	87	0	0
104	Yellowbilled Duck	4	7	4	12		395	Marsh Owl	0	0	0	1
106	Cape Teal	7	9	25	64		713	Cape Wagtail	5	14	19	32
107	Hottentot Teal	1	2	3	8			Total	1964	2630	1175	1769
108	Redbilled Teal	7	12	6	16			No. of species		50		

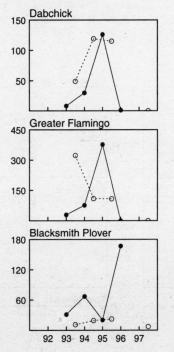

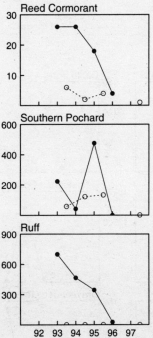

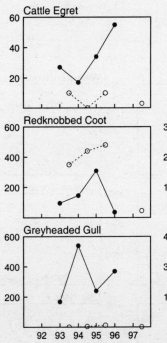

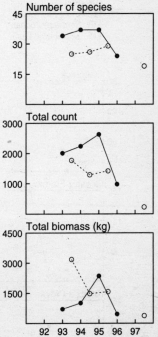

Barberspan, Delareyville, North West
26° 35' S 25° 35' E (2625DA)

An IBA and Ramsar site, protected within Barberspan Nature Reserve; it has an important bird ringing station. A shallow alkaline pan with a basin area of 1406 ha; littoral vegetation predominantly *Cyperus, Scirpus* and *Juncus*. Important stopover site for aquatic birds and sanctuary for moulting waterfowl; provides perennial water in an area of seasonal wetlands. Over 320 bird species recorded; has held globally significant numbers of Great Crested Grebe (1993), and of Redknobbed Coot in summer, and nationally significant numbers of African Spoonbill, Egyptian Goose and South African Shelduck. Counts show peak numbers of cormorants, herons and most egrets in summer, high counts of Kittlitz's and Blacksmith Plovers (more in winter), and exceptional numbers of waterfowl, and Dabchick, in winter 1994. Powerlines and recreational activities are threats. Pollution from the catchment area and the build up of salt are potential problems.

		Summer (4)		Winter (2)	
		Mean	Max.	Mean	Max.
006	Great Crested Grebe	29*	101**	62**	115**
007	Blacknecked Grebe	0	0	9	15
008	Dabchick	1	2	147	172
049	White Pelican	1	2	0	0
050	Pinkbacked Pelican	17	38	0	0
055	Whitebreasted Cormorant	335	457	90	179
058	Reed Cormorant	46	121	19	38
060	Darter	1	2	2	3
062	Grey Heron	10	20	5	5
063	Blackheaded Heron	27	64	16	20
064	Goliath Heron	6	9	9	12
066	Great White Heron	17	32	0	0
067	Little Egret	7	24	0	0
068	Yellowbilled Egret	1	2	0	0
069	Black Egret	1	2	0	0
071	Cattle Egret	3	9	67	132
090	Yellowbilled Stork	10	24	0	0
091	Sacred Ibis	0	0	1	1
094	Hadeda Ibis	1	3	4	8
095	African Spoonbill	60	87*	8	15
096	Greater Flamingo	82	180	115	118
097	Lesser Flamingo	110	267	48	95
099	Whitefaced Duck	2	7	1	2
102	Egyptian Goose	194	325	1690	2117*
103	South African Shelduck	123	213*	20	36
104	Yellowbilled Duck	81	163	488	726
106	Cape Teal	6	20	17	19
107	Hottentot Teal	2	6	2	4
108	Redbilled Teal	6	9	41	70
112	Cape Shoveller	33	64	17	18
113	Southern Pochard	37	122	8	14
115	Knobbilled Duck	0	1	0	0

		Summer (4)		Winter (2)	
		Mean	Max.	Mean	Max.
116	Spurwinged Goose	24	65	134	177
148	African Fish Eagle	0	0	2	3
223	Purple Gallinule	0	0	1	1
226	Moorhen	1	2	3	4
228	Redknobbed Coot	5729**	14826**	2167	2883*
245	Ringed Plover	6	18	2	4
246	Whitefronted Plover	1	5	0	0
247	Chestnutbanded Plover	0	0	7	11
248	Kittlitz's Plover	136	329	183	224
249	Threebanded Plover	3	11	29	46
258	Blacksmith Plover	68	122	134	138
264	Common Sandpiper	5	13	15	29
266	Wood Sandpiper	2	7	0	0
269	Marsh Sandpiper	1	2	0	0
270	Greenshank	0	0	1	2
272	Curlew Sandpiper	5	18	0	0
274	Little Stint	145	480	0	0
281	Sanderling	32	129	0	0
284	Ruff	15	55	0	0
286	Ethiopian Snipe	0	0	1	1
287	Blacktailed Godwit	0	1	0	0
289	Curlew	1	2	0	0
294	Avocet	0	0	1	1
295	Blackwinged Stilt	1	2	16	31
315	Greyheaded Gull	50	140	48	66
322	Caspian Tern	11	26	0	0
393	Grass Owl	0	1	0	0
395	Marsh Owl	0	1	0	0
713	Cape Wagtail	2	4	29	50
	Total	7480	16566	5647	7190
	No. of species		61		

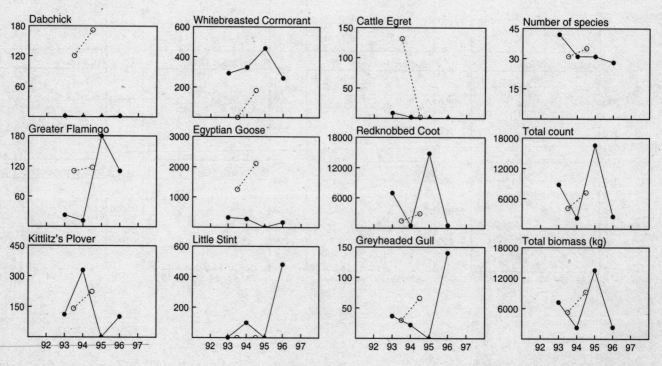

Hartbeespoort Dam, Hartbeespoort, North West
25° 45' S 27° 52' E (2527DD)

Only one count is available for this dam, for summer 1995, when small numbers of 20 species were recorded, the commonest bird being Whiskered Tern. There is great disturbance from human activities such as boating, water-skiing and fishing.

		Summer (1)		Winter (0)				Summer (1)		Winter (0)	
		Mean	Max.	Mean	Max.			Mean	Max.	Mean	Max.
055	Whitebreasted Cormorant	2	2	–	–	099	Whitefaced Duck	3	3	–	–
058	Reed Cormorant	2	2	–	–	102	Egyptian Goose	3	3	–	–
060	Darter	1	1	–	–	104	Yellowbilled Duck	5	5	–	–
062	Grey Heron	2	2	–	–	108	Redbilled Teal	3	3	–	–
063	Blackheaded Heron	1	1	–	–	228	Redknobbed Coot	5	5	–	–
066	Great White Heron	3	3	–	–	338	Whiskered Tern	20	20	–	–
067	Little Egret	4	4	–	–	428	Pied Kingfisher	6	6	–	–
068	Yellowbilled Egret	4	4	–	–	429	Giant Kingfisher	3	3	–	–
069	Black Egret	2	2	–	–		Total	79	79	–	–
071	Cattle Egret	10	10	–	–		No. of species		18		

Klipvoor Dam, Brits, North West
25° 10' S 27° 51' E (2527BB)

A large dam on the Morotele River in Borakalalo National Park. Has fringing reedbeds; when water level is low there is shoreline habitat for waders. Holds an excellent variety of waterbirds, including globally significant numbers of Great Crested Grebe in winter. Large numbers of Yellowbilled Stork occur in summer, and good numbers of cormorants occur, especially in winter (Whitebreasted breeds). Grebes, Darter, Sacred Ibis, waterfowl, Redknobbed Coot, and Threebanded, Blacksmith and Wattled Plovers are commoner in winter. Summer counts have increased during the survey period. Pollution and siltation are mild threats.

		Summer (4)		Winter (3)				Summer (4)		Winter (3)	
		Mean	Max.	Mean	Max.			Mean	Max.	Mean	Max.
006	Great Crested Grebe	2	3	46*	63**	115	Knobbilled Duck	1	4	1	2
008	Dabchick	4	8	82	122	116	Spurwinged Goose	2	8	55	104
055	Whitebreasted Cormorant	38	56	203	477	148	African Fish Eagle	8	14	8	9
058	Reed Cormorant	29	42	57	123	165	African Marsh Harrier	2	4	0	1
060	Darter	26	56	42	62	170	Osprey	1	1	0	0
062	Grey Heron	10	20	13	24	213	Black Crake	1	1	2	5
063	Blackheaded Heron	5	10	9	16	223	Purple Gallinule	0	0	1	2
064	Goliath Heron	2	4	2	3	226	Moorhen	0	0	0	1
065	Purple Heron	0	0	1	2	227	Lesser Moorhen	0	1	0	0
066	Great White Heron	8	15	10	18	228	Redknobbed Coot	4	10	350	395
067	Little Egret	10	18	2	6	229	African Finfoot	0	1	0	0
068	Yellowbilled Egret	1	2	3	10	240	African Jacana	1	2	4	6
069	Black Egret	2	8	0	0	242	Painted Snipe	1	4	0	0
071	Cattle Egret	50	172	4	7	248	Kittlitz's Plover	1	5	3	7
072	Squacco Heron	1	2	1	3	249	Threebanded Plover	5	6	17	28
074	Greenbacked Heron	3	7	5	10	258	Blacksmith Plover	14	16	58	74
076	Blackcrowned Night Heron	5	15	0	0	260	Wattled Plover	1	2	7	12
078	Little Bittern	0	0	0	1	264	Common Sandpiper	4	5	0	0
081	Hamerkop	1	2	3	7	266	Wood Sandpiper	4	5	1	2
090	Yellowbilled Stork	37	106	0	1	269	Marsh Sandpiper	1	3	0	0
091	Sacred Ibis	3	11	12	22	270	Greenshank	11	28	1	2
093	Glossy Ibis	1	2	0	0	274	Little Stint	3	12	0	0
094	Hadeda Ibis	1	4	6	8	284	Ruff	25	67	0	0
095	African Spoonbill	19	41	19	46	294	Avocet	1	2	0	0
097	Lesser Flamingo	0	0	0	1	295	Blackwinged Stilt	2	5	19	27
099	Whitefaced Duck	22	44	155	258	335	Little Tern	0	1	0	0
102	Egyptian Goose	201	375	181	232	338	Whiskered Tern	1	2	0	0
104	Yellowbilled Duck	4	13	20	36	339	Whitewinged Tern	7	23	1	4
105	African Black Duck	1	3	2	7	428	Pied Kingfisher	5	7	9	14
106	Cape Teal	0	0	17	52	429	Giant Kingfisher	1	3	1	1
107	Hottentot Teal	0	0	1	3	431	Malachite Kingfisher	0	1	0	0
108	Redbilled Teal	1	2	59	89	713	Cape Wagtail	0	0	7	21
112	Cape Shoveller	0	0	10	21		Total	588	769	1515	1802
113	Southern Pochard	0	0	6	19		No. of species		66		

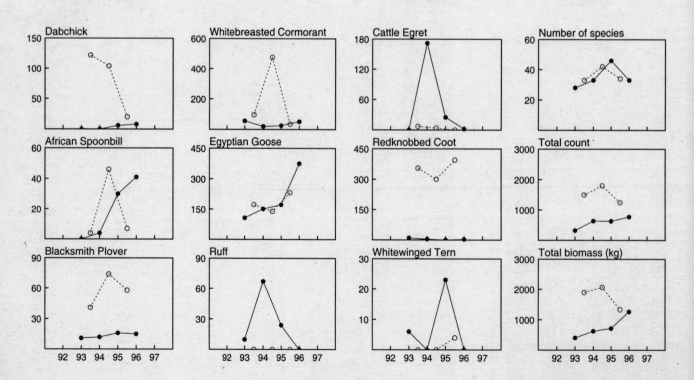

Leeupan, Delareyville, North West
26° 32' S 25° 36' E (2625DA)

An open seasonal pan, with a rocky and sandy shoreline; shore vegetation dominated by *Cyperus, Scirpus* and *Juncus*; there are also some small *Phragmites* patches. Two winter and three summer counts in 1993–1995 produced small to very large numbers of 20 species, the 1994 counts being particularly good. A globally significant count of Greater Flamingo was recorded in winter 1994 and nationally significant numbers of this species, and of Blacknecked Grebe, in summer 1994. Also noteworthy are 10 Great Crested Grebe (summer), good numbers of Lesser Flamingo ((more in winter), 150 Avocet (summer 1994) and a small population of Chestnutbanded Plover ((more in winter). No threats have been identified.

		Summer (3)		Winter (2)				Summer (3)		Winter (2)	
		Mean	Max.	Mean	Max.			Mean	Max.	Mean	Max.
006	Great Crested Grebe	3	10	0	0	228	Redknobbed Coot	2	6	0	0
007	Blacknecked Grebe	68	204*	0	0	247	Chestnutbanded Plover	2	5	6	12
008	Dabchick	3	9	0	0	248	Kittlitz's Plover	3	8	12	24
096	Greater Flamingo	266	799*	913*	1825**	258	Blacksmith Plover	1	3	0	0
097	Lesser Flamingo	55	164	266	532	274	Little Stint	1	4	0	0
102	Egyptian Goose	17	50	0	0	294	Avocet	50	150	2	3
103	South African Shelduck	17	50	0	0	295	Blackwinged Stilt	0	0	9	17
104	Yellowbilled Duck	3	8	2	4	315	Greyheaded Gull	1	4	0	0
106	Cape Teal	1	2	0	0	713	Cape Wagtail	0	0	1	2
108	Redbilled Teal	4	12	0	0		Total	496	1488	1212	2423
112	Cape Shoveller	0	0	2	4		No. of species		20		

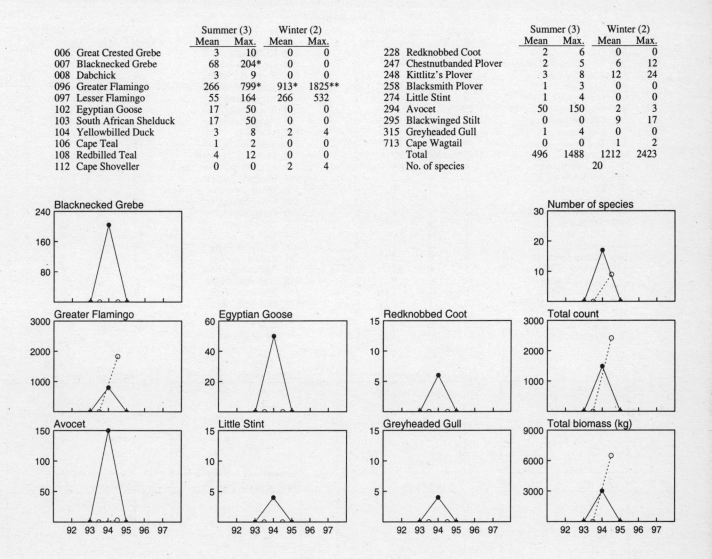

Prozesky Bird Sanctuary, Potchefstroom, North West
26° 45' S 27° 06' E (2627CC)

This site has open water, fringing and emergent vegetation, and shoreline habitat for waders. The good summer 1993 total of 3038 birds included 2363 Cattle Egrets and the maximum counts for Glossy Ibis and Ruff. The summer 1995 count of 1730 birds included 1131 Cattle Egrets. Fulvous Duck were numerous in summer 1994, when maximum counts of Little Stint and Blackwinged Stilt were recorded. Sacred Ibis and Whitefaced Duck are more numerous in winter, while moderate numbers of Redbilled Teal and Southern Pochard occur in summer. The reedbeds contain Purple Heron, Little Bittern, African Rail, Black Crake and Purple Gallinule. Threats are eutrophication, pollution by domestic sewage and pesticides, and overhead powerlines.

		Summer (3)		Winter (3)					Summer (3)		Winter (3)	
		Mean	Max.	Mean	Max.				Mean	Max.	Mean	Max.
008	Dabchick	5	12	5	6		108	Redbilled Teal	14	33	10	19
055	Whitebreasted Cormorant	5	11	0	0		112	Cape Shoveller	9	15	8	9
058	Reed Cormorant	23	59	6	9		113	Southern Pochard	18	51	9	20
062	Grey Heron	0	0	1	1		165	African Marsh Harrier	0	1	0	0
063	Blackheaded Heron	2	4	2	3		210	African Rail	1	3	1	2
065	Purple Heron	0	1	0	1		213	Black Crake	2	3	5	6
066	Great White Heron	1	1	0	0		223	Purple Gallinule	8	14	8	11
067	Little Egret	2	4	1	3		226	Moorhen	18	21	21	29
069	Black Egret	7	12	0	1		228	Redknobbed Coot	43	65	30	37
071	Cattle Egret	1165	2363	83	242		249	Threebanded Plover	0	1	2	4
072	Squacco Heron	6	16	0	1		258	Blacksmith Plover	4	8	2	2
076	Blackcrowned Night Heron	0	0	1	2		264	Common Sandpiper	0	0	0	1
078	Little Bittern	1	1	0	0		266	Wood Sandpiper	5	12	0	0
081	Hamerkop	1	2	2	5		269	Marsh Sandpiper	2	5	0	0
090	Yellowbilled Stork	1	2	0	0		270	Greenshank	7	22	0	0
091	Sacred Ibis	12	29	42	109		274	Little Stint	164	432	0	1
093	Glossy Ibis	77	203	0	1		284	Ruff	87	250	0	0
094	Hadeda Ibis	0	0	1	2		286	Ethiopian Snipe	0	1	1	2
095	African Spoonbill	0	0	2	4		294	Avocet	0	1	0	0
099	Whitefaced Duck	6	9	45	68		295	Blackwinged Stilt	25	59	4	8
100	Fulvous Duck	51	136	0	1		315	Greyheaded Gull	0	0	1	2
102	Egyptian Goose	5	11	2	4		338	Whiskered Tern	0	1	0	0
103	South African Shelduck	0	1	0	0		428	Pied Kingfisher	1	2	1	3
104	Yellowbilled Duck	16	24	18	19		713	Cape Wagtail	0	1	2	6
106	Cape Teal	0	0	1	2			Total	1805	3050	321	543
107	Hottentot Teal	11	22	4	7			No. of species		50		

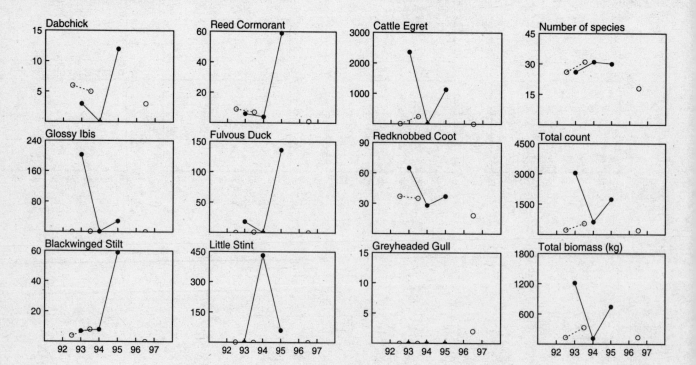

Vaalkop Dam, Brits, North West
25° 20' S 27° 28' E (2527DB)

A dam on the Elands River, partly within Vaalkops Nature Reserve; it has some fringing reedbeds, and several islands. Holds a good variety of waterbirds, but small numbers of most waterfowl and shorebirds. A nationally significant count of Great Crested Grebe was recorded in winter 1995. Numbers of grebes, cormorants, herons, African Spoonbill, Whitefaced Duck, and Egyptian and Spurwinged Geese, are higher in winter and the biomass graph reflects the concentration of these large waterbirds in this season. The high total count in winter 1997 reflects the presence of 895 Redknobbed Coot. Blacksmith Plover is fairly common all year, and Black Crake and Purple Gallinule are recorded. Low flying by microlight aircraft is a serious threat; boating, and pollution with anglers' waste, are also problems.

		Summer (4)		Winter (5)				Summer (4)		Winter (5)	
		Mean	Max.	Mean	Max.			Mean	Max.	Mean	Max.
006	Great Crested Grebe	0	1	7	26*	112	Cape Shoveller	0	0	2	3
008	Dabchick	1	5	22	75	113	Southern Pochard	0	1	0	2
055	Whitebreasted Cormorant	18	46	114	215	115	Knobbilled Duck	0	1	3	8
058	Reed Cormorant	38	141	70	247	116	Spurwinged Goose	2	3	53	119
060	Darter	6	18	24	47	148	African Fish Eagle	2	4	1	3
062	Grey Heron	11	18	42	69	170	Osprey	0	0	0	1
063	Blackheaded Heron	4	8	23	66	213	Black Crake	0	1	1	2
064	Goliath Heron	1	2	1	2	223	Purple Gallinule	0	1	0	0
066	Great White Heron	9	20	9	19	226	Moorhen	0	0	2	8
067	Little Egret	9	12	3	5	228	Redknobbed Coot	48	160	298	895
068	Yellowbilled Egret	1	2	2	6	240	African Jacana	2	6	2	11
069	Black Egret	3	8	0	0	248	Kittlitz's Plover	0	0	1	5
070	Slaty Egret	0	1	0	0	249	Threebanded Plover	1	2	5	21
071	Cattle Egret	192	409	21	50	258	Blacksmith Plover	27	61	23	39
072	Squacco Heron	0	1	0	2	264	Common Sandpiper	0	1	0	0
074	Greenbacked Heron	1	1	1	2	266	Wood Sandpiper	2	4	0	0
076	Blackcrowned Night Heron	1	3	1	3	270	Greenshank	1	2	1	1
081	Hamerkop	1	2	2	5	272	Curlew Sandpiper	1	4	0	0
090	Yellowbilled Stork	0	0	0	2	274	Little Stint	1	2	0	0
091	Sacred Ibis	19	55	17	31	284	Ruff	1	1	0	0
093	Glossy Ibis	0	1	0	0	295	Blackwinged Stilt	0	0	1	3
094	Hadeda Ibis	0	1	4	20	298	Water Dikkop	0	0	1	3
095	African Spoonbill	1	3	24	68	339	Whitewinged Tern	147	327	10	40
099	Whitefaced Duck	9	18	22	100	428	Pied Kingfisher	6	8	9	16
100	Fulvous Duck	0	0	0	2	431	Malachite Kingfisher	1	3	1	2
102	Egyptian Goose	15	21	43	89	711	African Pied Wagtail	0	0	0	2
104	Yellowbilled Duck	3	6	7	14	713	Cape Wagtail	2	4	4	8
105	African Black Duck	1	3	1	3		Total	585	889	884	1526
106	Cape Teal	0	0	0	2		No. of species			57	
108	Redbilled Teal	0	0	6	25						

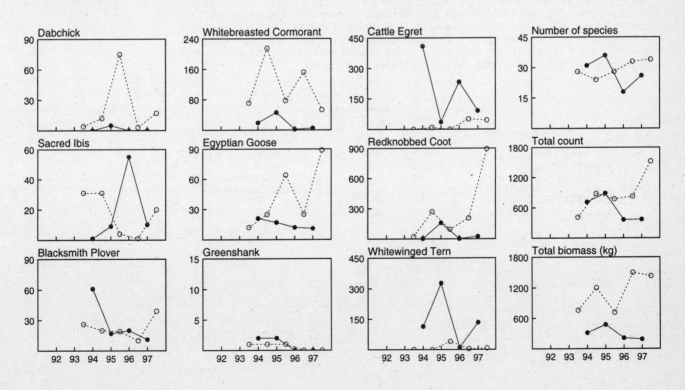

Benfontein Pan, Kimberley, Northern Cape
28° 50' S 24° 47' E (2824DD)

An open, ephemeral pan, with little vegetation. Counts indicate that it sometimes has much foraging habitat for shorebirds; when inundated it is capable of supporting a large bird population. Four counts are available, from summer 1996 to winter 1997. After summer 1996 the counts produced almost no birds and conditions were obviously very dry. The summer 1996 count produced good numbers of Palearctic waders such as Greenshank, Curlew Sandpiper and Little Stint, and smaller numbers of other shorebirds; the commonest waterbirds were Egyptian Goose and Redknobbed Coot. A possible mild threat is a dam wall built through the centre of the pan, possibly to allow water to accumulate in a smaller area; its effect on the pan's ecology is unknown.

		Summer (2) Mean	Max.	Winter (2) Mean	Max.			Summer (2) Mean	Max.	Winter (2) Mean	Max.
093	Glossy Ibis	5	9	0	0	266	Wood Sandpiper	1	1	0	0
096	Greater Flamingo	1	1	0	0	269	Marsh Sandpiper	1	1	0	0
102	Egyptian Goose	10	17	0	0	270	Greenshank	45	89	0	0
103	South African Shelduck	1	2	2	4	272	Curlew Sandpiper	82	164	0	0
104	Yellowbilled Duck	2	3	0	0	274	Little Stint	318	636	0	0
106	Cape Teal	1	2	0	0	284	Ruff	28	55	0	0
108	Redbilled Teal	3	5	0	0	294	Avocet	1	2	0	0
112	Cape Shoveller	3	5	0	0	295	Blackwinged Stilt	19	38	0	0
228	Redknobbed Coot	26	51	0	0		Total	554	1099	3	6
249	Threebanded Plover	1	2	0	0		No. of species			19	
258	Blacksmith Plover	12	16	1	2						

Bosduiwekop Dam, Petrusville, Northern Cape
30° 15' S 24° 45' E (3024BB)

A farm dam; shoreline open, predominantly rocky, with no vegetation. Counts are available only for 1996-97. During 1996 small numbers of 14 species were recorded, 11 species in summer and 7 in winter. The bulk of the summer total was made up of four waterfowl species: Egyptian Goose, South African Shelduck, Yellowbilled Duck and Spurwinged Goose. The dam was dry in the winter, when the count was low and the commonest species was Cape Wagtail; 9 Avocet and 7 Egyptian Goose were also recorded. A mild threat is livestock grazing and trampling. No birds were recorded during 1997 as the dam was dry.

		Summer (2) Mean	Max.	Winter (2) Mean	Max.			Summer (2) Mean	Max.	Winter (2) Mean	Max.
055	Whitebreasted Cormorant	2	2	0	0	148	African Fish Eagle	0	0	1	1
062	Grey Heron	1	1	1	1	228	Redknobbed Coot	1	1	0	0
091	Sacred Ibis	1	1	0	0	258	Blacksmith Plover	2	2	0	0
095	African Spoonbill	1	1	0	0	294	Avocet	0	0	9	9
102	Egyptian Goose	13	13	7	7	295	Blackwinged Stilt	2	2	1	1
103	South African Shelduck	29	29	2	2	713	Cape Wagtail	0	0	31	31
104	Yellowbilled Duck	28	28	0	0		Total	124	124	52	52
116	Spurwinged Goose	44	44	0	0		No. of species			14	

Dampoort Dam, Warrenton, Northern Cape
28° 11' S 24° 29' E (2824AB)

A farm dam with open shoreline, some habitat for shorebirds and no fringing vegetation. Counts are available for 1996 and 1997 and show mainly small numbers of 25 species; large totals were obtained only for Dabchick and Egyptian Goose, while Whitebreasted Cormorant, South African Shelduck, Yellowbilled Duck, Cape Shoveller and Redknobbed Coot were recorded in numbers ranging from 10 to 22 birds; all these counts were in winter. The relatively high count in winter 1996 was due to the large number (212) of Egyptian Geese. Very small numbers of Greater and Lesser Flamingo, and Yellowbilled Stork, have occurred. Movements possibly occur between this site and Spitskop Dam. Grazing and trampling by livestock constitute a significant threat; human disturbance is a mild threat.

		Summer (2)		Winter (2)				Summer (2)		Winter (2)	
		Mean	Max.	Mean	Max.			Mean	Max.	Mean	Max.
008	Dabchick	0	0	39	57	108	Redbilled Teal	1	2	2	3
055	Whitebreasted Cormorant	1	2	5	10	112	Cape Shoveller	1	1	11	11
058	Reed Cormorant	2	3	0	0	116	Spurwinged Goose	0	0	4	7
060	Darter	9	18	2	3	148	African Fish Eagle	1	1	0	0
062	Grey Heron	2	3	0	0	228	Redknobbed Coot	1	2	6	10
071	Cattle Egret	9	18	0	0	249	Threebanded Plover	0	0	1	1
090	Yellowbilled Stork	2	3	0	0	258	Blacksmith Plover	4	5	3	5
095	African Spoonbill	2	2	1	1	264	Common Sandpiper	1	1	0	0
096	Greater Flamingo	0	0	1	1	295	Blackwinged Stilt	0	0	3	3
097	Lesser Flamingo	0	0	2	4	339	Whitewinged Tern	2	3	0	0
102	Egyptian Goose	2	2	127	212	713	Cape Wagtail	1	1	1	1
103	South African Shelduck	0	0	12	22		Total	38	41	220	296
104	Yellowbilled Duck	1	2	5	10		No. of species		25		
106	Cape Teal	0	0	1	2						

Du Toit's Pan, Kimberley, Northern Cape
28° 46' S 24° 48' E (2824DD)

A pan in a mining area near Kimberley; receives water from mines and a sewage farm. Comprises two pans separated by *Phragmites* reedbeds; one has open water and reeds, the other has mudflats when water is low. Counts have been in progress since summer 1996 and have identified 30 waterbird species. The summer 1997 count totalled only 75 birds, whereas in summer 1996, 643 birds were counted, including the maximum counts of all the Palearctic shorebirds except Little Stint, and also the maxima for Blackwinged Stilt, Whitewinged Tern, Yellowbilled Duck, Cape and Redbilled Teal, and Cape Shoveller. Numbers of Dabchick, Reed Cormorant, Darter, Moorhen and Redknobbed Coot peak in winter, and the only record of Lesser Flamingo, 289 birds, was in winter 1996. Bird movements occur between this pan and other wetlands in the Kimberley area, including Kamfers Dam. An important threat is pollution from sewage; mild threats are reed encroachment, and boating on the open pan.

		Summer (2)		Winter (2)				Summer (2)		Winter (2)	
		Mean	Max.	Mean	Max.			Mean	Max.	Mean	Max.
008	Dabchick	0	0	10	20	148	African Fish Eagle	0	0	1	1
055	Whitebreasted Cormorant	8	13	0	0	226	Moorhen	4	5	13	23
058	Reed Cormorant	0	0	10	19	228	Redknobbed Coot	5	10	95	188
060	Darter	1	1	7	12	249	Threebanded Plover	1	1	0	0
064	Goliath Heron	3	4	2	2	258	Blacksmith Plover	6	6	4	7
065	Purple Heron	1	1	1	1	266	Wood Sandpiper	2	3	0	0
071	Cattle Egret	1	2	0	0	269	Marsh Sandpiper	37	66	0	0
097	Lesser Flamingo	0	0	145	289	272	Curlew Sandpiper	15	27	0	0
102	Egyptian Goose	3	5	2	3	274	Little Stint	11	18	0	0
103	South African Shelduck	1	1	4	4	284	Ruff	117	228	0	0
104	Yellowbilled Duck	17	24	2	3	294	Avocet	0	0	1	2
106	Cape Teal	17	26	1	2	295	Blackwinged Stilt	28	51	4	7
108	Redbilled Teal	3	5	0	0	315	Greyheaded Gull	6	12	2	4
112	Cape Shoveller	10	20	4	5	339	Whitewinged Tern	69	137	0	0
113	Southern Pochard	0	0	4	7		Total	361	645	308	360
116	Spurwinged Goose	0	0	1	2		No. of species		30		

Daniëlskuil Dams, Daniëlskuil, Northern Cape
28° 11' S 23° 33' E (2823BA)

Two dams and a dam/pan with open shoreline, some shorebird habitat, and almost no fringing vegetation, adjacent to Danielskuil. Formerly, the dam/pan received water from local sewage works. Counts are available for 1996 and 1997, when mainly small numbers of 17 species were recorded, 16 species in summer (only South African Shelduck being missing) and only 3 in winter (SA Shelduck, Threebanded Plover and Cape Wagtail). The most numerous birds in summer were Whitefaced Duck, Blacksmith Plover (a good count of 47 birds in 1997), Curlew Sandpiper and Little Stint. Pollution by sewage and domestic refuse is an important threat; mild threats are fishing, and overhead powerlines.

		Summer (2)		Winter (2)					Summer (2)		Winter (2)	
		Mean	Max.	Mean	Max.				Mean	Max.	Mean	Max.
062	Grey Heron	3	3	0	0		249	Threebanded Plover	4	8	1	2
071	Cattle Egret	1	1	0	0		258	Blacksmith Plover	29	47	0	0
093	Glossy Ibis	1	2	0	0		264	Common Sandpiper	2	2	0	0
094	Hadeda Ibis	1	1	0	0		269	Marsh Sandpiper	3	6	0	0
099	Whitefaced Duck	8	15	0	0		272	Curlew Sandpiper	20	39	0	0
102	Egyptian Goose	1	2	0	0		274	Little Stint	23	42	0	0
103	South African Shelduck	0	0	2	2		713	Cape Wagtail	6	7	2	4
104	Yellowbilled Duck	4	5	0	0			Total	103	128	5	8
106	Cape Teal	1	1	0	0			No. of species			17	
245	Ringed Plover	1	2	0	0							

Espagsdrift Vlei, Jan Kempdorp, Northern Cape
27° 56' S 24° 44' E (2724DC)

A farm dam, using water from the Vaalharts irrigation scheme; has submergent vegetation, a few reedbeds, some sedges, and extensive muddy shoreline. Counts for 1996 and 1997 are available. In this period 38 species were recorded, including Squacco Heron, Lesser Flamingo, Yellowbilled Stork, and Whitebacked and Knobbilled Ducks; Whitebacked Duck is always present. Most species occur in small numbers, but Redknobbed Coot occurs in good numbers in both seasons, and breeds. Some shorebirds are also quite numerous, and the highest counts of Blacksmith Plover ((which breeds here), Wood Sandpiper and Ruff were recorded in summer 1997, but of Little Stint in summer 1996. Livestock grazing/trampling is an important threat; eutrophication, pollution by pesticide runoff, and overhead power lines are lesser threats.

		Summer (2)		Winter (2)					Summer (2)		Winter (2)	
		Mean	Max.	Mean	Max.				Mean	Max.	Mean	Max.
008	Dabchick	9	18	7	10		116	Spurwinged Goose	0	0	1	1
062	Grey Heron	2	2	0	0		223	Purple Gallinule	1	1	0	0
067	Little Egret	1	1	0	0		226	Moorhen	1	2	5	7
069	Black Egret	2	2	0	0		228	Redknobbed Coot	143	190	161	163
071	Cattle Egret	22	43	1	1		245	Ringed Plover	1	1	0	0
072	Squacco Heron	1	1	0	0		248	Kittlitz's Plover	1	1	1	2
090	Yellowbilled Stork	1	2	0	0		249	Threebanded Plover	0	0	1	1
093	Glossy Ibis	2	4	2	3		258	Blacksmith Plover	37	62	5	6
095	African Spoonbill	4	7	0	0		266	Wood Sandpiper	25	47	0	0
097	Lesser Flamingo	0	0	4	8		269	Marsh Sandpiper	1	2	0	0
099	Whitefaced Duck	1	2	0	0		272	Curlew Sandpiper	1	2	0	0
101	Whitebacked Duck	2	3	1	1		274	Little Stint	186	372	0	0
102	Egyptian Goose	5	6	2	2		284	Ruff	38	49	0	0
103	South African Shelduck	0	0	4	6		286	Ethiopian Snipe	0	0	1	1
104	Yellowbilled Duck	15	20	8	10		295	Blackwinged Stilt	8	8	2	4
106	Cape Teal	0	0	1	2		339	Whitewinged Tern	5	7	0	0
108	Redbilled Teal	14	21	5	10		428	Pied Kingfisher	2	3	0	0
112	Cape Shoveller	7	9	9	13		713	Cape Wagtail	0	0	9	15
113	Southern Pochard	7	14	1	1			Total	539	613	225	226
115	Knobbilled Duck	1	1	0	0			No. of species			38	

Faugh A Ballagh Dam, Hanover, Northern Cape
30° 52' S 24° 38' E (3024DC)

A large farm dam on the Seekoei River, with an open shoreline but extensive *Phragmites* reedbeds towards the inlet. When the water level is low, good foraging habitat for shorebirds is exposed. Counts were made in winter 1996, summer 1997, and winter 1997 when the water level was low. In summer only nine species were recorded, Egyptian Goose and South African Shelduck being more numerous than in winter, while numbers of four other waterfowl species peaked in winter. In winter 1997, peak numbers of all six shorebird species were counted, including 42 Avocet; of these species, only Kittlitz's Plover was recorded in summer 1997. Good numbers of Cape Wagtail occur in winter. Other species of note are Osprey and Caspian Tern. Overhead powerlines are an important threat; mild threats are livestock grazing and trampling, barrage construction, and angling.

		Summer (1) Mean	Max.	Winter (2) Mean	Max.			Summer (1) Mean	Max.	Winter (2) Mean	Max.
049	White Pelican	1	1	0	0	116	Spurwinged Goose	1	1	5	5
055	Whitebreasted Cormorant	0	0	8	16	148	African Fish Eagle	0	0	1	2
058	Reed Cormorant	0	0	1	2	170	Osprey	0	0	1	1
081	Hamerkop	1	1	1	2	248	Kittlitz's Plover	9	9	6	11
091	Sacred Ibis	3	3	2	3	249	Threebanded Plover	0	0	20	35
094	Hadeda Ibis	0	0	3	5	258	Blacksmith Plover	0	0	28	55
095	African Spoonbill	1	1	4	7	274	Little Stint	0	0	17	34
096	Greater Flamingo	0	0	1	1	294	Avocet	0	0	21	42
102	Egyptian Goose	143	143	82	152	295	Blackwinged Stilt	0	0	10	19
103	South African Shelduck	74	74	49	53	322	Caspian Tern	0	0	1	1
104	Yellowbilled Duck	0	0	350	357	713	Cape Wagtail	3	3	108	124
108	Redbilled Teal	0	0	17	31		Total	236	236	741	941
112	Cape Shoveller	0	0	11	20		No. of species			24	

Grootdam (Rooipoort), Schmidtsdrif, Northern Cape
28° 43' S 24° 15' E (2824CA)

A small farm dam on Rooipoort Nature Reserve, with an open shoreline, muddy water and a few fringing trees and shrubs. Counts in 1996–97 yielded small numbers of five bird species in summer and nine in winter, when in 1997 Dabchick, Yellowbilled Duck and Threebanded Plover made up 80% of the highest count of 37 birds. No threats have been identified.

		Summer (2) Mean	Max.	Winter (2) Mean	Max.			Summer (2) Mean	Max.	Winter (2) Mean	Max.
008	Dabchick	3	5	5	10	258	Blacksmith Plover	1	2	1	2
102	Egyptian Goose	2	2	1	2	269	Marsh Sandpiper	0	0	1	1
104	Yellowbilled Duck	1	2	6	12	713	Cape Wagtail	0	0	1	1
108	Redbilled Teal	0	0	1	2		Total	7	8	19	37
226	Moorhen	0	0	1	1		No. of species			9	
249	Threebanded Plover	1	1	4	7						

Ganspan Pans & Vlei, Jan Kempdorp, Northern Cape
27° 55' S 24° 46' E (2724DD)

This site comprises Ganspan A, a pan with inflow from Vaalharts irrigation scheme and an overgrown vlei, and Ganspan B, a permanent marsh with reedbeds and some mud and open water. Together the sites hold a wide range of wetland habitats and support a good number of bird species. Two summer and two winter counts yielded good totals of Reed Cormorant, Greater and Lesser Flamingos, Moorhen and Redknobbed Coot (all peaking in winter), and Glossy Ibis, Ruff and Whitewinged Tern (peaking in summer). There were good counts of waterfowl, notably of White-faced and Yellowbilled Duck, Hottentot and Redbilled Teal, and Cape Shoveller; numbers of all these ducks peaked in winter. Occurrences of Great Crested Grebe, Goliath Heron, Black Egret, Little Bittern, Maccoa Duck, African Rail, Black Crake and Caspian Tern contribute to the excellent variety of species recorded. Important threats to all wetlands include reed encroachment, and pollution by pesticides and fertilisers; other threats are eutrophication and boating (Ganspan A), livestock grazing/trampling (Ganspan B), and overhead powerlines (Ganspan A and B).

		Summer (2)		Winter (2)					Summer (2)		Winter (2)	
		Mean	Max.	Mean	Max.				Mean	Max.	Mean	Max.
006	Great Crested Grebe	3	4	5	9		113	Southern Pochard	4	8	0	0
008	Dabchick	22	25	23	33		116	Spurwinged Goose	1	1	3	4
055	Whitebreasted Cormorant	33	54	0	0		117	Maccoa Duck	1	1	2	4
058	Reed Cormorant	29	54	204	209		148	African Fish Eagle	0	0	1	1
060	Darter	4	4	10	11		165	African Marsh Harrier	0	0	1	2
062	Grey Heron	2	2	1	2		210	African Rail	0	0	1	1
064	Goliath Heron	2	3	1	1		213	Black Crake	0	0	1	1
065	Purple Heron	1	1	1	1		223	Purple Gallinule	3	3	5	9
067	Little Egret	1	1	0	0		226	Moorhen	17	24	43	50
068	Yellowbilled Egret	0	0	1	1		228	Redknobbed Coot	258	435	516	566
069	Black Egret	1	1	1	2		248	Kittlitz's Plover	0	0	1	2
072	Squacco Heron	2	3	1	1		249	Threebanded Plover	0	0	3	4
076	Blackcrowned Night Heron	1	1	0	0		258	Blacksmith Plover	11	16	4	6
078	Little Bittern	1	1	0	0		266	Wood Sandpiper	5	9	1	1
081	Hamerkop	1	1	0	0		269	Marsh Sandpiper	21	38	0	0
090	Yellowbilled Stork	4	6	0	0		274	Little Stint	1	2	0	0
091	Sacred Ibis	1	1	19	26		284	Ruff	170	318	1	1
093	Glossy Ibis	42	83	10	16		287	Blacktailed Godwit	1	1	0	0
095	African Spoonbill	9	16	9	14		294	Avocet	6	11	6	9
096	Greater Flamingo	97	190	182	343		295	Blackwinged Stilt	28	55	12	12
097	Lesser Flamingo	0	0	274	483		305	Blackwinged Pratincole	1	1	0	0
099	Whitefaced Duck	1	2	16	16		315	Greyheaded Gull	0	0	1	1
102	Egyptian Goose	9	17	9	10		322	Caspian Tern	1	1	0	0
103	South African Shelduck	12	17	8	10		339	Whitewinged Tern	150	249	0	0
104	Yellowbilled Duck	38	61	160	313		428	Pied Kingfisher	2	2	2	2
106	Cape Teal	0	0	3	5		713	Cape Wagtail	1	1	4	5
107	Hottentot Teal	6	12	21	35			Total	1020	1515	1666	2232
108	Redbilled Teal	6	10	75	148			No. of species			55	
112	Cape Shoveller	24	29	37	59							

Kriegerspoort Dam, Hanover, Northern Cape
31° 17' S 24° 33' E (3124BC)

An open dam with a bare shoreline. Summer and winter counts in 1997 recorded the presence of 14 species of waterbird. Of the commonest species, good numbers of South African Shelduck were present, the winter count being the higher, while Egyptian Goose numbers peaked in summer and Redknobbed Coot was recorded only in summer. White-breasted Cormorant, African Spoonbill, Greater Flamingo, Avocet and Blackwinged Stilt also occurred only in summer, in small numbers, and a good total of 41 Cape Wagtail was recorded in winter. The only Palearctic shorebird recorded was Common Sandpiper. A mild threat is posed by livestock grazing and trampling.

		Summer (1)		Winter (1)					Summer (1)		Winter (1)	
		Mean	Max.	Mean	Max.				Mean	Max.	Mean	Max.
055	Whitebreasted Cormorant	6	6	0	0		228	Redknobbed Coot	39	39	0	0
095	African Spoonbill	6	6	0	0		258	Blacksmith Plover	3	3	10	10
096	Greater Flamingo	13	13	0	0		264	Common Sandpiper	7	7	0	0
099	Whitefaced Duck	3	3	0	0		294	Avocet	3	3	1	1
102	Egyptian Goose	104	104	53	53		295	Blackwinged Stilt	16	16	0	0
103	South African Shelduck	43	43	64	64		713	Cape Wagtail	0	0	41	41
104	Yellowbilled Duck	0	0	6	6			Total	243	243	179	179
116	Spurwinged Goose	0	0	4	4			No. of species			14	

Kamfers Dam, Kimberley, Northern Cape
28° 40' S 24° 46' E (2824DB)

An IBA. A large pan with *Phragmites* reedbeds, mudflats, and emergent grass; was ephemeral but now supplemented by sewage water inflow. Excellent habitat for waterbirds, many of which breed, including Chestnutbanded Plover. Globally significant counts of Blacknecked Grebe ((large numbers bred recently); nationally significant numbers of Dabchick, and of Greater Flamingo (one globally significant count) which sometimes attempts to breed; large numbers of Lesser Flamingo. Glossy Ibis, South African Shelduck, Cape and Hottentot Teal, Cape Shoveller, Blacksmith Plover, Blackwinged Stilt and Greyheaded Gull peak in summer. In winter, peak numbers of Yellowbilled Duck, Redbilled Teal, Egyptian and Spurwinged Geese, Moorhen, Redknobbed Coot, and Whiskered Tern occur. Eutrophication and reed encroachment are severe threats. Important threats are domestic dogs and cats, poaching and overhead powerlines; livestock grazing/trampling is a mild threat.

		Summer (3)		Winter (3)				Summer (3)		Winter (3)	
		Mean	Max.	Mean	Max.			Mean	Max.	Mean	Max.
007	Blacknecked Grebe	32	95	94	282**	165	African Marsh Harrier	1	2	0	0
008	Dabchick	3	8	119	358*	213	Black Crake	0	0	0	1
058	Reed Cormorant	3	9	0	0	223	Purple Gallinule	4	11	3	4
062	Grey Heron	1	2	2	3	226	Moorhen	16	24	46	111
063	Blackheaded Heron	2	5	1	1	228	Redknobbed Coot	37	85	79	226
064	Goliath Heron	0	0	0	1	245	Ringed Plover	6	11	0	0
065	Purple Heron	0	0	0	1	247	Chestnutbanded Plover	5	8	11	18
071	Cattle Egret	43	122	0	0	248	Kittlitz's Plover	5	14	11	22
076	Blackcrowned Night Heron	0	1	0	1	249	Threebanded Plover	8	15	11	19
090	Yellowbilled Stork	1	4	0	0	258	Blacksmith Plover	44	76	23	32
091	Sacred Ibis	4	11	5	13	266	Wood Sandpiper	21	48	0	1
093	Glossy Ibis	28	67	11	18	269	Marsh Sandpiper	83	109	0	0
094	Hadeda Ibis	0	1	4	5	270	Greenshank	12	30	0	1
095	African Spoonbill	0	1	0	0	272	Curlew Sandpiper	64	86	21	62
096	Greater Flamingo	1032*	1467**	463	823*	274	Little Stint	337	497	0	0
097	Lesser Flamingo	1875	2820	2034	3668	284	Ruff	423	612	0	0
099	Whitefaced Duck	51	83	151	241	286	Ethiopian Snipe	4	7	6	15
102	Egyptian Goose	10	15	23	55	294	Avocet	19	24	15	24
103	South African Shelduck	58	129	29	54	295	Blackwinged Stilt	162	229	58	85
104	Yellowbilled Duck	49	78	102	229	315	Greyheaded Gull	65	181	2	7
106	Cape Teal	34	99	43	75	338	Whiskered Tern	0	1	15	45
107	Hottentot Teal	7	18	3	5	339	Whitewinged Tern	174	268	0	0
108	Redbilled Teal	36	64	53	116	395	Marsh Owl	1	2	0	0
112	Cape Shoveller	53	107	43	64	431	Malachite Kingfisher	0	0	1	2
113	Southern Pochard	0	0	4	13	713	Cape Wagtail	10	15	36	63
116	Spurwinged Goose	5	13	20	49		Total	4829	5948	3549	5435
117	Maccoa Duck	0	1	5	16		No. of species		52		

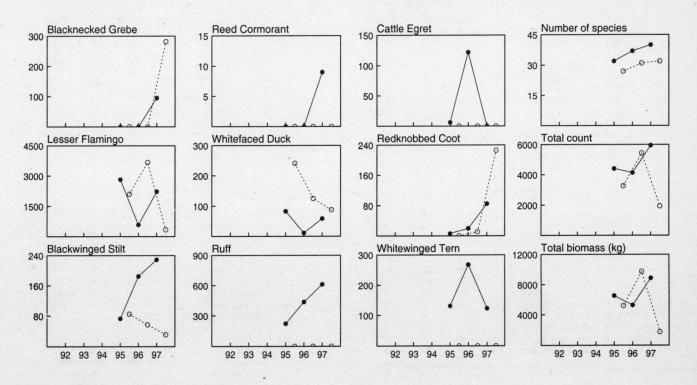

Nantwich Saltpan, Kimberley, Northern Cape
28° 29' S 24° 46' E (2824BD)

A pan at the Nantwich Saltworks. Summer and winter counts for 1996 and 1997 have yielded small numbers of 10 waterbird species, including two waterfowl species, four plovers and three other shorebird species. The only inland site in the Northern Cape where Chestnutbanded Plover is regular; it is the second commonest species recorded, with 5–9 birds present throughout the year; up to 14 Little Stint are recorded in summer. A severe threat is landfill/reclamation at the saltworks; human disturbance is an important threat, and livestock grazing/trampling a mild threat.

		Summer (2)		Winter (2)				Summer (2)		Winter (2)	
		Mean	Max.	Mean	Max.			Mean	Max.	Mean	Max.
106	Cape Teal	1	2	0	0	274	Little Stint	9	14	0	0
116	Spurwinged Goose	1	2	0	0	284	Ruff	2	3	0	0
247	Chestnutbanded Plover	7	8	8	9	295	Blackwinged Stilt	1	2	5	8
248	Kittlitz's Plover	3	6	0	0	713	Cape Wagtail	1	1	2	3
249	Threebanded Plover	4	7	0	0		Total	29	29	16	16
258	Blacksmith Plover	2	3	2	3		No. of species		10		

Orange River Estuary, Alexander Bay, Northern Cape
28° 38' S 16° 27' E (2816CB)

IBA and Ramsar site, important for bird breeding and migration stopover. A delta-type river mouth with a braided channel during low flow months. Has sandbars, tidal basin, narrow floodplain, marshes (*Phragmites, Scirpus, Sporobolus, Sarcocornia*), pans, and a saltmarsh on one bank of the river mouth. Two counts (summer and winter 1997) are available, recording a large variety of waterbirds, including globally significant counts of Kelp and Hartlaub's Gulls, and nationally significant numbers of South African Shelduck and Cape Shoveller. Large numbers of Cape Teal, Avocet, Whitefronted, Chestnutbanded, Kittlitz's and Blacksmith Plovers, and Cape Wagtail, recorded; also good numbers of White Pelican and both flamingos. A severe threat is degradation of the salt marsh through mining; important threats are hunting/poaching, boating, fishing, livestock grazing/trampling, and siltation.

		Summer (1)		Winter (1)				Summer (1)		Winter (1)	
		Mean	Max.	Mean	Max.			Mean	Max.	Mean	Max.
007	Blacknecked Grebe	0	0	16	16	213	Black Crake	0	0	1	1
008	Dabchick	0	0	30	30	226	Moorhen	0	0	5	5
049	White Pelican	17	17	110	110	228	Redknobbed Coot	0	0	72	72
055	Whitebreasted Cormorant	0	0	55	55	244	African Black Oystercatcher	0	0	9	9
056	Cape Cormorant	0	0	29	29	246	Whitefronted Plover	0	0	113	113
058	Reed Cormorant	2	2	3	3	247	Chestnutbanded Plover	0	0	61	61
060	Darter	1	1	79	79	248	Kittlitz's Plover	0	0	190	190
062	Grey Heron	2	2	23	23	249	Threebanded Plover	0	0	49	49
063	Blackheaded Heron	2	2	4	4	258	Blacksmith Plover	34	34	459	459
064	Goliath Heron	2	2	6	6	262	Turnstone	0	0	4	4
065	Purple Heron	0	0	1	1	264	Common Sandpiper	6	6	0	0
067	Little Egret	10	10	32	32	270	Greenshank	0	0	7	7
071	Cattle Egret	0	0	246	246	272	Curlew Sandpiper	0	0	793	793
076	Blackcrowned Night Heron	0	0	24	24	274	Little Stint	2	2	1	1
081	Hamerkop	1	1	4	4	284	Ruff	0	0	3	3
093	Glossy Ibis	0	0	1	1	294	Avocet	0	0	510	510
094	Hadeda Ibis	3	3	0	0	295	Blackwinged Stilt	0	0	75	75
095	African Spoonbill	5	5	66	66	312	Kelp Gull	7	7	453**	453**
096	Greater Flamingo	0	0	99	99	315	Greyheaded Gull	0	0	2	2
097	Lesser Flamingo	0	0	259	259	316	Hartlaub's Gull	0	0	397**	397**
102	Egyptian Goose	150	150	873	873	322	Caspian Tern	0	0	8	8
103	South African Shelduck	51	51	341*	341*	324	Swift Tern	0	0	82	82
104	Yellowbilled Duck	96	96	106	106	326	Sandwich Tern	0	0	20	20
105	African Black Duck	0	0	8	8	428	Pied Kingfisher	5	5	56	56
106	Cape Teal	0	0	297	297	431	Malachite Kingfisher	0	0	1	1
108	Redbilled Teal	35	35	97	97	711	African Pied Wagtail	3	3	2	2
112	Cape Shoveller	0	0	269*	269*	713	Cape Wagtail	25	25	222	222
116	Spurwinged Goose	19	19	116	116	891	Mallard	0	0	1	1
117	Maccoa Duck	0	0	9	9		Total	483	483	6801	6801
148	African Fish Eagle	4	4	1	1		No. of species		59		
170	Osprey	1	1	1	1						

Platfontein Pans, Kimberley, Northern Cape
28° 39' S 24° 37' E (2824DA)

Six ephemeral pans, infrequently inundated; shoreline open, with mud and short vegetation. Summer and winter counts in 1997 produced an impressive 42 waterbird species, with large totals for some. Nationally significant numbers of Greater Flamingo, South African Shelduck, Southern Pochard and Blackwinged Stilt occurred in summer, and of the flamingo also in winter. In summer there were also good numbers of Blacknecked Grebe, Dabchick, Glossy Ibis, Redbilled Teal, Cape Shoveller and Redknobbed Coot (breeds), high counts of Palearctic shorebirds ((particularly Marsh Sandpiper and Ruff), an exceptional 530 Avocet, and good numbers of Greyheaded Gull and Whitewinged Tern. The winter count produced large totals of Whitefaced and Yellowbilled Ducks, increased numbers of Redbilled Teal and Cape Shoveller, large counts of Kittlitz's and Blacksmith Plovers, 280 Curlew Sandpiper, and reasonable counts of Avocet and Blackwinged Stilt. Important threats are posed by overhead powerlines and by livestock grazing/trampling.

	Summer (1) Mean	Max.	Winter (1) Mean	Max.			Summer (1) Mean	Max.	Winter (1) Mean	Max.
006 Great Crested Grebe	1	1	1	1	148 African Fish Eagle		1	1	2	2
007 Blacknecked Grebe	52	52	32	32	226 Moorhen		4	4	0	0
008 Dabchick	95	95	28	28	228 Redknobbed Coot		2224	2224	1235	1235
058 Reed Cormorant	1	1	0	0	245 Ringed Plover		9	9	0	0
062 Grey Heron	1	1	0	0	248 Kittlitz's Plover		20	20	115	115
063 Blackheaded Heron	1	1	0	0	249 Threebanded Plover		16	16	23	23
067 Little Egret	1	1	0	0	254 Grey Plover		1	1	0	0
091 Sacred Ibis	1	1	0	0	258 Blacksmith Plover		40	40	94	94
093 Glossy Ibis	243	243	28	28	266 Wood Sandpiper		4	4	0	0
095 African Spoonbill	20	20	0	0	269 Marsh Sandpiper		208	208	1	1
096 Greater Flamingo	788*	788*	691*	691*	270 Greenshank		27	27	0	0
097 Lesser Flamingo	0	0	1	1	272 Curlew Sandpiper		372	372	283	283
099 Whitefaced Duck	22	22	177	177	274 Little Stint		243	243	0	0
102 Egyptian Goose	158	158	74	74	284 Ruff		1531	1531	1	1
103 South African Shelduck	237*	237*	124	124	294 Avocet		530	530	57	57
104 Yellowbilled Duck	26	26	200	200	295 Blackwinged Stilt		774*	774*	258	258
106 Cape Teal	69	69	64	64	305 Blackwinged Pratincole		1	1	0	0
107 Hottentot Teal	5	5	0	0	315 Greyheaded Gull		248	248	0	0
108 Redbilled Teal	264	264	793	793	339 Whitewinged Tern		509	509	0	0
112 Cape Shoveller	101	101	167	167	713 Cape Wagtail		5	5	20	20
113 Southern Pochard	280*	280*	31	31	Total		9150	9150	4569	4569
116 Spurwinged Goose	15	15	55	55	No. of species			43		
117 Maccoa Duck	2	2	14	14						

So Ver Myn Dam, Windsorton, Northern Cape
28° 13' S 24° 31' E (2824BA)

A farm dam, with an open shoreline, fairly suitable for waders. Summer and winter counts for 1996–97 yielded small numbers of a reasonable variety of waterbirds, with Dabchick being more numerous in winter and cormorants in summer. Some waterfowl, and Redknobbed Coot, have higher summer counts, others are more numerous in winter, but numbers are too small to give a good indication of patterns of occurrence. Non-Palearctic shorebirds are commoner in winter, when peaks of Kittlitz's and Threebanded Plovers, Avocet and Blackwinged Stilt are recorded. No threats have been identified.

	Summer (2) Mean	Max.	Winter (2) Mean	Max.			Summer (2) Mean	Max.	Winter (2) Mean	Max.
006 Great Crested Grebe	1	1	0	0	112 Cape Shoveller		8	8	0	0
008 Dabchick	16	31	35	69	113 Southern Pochard		0	0	1	1
055 Whitebreasted Cormorant	9	17	0	0	117 Maccoa Duck		0	0	1	2
058 Reed Cormorant	8	16	0	0	228 Redknobbed Coot		55	93	33	66
060 Darter	0	0	1	1	248 Kittlitz's Plover		0	0	6	12
062 Grey Heron	1	1	1	1	249 Threebanded Plover		1	2	7	13
066 Great White Heron	1	2	1	1	258 Blacksmith Plover		8	8	5	9
091 Sacred Ibis	0	0	1	1	269 Marsh Sandpiper		1	1	0	0
093 Glossy Ibis	1	2	0	0	272 Curlew Sandpiper		13	25	0	0
095 African Spoonbill	0	0	1	1	284 Ruff		3	5	1	2
099 Whitefaced Duck	1	2	0	0	294 Avocet		0	0	2	4
102 Egyptian Goose	3	4	2	2	295 Blackwinged Stilt		2	3	5	7
103 South African Shelduck	2	3	1	2	339 Whitewinged Tern		38	75	0	0
104 Yellowbilled Duck	7	11	15	22	Total		179	220	117	178
108 Redbilled Teal	6	7	3	3	No. of species			28		

Sakrivierspoort Wetlands, Loxton, Northern Cape
31° 50' S 22° 08' E (3122CC)

Two dams and a seasonal wetland on the Sakrivier. Counts from summer 1995 to summer 1997 have yielded small to moderate numbers of a good selection of waterbirds, including good totals of South African Shelduck. Shorebird numbers are highest in summer, as are numbers of Reed Cormorant, ibises, Moorhen and several duck species; Egyptian and Spurwinged Geese are commoner in winter. Numbers of Sacred Ibis and Blacksmith Plover have increased in summer, and Cape Wagtail counts have increased in both seasons. Threats are agriculture along drying margins, livestock trampling/grazing, and dam construction.

		Summer (3)		Winter (2)				Summer (3)		Winter (2)	
		Mean	Max.	Mean	Max.			Mean	Max.	Mean	Max.
006	Great Crested Grebe	2	6	0	0	112	Cape Shoveller	4	8	4	5
007	Blacknecked Grebe	5	9	2	2	116	Spurwinged Goose	0	0	4	8
008	Dabchick	7	9	7	8	117	Maccoa Duck	1	2	5	10
055	Whitebreasted Cormorant	1	2	0	0	165	African Marsh Harrier	0	1	0	0
058	Reed Cormorant	24	27	4	6	226	Moorhen	10	10	5	8
060	Darter	0	1	0	0	228	Redknobbed Coot	32	33	45	55
062	Grey Heron	5	6	0	0	248	Kittlitz's Plover	14	18	12	22
063	Blackheaded Heron	1	2	0	0	249	Threebanded Plover	21	28	13	14
067	Little Egret	2	2	0	0	258	Blacksmith Plover	40	50	30	31
071	Cattle Egret	1	3	6	9	264	Common Sandpiper	0	1	0	0
076	Blackcrowned Night Heron	1	2	0	0	266	Wood Sandpiper	1	2	0	0
078	Little Bittern	2	3	0	0	269	Marsh Sandpiper	1	1	0	0
084	Black Stork	0	1	0	0	270	Greenshank	3	5	1	1
090	Yellowbilled Stork	1	2	0	0	272	Curlew Sandpiper	1	1	0	0
091	Sacred Ibis	26	37	1	1	274	Little Stint	38	44	0	0
094	Hadeda Ibis	6	8	2	2	284	Ruff	1	1	0	0
095	African Spoonbill	8	19	1	2	286	Ethiopian Snipe	1	3	1	2
096	Greater Flamingo	0	0	1	1	294	Avocet	5	15	0	0
099	Whitefaced Duck	1	2	0	0	295	Blackwinged Stilt	4	12	0	0
102	Egyptian Goose	98	120	189	245	338	Whiskered Tern	1	3	0	0
103	South African Shelduck	65	93	48	53	428	Pied Kingfisher	6	12	3	3
104	Yellowbilled Duck	41	49	16	16	431	Malachite Kingfisher	0	1	2	2
105	African Black Duck	3	5	2	2	713	Cape Wagtail	69	89	62	80
106	Cape Teal	0	0	3	5		Total	557	599	464	505
108	Redbilled Teal	6	13	2	3		No. of species			48	

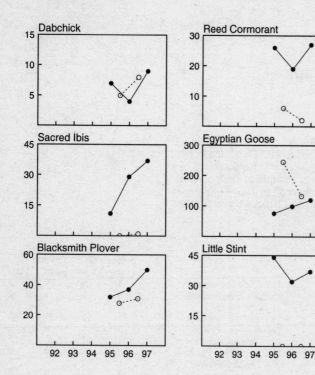

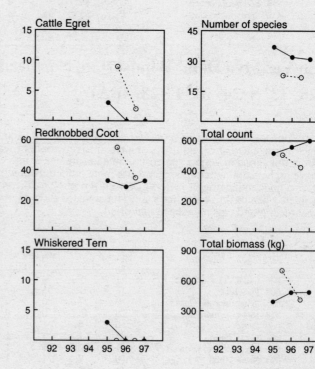

Spitskop Dam, Spitskop, Northern Cape
28° 04' S 24° 33' E (2824BA)

Summer and winter counts for 1996–97 show that this IBA is important for waterbirds, usually holding higher numbers than any other Northern Cape site. A large dam on the Harts River; varied shoreline habitats, including grass, reeds and mud. Cormorants and Darter breed. Globally significant numbers of Great Crested Grebe, Dabchick and Darter in winter, of African Spoonbill and South African Shelduck in summer, and of Redknobbed Coot all year. Nationally significant numbers of Darter, Cape Shoveller and Whitewinged Tern in summer. High counts of cormorants and flamingos, especially in winter, and of Goliath Heron all year. Good summer counts of Cattle Egret, Squacco Heron, Yellowbilled Stork, ibises, Blackwinged Stilt and Greyheaded Gull. Numbers of Egyptian Goose peak in summer, of Spurwinged Goose, Yellowbilled Duck and Redbilled Teal in winter. Important threats include pesticide and fertiliser pollution, and fishing; mild threats are siltation, hunting/poaching and livestock grazing/trampling.

		Summer (2) Mean	Max.	Winter (2) Mean	Max.			Summer (2) Mean	Max.	Winter (2) Mean	Max.
006	Great Crested Grebe	8	9	99**	134**	104	Yellowbilled Duck	160	166	569	834
007	Blacknecked Grebe	1	1	0	0	106	Cape Teal	26	50	4	7
008	Dabchick	12	23	543**	949**	108	Redbilled Teal	18	25	207	299
050	Pinkbacked Pelican	39	41	0	0	112	Cape Shoveller	232*	292*	151	160
055	Whitebreasted Cormorant	457	780	644	701	113	Southern Pochard	0	0	1	2
058	Reed Cormorant	248	393	890	1168	116	Spurwinged Goose	1	1	275	299
060	Darter	306*	346*	522**	569**	148	African Fish Eagle	3	3	2	2
062	Grey Heron	14	16	17	20	213	Black Crake	2	3	2	4
063	Blackheaded Heron	1	1	5	5	223	Purple Gallinule	4	7	2	4
064	Goliath Heron	27	41	22	35	226	Moorhen	17	30	23	39
065	Purple Heron	1	1	2	3	228	Redknobbed Coot	4868*	6279**	5961**	6497**
066	Great White Heron	9	17	3	5	245	Ringed Plover	1	1	0	0
067	Little Egret	4	4	0	0	248	Kittlitz's Plover	4	7	8	13
068	Yellowbilled Egret	0	0	3	5	249	Threebanded Plover	1	1	0	0
069	Black Egret	10	12	0	0	258	Blacksmith Plover	169	180	72	109
071	Cattle Egret	606	1000	0	0	266	Wood Sandpiper	10	19	0	0
072	Squacco Heron	31	57	3	5	269	Marsh Sandpiper	1	2	0	0
076	Blackcrowned Night Heron	9	17	0	0	272	Curlew Sandpiper	14	28	0	0
078	Little Bittern	3	5	0	0	274	Little Stint	21	40	0	0
090	Yellowbilled Stork	34	34	0	0	284	Ruff	100	200	0	0
091	Sacred Ibis	18	32	51	71	295	Blackwinged Stilt	82	88	28	39
093	Glossy Ibis	36	39	4	7	315	Greyheaded Gull	220	256	43	61
094	Hadeda Ibis	0	0	2	3	322	Caspian Tern	29	45	9	16
095	African Spoonbill	186**	257**	43	44	338	Whiskered Tern	6	12	7	14
096	Greater Flamingo	113	210	244	357	339	Whitewinged Tern	587	1128*	0	0
097	Lesser Flamingo	55	110	819	919	428	Pied Kingfisher	2	2	4	6
099	Whitefaced Duck	4	8	0	0	713	Cape Wagtail	2	3	31	32
101	Whitebacked Duck	1	2	2	4		Total	10237	12859	11727	12838
102	Egyptian Goose	693	854	335	447		No. of species		57		
103	South African Shelduck	745**	1184**	84	137						

Strydenburg Pan, Strydenburg, Northern Cape
29° 56' S 23° 41' E (2923DC)

An open, ephemeral pan with little vegetation; adjacent to Strydenburg town. Good wader and flamingo habitat; Greater Flamingo has bred here. One winter count, in 1997, produced a substantial number of waterbirds of 18 species, the largest totals being of Greater and Lesser Flamingo, and Redknobbed Coot, with good numbers of South African Shelduck, Cape Teal, Blacksmith Plover, Avocet and Blackwinged Stilt; even 24 Curlew Sandpipers and a Ruff were present. Mild threats are posed by human disturbance and domestic dogs and cats.

		Summer (0) Mean	Max.	Winter (1) Mean	Max.			Summer (0) Mean	Max.	Winter (1) Mean	Max.
008	Dabchick	–	–	1	1	248	Kittlitz's Plover	–	–	8	8
096	Greater Flamingo	–	–	101	101	249	Threebanded Plover	–	–	10	10
097	Lesser Flamingo	–	–	155	155	258	Blacksmith Plover	–	–	41	41
099	Whitefaced Duck	–	–	1	1	272	Curlew Sandpiper	–	–	24	24
102	Egyptian Goose	–	–	6	6	284	Ruff	–	–	1	1
103	South African Shelduck	–	–	10	10	294	Avocet	–	–	50	50
104	Yellowbilled Duck	–	–	3	3	295	Blackwinged Stilt	–	–	57	57
106	Cape Teal	–	–	34	34	713	Cape Wagtail	–	–	8	8
112	Cape Shoveller	–	–	15	15		Total	–	–	960	960
228	Redknobbed Coot	–	–	435	435		No. of species		18		

Springbok Sewage Works, Springbok, Northern Cape
29° 40' S 17° 53' E (2917DB)

A small site; sewage ponds, with open water and a little fringing vegetation of reeds. Two summer and two winter counts show mainly small numbers of the commoner wetland bird species, and also Great Crested and Blacknecked Grebes (in summer only). The most numerous species has been Cape Teal, with good counts both in summer and winter. The small amount of data available give little indication of seasonality of occurrence in most species, although both Palearctic and other shorebirds are more numerous in summer. No threats have been identified.

		Summer (2) Mean	Summer (2) Max.	Winter (2) Mean	Winter (2) Max.			Summer (2) Mean	Summer (2) Max.	Winter (2) Mean	Winter (2) Max.
006	Great Crested Grebe	2	4	0	0	226	Moorhen	11	12	10	19
007	Blacknecked Grebe	2	4	0	0	228	Redknobbed Coot	8	13	12	15
008	Dabchick	16	20	13	16	249	Threebanded Plover	7	11	2	3
062	Grey Heron	0	0	1	1	258	Blacksmith Plover	22	37	10	17
063	Blackheaded Heron	2	2	2	3	264	Common Sandpiper	1	1	0	0
091	Sacred Ibis	1	2	1	1	266	Wood Sandpiper	3	4	0	0
102	Egyptian Goose	4	6	0	0	269	Marsh Sandpiper	2	3	0	0
103	South African Shelduck	2	3	2	4	270	Greenshank	2	2	0	0
105	African Black Duck	0	0	4	7	295	Blackwinged Stilt	16	25	4	4
106	Cape Teal	37	47	42	52	713	Cape Wagtail	15	23	9	12
108	Redbilled Teal	0	0	3	5		Total	153	186	116	152
112	Cape Shoveller	1	2	4	5		No. of species		23		
117	Maccoa Duck	2	3	1	2						

Vaalharts Weir, Warrenton, Northern Cape
28° 07' S 24° 55' E (2824BB)

An oxbow lake permanently connected to the Vaal River above the Vaalharts Weir, with extensive fringing reedbeds of *Phragmites, Typha*, etc., and adjacent flooded grass. Two summer and two winter counts are available, starting in summer 1996. The site holds a good variety of waterbird species, including Goliath and Squacco Herons, while Black Crake and Purple Gallinule occur in the reedbeds. The winter 1997 count of 2151 birds was more than twice that in 1996 and almost three times the summer 1997 total, and reflects peak numbers of waterfowl and Redknobbed Coot. Summer 1997 gave high counts of Glossy Ibis, Redbilled Teal, Ruff and Whiskered Tern. Numbers of Dabchick, and of most waterfowl, peak in winter, when Moorhen also seem to be considerably more numerous. A severe threat is infestation by alien water plants (*Eichhornia, Myriophyllum aquaticum*); other threats include reed encroachment resulting from nutrient enrichment from fertiliser runoff, and pollution by pesticides.

		Summer (2) Mean	Summer (2) Max.	Winter (2) Mean	Winter (2) Max.			Summer (2) Mean	Summer (2) Max.	Winter (2) Mean	Winter (2) Max.
008	Dabchick	3	5	153	166	165	African Marsh Harrier	0	0	1	1
055	Whitebreasted Cormorant	3	3	1	1	213	Black Crake	0	0	1	1
058	Reed Cormorant	9	9	7	14	223	Purple Gallinule	0	0	1	1
060	Darter	10	12	4	4	226	Moorhen	6	8	51	68
062	Grey Heron	0	0	4	6	228	Redknobbed Coot	43	81	1074	1532
064	Goliath Heron	3	5	3	4	240	African Jacana	1	1	1	1
065	Purple Heron	1	1	0	0	249	Threebanded Plover	4	4	2	3
068	Yellowbilled Egret	1	1	0	0	258	Blacksmith Plover	18	21	8	9
069	Black Egret	1	1	1	1	266	Wood Sandpiper	3	3	0	0
071	Cattle Egret	1	1	0	0	269	Marsh Sandpiper	6	11	0	0
072	Squacco Heron	9	14	11	20	270	Greenshank	1	2	0	0
093	Glossy Ibis	30	59	8	16	284	Ruff	206	407	0	0
094	Hadeda Ibis	6	6	1	1	286	Ethiopian Snipe	0	0	1	1
095	African Spoonbill	1	1	1	1	294	Avocet	0	0	2	4
099	Whitefaced Duck	5	5	4	7	295	Blackwinged Stilt	11	21	10	11
102	Egyptian Goose	3	5	51	100	305	Blackwinged Pratincole	1	1	0	0
103	South African Shelduck	0	0	8	15	322	Caspian Tern	2	3	1	2
104	Yellowbilled Duck	18	29	69	97	338	Whiskered Tern	24	47	7	14
106	Cape Teal	1	1	2	3	339	Whitewinged Tern	54	100	0	0
107	Hottentot Teal	1	2	1	2	428	Pied Kingfisher	1	1	1	2
108	Redbilled Teal	12	22	7	11	431	Malachite Kingfisher	0	0	1	1
112	Cape Shoveller	0	0	14	20	713	Cape Wagtail	1	1	11	14
116	Spurwinged Goose	1	2	37	68		Total	490	791	1552	2152
148	African Fish Eagle	1	1	2	2		No. of species		46		

Vanderkloof Dam, Vanderkloof, Northern Cape
30° 10' S 24° 55' E (3024BB)

A very large, state-owned impoundment on the Orange River, partly within the Rolfontein and Doornkloof Nature Reserves. Shoreline character variable, depending on water level: when level low, muddy substrate in bays is exposed; when dam full, water reaches base of Karoo koppies. No submergent vegetation, hence lack of Redknobbed Coot: only 1 recorded, in summer. Cormorant, Darter, and Goliath Herons breed, as probably do Egyptian Goose and Yellowbilled Duck. Counts in winter 1996 and summer 1997, when water level was high, produced very few shorebirds but small to good numbers of 30 waterfowl species. Cormorant, Darter, heron and egret numbers peaked in summer, when a count of 112 Darter was noteworthy. Egyptian Goose was common in both seasons, but Yellowbilled Duck was commoner in winter; summer also produced small numbers of six shorebird species. A noteworthy feature was the total of eight Fish Eagles on both counts; several pairs breed here. No threats have been identified.

	Summer (1)		Winter (1)				Summer (1)		Winter (1)	
	Mean	Max.	Mean	Max.			Mean	Max.	Mean	Max.
055 Whitebreasted Cormorant	16	16	4	4	115	Knobbilled Duck	0	0	1	1
058 Reed Cormorant	58	58	10	10	148	African Fish Eagle	8	8	8	8
060 Darter	112	112	50	50	170	Osprey	3	3	1	1
062 Grey Heron	29	29	1	1	228	Redknobbed Coot	1	1	0	0
063 Blackheaded Heron	2	2	1	1	248	Kittlitz's Plover	1	1	0	0
064 Goliath Heron	20	20	5	5	249	Threebanded Plover	4	4	0	0
071 Cattle Egret	8	8	0	0	258	Blacksmith Plover	10	10	1	1
081 Hamerkop	0	0	1	1	264	Common Sandpiper	4	4	0	0
084 Black Stork	0	0	2	2	270	Greenshank	2	2	0	0
094 Hadeda Ibis	0	0	1	1	284	Ruff	7	7	0	0
095 African Spoonbill	0	0	1	1	428	Pied Kingfisher	6	6	0	0
102 Egyptian Goose	261	261	246	246	429	Giant Kingfisher	0	0	1	1
103 South African Shelduck	17	17	7	7	711	African Pied Wagtail	11	11	17	17
104 Yellowbilled Duck	34	34	178	178	713	Cape Wagtail	4	4	19	19
105 African Black Duck	2	2	0	0		Total	620	620	557	557
112 Cape Shoveller	0	0	2	2		No. of species		30		

Volstruis Pan, Schmidtsdrif, Northern Cape
28° 40' S 24° 10' E (2824CA)

A large open pan on Rooipoort Nature Reserve. Some vegetation on pan floor, mainly grasses; shoreline open, providing good habitat for shorebirds. Infrequently inundated (possibly full only every 10 years). Two summer and two winter counts available, showing reasonable numbers of a relatively good variety of waterfowl and shorebirds. In summer, small to moderate numbers of Palearctic waders recorded, together with a few Avocet, and a good number of Blackwinged Stilt in summer 1997; in winter fewer stilt are recorded, and in 1997 there were reasonable counts of Kittlitz's and Blacksmith Plovers. A greater diversity of waterfowl has occurred in summer: 7 species, plus Redknobbed Coot; in winter 5 of those species were recorded (including 210 Egyptian Goose in 1997) and no coot. All other waterbirds occurred only in summer; 52 Glossy Ibis in 1997 are noteworthy. No threats have been identified.

	Summer (2)		Winter (2)				Summer (2)		Winter (2)	
	Mean	Max.	Mean	Max.			Mean	Max.	Mean	Max.
008 Dabchick	9	18	0	0	248	Kittlitz's Plover	1	1	17	33
066 Great White Heron	1	1	0	0	249	Threebanded Plover	0	0	1	2
093 Glossy Ibis	26	52	0	0	258	Blacksmith Plover	1	2	9	17
095 African Spoonbill	1	1	0	0	269	Marsh Sandpiper	4	8	1	1
096 Greater Flamingo	13	25	0	0	270	Greenshank	6	11	0	0
102 Egyptian Goose	11	21	105	210	274	Little Stint	10	20	0	0
103 South African Shelduck	3	5	3	5	284	Ruff	37	73	0	0
104 Yellowbilled Duck	5	9	20	39	294	Avocet	3	6	0	0
108 Redbilled Teal	15	30	11	22	295	Blackwinged Stilt	27	53	10	19
112 Cape Shoveller	3	5	2	3	713	Cape Wagtail	0	0	7	13
113 Southern Pochard	2	3	0	0		Total	194	387	182	364
116 Spurwinged Goose	8	15	0	0		No. of species		23		
228 Redknobbed Coot	14	28	0	0						

Allemanskraal Dam, Ventersburg, Free State
28° 18' S 27° 12' E (2827AC)

A large state dam on the Sand River, within the Willem Pretorius Game Reserve, an IBA. Globally significant numbers of Egyptian Goose are recorded, and nationally significant numbers of Cattle Egret, African Spoonbill, South African Shelduck and Cape Shoveller (in summer) and Spurwinged Goose (in winter). Most waterfowl, and also Darter, Goliath Heron, Sacred Ibis, Redknobbed Coot, plovers and Greyheaded Gull, are more numerous in summer; Dabchick and Whitebreasted Cormorant are commoner in winter. The high biomass total for winter 1993 reflects exceptionally high counts of Egyptian and Spurwinged Geese. Numbers of Darter and Egyptian Goose are apparently declining. Mild threats are posed by siltation, agrochemical pollution, *Eucalyptus* encroachment on islands and shoreline, boating, and hunting/poaching.

		Summer (6) Mean	Summer (6) Max.	Winter (6) Mean	Winter (6) Max.
008	Dabchick	1	2	29	61
055	Whitebreasted Cormorant	3	15	26	47
058	Reed Cormorant	15	35	3	12
060	Darter	52	108	14	42
062	Grey Heron	15	26	10	19
063	Blackheaded Heron	5	12	1	7
064	Goliath Heron	28	42	6	12
067	Little Egret	0	1	0	1
068	Yellowbilled Egret	1	7	0	0
071	Cattle Egret	1733	5400*	3	14
076	Blackcrowned Night Heron	0	1	0	0
081	Hamerkop	1	4	0	1
090	Yellowbilled Stork	8	33	0	0
091	Sacred Ibis	110	240	0	2
093	Glossy Ibis	1	3	0	0
094	Hadeda Ibis	3	15	5	18
095	African Spoonbill	45	105*	6	14
096	Greater Flamingo	1	4	3	11
097	Lesser Flamingo	0	1	1	3
099	Whitefaced Duck	4	16	2	9
102	Egyptian Goose	1970*	4481**	1900*	3851**
103	South African Shelduck	165	332*	13	35
104	Yellowbilled Duck	179	238	102	249
105	African Black Duck	1	4	0	0
106	Cape Teal	12	22	5	15
108	Redbilled Teal	59	327	12	32
112	Cape Shoveller	67	239*	17	39

		Summer (6) Mean	Summer (6) Max.	Winter (6) Mean	Winter (6) Max.
116	Spurwinged Goose	17	51	885	2654*
148	African Fish Eagle	1	2	1	2
228	Redknobbed Coot	494	1527	203	408
248	Kittlitz's Plover	35	144	27	121
249	Threebanded Plover	45	227	7	13
254	Grey Plover	0	1	0	0
258	Blacksmith Plover	247	577	52	86
264	Common Sandpiper	1	2	0	0
266	Wood Sandpiper	0	0	0	1
269	Marsh Sandpiper	3	15	0	1
270	Greenshank	6	21	0	1
272	Curlew Sandpiper	115	489	13	51
274	Little Stint	100	261	10	59
284	Ruff	52	128	0	0
286	Ethiopian Snipe	0	0	0	1
289	Curlew	1	3	0	0
294	Avocet	2	6	2	4
295	Blackwinged Stilt	0	0	3	15
305	Blackwinged Pratincole	0	1	0	0
315	Greyheaded Gull	49	83	3	11
322	Caspian Tern	1	6	1	4
339	Whitewinged Tern	101	252	3	16
428	Pied Kingfisher	0	2	0	0
711	African Pied Wagtail	0	1	0	0
713	Cape Wagtail	7	29	58	255
	Total	5755	8649	3424	7202
	No. of species		52		

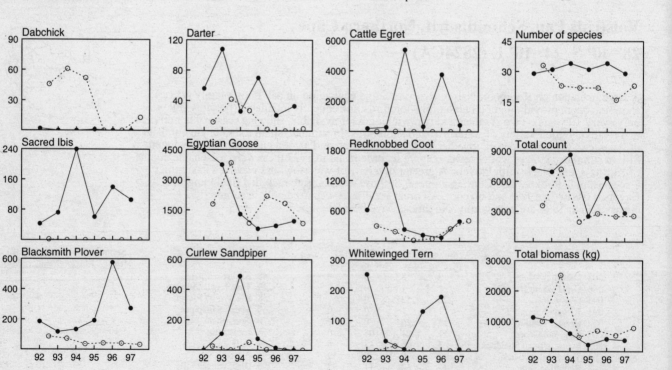

Bloemhof Dam, Bloemhof, Free State
27° 41' S 25° 40' E (2725DA)

A sub-regional IBA. A state dam on the Vaal River, partly within two nature reserves. It regularly supports over 5000, sometimes over 10 000, waterbirds. There are globally significant counts of Dabchick, Darter, African Spoonbill, Greater Flamingo and Cape Shoveller, and nationally significant counts of six other species, including Goliath Heron. Good numbers of Blacksmith Plover, Blackwinged Stilt and Greyheaded Gull also occur. Large numbers of herons, egrets and cormorants breed. Numbers of most waterfowl peak in winter; counts of most other waterbirds are higher in summer, except for Dabchick, flamingos, Redknobbed Coot, Avocet and Whiskered Tern. Black Egret and Saddlebilled Stork are recorded. Important threats are pollution and eutrophication; mild threats are posed by fishing and boating.

		Summer (6) Mean	Summer (6) Max.	Winter (6) Mean	Winter (6) Max.			Summer (6) Mean	Summer (6) Max.	Winter (6) Mean	Winter (6) Max.
006	Great Crested Grebe	0	0	0	2	104	Yellowbilled Duck	149	280	445	703
007	Blacknecked Grebe	0	0	1	4	106	Cape Teal	25	68	30	55
008	Dabchick	1	5	159	540**	108	Redbilled Teal	97	510	609	1676
049	White Pelican	0	1	0	0	112	Cape Shoveller	35	153	156	490**
050	Pinkbacked Pelican	8	21	0	0	113	Southern Pochard	0	0	42	175
055	Whitebreasted Cormorant	267	504	206	640	115	Knobbilled Duck	0	1	17	79
058	Reed Cormorant	205	456	39	112	116	Spurwinged Goose	63	163	653	1580
060	Darter	228	610**	117	280*	148	African Fish Eagle	6	13	4	7
062	Grey Heron	57	95	7	12	165	African Marsh Harrier	0	1	0	1
063	Blackheaded Heron	8	24	7	20	170	Osprey	0	1	0	0
064	Goliath Heron	76	168*	37	79	226	Moorhen	0	0	1	3
065	Purple Heron	0	1	0	0	228	Redknobbed Coot	347	1576	1817	3854*
066	Great White Heron	38	109	0	2	248	Kittlitz's Plover	5	25	4	20
067	Little Egret	18	50	3	15	249	Threebanded Plover	1	2	2	7
068	Yellowbilled Egret	2	9	1	3	258	Blacksmith Plover	121	287	113	303
069	Black Egret	5	28	0	1	264	Common Sandpiper	0	1	0	1
071	Cattle Egret	1217	6233*	0	1	270	Greenshank	1	5	1	2
072	Squacco Heron	3	10	0	0	272	Curlew Sandpiper	2	8	66	350
076	Blackcrowned Night Heron	0	1	0	0	274	Little Stint	20	118	1	5
090	Yellowbilled Stork	38	94	0	1	284	Ruff	51	243	117	700
091	Sacred Ibis	16	38	18	52	294	Avocet	61	360	131	716*
093	Glossy Ibis	2	9	2	8	295	Blackwinged Stilt	42	169	90	355
094	Hadeda Ibis	2	4	17	66	315	Greyheaded Gull	193	423	41	69
095	African Spoonbill	63	193**	9	20	322	Caspian Tern	19	61	2	4
096	Greater Flamingo	119	489	507	1632**	338	Whiskered Tern	1	5	27	155
097	Lesser Flamingo	17	79	158	707	339	Whitewinged Tern	853	1420*	7	32
099	Whitefaced Duck	4	23	291	714	395	Marsh Owl	0	0	1	2
100	Fulvous Duck	11	49	69	294	428	Pied Kingfisher	0	2	0	1
101	Whitebacked Duck	0	0	1	7	713	Cape Wagtail	9	50	4	10
102	Egyptian Goose	300	767	1481	2543*		Total	4913	8540	7585	11081
103	South African Shelduck	106	348*	77	400*		No. of species		60		

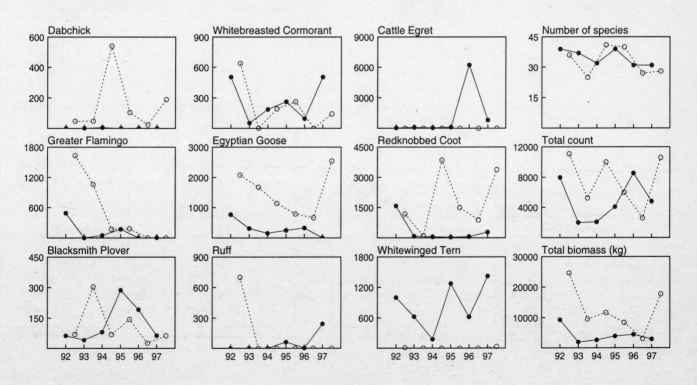

Erfenis Dam, Winburg, Free State
28° 34' S 26° 50' E (2826DB)

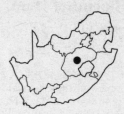

A large state dam with little fringing emergent vegetation; good shorebird habitat in some years, e.g. in summer 1994 large counts of Blacksmith Plover, Curlew Sandpiper, Little Stint and Ruff recorded. Dabchick noted only in winter, in declining numbers; Cattle Egret occur only in summer, in increasing numbers. Cormorants, herons, egrets, ibises and African Spoonbill commoner in summer; flamingos and most waterfowl commoner in winter. High winter counts of Common Sandpiper and Little Stint in 1992. In winter, total number of species has remained fairly constant, and total count and total biomass curves closely follow those for the three commonest large waterfowl species, namely Egyptian Goose, Spurwinged Goose and Redknobbed Coot. Mild threats are posed by pollution, siltation, boating, hunting/poaching and domestic dogs.

		Summer (6)		Winter (6)				Summer (6)		Winter (6)	
		Mean	Max.	Mean	Max.			Mean	Max.	Mean	Max.
006	Great Crested Grebe	0	0	0	1	108	Redbilled Teal	54	206	69	322
008	Dabchick	0	0	30	79	112	Cape Shoveller	15	44	9	17
055	Whitebreasted Cormorant	1	4	6	33	113	Southern Pochard	5	26	23	133
056	Cape Cormorant	0	1	0	0	116	Spurwinged Goose	19	41	326	994
058	Reed Cormorant	14	56	1	2	148	African Fish Eagle	1	3	1	3
060	Darter	15	31	5	17	170	Osprey	0	1	0	1
062	Grey Heron	18	33	4	10	228	Redknobbed Coot	420	852	372	1144
063	Blackheaded Heron	1	3	0	1	245	Ringed Plover	2	9	0	1
064	Goliath Heron	15	20	5	9	248	Kittlitz's Plover	15	47	40	201
065	Purple Heron	0	2	0	0	249	Threebanded Plover	3	10	7	21
066	Great White Heron	0	2	0	0	258	Blacksmith Plover	168	316	91	174
067	Little Egret	1	2	0	0	264	Common Sandpiper	1	6	22	134
068	Yellowbilled Egret	1	4	0	0	266	Wood Sandpiper	0	1	0	1
071	Cattle Egret	193	412	0	0	269	Marsh Sandpiper	3	11	0	0
076	Blackcrowned Night Heron	0	1	0	0	270	Greenshank	3	8	0	1
081	Hamerkop	0	1	0	1	272	Curlew Sandpiper	77	330	3	18
090	Yellowbilled Stork	5	17	0	0	274	Little Stint	195	936	24	141
091	Sacred Ibis	7	29	0	0	284	Ruff	256	1295	0	0
093	Glossy Ibis	3	14	0	0	294	Avocet	1	2	2	6
094	Hadeda Ibis	1	3	1	3	295	Blackwinged Stilt	1	5	4	9
095	African Spoonbill	37	43	6	25	305	Blackwinged Pratincole	0	1	0	0
096	Greater Flamingo	3	6	21	63	315	Greyheaded Gull	1	6	7	19
097	Lesser Flamingo	1	2	14	84	322	Caspian Tern	4	22	1	5
099	Whitefaced Duck	2	5	36	211	339	Whitewinged Tern	250	486	3	17
100	Fulvous Duck	0	0	1	3	428	Pied Kingfisher	0	1	0	0
102	Egyptian Goose	815	1378	1691	3152*	429	Giant Kingfisher	0	1	0	0
103	South African Shelduck	148	427**	6	16	431	Malachite Kingfisher	0	0	0	1
104	Yellowbilled Duck	105	203	180	342	713	Cape Wagtail	4	11	32	81
105	African Black Duck	3	11	3	9		Total	2903	4737	3054	5275
106	Cape Teal	21	98	10	27		No. of species			58	

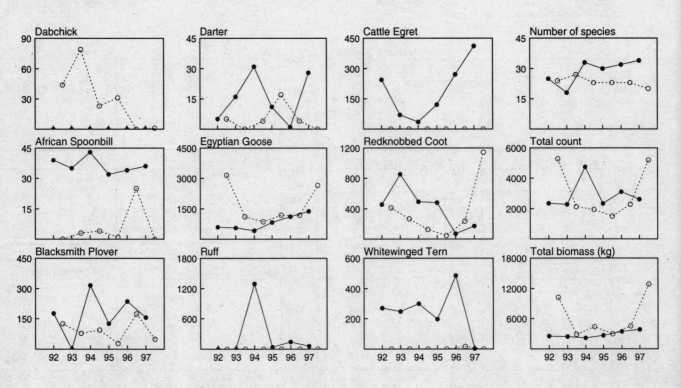

Gariep Dam (West), Gariep Dam (town), Free State
30° 37' S 25° 37' E (3025DA)

A large, state-owned dam surrounded by nature reserves, which comprise an IBA. Most of shoreline unsuitable for shorebirds, but the dam supports large numbers of waterbirds. Globally significant numbers of South African Shelduck occur in summer (this is a moulting site) and of Yellowbilled Duck all year, and nationally significant numbers of Egyptian Goose are recorded in summer. Good numbers of Redbilled Teal occur in summer, and of Cape Shoveller and Spurwinged Goose in winter. High counts of Grey and Goliath Herons, and African Spoonbill, are recorded, especially in summer, and of Caspian Tern in winter. African Fish Eagle is resident in good numbers. A good count of 22 Yellowbilled Stork was made in summer 1996. Summer counts of several species increased during survey period (see graphs). An important threat is the diversion of water in the catchment by dam building in Lesotho; mild threats are posed by boating, fishing and siltation.

		Summer (6)		Winter (6)	
		Mean	Max.	Mean	Max.
008	Dabchick	0	0	2	10
055	Whitebreasted Cormorant	18	31	6	19
058	Reed Cormorant	6	20	0	0
060	Darter	23	48	3	11
062	Grey Heron	48	84	16	62
063	Blackheaded Heron	1	2	0	0
064	Goliath Heron	21	29	9	14
066	Great White Heron	0	2	0	0
067	Little Egret	1	3	1	4
071	Cattle Egret	15	48	0	0
076	Blackcrowned Night Heron	0	0	0	1
090	Yellowbilled Stork	3	17	0	0
091	Sacred Ibis	28	89	1	4
094	Hadeda Ibis	1	6	0	0
095	African Spoonbill	38	64	4	9
099	Whitefaced Duck	32	189	1	7
102	Egyptian Goose	611	1339	336	623
103	South African Shelduck	368*	1287**	14	57
104	Yellowbilled Duck	328	1479*	469	1993**
105	African Black Duck	0	0	0	2
106	Cape Teal	2	13	0	0
108	Redbilled Teal	95	570	1	4

		Summer (6)		Winter (6)	
		Mean	Max.	Mean	Max.
112	Cape Shoveller	0	0	20	121
116	Spurwinged Goose	20	62	105	186
148	African Fish Eagle	13	20	11	22
228	Redknobbed Coot	4	18	0	0
248	Kittlitz's Plover	2	12	0	0
249	Threebanded Plover	0	1	0	2
258	Blacksmith Plover	1	4	8	30
264	Common Sandpiper	0	2	0	0
270	Greenshank	0	1	0	0
272	Curlew Sandpiper	1	3	0	0
274	Little Stint	4	22	0	0
295	Blackwinged Stilt	1	3	5	16
315	Greyheaded Gull	0	2	2	7
322	Caspian Tern	0	2	2	8
339	Whitewinged Tern	0	0	1	4
428	Pied Kingfisher	0	0	2	9
429	Giant Kingfisher	0	1	1	4
711	African Pied Wagtail	1	4	1	4
713	Cape Wagtail	4	12	2	11
	Total	1687	3469	1024	3124
	No. of species		41		

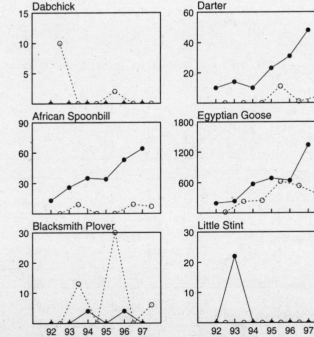

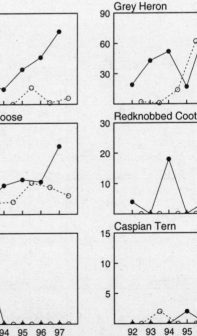

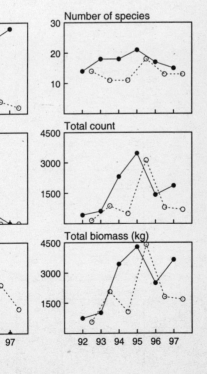

Kalkfontein Dam, Koffiefontein, Free State
29° 32' S 25° 15' E (2925CB)

An IBA. Large, permanent waterbody in an area of seasonal pans and hardly any watercourses; regularly holds 10 000+ waterbirds. Exceptional count of 18 355 birds in summer 1995, when globally significant counts of Redknobbed Coot (7666) and Yellowbilled Stork (191) were made, and peak numbers of African Spoonbill, Greater Flamingo, Cape Teal, Cape Shoveller, Curlew Sandpiper, Little Stint and Ruff were present. Nationally significant summer counts of Caspian and White-winged Terns; good numbers of Goliath Heron all year. Substantial numbers of shorebirds in summer, and of African plovers and Blackwinged Stilt in winter; high count of Curlew Sandpiper in July 1994; Chestnutbanded Plover also occurs. Over-utilization of water an important threat; mild threats are eutrophication, agrochemical pollution, fishing and boating.

		Summer (6)		Winter (6)	
		Mean	Max.	Mean	Max.
006	Great Crested Grebe	4	10	20	52**
007	Blacknecked Grebe	0	2	5	16
008	Dabchick	3	13	91	339*
055	Whitebreasted Cormorant	261	615	180	601
058	Reed Cormorant	65	229	33	100
060	Darter	30	73	31	45
062	Grey Heron	44	69	27	65
063	Blackheaded Heron	1	2	0	0
064	Goliath Heron	28	38	19	36
066	Great White Heron	2	9	0	0
067	Little Egret	6	19	0	0
071	Cattle Egret	10	56	0	0
090	Yellowbilled Stork	12	41	0	0
091	Sacred Ibis	8	23	6	10
093	Glossy Ibis	0	1	0	0
094	Hadeda Ibis	0	1	4	15
095	African Spoonbill	62	191**	4	14
096	Greater Flamingo	52	253	38	71
097	Lesser Flamingo	0	0	4	24
099	Whitefaced Duck	3	15	1	6
102	Egyptian Goose	875	1638	916	1816*
103	South African Shelduck	1316**	2721**	121	208
104	Yellowbilled Duck	152	448	169	482
105	African Black Duck	2	4	1	2
106	Cape Teal	53	169	55	89
107	Hottentot Teal	0	0	0	2
108	Redbilled Teal	8	23	11	40
112	Cape Shoveller	86	258*	54	134

		Summer (6)		Winter (6)	
		Mean	Max.	Mean	Max.
113	Southern Pochard	0	0	17	46
116	Spurwinged Goose	73	250	132	294
148	African Fish Eagle	4	10	7	10
170	Osprey	2	4	1	1
228	Redknobbed Coot	2852*	7666**	1853	3116*
245	Ringed Plover	1	4	0	0
247	Chestnutbanded Plover	0	2	3	11
248	Kittlitz's Plover	21	88	156	331
249	Threebanded Plover	3	5	13	30
258	Blacksmith Plover	54	90	160	305
264	Common Sandpiper	12	60	0	0
266	Wood Sandpiper	1	3	1	2
269	Marsh Sandpiper	12	71	0	1
270	Greenshank	4	18	1	2
272	Curlew Sandpiper	155	350	68	246
274	Little Stint	688	1222	12	51
284	Ruff	356	2038	0	2
294	Avocet	10	52	9	22
295	Blackwinged Stilt	11	44	16	43
315	Greyheaded Gull	136	175	62	90
322	Caspian Tern	49	152*	10	19
339	Whitewinged Tern	727	1806*	4	17
428	Pied Kingfisher	0	2	1	3
429	Giant Kingfisher	0	0	0	1
711	African Pied Wagtail	1	2	1	4
713	Cape Wagtail	7	20	174	373
	Total	8261	18356	4488	6725
	No. of species		54		

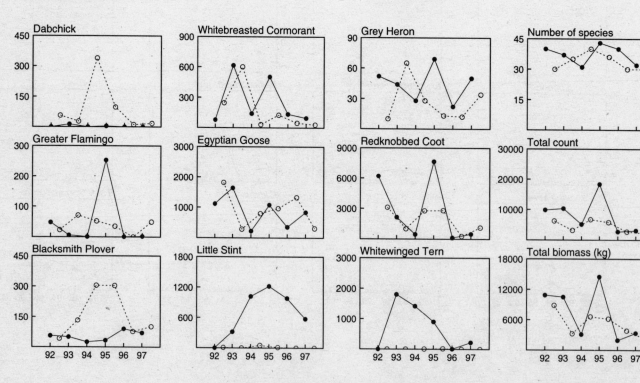

Knellpoort Dam, Wepener, Free State
29° 46' S 26° 53' E (2926DD)

A large state dam on the Rietspruit River. Spurwinged Goose is common in winter, when the highest numbers of Egyptian Goose are also recorded. Moderate numbers of South African Shelduck occur in summer, while Threebanded Plover is more numerous in winter. Six years of counts show some decline in the number of species recorded, especially in winter, and notable summer and winter declines in total count and biomass figures. A nationally significant count of Yellowbilled Duck was recorded in summer 1992, when 127 Darter were also present, but from 1993, summer counts of these species, winter counts of Dabchick, and all counts of Redknobbed Coot, have been very low. Mild threats are posed by power boats, pollution and overhead powerlines.

		Summer (6)		Winter (6)				Summer (6)		Winter (6)	
		Mean	Max.	Mean	Max.			Mean	Max.	Mean	Max.
008	Dabchick	3	18	18	74	113	Southern Pochard	0	0	5	17
055	Whitebreasted Cormorant	7	12	5	19	116	Spurwinged Goose	3	11	166	290
058	Reed Cormorant	9	22	2	7	148	African Fish Eagle	1	4	1	3
060	Darter	35	127	7	19	228	Redknobbed Coot	335	1669	228	1140
062	Grey Heron	2	8	3	7	248	Kittlitz's Plover	0	1	4	9
063	Blackheaded Heron	1	3	0	1	249	Threebanded Plover	1	4	10	26
064	Goliath Heron	3	5	5	8	258	Blacksmith Plover	9	21	10	17
066	Great White Heron	1	3	0	0	264	Common Sandpiper	1	8	0	0
067	Little Egret	6	35	0	0	270	Greenshank	2	6	0	0
071	Cattle Egret	16	47	0	0	272	Curlew Sandpiper	13	77	0	0
091	Sacred Ibis	1	5	0	0	274	Little Stint	8	41	0	0
094	Hadeda Ibis	1	2	1	3	284	Ruff	19	74	0	1
095	African Spoonbill	1	4	2	6	286	Ethiopian Snipe	0	0	1	4
099	Whitefaced Duck	0	0	2	13	295	Blackwinged Stilt	0	0	1	1
102	Egyptian Goose	364	520	540	1300	339	Whitewinged Tern	5	21	0	0
103	South African Shelduck	31	77	3	8	428	Pied Kingfisher	1	2	0	0
104	Yellowbilled Duck	203	1087*	61	148	429	Giant Kingfisher	0	1	0	0
105	African Black Duck	1	3	3	16	713	Cape Wagtail	2	8	17	43
108	Redbilled Teal	2	10	5	12		Total	1088	3496	1098	2674
112	Cape Shoveller	3	19	1	4		No. of species			38	

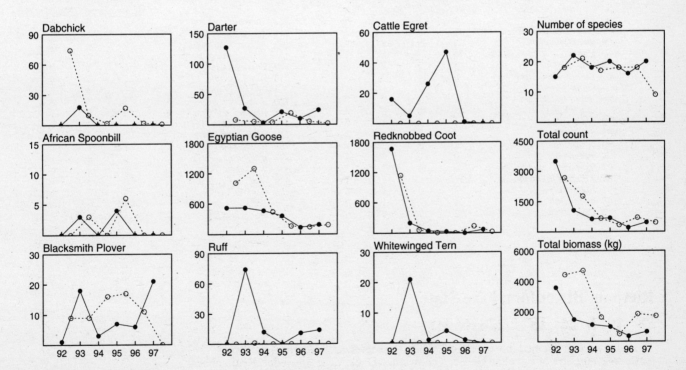

Benfontein Dam, Kimberley (N. Cape), Free State
28° 50' S 24° 50' E (2824DD)

A farm dam, with no vegetation; shoreline open, but rock wall along 30-40% of perimeter. Summer and winter counts for 1996 and winter count for 1997 available. These produced few birds, of only seven species in summer and 10 species in winter. Waterfowl were almost absent in summer, when the commonest species were Cattle Egret and Redknobbed Coot, and small numbers of four shorebird species were present, including 7 Blackwinged Stilt. Coot were absent in winter, when the commonest birds were Yellowbilled Duck and Spurwinged Goose. No threats have been identified.

		Summer (2)		Winter (2)					Summer (2)		Winter (2)	
		Mean	Max.	Mean	Max.				Mean	Max.	Mean	Max.
071	Cattle Egret	6	11	0	0		258	Blacksmith Plover	1	2	1	2
102	Egyptian Goose	1	2	2	2		270	Greenshank	1	2	0	0
103	South African Shelduck	0	0	2	2		272	Curlew Sandpiper	0	0	1	1
104	Yellowbilled Duck	0	0	6	11		295	Blackwinged Stilt	4	7	1	2
112	Cape Shoveller	0	0	1	2		713	Cape Wagtail	0	0	1	1
116	Spurwinged Goose	0	0	5	9			Total	19	37	19	21
228	Redknobbed Coot	6	12	0	0			No. of species			13	

Loch Athlone, Bethlehem, Free State
28° 16' S 28° 19' E (2828AD)

Counts were made at this dam only from summer 1993 to winter 1994. Of the 34 waterbird species recorded, the commonest were Whitebreasted Cormorant, Cattle Egret, Yellowbilled Duck and Redknobbed Coot; of these four species, Whitebreasted Cormorant was the only one to be more numerous in winter. Reed Cormorant and Darter were more numerous in summer. Total counts declined during the survey period. Threats include sedimentation and the accumulation of pesticides and fertilizers.

		Summer (2)		Winter (2)					Summer (2)		Winter (2)	
		Mean	Max.	Mean	Max.				Mean	Max.	Mean	Max.
008	Dabchick	1	1	9	10		113	Southern Pochard	0	0	2	4
055	Whitebreasted Cormorant	8	13	30	52		116	Spurwinged Goose	1	1	4	5
058	Reed Cormorant	27	39	18	29		148	African Fish Eagle	0	0	1	1
060	Darter	26	28	18	21		165	African Marsh Harrier	0	0	1	1
062	Grey Heron	2	2	2	2		209	Crowned Crane	1	1	0	0
063	Blackheaded Heron	6	10	8	15		213	Black Crake	1	1	0	0
064	Goliath Heron	2	2	1	1		223	Purple Gallinule	1	1	2	3
068	Yellowbilled Egret	1	1	0	0		226	Moorhen	3	4	4	6
071	Cattle Egret	55	70	0	0		228	Redknobbed Coot	38	45	19	22
072	Squacco Heron	1	1	1	2		249	Threebanded Plover	1	1	0	0
091	Sacred Ibis	3	5	1	1		258	Blacksmith Plover	2	2	1	2
093	Glossy Ibis	2	3	0	0		286	Ethiopian Snipe	1	2	2	3
094	Hadeda Ibis	0	0	2	4		295	Blackwinged Stilt	0	0	1	1
102	Egyptian Goose	6	10	7	7		338	Whiskered Tern	8	14	0	0
104	Yellowbilled Duck	53	100	33	37		429	Giant Kingfisher	0	0	1	2
107	Hottentot Teal	3	6	1	2		713	Cape Wagtail	0	0	1	1
108	Redbilled Teal	1	2	1	2			Total	249	279	164	182
112	Cape Shoveller	2	2	0	0			No. of species			34	

Rietpan, Brandfort, Free State
28° 40' S 26° 18' E (2826CB)

This pan was first counted in winter 1997, when 15 species were recorded, including reasonable numbers of Egyptian Goose, Yellowbilled Duck, Cape Shoveller, Redknobbed Coot, Kittlitz's Plover and Cape Wagtail, and a few Lesser Flamingo. Mild threats are posed by livestock grazing/trampling, and hunting/poaching.

		Summer (0)		Winter (1)					Summer (0)		Winter (1)	
		Mean	Max.	Mean	Max.				Mean	Max.	Mean	Max.
062	Grey Heron	–	–	1	1		228	Redknobbed Coot	–	–	68	68
095	African Spoonbill	–	–	1	1		248	Kittlitz's Plover	–	–	13	13
096	Greater Flamingo	–	–	1	1		258	Blacksmith Plover	–	–	11	11
097	Lesser Flamingo	–	–	9	9		295	Blackwinged Stilt	–	–	1	1
102	Egyptian Goose	–	–	56	56		395	Marsh Owl	–	–	1	1
103	South African Shelduck	–	–	7	7		713	Cape Wagtail	–	–	23	23
104	Yellowbilled Duck	–	–	43	43			Total	–	–	268	268
108	Redbilled Teal	–	–	9	9			No. of species			15	

Rusfontein Dam, Thaba Nchu, Free State
29° 18' S   26° 37' E (2926BC)

A large state dam in the Rustfontein Nature Reserve. Numbers of cormorants, South African Shelduck, Redbilled Teal and Southern Pochard are higher in summer, while Dabchick, Egyptian and Spurwinged Geese, and Threebanded Plover are commoner in winter. The number of species observed has remained fairly constant in summer but has declined in winter, while total count and biomass figures show a decline in summer. The high total count and biomass for summer 1992 and 1993, and winter 1997, reflect large numbers of Redknobbed Coot (a nationally significant count in 1997); in summer 1993 there was also a high count of Whitebreasted Cormorant. Important threats are fishing (especially planned commercial netting) and boating; hunting/poaching is a mild threat.

		Summer (6)		Winter (6)	
		Mean	Max.	Mean	Max.
008	Dabchick	1	2	32	53
050	Pinkbacked Pelican	0	1	0	1
055	Whitebreasted Cormorant	77	233	37	143
058	Reed Cormorant	24	73	13	25
060	Darter	17	36	53	93
062	Grey Heron	10	17	7	18
063	Blackheaded Heron	0	1	0	1
064	Goliath Heron	12	19	8	11
065	Purple Heron	0	1	0	0
066	Great White Heron	0	1	0	0
067	Little Egret	0	1	0	1
071	Cattle Egret	1	2	1	4
076	Blackcrowned Night Heron	0	1	0	0
081	Hamerkop	0	0	0	1
090	Yellowbilled Stork	2	8	0	0
091	Sacred Ibis	1	2	0	1
093	Glossy Ibis	1	6	1	5
094	Hadeda Ibis	0	0	0	2
095	African Spoonbill	10	17	4	10
097	Lesser Flamingo	0	0	2	9
099	Whitefaced Duck	6	32	0	1
102	Egyptian Goose	322	549	477	641
103	South African Shelduck	145	234*	62	205
104	Yellowbilled Duck	149	385	121	256
105	African Black Duck	1	5	1	3
106	Cape Teal	0	2	2	6
107	Hottentot Teal	0	0	0	2
108	Redbilled Teal	32	91	17	38
112	Cape Shoveller	11	28	16	39
113	Southern Pochard	15	91	2	7
116	Spurwinged Goose	10	31	20	70

		Summer (6)		Winter (6)	
		Mean	Max.	Mean	Max.
148	African Fish Eagle	2	2	1	2
165	African Marsh Harrier	0	0	0	1
170	Osprey	0	1	0	0
209	Crowned Crane	1	2	0	0
228	Redknobbed Coot	1020	2406	975	2709*
245	Ringed Plover	0	0	1	8
248	Kittlitz's Plover	19	83	18	51
249	Threebanded Plover	4	9	17	53
254	Grey Plover	0	2	0	0
258	Blacksmith Plover	85	143	66	93
264	Common Sandpiper	2	4	0	0
266	Wood Sandpiper	0	1	0	1
269	Marsh Sandpiper	4	10	0	0
270	Greenshank	3	5	0	1
272	Curlew Sandpiper	103	354	25	131
274	Little Stint	257	660	0	2
284	Ruff	97	212	0	1
286	Ethiopian Snipe	0	0	1	2
294	Avocet	0	0	2	6
295	Blackwinged Stilt	9	30	7	16
315	Greyheaded Gull	2	4	2	4
322	Caspian Tern	1	3	0	1
339	Whitewinged Tern	93	162	0	1
395	Marsh Owl	0	0	0	1
428	Pied Kingfisher	2	8	1	2
429	Giant Kingfisher	0	0	0	1
431	Malachite Kingfisher	0	1	0	0
713	Cape Wagtail	10	38	29	57
	Total	2558	4174	2018	3941
	No. of species		59		

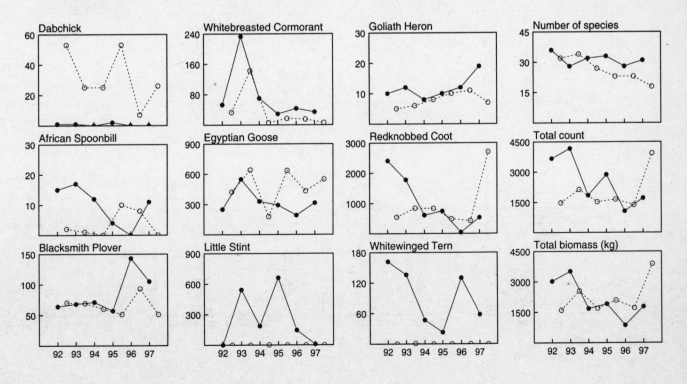

Seekoeivlei, Memel, Free State
27° 35' S 29° 35' E (2729DA)

A Ramsar site and part of the Seekoeivlei Nature Reserve; supports large numbers and wide variety of waterbirds. Floodplain 20 km long, drained by Klip River; extensive marshes (*Phragmites, Typha, Cyperus, Leersia*, etc.) and many seasonal oxbow lakes. Three crane species occur; Bittern probably breeds. Breeding colonies of egrets, African Spoonbill and Blackcrowned Night Heron. Good numbers of Glossy Ibis, Squacco Heron, Little Bittern and Ethiopian Snipe recorded. Whitewinged Flufftail and Baillon's Crake occur; African Rail, Moorhen and Purple Gallinule common; Lesser Moorhen in summer 1997. High biomass in winter 1994, when Spurwinged Geese were numerous. Winter counts have declined since 1994, mainly owing to decline in numbers of common waterfowl. Domestic dogs and cats pose an important threat; pollution from plastics, and hunting/poaching, are mild threats.

		Summer (5) Mean	Summer (5) Max.	Winter (5) Mean	Winter (5) Max.			Summer (5) Mean	Summer (5) Max.	Winter (5) Mean	Winter (5) Max.
006	Great Crested Grebe	1	7	0	2	112	Cape Shoveller	12	21	20	54
008	Dabchick	1	3	6	20	113	Southern Pochard	3	10	3	14
055	Whitebreasted Cormorant	3	8	5	19	116	Spurwinged Goose	137	520	457*	1308
058	Reed Cormorant	46	67	15	38	117	Maccoa Duck	0	1	0	0
060	Darter	8	13	2	6	148	African Fish Eagle	0	1	0	1
062	Grey Heron	4	8	8	30	170	Osprey	0	0	0	1
063	Blackheaded Heron	7	14	5	16	207	Wattled Crane	5	24	1	2
064	Goliath Heron	1	1	1	3	209	Crowned Crane	12	31	74	180
065	Purple Heron	2	8	2	4	213	Black Crake	0	0	0	2
066	Great White Heron	2	5	5	10	223	Purple Gallinule	27	84*	22	47
067	Little Egret	19	55	23	87	226	Moorhen	25	64	64	235
068	Yellowbilled Egret	12	18	3	8	228	Redknobbed Coot	255	707	227	556
069	Black Egret	0	1	0	0	248	Kittlitz's Plover	0	0	1	3
071	Cattle Egret	1338	5000*	5	21	249	Threebanded Plover	3	10	11	50
072	Squacco Heron	2	8	1	4	258	Blacksmith Plover	54	149	36	73
076	Blackcrowned Night Heron	1	5	2	9	260	Wattled Plover	12	42	0	0
078	Little Bittern	1	2	0	0	266	Wood Sandpiper	2	9	0	0
081	Hamerkop	4	5	2	4	270	Greenshank	5	22	0	2
091	Sacred Ibis	57	152	85	356	284	Ruff	5	23	0	0
093	Glossy Ibis	183	560	9	24	286	Ethiopian Snipe	18	62	0	0
094	Hadeda Ibis	41	83	22	32	294	Avocet	2	4	2	5
095	African Spoonbill	19	49	25	51	295	Blackwinged Stilt	4	16	3	12
096	Greater Flamingo	0	0	4	17	338	Whiskered Tern	23	86	0	0
099	Whitefaced Duck	2	12	0	2	339	Whitewinged Tern	0	2	0	0
101	Whitebacked Duck	2	10	0	0	393	Grass Owl	1	2	0	2
102	Egyptian Goose	53	102	122	329	395	Marsh Owl	0	0	0	1
103	South African Shelduck	2	10	8	20	428	Pied Kingfisher	2	4	2	4
104	Yellowbilled Duck	153	409	244	676	429	Giant Kingfisher	0	1	1	3
105	African Black Duck	3	8	9	34	431	Malachite Kingfisher	0	2	1	2
106	Cape Teal	1	6	0	0	713	Cape Wagtail	8	22	10	24
107	Hottentot Teal	19	53	28	81		Total	2611	7625	1593	3803
108	Redbilled Teal	6	10	15	57		No. of species		62		

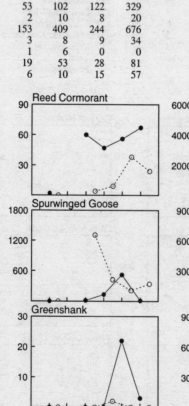

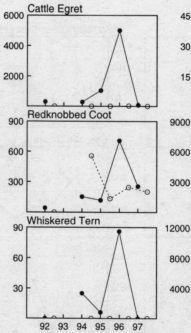

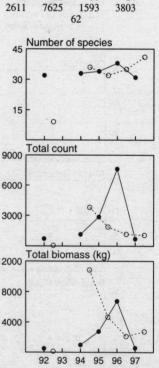

Sterkfontein Dam, Harrismith, Free State
28° 26' S 29° 01' E (2829AC)

An IBA and provincial nature reserve. A large dam in high-altitude sour grassland, with predominantly open shoreline but with no significant foraging habitat for Palearctic shorebirds. Cormorant counts are greater in summer, while Dabchick and most waterfowl species seem to attain higher numbers in winter, although numbers of some waterfowl (e.g. Spurwinged and Egyptian Goose, Yellowbilled Duck and Redbilled Teal) show great variations in both seasons. Numbers of Greyheaded Gull appear to be increasing and those of Dabchick declining. Goliath Heron is regularly recorded in small numbers. Black Stork and Grass Owl occur. Recreational facilities including boating and water-skiing pose only mild threats to the avifauna.

		Summer (6) Mean	Summer (6) Max.	Winter (6) Mean	Winter (6) Max.			Summer (6) Mean	Summer (6) Max.	Winter (6) Mean	Winter (6) Max.
006	Great Crested Grebe	0	0	1	2	165	African Marsh Harrier	0	1	0	0
008	Dabchick	2	6	32	78	170	Osprey	2	4	1	1
055	Whitebreasted Cormorant	54	92	3	7	209	Crowned Crane	1	6	0	0
058	Reed Cormorant	24	54	6	14	228	Redknobbed Coot	16	33	63	209
060	Darter	12	23	9	12	248	Kittlitz's Plover	0	0	5	12
062	Grey Heron	2	6	1	3	249	Threebanded Plover	0	1	1	3
063	Blackheaded Heron	4	22	1	2	254	Grey Plover	0	1	0	0
064	Goliath Heron	1	3	3	4	258	Blacksmith Plover	3	6	15	37
071	Cattle Egret	12	71	0	0	264	Common Sandpiper	1	2	0	0
081	Hamerkop	0	0	0	1	266	Wood Sandpiper	0	1	0	0
094	Hadeda Ibis	0	2	2	4	270	Greenshank	3	17	0	0
099	Whitefaced Duck	0	2	12	36	274	Little Stint	3	17	0	0
102	Egyptian Goose	210	438	109	345	284	Ruff	0	1	0	0
103	South African Shelduck	0	2	0	2	315	Greyheaded Gull	8	17	8	26
104	Yellowbilled Duck	141	348	228	491	339	Whitewinged Tern	0	1	0	0
105	African Black Duck	0	1	1	2	428	Pied Kingfisher	1	3	0	1
108	Redbilled Teal	1	2	14	49	429	Giant Kingfisher	0	0	0	1
113	Southern Pochard	4	24	3	12	713	Cape Wagtail	7	22	13	42
116	Spurwinged Goose	25	63	75	161		Total	541	1027	605	887
148	African Fish Eagle	2	6	2	4		No. of species			38	

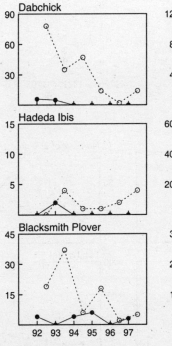

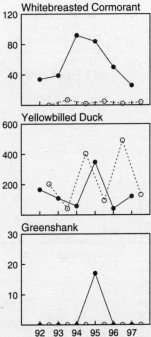

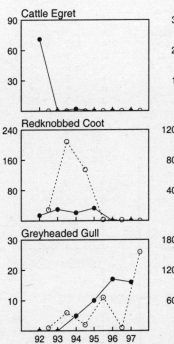

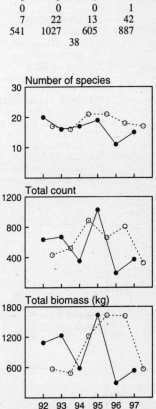

Welbedacht Dam, Wepener, Free State
29° 52' S 26° 53' E (2926DD)

Large dam with reeds, and sometimes good shorebird habitat. Globally significant count of Yellowbilled Duck made in winter 1995 (hence high total count and biomass for that survey), when Redbilled Teal and Cape Shoveller were also present in large numbers. Nationally significant numbers of African Spoonbill and South African Shelduck recorded. Some good counts of Palearctic shorebirds in summer 1994 and 1997; Avocet numbers are sometimes high in winter and summer. Numbers of herons, egrets and ibises higher in summer; Dabchick and most waterfowl more numerous in winter (exceptions being Egyptian Goose and South African Shelduck). Siltation is a severe threat, and the consequent invasion by reeds and willows *Salix babylonica* is an important threat.

		Summer (6) Mean	Summer (6) Max.	Winter (6) Mean	Winter (6) Max.			Summer (6) Mean	Summer (6) Max.	Winter (6) Mean	Winter (6) Max.
008	Dabchick	1	7	11	28	117	Maccoa Duck	0	0	1	7
055	Whitebreasted Cormorant	5	20	17	55	148	African Fish Eagle	2	8	1	3
058	Reed Cormorant	12	51	7	23	170	Osprey	0	1	0	0
060	Darter	4	20	2	8	209	Crowned Crane	1	3	0	0
062	Grey Heron	12	37	1	5	223	Purple Gallinule	0	1	1	3
063	Blackheaded Heron	4	20	0	2	226	Moorhen	1	4	1	5
064	Goliath Heron	5	9	1	2	228	Redknobbed Coot	17	84	24	35
065	Purple Heron	1	2	0	0	248	Kittlitz's Plover	1	4	8	21
066	Great White Heron	0	1	0	0	249	Threebanded Plover	3	12	15	64
067	Little Egret	2	6	0	0	258	Blacksmith Plover	19	46	13	41
068	Yellowbilled Egret	0	1	0	0	264	Common Sandpiper	2	13	0	0
071	Cattle Egret	232	1052	0	0	266	Wood Sandpiper	0	1	0	0
076	Blackcrowned Night Heron	0	1	0	0	269	Marsh Sandpiper	0	1	0	0
079	Dwarf Bittern	1	5	0	0	270	Greenshank	2	11	2	9
090	Yellowbilled Stork	5	28	0	0	272	Curlew Sandpiper	222	1018	3	18
091	Sacred Ibis	5	21	0	1	274	Little Stint	58	150	0	0
093	Glossy Ibis	2	12	0	0	284	Ruff	58	169	0	0
094	Hadeda Ibis	2	12	4	16	286	Ethiopian Snipe	0	0	4	24
095	African Spoonbill	48	147*	8	28	290	Whimbrel	0	1	0	0
099	Whitefaced Duck	0	2	0	0	294	Avocet	12	64	47	158
100	Fulvous Duck	1	5	0	0	295	Blackwinged Stilt	5	14	7	25
101	Whitebacked Duck	0	2	0	0	315	Greyheaded Gull	0	0	1	3
102	Egyptian Goose	225	386	211	732	339	Whitewinged Tern	28	166	4	21
103	South African Shelduck	68	269*	22	94	428	Pied Kingfisher	1	2	2	5
104	Yellowbilled Duck	214	502	1104*	4822**	429	Giant Kingfisher	0	2	0	2
105	African Black Duck	2	9	14	40	431	Malachite Kingfisher	0	2	0	0
107	Hottentot Teal	0	0	1	5	711	African Pied Wagtail	0	0	1	5
108	Redbilled Teal	1	2	42	239	713	Cape Wagtail	9	42	25	104
112	Cape Shoveller	0	2	27	140		Total	1296	1821	1705	6411
113	Southern Pochard	0	2	13	50		No. of species			59	
116	Spurwinged Goose	3	5	62	164						

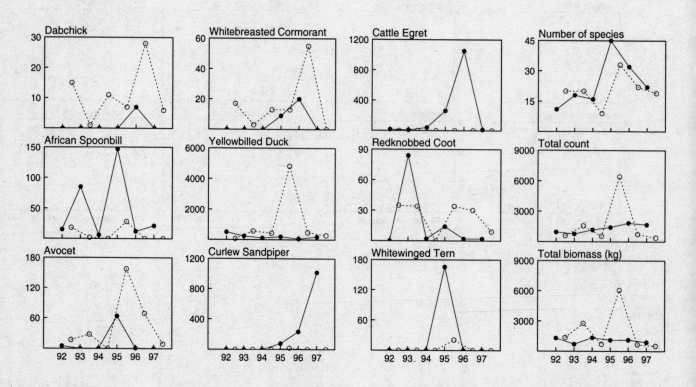

Albert Falls Dam, Pietermaritzburg, KwaZulu–Natal
29° 26' S 30° 24' E (2930AD)

A large water supply dam with mostly open, rather barren shoreline of earth/stones, but some muddy areas with wet grass, and a little fringing reed/sedge cover, especially at inlets. White-breasted Cormorant breeds. Attracts a good variety of waterbirds. Water level very low 1992–93; largest counts of Dabchick, Egyptian and Spurwinged Geese, Crowned Crane, Kittlitz's Plover and Cape Wagtail recorded winter 1993. High count and biomass totals in winters of 1993–94 due to good numbers of cormorants, geese and cranes (largest counts of Whitebreasted Cormorant and Little Egret in winter 1994, plus 295 Spurwinged Geese). High count of Blacksmith Plover in summer 1997. Osprey and Wattled Plover regular; occasional good numbers of Marsh Owl recorded. Occasional fishing competitions on the dam cause mild disturbance.

		Summer (4)		Winter (4)				Summer (4)		Winter (4)	
		Mean	Max.	Mean	Max.			Mean	Max.	Mean	Max.
008	Dabchick	0	0	3	10	209	Crowned Crane	5	18	7	26
055	Whitebreasted Cormorant	18	32	98	270	213	Black Crake	0	0	0	1
058	Reed Cormorant	11	36	28	105	228	Redknobbed Coot	0	0	3	10
060	Darter	5	9	27	56	240	African Jacana	0	0	1	3
062	Grey Heron	7	14	10	22	248	Kittlitz's Plover	0	0	29	90
063	Blackheaded Heron	2	5	1	3	249	Threebanded Plover	1	4	4	6
064	Goliath Heron	1	3	0	1	258	Blacksmith Plover	33	106	28	42
065	Purple Heron	0	0	1	1	260	Wattled Plover	1	2	0	0
066	Great White Heron	0	0	0	1	264	Common Sandpiper	6	16	0	0
067	Little Egret	6	13	11	37	266	Wood Sandpiper	8	26	0	0
068	Yellowbilled Egret	0	0	1	3	269	Marsh Sandpiper	1	2	0	0
071	Cattle Egret	7	15	7	22	270	Greenshank	2	4	0	0
081	Hamerkop	0	1	1	3	274	Little Stint	3	10	0	0
091	Sacred Ibis	1	5	3	6	284	Ruff	7	21	0	0
094	Hadeda Ibis	20	55	12	21	286	Ethiopian Snipe	0	0	0	1
095	African Spoonbill	3	12	10	19	298	Water Dikkop	0	1	0	1
099	Whitefaced Duck	11	20	3	13	315	Greyheaded Gull	0	0	0	1
102	Egyptian Goose	93	140	71	169	428	Pied Kingfisher	2	8	8	14
103	South African Shelduck	0	0	0	1	429	Giant Kingfisher	1	2	1	2
104	Yellowbilled Duck	8	14	6	11	431	Malachite Kingfisher	1	2	2	3
108	Redbilled Teal	1	2	1	3	711	African Pied Wagtail	2	7	1	2
116	Spurwinged Goose	9	18	191	377	713	Cape Wagtail	2	9	21	40
148	African Fish Eagle	3	5	3	4	891	Mallard	0	0	1	3
165	African Marsh Harrier	0	0	1	3		Total	280	393	593	896
170	Osprey	2	3	1	2		No. of species		48		

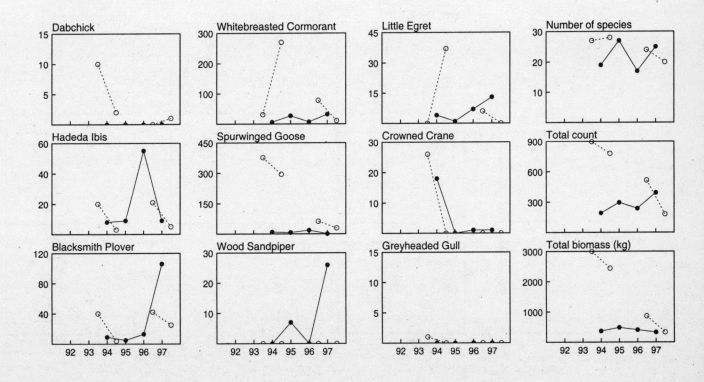

Banzi Pan (Ndumo), Ingwavuma, KwaZulu–Natal
26° 52' S 32° 17' E (2632CD)

Banzi, Shokwe and Nyamithi pans are in Ndumo Game Reserve, an Important Bird Area and Ramsar site. Large pan fed by Usutu River; extensively fringed by *Phragmites*, allowing only limited viewing; also emergent sedges, and much *Nymphaea* at one end. Flooding regime subjected to recent changes, affecting seasonal water levels. Good numbers of Pygmy Goose in winter. Exceptional numbers of Fulvous and Whitefaced Duck in winter 1994 probably reflect good edge habitat with falling water level; large numbers of Openbilled Stork, Glossy Ibis, White Pelican, Ruff and Egyptian Goose in summer 1995 occurred when lower water level provided good foraging habitats for these species; biomass figure for this count thus also very high. Large count of Kittlitz's Plover in winter 1995 probably reflects very dry conditions. Sedimentation is a threat.

		Summer (4)		Winter (5)				Summer (4)		Winter (5)	
		Mean	Max.	Mean	Max.			Mean	Max.	Mean	Max.
049	White Pelican	106	424	5	18	100	Fulvous Duck	13	50	157	720
058	Reed Cormorant	1	3	19	41	102	Egyptian Goose	31	113	9	36
060	Darter	1	2	3	13	114	Pygmy Goose	0	0	73	320
062	Grey Heron	0	1	3	9	115	Knobbilled Duck	0	0	1	5
064	Goliath Heron	5	16	1	3	116	Spurwinged Goose	19	77	51	135
065	Purple Heron	0	0	0	2	148	African Fish Eagle	2	2	2	4
066	Great White Heron	2	6	2	7	213	Black Crake	0	0	0	2
067	Little Egret	3	5	0	2	226	Moorhen	0	0	0	1
071	Cattle Egret	0	0	3	16	240	African Jacana	4	10	16	38
072	Squacco Heron	2	4	0	1	248	Kittlitz's Plover	0	0	27	136
074	Greenbacked Heron	0	1	0	0	249	Threebanded Plover	0	0	1	6
081	Hamerkop	1	1	0	1	258	Blacksmith Plover	1	2	1	2
086	Woollynecked Stork	2	9	0	0	264	Common Sandpiper	1	2	2	8
087	Openbilled Stork	68	270	1	6	270	Greenshank	0	0	0	2
088	Saddlebilled Stork	0	0	0	1	274	Little Stint	8	32	0	0
090	Yellowbilled Stork	9	31	0	2	284	Ruff	45	180	0	0
091	Sacred Ibis	0	0	2	6	295	Blackwinged Stilt	3	10	3	14
093	Glossy Ibis	83	332	0	2	298	Water Dikkop	2	6	2	5
094	Hadeda Ibis	3	4	1	4	428	Pied Kingfisher	5	13	4	11
095	African Spoonbill	1	4	1	4	431	Malachite Kingfisher	1	2	0	0
096	Greater Flamingo	13	51	22	110	711	African Pied Wagtail	1	5	2	4
097	Lesser Flamingo	0	0	9	46		Total	486	1829	608	1874
099	Whitefaced Duck	56	222	182	577		No. of species			44	

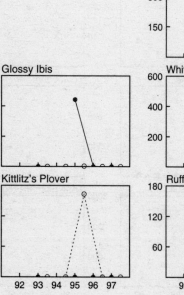

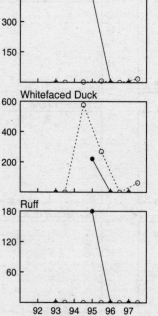

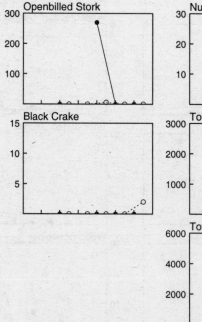

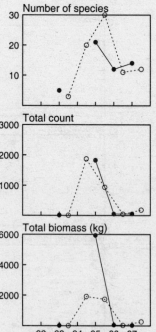

Blood River Vlei, Vryheid, KwaZulu–Natal
27° 50' S 30° 35' E (2730DC)

An important wetland for water purification and streamflow regulation. Extensive reedmarsh/sedgemarsh occurs above the breached dam wall, and downstream at the Lynspruit confluence; it also has open water and wet grassland habitats. It supports good populations of waterfowl, shorebirds (including Ethiopian Snipe) and other waterbirds. Existing counts are too few to highlight the site's importance; other studies confirm the occurrence of significant numbers of Little Bittern and secretive rails. Dam wall building is a serious threat; gulley erosion is a potential threat; minor threats include drainage and agricultural development.

		Summer (1)		Winter (1)	
		Mean	Max.	Mean	Max.
008	Dabchick	6	6	4	4
055	Whitebreasted Cormorant	3	3	0	0
058	Reed Cormorant	12	12	6	6
060	Darter	3	3	0	0
062	Grey Heron	8	8	5	5
063	Blackheaded Heron	0	0	4	4
065	Purple Heron	7	7	0	0
066	Great White Heron	8	8	1	1
067	Little Egret	3	3	0	0
068	Yellowbilled Egret	2	2	0	0
071	Cattle Egret	260	260	0	0
072	Squacco Heron	6	6	0	0
076	Blackcrowned Night Heron	2	2	0	0
078	Little Bittern	1	1	0	0
081	Hamerkop	1	1	0	0
091	Sacred Ibis	2	2	7	7
093	Glossy Ibis	13	13	0	0
094	Hadeda Ibis	14	14	89	89
102	Egyptian Goose	2	2	321	321
103	South African Shelduck	0	0	2	2
104	Yellowbilled Duck	32	32	127	127
107	Hottentot Teal	16	16	17	17
108	Redbilled Teal	5	5	10	10
112	Cape Shoveller	0	0	26	26
116	Spurwinged Goose	0	0	207	207
165	African Marsh Harrier	2	2	3	3
209	Crowned Crane	5	5	7	7
210	African Rail	10	10	19	19
213	Black Crake	4	4	0	0
217	Redchested Flufftail	4	4	0	0
223	Purple Gallinule	1	1	0	0
226	Moorhen	6	6	11	11
228	Redknobbed Coot	0	0	16	16
241	Lesser Jacana	0	0	1	1
245	Ringed Plover	1	1	0	0
248	Kittlitz's Plover	3	3	0	0
249	Threebanded Plover	11	11	12	12
258	Blacksmith Plover	20	20	40	40
260	Wattled Plover	3	3	5	5
264	Common Sandpiper	9	9	0	0
266	Wood Sandpiper	5	5	0	0
269	Marsh Sandpiper	4	4	0	0
270	Greenshank	6	6	2	2
274	Little Stint	7	7	0	0
284	Ruff	4	4	0	0
286	Ethiopian Snipe	26	26	3	3
431	Malachite Kingfisher	1	1	1	1
713	Cape Wagtail	7	7	14	14
714	Yellow Wagtail	2	2	0	0
	Total	547	547	960	960
	No. of species		49		

Bushlands Pan, Hluhluwe, KwaZulu–Natal
28° 05' S 32° 18' E (2832AB)

Formerly open water with reedbeds, islands where duck bred, and emergent grass (increased during drought in 1992–93). Now surrounded by *Eucalyptus* trees, planted 5–6 years ago; as trees grew, pan dried out and open water disappeared; counts were discontinued in 1994. Formerly excellent for waterfowl and shorebirds; even in 1993–94 good counts were made of White Pelican, Whitefaced Duck, African Jacana, Kittlitz's and Threebanded Plovers, Redwinged Pratincole, and Whiskered and Whitewinged Tern. Longtoed Plover occurred formerly. The pan basin is still moist to wet, with dense, grass-dominated vegetation and some *Typha*; Black Crake and Redchested Flufftail were heard in 1997 (T. Wood). The site will probably dry out completely with further tree growth.

		Summer (2)		Winter (1)	
		Mean	Max.	Mean	Max.
008	Dabchick	1	2	0	0
049	White Pelican	23	45	0	0
050	Pinkbacked Pelican	0	0	1	1
060	Darter	1	2	0	0
062	Grey Heron	0	0	1	1
081	Hamerkop	0	0	1	1
088	Saddlebilled Stork	1	1	0	0
091	Sacred Ibis	0	0	1	1
094	Hadeda Ibis	0	0	2	2
099	Whitefaced Duck	74	96	0	0
101	Whitebacked Duck	1	1	0	0
102	Egyptian Goose	0	0	2	2
114	Pygmy Goose	3	4	0	0
116	Spurwinged Goose	3	4	0	0
148	African Fish Eagle	2	2	1	1
165	African Marsh Harrier	1	1	0	0
213	Black Crake	2	2	0	0
240	African Jacana	11	14	0	0
248	Kittlitz's Plover	0	0	50	50
249	Threebanded Plover	0	0	75	75
258	Blacksmith Plover	0	0	3	3
260	Wattled Plover	0	0	3	3
266	Wood Sandpiper	2	4	0	0
286	Ethiopian Snipe	0	0	3	3
295	Blackwinged Stilt	7	14	0	0
304	Redwinged Pratincole	0	0	10	10
338	Whiskered Tern	65	130	0	0
339	Whitewinged Tern	60	120	0	0
428	Pied Kingfisher	1	2	0	0
713	Cape Wagtail	0	0	10	10
	Total	256	393	163	163
	No. of species		30		

Chelmsford Dam, Newcastle, KwaZulu–Natal
27° 57' S 29° 57' E (2729DD)

A global Important Bird Area. A large dam with grassy shores, some fringing reedbeds and some sedges; counted by boat. All three crane species occur; Corncrake and Grass Owl recorded; large breeding colony of Cattle Egret and cormorants. Important moulting site for waterfowl. Only one summer and 3 winter counts available. Summer 1997 count notable for large numbers of Darter and Cattle Egret. Winter counts of Yellowbilled Duck increasing: nationally significant numbers of this species were present in winter 1997, when the largest counts of Grey Heron, Whitefaced Duck, Redbilled Teal and Hadeda Ibis were also recorded; Spurwinged Goose peaked in winter 1995, and Egyptian Goose and Redknobbed Coot in winter 1996. 40 Lesser Flamingo were present in winter 1995. No threats have been identified.

		Summer (2)		Winter (3)					Summer (2)		Winter (3)	
		Mean	Max.	Mean	Max.				Mean	Max.	Mean	Max.
006	Great Crested Grebe	0	0	1	3		113	Southern Pochard	0	0	5	10
008	Dabchick	0	0	9	13		115	Knobbilled Duck	0	0	15	31
055	Whitebreasted Cormorant	6	11	29	40		116	Spurwinged Goose	10	19	458	669
058	Reed Cormorant	8	16	143	282		148	African Fish Eagle	1	1	0	0
060	Darter	113	225	20	22		170	Osprey	1	1	0	0
062	Grey Heron	5	9	15	30		209	Crowned Crane	0	0	5	9
063	Blackheaded Heron	2	4	9	12		223	Purple Gallinule	2	3	0	0
064	Goliath Heron	3	6	2	4		226	Moorhen	0	0	1	4
065	Purple Heron	1	2	2	4		228	Redknobbed Coot	0	0	66	90
066	Great White Heron	2	4	15	32		249	Threebanded Plover	0	0	3	7
067	Little Egret	0	0	1	4		258	Blacksmith Plover	8	16	26	32
068	Yellowbilled Egret	0	0	1	2		264	Common Sandpiper	1	1	0	0
071	Cattle Egret	1171	2342	25	32		266	Wood Sandpiper	1	1	0	0
072	Squacco Heron	0	0	1	3		286	Ethiopian Snipe	0	0	2	5
091	Sacred Ibis	0	0	8	16		294	Avocet	0	0	2	5
094	Hadeda Ibis	1	2	35	98		295	Blackwinged Stilt	0	0	2	7
095	African Spoonbill	0	0	9	17		315	Greyheaded Gull	0	0	1	3
096	Greater Flamingo	0	0	1	2		322	Caspian Tern	0	0	3	8
097	Lesser Flamingo	0	0	13	40		339	Whitewinged Tern	1	2	1	2
099	Whitefaced Duck	0	0	69	207		395	Marsh Owl	0	0	1	2
100	Fulvous Duck	1	2	6	18		428	Pied Kingfisher	3	6	0	0
102	Egyptian Goose	5	10	561	973		431	Malachite Kingfisher	1	1	0	0
104	Yellowbilled Duck	20	40	725	1162*		713	Cape Wagtail	6	12	13	22
107	Hottentot Teal	1	1	4	8			Total	1369	2737	2386	2844
108	Redbilled Teal	0	0	78	202			No. of species			49	
112	Cape Shoveller	0	0	3	4							

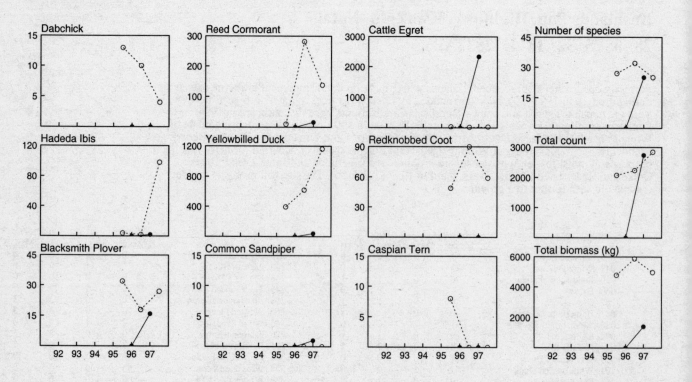

Collin's Lake, Mtubatuba, KwaZulu–Natal
28° 26' S 32° 10' E (2832AC)

An irrigation dam, with deep water, some fringing reeds and little floating vegetation. Counts are very low, with a maximum of 40 birds (winter 1995). Surrounding human activity poses a serious threat (squatter camps, rubbish dump, fishing); the site has not been counted since summer 1997 because of lack of security.

		Summer (3)		Winter (2)				Summer (3)		Winter (2)	
		Mean	Max.	Mean	Max.			Mean	Max.	Mean	Max.
008	Dabchick	0	0	2	3	223	Purple Gallinule	0	1	0	0
050	Pinkbacked Pelican	0	0	1	2	226	Moorhen	3	7	0	0
058	Reed Cormorant	0	1	2	2	228	Redknobbed Coot	0	0	9	17
063	Blackheaded Heron	0	0	3	6	240	African Jacana	2	7	0	0
065	Purple Heron	0	1	0	0	264	Common Sandpiper	0	1	0	0
067	Little Egret	0	1	1	1	266	Wood Sandpiper	0	1	0	0
072	Squacco Heron	0	1	0	0	338	Whiskered Tern	2	5	0	0
074	Greenbacked Heron	0	1	0	0	339	Whitewinged Tern	0	1	0	0
084	Black Stork	0	0	1	1	428	Pied Kingfisher	1	2	0	0
099	Whitefaced Duck	1	3	0	0	431	Malachite Kingfisher	1	2	0	0
102	Egyptian Goose	1	2	0	0		Total	14	34	21	40
114	Pygmy Goose	1	2	4	8		No. of species			22	

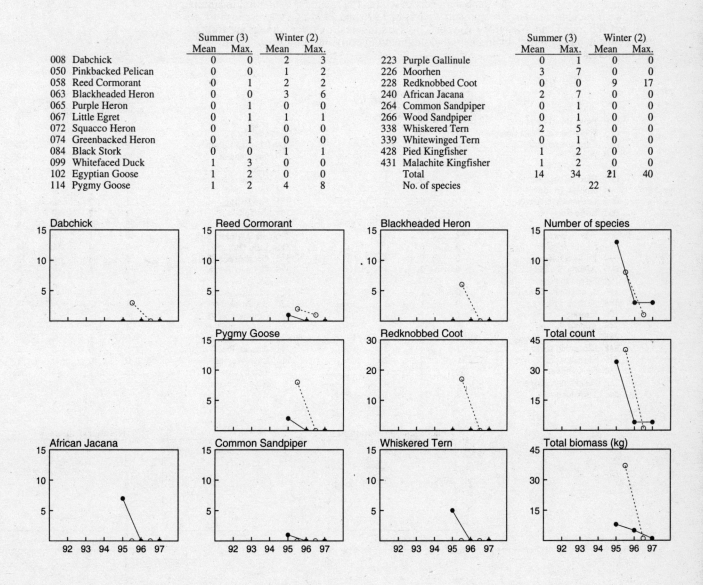

Durban Bayhead, Durban, KwaZulu–Natal
29° 53' S 31° 01' E (2931CC)

Open estuary, with mud and a tiny remnant of what was once the largest mangrove swamp in the province; completely surrounded by industrial development. Moderate numbers of Palearctic shorebirds in summer, especially Ringed and Grey Plovers, and Terek and Curlew Sandpipers. Counts of Grey Plover and Terek Sandpiper increasing, of Turnstone and Curlew Sandpiper decreasing. 44 Common Sandpipers in winter 1995, and 50 Whimbrel in summer 1997, were exceptional. High biomass in winters of 1996 and 1997 due to presence of Kelp Gull and White Pelican. Mangrove Kingfisher occurs in winter. Critical threats are further development, and pollution by industrial waste (including oil) and solid waste; disturbance is a mild threat.

		Summer (5) Mean	Summer (5) Max.	Winter (5) Mean	Winter (5) Max.			Summer (5) Mean	Summer (5) Max.	Winter (5) Mean	Winter (5) Max.
050	Pinkbacked Pelican	0	2	3	10	263	Terek Sandpiper	18	35	0	1
055	Whitebreasted Cormorant	7	10	2	7	264	Common Sandpiper	0	1	9	44
056	Cape Cormorant	0	0	2	11	269	Marsh Sandpiper	2	8	0	0
060	Darter	0	0	1	5	270	Greenshank	30	53	5	12
062	Grey Heron	3	10	3	4	271	Knot	0	1	0	0
063	Blackheaded Heron	0	0	1	3	272	Curlew Sandpiper	208	288	5	10
064	Goliath Heron	1	3	2	3	274	Little Stint	12	30	0	0
066	Great White Heron	0	0	0	1	281	Sanderling	1	2	0	0
067	Little Egret	0	1	2	7	284	Ruff	1	2	0	0
071	Cattle Egret	0	0	3	15	290	Whimbrel	23	50	4	8
086	Woollynecked Stork	1	5	1	5	295	Blackwinged Stilt	0	1	0	2
091	Sacred Ibis	0	0	0	1	312	Kelp Gull	7	24	11	24
094	Hadeda Ibis	0	0	1	3	315	Greyheaded Gull	75	93	5	17
095	African Spoonbill	0	1	1	3	322	Caspian Tern	2	8	1	2
102	Egyptian Goose	2	10	2	9	324	Swift Tern	2	5	2	8
116	Spurwinged Goose	0	1	0	0	325	Lesser Crested Tern	0	1	0	0
148	African Fish Eagle	0	1	1	3	326	Sandwich Tern	1	2	0	1
170	Osprey	1	1	1	2	327	Common Tern	4	12	4	10
245	Ringed Plover	49	87	0	0	428	Pied Kingfisher	1	2	2	7
246	Whitefronted Plover	5	20	3	10	429	Giant Kingfisher	0	1	0	0
248	Kittlitz's Plover	1	4	3	10	711	African Pied Wagtail	0	0	0	2
249	Threebanded Plover	0	2	2	3	713	Cape Wagtail	0	0	0	1
254	Grey Plover	59	87	6	15		Total	533	582	94	156
258	Blacksmith Plover	4	17	4	13		No. of species			47	
262	Turnstone	10	26	1	6						

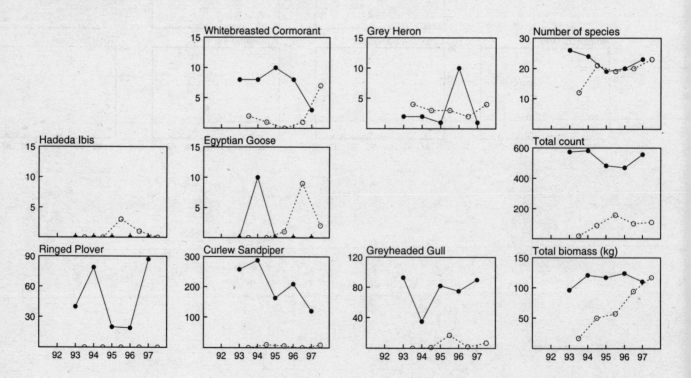

Hlatikulu Vlei, Hlatikulu, KwaZulu–Natal
29° 15' S 29° 41' E (2929BA)

A degraded and fragmented vlei system, in highly modified highland sour grassland. Patchy *Phragmites* reed swamp and *Typha* marsh, and many sedge meadows with *Carex, Cyperus, Schoenoplectus, Eleocharis*, rushes (*Juncus*), grasses and forbs. In Hlatikulu Nature Reserve, wetland rehabilitation has been attempted by building three dams, and many "damlets" in existing drains/furrows. Notable as a breeding site and sanctuary for cranes. Only three counts are available, for 1993–94, showing good summer numbers of cormorants and Darter, good winter numbers of Egyptian and Spurwinged Geese and Yellowbilled Duck, and good numbers of Dabchick and Redknobbed Coot throughout the year. A good selection of migratory shorebirds occurs in summer. Breeding of Bittern and Grass Owl is recorded. Threats include uncontrolled human access, cattle grazing, and bird snaring.

		Summer (2)		Winter (1)				Summer (2)		Winter (1)	
		Mean	Max.	Mean	Max.			Mean	Max.	Mean	Max.
008	Dabchick	71	107	80	80	165	African Marsh Harrier	2	4	1	1
055	Whitebreasted Cormorant	13	13	1	1	207	Wattled Crane	0	0	6	6
058	Reed Cormorant	135	253	7	7	209	Crowned Crane	3	6	2	2
060	Darter	34	67	0	0	213	Black Crake	0	0	1	1
062	Grey Heron	4	4	1	1	217	Redchested Flufftail	2	3	0	0
063	Blackheaded Heron	23	30	30	30	223	Purple Gallinule	3	5	3	3
065	Purple Heron	2	3	1	1	226	Moorhen	5	9	2	2
066	Great White Heron	8	9	5	5	228	Redknobbed Coot	334	506	551	551
067	Little Egret	3	3	0	0	242	Painted Snipe	1	1	0	0
068	Yellowbilled Egret	1	1	0	0	249	Threebanded Plover	5	7	15	15
071	Cattle Egret	51	82	0	0	258	Blacksmith Plover	50	75	34	34
076	Blackcrowned Night Heron	2	3	0	0	260	Wattled Plover	9	11	2	2
080	Bittern	0	0	1	1	264	Common Sandpiper	11	19	0	0
081	Hamerkop	1	1	0	0	266	Wood Sandpiper	35	54	0	0
091	Sacred Ibis	27	43	17	17	269	Marsh Sandpiper	11	22	0	0
093	Glossy Ibis	1	1	3	3	270	Greenshank	10	19	0	0
094	Hadeda Ibis	26	26	23	23	272	Curlew Sandpiper	14	27	0	0
095	African Spoonbill	13	15	4	4	274	Little Stint	108	213	0	0
099	Whitefaced Duck	1	2	0	0	284	Ruff	28	56	1	1
101	Whitebacked Duck	0	0	5	5	286	Ethiopian Snipe	18	22	5	5
102	Egyptian Goose	57	66	446	446	295	Blackwinged Stilt	8	16	9	9
103	South African Shelduck	4	7	7	7	338	Whiskered Tern	16	27	0	0
104	Yellowbilled Duck	245	316	513	513	428	Pied Kingfisher	6	8	1	1
106	Cape Teal	2	4	0	0	429	Giant Kingfisher	1	2	0	0
107	Hottentot Teal	5	7	10	10	431	Malachite Kingfisher	2	4	0	0
108	Redbilled Teal	46	83	9	9	713	Cape Wagtail	22	30	48	48
112	Cape Shoveller	19	32	11	11		Total	1520	1985	1989	1989
113	Southern Pochard	4	4	0	0		No. of species		55		
116	Spurwinged Goose	32	42	134	134						

Klipspruit Dam Complex, Vryheid, KwaZulu–Natal
27° 55' S 30° 35' E (2730DC)

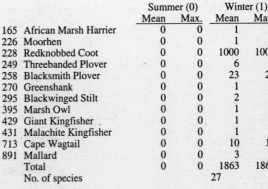

Two dams, with open water and some fringing vegetation. Only one count available (winter 1997), which, although only 15% of shoreline and 35% of open water were covered, produced large numbers of Egyptian and Spurwinged Geese, Yellowbilled Duck and Redknobbed Coot, and reasonable numbers of Redbilled Teal and Cape Shoveller; Marsh Owl was also recorded. Threats include agriculture along dam margins, and overhead power lines.

		Summer (0)		Winter (1)				Summer (0)		Winter (1)	
		Mean	Max.	Mean	Max.			Mean	Max.	Mean	Max.
008	Dabchick	0	0	30	30	165	African Marsh Harrier	0	0	1	1
055	Whitebreasted Cormorant	0	0	10	10	226	Moorhen	0	0	1	1
058	Reed Cormorant	0	0	13	13	228	Redknobbed Coot	0	0	1000	1000
060	Darter	0	0	3	3	249	Threebanded Plover	0	0	6	6
062	Grey Heron	0	0	1	1	258	Blacksmith Plover	0	0	23	23
063	Blackheaded Heron	0	0	5	5	270	Greenshank	0	0	1	1
091	Sacred Ibis	0	0	6	6	295	Blackwinged Stilt	0	0	2	2
094	Hadeda Ibis	0	0	21	21	395	Marsh Owl	0	0	1	1
102	Egyptian Goose	0	0	174	174	429	Giant Kingfisher	0	0	1	1
103	South African Shelduck	0	0	9	9	431	Malachite Kingfisher	0	0	1	1
104	Yellowbilled Duck	0	0	179	179	713	Cape Wagtail	0	0	10	10
108	Redbilled Teal	0	0	63	63	891	Mallard	0	0	3	3
112	Cape Shoveller	0	0	35	35		Total	0	0	1863	1863
116	Spurwinged Goose	0	0	263	263		No. of species		27		
148	African Fish Eagle	0	0	1	1						

Hlonhlela Pan, Mkuze, KwaZulu–Natal
27° 36' S 32° 12' E (2732CA)

A freshwater pan in Mkuzi Game Reserve. Extensively fringed with emergent *Echinochloa* grass; some *Phragmites* stands; some *Polygonum* and *Nymphaea*. An exceptional winter count (1416 birds) in 1992 included a nationally significant number of White Pelican and good numbers of Whitefaced Duck, Spurwinged Goose and Hadeda Ibis, plus Yellowbilled Stork and Darter; the largest other count is 79 birds in summer 1996, when good numbers of Greenbacked Heron, Black Crake and African Jacana were recorded. Numbers of most waterfowl appear to peak in winter, but Pygmy Goose numbers peak in summer, when floating vegetation must be more extensive. 20 Curlew occurred in July 1994. No threats have been identified.

		Summer (5)		Winter (6)	
		Mean	Max.	Mean	Max.
008	Dabchick	0	2	1	3
049	White Pelican	0	0	167	1000*
058	Reed Cormorant	1	4	0	1
060	Darter	0	1	2	10
062	Grey Heron	0	2	1	2
064	Goliath Heron	0	1	0	2
071	Cattle Egret	0	0	2	8
072	Squacco Heron	0	1	0	1
074	Greenbacked Heron	2	9	0	0
078	Little Bittern	0	2	0	0
081	Hamerkop	1	4	0	1
087	Openbilled Stork	1	2	0	0
089	Marabou Stork	0	0	0	1
090	Yellowbilled Stork	0	0	2	10
091	Sacred Ibis	0	1	0	0
093	Glossy Ibis	0	0	0	2
094	Hadeda Ibis	2	5	12	50
095	African Spoonbill	0	0	1	8
099	Whitefaced Duck	11	35	29	160

		Summer (5)		Winter (6)	
		Mean	Max.	Mean	Max.
102	Egyptian Goose	1	3	8	22
114	Pygmy Goose	4	13	2	9
116	Spurwinged Goose	0	1	24	140
148	African Fish Eagle	0	1	0	2
213	Black Crake	4	15	0	2
240	African Jacana	9	24	4	10
249	Threebanded Plover	0	0	0	2
258	Blacksmith Plover	0	0	1	4
266	Wood Sandpiper	0	1	0	0
269	Marsh Sandpiper	0	0	0	2
289	Curlew	0	0	3	20
403	Pel's Fishing Owl	0	0	0	1
428	Pied Kingfisher	2	3	1	5
429	Giant Kingfisher	0	1	1	2
431	Malachite Kingfisher	0	0	0	1
711	African Pied Wagtail	0	0	0	1
	Total	41	81	261	1417
	No. of species			35	

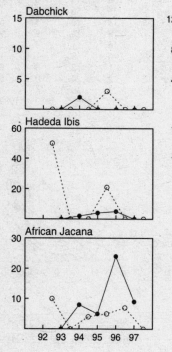

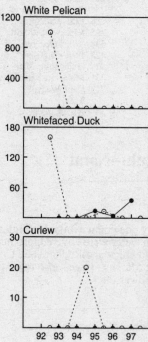

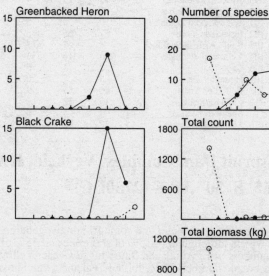

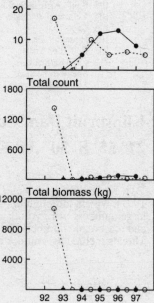

Hluhluwe River Vlei & Floodplain, Hluhluwe, KwaZulu–Natal
28° 05' S 32° 20' E (2832AB)

The floodplain of the Hluhluwe River, entering False Bay. A meandering river, with muddy margins, wet grassland and some fringing reeds. Pinkbacked Pelican formerly bred, and still occurs; Pygmy Goose also occurs; reedbeds near the floodplain hold African Rail, Black Crake and Purple Gallinule. Only two counts are available (winter 1994 and summer 1995): good numbers of White Pelican, Ringed Plover and Redwinged Pratincole (which has bred here) were recorded in summer, and of Lesser Flamingo, Redwinged Pratincole and Caspian Tern in winter. Counts were discontinued in 1995 but should be reinstated. Threats include excessive grazing and trampling by cattle, which have eliminated open water areas and have severely affected the vegetation, resulting in a falloff in duck numbers, although shorebird habitat is probably still good.

		Summer (2)		Winter (1)				Summer (2)		Winter (1)	
		Mean	Max.	Mean	Max.			Mean	Max.	Mean	Max.
049	White Pelican	60	120	12	12	213	Black Crake	2	3	3	3
055	Whitebreasted Cormorant	0	0	2	2	226	Moorhen	1	1	3	3
056	Cape Cormorant	0	0	1	1	240	African Jacana	1	2	1	1
058	Reed Cormorant	2	3	19	19	245	Ringed Plover	20	40	0	0
060	Darter	1	1	5	5	248	Kittlitz's Plover	15	30	5	5
062	Grey Heron	2	4	10	10	249	Threebanded Plover	1	2	7	7
063	Blackheaded Heron	2	4	5	5	258	Blacksmith Plover	1	2	0	0
064	Goliath Heron	2	3	5	5	260	Wattled Plover	4	7	9	9
065	Purple Heron	1	2	6	6	264	Common Sandpiper	7	13	0	0
066	Great White Heron	1	1	7	7	266	Wood Sandpiper	2	3	0	0
067	Little Egret	2	4	11	11	269	Marsh Sandpiper	1	1	5	5
068	Yellowbilled Egret	0	0	1	1	270	Greenshank	19	37	9	9
069	Black Egret	1	1	0	0	272	Curlew Sandpiper	60	120	0	0
071	Cattle Egret	20	39	11	11	274	Little Stint	77	153	0	0
074	Greenbacked Heron	2	3	2	2	284	Ruff	20	40	0	0
081	Hamerkop	1	1	2	2	294	Avocet	2	3	12	12
090	Yellowbilled Stork	5	9	9	9	295	Blackwinged Stilt	1	1	29	29
091	Sacred Ibis	3	6	2	2	298	Water Dikkop	1	1	0	0
093	Glossy Ibis	0	0	3	3	304	Redwinged Pratincole	16	32	33	33
094	Hadeda Ibis	0	0	15	15	315	Greyheaded Gull	1	2	0	0
095	African Spoonbill	4	7	8	8	322	Caspian Tern	0	0	15	15
097	Lesser Flamingo	0	0	300	300	335	Little Tern	1	1	0	0
099	Whitefaced Duck	1	1	34	34	338	Whiskered Tern	0	0	3	3
102	Egyptian Goose	1	2	2	2	428	Pied Kingfisher	2	3	9	9
104	Yellowbilled Duck	16	31	7	7	431	Malachite Kingfisher	1	1	2	2
116	Spurwinged Goose	0	0	9	9	713	Cape Wagtail	0	0	6	6
148	African Fish Eagle	1	2	4	4		Total	372	744	647	647
165	African Marsh Harrier	1	2	4	4		No. of species		54		

Klipfontein Bird Sanctuary, Vryheid, KwaZulu–Natal
27° 48' S 30° 48' E (2730DD)

A permanent marsh below a sewage plant. Diverse habitats, including extensive reedbeds, a small dam and a river. The site was first counted in 1997; it is notable for the presence of African Rail (the larger number counted in winter is unusual), Black Crake and Redchested Flufftail, and for good counts of Yellowbilled Duck (winter) and Blacksmith Plover (summer). The site obviously has potential to hold more species. Important threats are vandalism, refuse dumping, informal settlement, and the spread of alien plants.

		Summer (1)		Winter (1)				Summer (1)		Winter (1)	
		Mean	Max.	Mean	Max.			Mean	Max.	Mean	Max.
008	Dabchick	2	2	1	1	213	Black Crake	0	0	5	5
058	Reed Cormorant	0	0	2	2	217	Redchested Flufftail	5	5	4	4
063	Blackheaded Heron	3	3	1	1	226	Moorhen	4	4	6	6
071	Cattle Egret	1	1	1	1	249	Threebanded Plover	3	3	7	7
074	Greenbacked Heron	0	0	1	1	258	Blacksmith Plover	36	36	10	10
081	Hamerkop	0	0	2	2	260	Wattled Plover	0	0	1	1
094	Hadeda Ibis	10	10	13	13	264	Common Sandpiper	3	3	0	0
102	Egyptian Goose	0	0	10	10	428	Pied Kingfisher	0	0	2	2
104	Yellowbilled Duck	19	19	47	47	429	Giant Kingfisher	1	1	0	0
105	African Black Duck	2	2	2	2	431	Malachite Kingfisher	2	2	0	0
116	Spurwinged Goose	5	5	0	0	713	Cape Wagtail	4	4	7	7
209	Crowned Crane	2	2	0	0		Total	108	108	135	135
210	African Rail	6	6	13	13		No. of species		24		

Kosi Bay Nature Reserve, Manguzi, KwaZulu–Natal
26° 58' S 32° 50' E (2632DD)

IBA and Ramsar site. Coastal lakes, most with little fringing vegetation, in grassland and marsh.. Summer and winter counts of individual species show considerable fluctuations, but there seems to be a trend of decreasing numbers and species variety in both seasons. Influx of Cape Cormorant recorded in winter 1994; high counts of Reed Cormorant in winter 1992 and of Whitefaced Duck in winters of 1992 and 1993. Good numbers of Knot for this coast. 20–50 pairs of Pygmy Goose breed, as do 3+ pairs of Pel's Fishing Owl. Whitebacked Night Heron, Rufousbellied Heron, Lesser Gallinule, African Finfoot and Grass Owl occur. Threats include sedimentation, eutrophication and afforestation. Human pressure is increasing; the lakes are traditional fishing areas and are used for tourism and recreation.

		Summer (5)		Winter (6)				Summer (5)		Winter (6)	
		Mean	Max.	Mean	Max.			Mean	Max.	Mean	Max.
008	Dabchick	1	5	0	1	226	Moorhen	0	1	1	2
055	Whitebreasted Cormorant	50	98	28	105	228	Redknobbed Coot	1	3	62	296
056	Cape Cormorant	0	0	117	700	240	African Jacana	5	7	7	13
058	Reed Cormorant	13	48	119	460	241	Lesser Jacana	0	2	0	0
060	Darter	3	7	13	45	246	Whitefronted Plover	12	45	6	23
062	Grey Heron	3	9	1	2	248	Kittlitz's Plover	1	7	0	0
063	Blackheaded Heron	1	2	0	1	249	Threebanded Plover	0	0	0	1
064	Goliath Heron	2	3	1	2	254	Grey Plover	1	5	0	0
065	Purple Heron	4	7	3	7	258	Blacksmith Plover	1	5	0	2
066	Great White Heron	1	2	1	2	260	Wattled Plover	1	2	1	3
067	Little Egret	2	7	6	10	262	Turnstone	10	43	1	5
068	Yellowbilled Egret	0	2	0	0	264	Common Sandpiper	4	10	0	1
071	Cattle Egret	22	50	520	903	270	Greenshank	10	50	0	0
072	Squacco Heron	0	1	0	0	271	Knot	20	100	0	0
074	Greenbacked Heron	1	4	1	2	272	Curlew Sandpiper	25	127	2	13
075	Rufousbellied Heron	0	1	0	0	281	Sanderling	19	93	0	0
078	Little Bittern	0	1	0	0	284	Ruff	0	1	0	0
079	Dwarf Bittern	0	1	0	0	290	Whimbrel	10	41	1	2
081	Hamerkop	0	1	0	0	295	Blackwinged Stilt	0	0	1	2
088	Saddlebilled Stork	1	2	1	2	315	Greyheaded Gull	5	10	6	13
091	Sacred Ibis	0	0	1	7	322	Caspian Tern	1	3	1	2
094	Hadeda Ibis	4	10	5	8	324	Swift Tern	11	57	0	0
095	African Spoonbill	0	0	1	4	325	Lesser Crested Tern	0	1	0	0
096	Greater Flamingo	10	25	157	335	327	Common Tern	3	16	9	51
097	Lesser Flamingo	0	0	2	13	335	Little Tern	20	100	0	0
099	Whitefaced Duck	1	7	103	419	428	Pied Kingfisher	15	19	17	24
104	Yellowbilled Duck	26	74	35	92	429	Giant Kingfisher	1	2	3	4
108	Redbilled Teal	0	0	1	8	430	Halfcollared Kingfisher	1	3	0	0
114	Pygmy Goose	5	21	36	181	431	Malachite Kingfisher	1	2	1	2
116	Spurwinged Goose	2	9	4	23	711	African Pied Wagtail	0	2	1	2
148	African Fish Eagle	4	8	6	10	713	Cape Wagtail	0	2	1	5
170	Osprey	3	4	1	2		Total	343	767	1284	2395
213	Black Crake	2	4	3	6		No. of species			65	
223	Purple Gallinule	0	2	2	8						

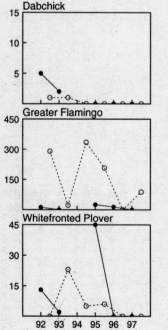

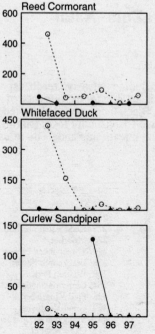

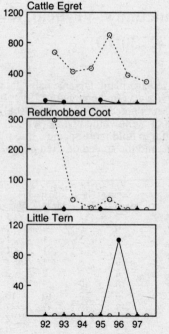

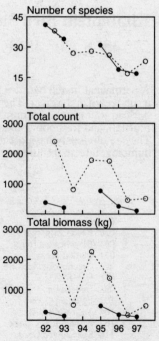

kuNdlebeni Pan, Mbazwane, KwaZulu–Natal
27° 42' S 32° 37' E (2732DA)

A shallow pan in dune slacks south of Ozabeni. Large fluctuations in water level; prone to dry out. Fringing grassland; little reed cover; some *Nymphaea* cover, resulting in the occurrence of African and Lesser Jacana. When flooded, the pan can hold large numbers of waterfowl, especially Spurwinged Goose (e.g. in winter 1992, when relatively high counts of several other species were also made). Noteworthy numbers of Redwinged Pratincole occurred in winter 1993. Pinkthroated Longclaw occurs. No threats have been identified.

		Summer (5) Mean	Summer (5) Max.	Winter (6) Mean	Winter (6) Max.
008	Dabchick	0	2	1	6
058	Reed Cormorant	0	0	1	6
060	Darter	0	0	1	3
065	Purple Heron	0	0	0	2
066	Great White Heron	0	1	2	10
067	Little Egret	0	0	0	1
071	Cattle Egret	9	34	0	1
072	Squacco Heron	0	1	1	3
081	Hamerkop	0	0	0	1
086	Woollynecked Stork	0	1	0	0
088	Saddlebilled Stork	0	1	0	0
091	Sacred Ibis	0	0	2	14
093	Glossy Ibis	0	0	0	1
095	African Spoonbill	0	0	0	1
099	Whitefaced Duck	4	19	7	39
102	Egyptian Goose	0	0	0	2
114	Pygmy Goose	0	0	0	1
116	Spurwinged Goose	1	4	188	1080
148	African Fish Eagle	0	0	1	1
165	African Marsh Harrier	0	0	1	1
213	Black Crake	0	0	1	6
223	Purple Gallinule	0	0	0	1
240	African Jacana	1	4	3	20
241	Lesser Jacana	0	0	1	5
248	Kittlitz's Plover	0	0	0	2
249	Threebanded Plover	0	0	1	2
258	Blacksmith Plover	4	14	3	10
260	Wattled Plover	2	4	1	3
264	Common Sandpiper	0	1	0	0
266	Wood Sandpiper	1	4	0	0
269	Marsh Sandpiper	0	1	0	0
270	Greenshank	1	3	0	0
284	Ruff	0	1	0	0
295	Blackwinged Stilt	0	0	0	2
304	Redwinged Pratincole	2	11	7	41
327	Common Tern	0	0	1	6
338	Whiskered Tern	0	1	2	10
339	Whitewinged Tern	0	1	0	0
428	Pied Kingfisher	0	0	1	2
713	Cape Wagtail	0	0	1	3
	Total	28	57	225	1220
	No. of species		40		

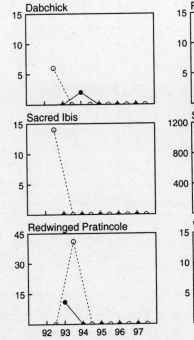
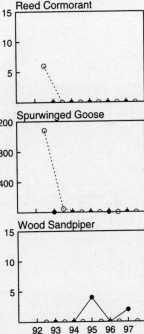
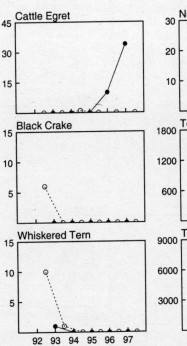
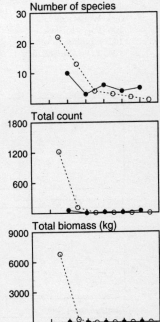

Lake Eteza, Mtubatuba, KwaZulu–Natal
28° 29' S 32° 09' E (2832AC)

An IBA and nature reserve. Seasonal brackish lake fed by the Msunduzi River; has open water, and submerged, emergent, fringing and floating vegetation. Counts since summer 1995 small, presumably owing to low water levels (lake may dry out during droughts). Good count of 3298 in winter 1994 (more water and good habitat): high numbers of White Pelican, African Spoonbill ((globally significant), Lesser Flamingo, waterfowl (notably Whitefaced and Fulvous Duck, and Spurwinged Goose), Avocet and Blackwinged Stilt, while 40 Greenshank also recorded. Bittern, Lesser Gallinule, Grass Owl and Natal Nightjar occur. Critical threats are siltation, and dredging/ erosion of outlet. Surrounded by sugar cane and gum tree plantation; water abstraction for cane is a threat, as is inflow of agricultural fertilisers.

	Summer (3)		Winter (4)				Summer (3)		Winter (4)	
	Mean	Max.	Mean	Max.			Mean	Max.	Mean	Max.
008 Dabchick	0	0	4	8		107 Hottentot Teal	0	0	0	1
049 White Pelican	0	0	68	270		108 Redbilled Teal	0	0	15	55
050 Pinkbacked Pelican	0	0	2	6		112 Cape Shoveller	0	0	7	28
055 Whitebreasted Cormorant	0	0	1	1		114 Pygmy Goose	2	6	4	15
058 Reed Cormorant	11	22	10	25		115 Knobbilled Duck	0	0	11	41
060 Darter	1	2	5	8		116 Spurwinged Goose	1	2	215	821
062 Grey Heron	0	1	3	10		148 African Fish Eagle	0	0	1	1
063 Blackheaded Heron	0	0	1	2		213 Black Crake	0	0	1	4
064 Goliath Heron	1	2	0	1		223 Purple Gallinule	3	4	0	0
065 Purple Heron	1	2	1	2		226 Moorhen	2	7	1	1
066 Great White Heron	0	0	2	5		228 Redknobbed Coot	0	0	6	21
067 Little Egret	0	0	1	3		240 African Jacana	9	14	11	21
068 Yellowbilled Egret	0	0	1	2		249 Threebanded Plover	0	0	0	1
071 Cattle Egret	16	40	0	0		258 Blacksmith Plover	0	0	1	3
072 Squacco Heron	0	0	1	3		270 Greenshank	0	0	10	40
081 Hamerkop	0	0	1	2		294 Avocet	0	0	7	26
090 Yellowbilled Stork	0	0	12	47		295 Blackwinged Stilt	0	0	21	84
091 Sacred Ibis	0	1	2	8		298 Water Dikkop	0	0	1	2
093 Glossy Ibis	0	0	1	2		339 Whitewinged Tern	5	15	0	1
095 African Spoonbill	0	0	52	206**		428 Pied Kingfisher	0	1	2	5
097 Lesser Flamingo	0	0	53	210		431 Malachite Kingfisher	0	0	1	1
099 Whitefaced Duck	0	0	186	688		713 Cape Wagtail	0	0	0	1
100 Fulvous Duck	0	0	137	536		Total	52	82	897	3299
102 Egyptian Goose	0	0	44	158		No. of species			47	
104 Yellowbilled Duck	0	0	2	5						

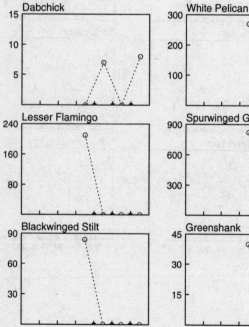
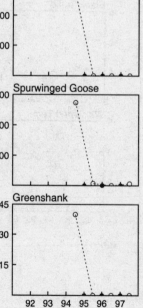
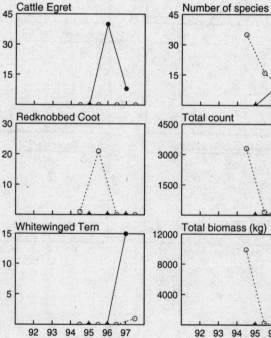
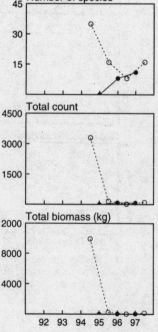

Lake Mfutululu, Mtubatuba, KwaZulu–Natal
28° 25' S 32° 15' E (2832AD)

A freshwater pan on the Mfolozi floodplain; water inflow is from a stream and by periodic backflooding from the Mfolozi River. Much emergent vegetation (*Scirpus*, *Echinochloa*, some papyrus) and variably extensive *Nymphaea* cover. An exceptionally high count in summer 1995, when the habitat was presumably excellent, included 1000 White Pelicans ((presumably a temporary influx of non-feeding birds) and the largest recorded numbers of Great White Heron, Black Stork (the only record), Yellowbilled Stork, Glossy Ibis, African Spoonbill, Whitefaced and Fulvous Ducks, and Egyptian and Spurwinged Geese. 200 Pygmy Goose occurred in winter 1995. Critical threats are posed by siltation and altered hydrology, less severe threats by chemical pollution and water abstraction.

		Summer (3)		Winter (2)					Summer (3)		Winter (2)	
		Mean	Max.	Mean	Max.				Mean	Max.	Mean	Max.
049	White Pelican	333	1000*	0	0		095	African Spoonbill	7	20	0	0
055	Whitebreasted Cormorant	1	3	1	1		099	Whitefaced Duck	141	424	13	25
058	Reed Cormorant	1	3	6	10		100	Fulvous Duck	117	350	0	0
060	Darter	0	0	1	1		101	Whitebacked Duck	0	0	37	63
062	Grey Heron	3	8	0	0		102	Egyptian Goose	26	78	5	10
064	Goliath Heron	0	1	0	0		104	Yellowbilled Duck	0	0	1	2
065	Purple Heron	1	2	0	0		114	Pygmy Goose	0	0	103	200
066	Great White Heron	8	23	0	0		116	Spurwinged Goose	69	207	18	30
067	Little Egret	0	0	1	2		148	African Fish Eagle	1	2	1	1
068	Yellowbilled Egret	0	0	1	1		223	Purple Gallinule	0	1	0	0
069	Black Egret	2	5	1	1		226	Moorhen	8	15	8	16
071	Cattle Egret	1	2	0	0		240	African Jacana	9	12	6	9
072	Squacco Heron	0	1	0	0		270	Greenshank	1	2	0	0
084	Black Stork	4	11	0	0		295	Blackwinged Stilt	3	10	0	0
086	Woollynecked Stork	2	6	2	4		339	Whitewinged Tern	1	3	0	0
090	Yellowbilled Stork	15	46	0	0		428	Pied Kingfisher	1	2	1	2
091	Sacred Ibis	2	6	0	0			Total	768	2248	202	355
093	Glossy Ibis	10	29	0	0			No. of species		35		
094	Hadeda Ibis	1	4	0	0							

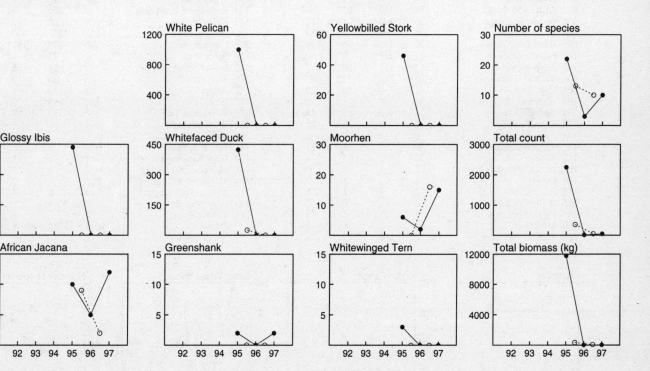

Lake St Lucia, Hlabisa, KwaZulu–Natal
28° 04' S 32° 27' E (2832AB)

A global IBA and Ramsar site; largest African estuarine system, with important populations of many species. Important for many bird species; globally significant numbers of breeding White Pelican and African Spoonbill, and Greater Flamingo; also significant breeding numbers of Goliath Heron, Saddle-billed Stork and African Fish Eagle. High counts of Lesser Flamingo, shorebirds, Redwinged Pratin-cole (formerly bred), Greyheaded Gull and terns. Figures show recent decline in counts and number of species. Threats include cessation of dredging at St Lucia mouth, human disturbance, reduced water inflow from catchment, pollution, and development.

		Summer (6)		Winter (6)	
		Mean	Max.	Mean	Max.
008	Dabchick	0	2	21	127
049	White Pelican	550	1916**	1416*	3978**
050	Pinkbacked Pelican	24	41	57	125
055	Whitebreasted Cormorant	27	69	112	217
056	Cape Cormorant	0	0	27	149
058	Reed Cormorant	78	341	66	163
060	Darter	10	32	26	109
062	Grey Heron	36	53	58	94
063	Blackheaded Heron	7	32	1	2
064	Goliath Heron	76	107	56	93
065	Purple Heron	3	8	5	15
066	Great White Heron	102	223	68	118
067	Little Egret	103	280	53	119
068	Yellowbilled Egret	2	9	1	3
069	Black Egret	7	23	0	0
071	Cattle Egret	81	221	25	89
072	Squacco Heron	3	9	2	6
074	Greenbacked Heron	1	1	0	1
076	Blackcrowned Night Heron	2	7	0	0
081	Hamerkop	2	5	1	3
086	Woollynecked Stork	12	33	6	17
088	Saddlebilled Stork	1	3	3	4
090	Yellowbilled Stork	78	139	8	21
091	Sacred Ibis	26	98	24	50
093	Glossy Ibis	73	391	19	78
094	Hadeda Ibis	5	8	9	27
095	African Spoonbill	92*	163**	93*	158**
096	Greater Flamingo	1314**	3095**	3535**	13173**
097	Lesser Flamingo	346	1000	2275	5758
099	Whitefaced Duck	90	135	85	259
100	Fulvous Duck	31	181	0	0
102	Egyptian Goose	262	571	180	307
104	Yellowbilled Duck	108	246	52	169
106	Cape Teal	2	9	16	29
107	Hottentot Teal	31	134	2	12
108	Redbilled Teal	18	65	16	61
112	Cape Shoveller	0	0	7	25
114	Pygmy Goose	0	0	0	2
116	Spurwinged Goose	30	116	28	85
148	African Fish Eagle	72	88	63	79
165	African Marsh Harrier	1	2	3	7
170	Osprey	1	2	1	2
213	Black Crake	2	8	1	6
215	Baillon's Crake	0	2	0	0
223	Purple Gallinule	5	23	3	15
226	Moorhen	0	2	3	15
228	Redknobbed Coot	0	0	70	420

		Summer (6)		Winter (6)	
		Mean	Max.	Mean	Max.
240	African Jacana	3	17	3	12
245	Ringed Plover	147	502	1	6
246	Whitefronted Plover	9	19	8	14
248	Kittlitz's Plover	11	24	32	77
249	Threebanded Plover	2	7	3	11
254	Grey Plover	10	53	1	5
258	Blacksmith Plover	6	16	22	44
260	Wattled Plover	7	23	12	25
262	Turnstone	0	2	1	3
263	Terek Sandpiper	0	1	0	0
264	Common Sandpiper	53	93	2	5
265	Green Sandpiper	0	1	0	0
266	Wood Sandpiper	13	25	1	5
269	Marsh Sandpiper	38	91	9	19
270	Greenshank	58	133	63	250
271	Knot	2	9	0	0
272	Curlew Sandpiper	1562	4117*	193	923
274	Little Stint	853	3721	90	478
281	Sanderling	0	1	0	0
284	Ruff	184	328	4	20
289	Curlew	0	1	0	0
290	Whimbrel	10	15	3	8
294	Avocet	69	254	180	300
295	Blackwinged Stilt	42	125	150	383
296	Crab Plover	0	1	0	0
298	Water Dikkop	9	15	7	19
304	Redwinged Pratincole	7	22	66	165
312	Kelp Gull	0	0	1	4
315	Greyheaded Gull	158	273	803*	1332**
322	Caspian Tern	220*	372**	188*	476**
324	Swift Tern	31	72	6	22
325	Lesser Crested Tern	12	24	8	45
326	Sandwich Tern	6	28	0	1
327	Common Tern	5	18	1	3
335	Little Tern	266	816*	7	35
338	Whiskered Tern	40	172	7	16
339	Whitewinged Tern	14	73	3	17
395	Marsh Owl	0	2	0	1
428	Pied Kingfisher	36	53	36	56
429	Giant Kingfisher	1	3	1	2
431	Malachite Kingfisher	2	6	0	1
434	Mangrove Kingfisher	0	0	0	2
711	African Pied Wagtail	2	6	2	4
713	Cape Wagtail	1	4	3	10
714	Yellow Wagtail	1	7	0	0
	Total	7604	13782	10408	25665
	No. of species			92	

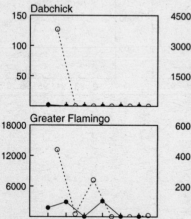

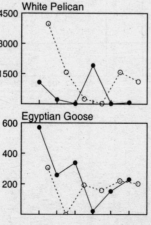

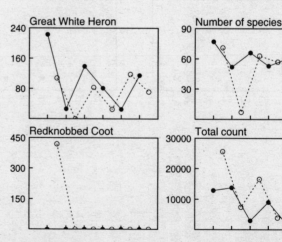

More graphs on next page.

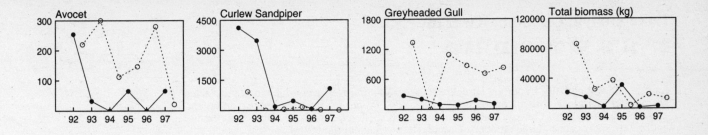

Mandini Sewage Works, Mandini, KwaZulu–Natal
29° 10' S 31° 25' E (2931AB)

Sewage treatment works near the Tugela River. Only two summer and three winter counts available, showing no unusually large concentrations of any species; the commoner ducks are more numerous in summer (compare with the nearby Sundumbili Sewage Works), when small numbers of Palearctic shorebirds also occur. Compared with Sundumbili Sewage Works, species diversity and bird numbers low, birds apparently preferring to use the Tugela River. Water hyacinth *Eichhornia* is a problem at times.

		Summer (2)		Winter (3)	
		Mean	Max.	Mean	Max.
058	Reed Cormorant	0	0	0	1
062	Grey Heron	0	0	0	1
071	Cattle Egret	0	0	4	11
081	Hamerkop	1	1	0	1
091	Sacred Ibis	0	0	0	1
099	Whitefaced Duck	10	20	0	1
102	Egyptian Goose	0	0	3	10
104	Yellowbilled Duck	8	15	0	0
107	Hottentot Teal	0	0	0	1
240	African Jacana	0	0	1	1
246	Whitefronted Plover	1	1	0	0

		Summer (2)		Winter (3)	
		Mean	Max.	Mean	Max.
249	Threebanded Plover	2	4	1	2
258	Blacksmith Plover	3	5	1	2
264	Common Sandpiper	1	1	0	0
266	Wood Sandpiper	2	3	0	0
269	Marsh Sandpiper	1	1	0	0
428	Pied Kingfisher	1	2	0	0
711	African Pied Wagtail	1	1	0	1
713	Cape Wagtail	2	2	3	6
	Total	30	55	14	25
	No. of species			19	

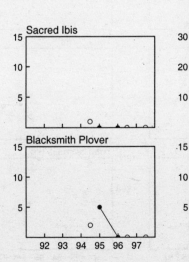

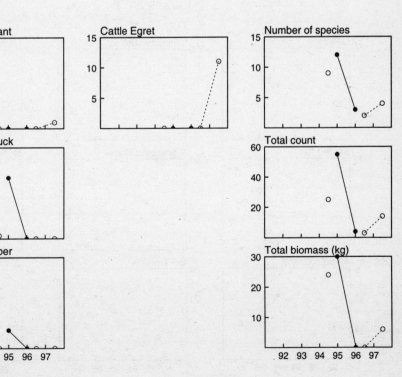

Lake Sibaya, Ubombo, KwaZulu–Natal
27° 21' S 32° 40' E (2732BC)

Ramsar site and globally Important Bird Area. Largest natural freshwater lake in South Africa. Deep water; marginal, fringing and floating vegetation (*Typha, Phragmites*, sedges, emergent grass, *Nymphaea*, etc.) is largely confined to inlets and sheltered shorelines. Diverse avifauna but few species occur in large numbers. Goliath Heron, Saddlebilled Stork, Lesser Jacana and Pinkthroated Longclaw occur, Natal Nightjar locally common. Pygmy Goose and African Jacana most numerous in winter, when other local waterbodies may become dry. Small numbers of Lesser Gallinule and Redchested Flufftail; Black Crake and Purple Gallinule locally common. Important source of permanent water for birds and mammals; supports appreciable number of rare/endangered plant and animal taxa. Also supports rural people and tourism; eutrophication is a threat.

		Summer (4)		Winter (6)	
		Mean	Max.	Mean	Max.
008	Dabchick	12	42	92	139
055	Whitebreasted Cormorant	372	466	92	201
058	Reed Cormorant	153	283	237	382
060	Darter	4	13	15	31
062	Grey Heron	5	8	2	3
064	Goliath Heron	4	6	3	5
065	Purple Heron	18	40	2	4
066	Great White Heron	1	2	4	5
067	Little Egret	17	46	20	34
068	Yellowbilled Egret	0	0	0	1
069	Black Egret	0	0	1	3
071	Cattle Egret	12	25	46	119
072	Squacco Heron	4	12	5	7
074	Greenbacked Heron	1	2	1	2
076	Blackcrowned Night Heron	0	0	0	1
081	Hamerkop	4	7	1	2
086	Woollynecked Stork	2	4	0	0
090	Yellowbilled Stork	0	1	0	0
091	Sacred Ibis	1	2	12	19
094	Hadeda Ibis	3	6	7	25
095	African Spoonbill	0	1	2	9
096	Greater Flamingo	4	14	0	0
099	Whitefaced Duck	15	31	41	133
102	Egyptian Goose	5	14	3	3
104	Yellowbilled Duck	9	19	4	11
114	Pygmy Goose	4	10	25	74
116	Spurwinged Goose	11	18	7	21
148	African Fish Eagle	13	18	11	13
165	African Marsh Harrier	0	0	0	1

		Summer (4)		Winter (6)	
		Mean	Max.	Mean	Max.
213	Black Crake	3	5	5	16
223	Purple Gallinule	2	4	4	10
224	Lesser Gallinule	0	0	0	2
226	Moorhen	10	21	4	13
228	Redknobbed Coot	0	0	2	14
240	African Jacana	14	21	22	30
241	Lesser Jacana	0	1	1	3
245	Ringed Plover	1	4	1	3
246	Whitefronted Plover	0	1	0	0
258	Blacksmith Plover	7	13	2	5
260	Wattled Plover	5	8	2	7
264	Common Sandpiper	2	6	1	3
270	Greenshank	14	21	3	11
274	Little Stint	2	7	0	0
294	Avocet	0	0	1	3
295	Blackwinged Stilt	16	37	16	40
298	Water Dikkop	3	7	0	0
304	Redwinged Pratincole	1	2	0	0
315	Greyheaded Gull	0	1	1	3
322	Caspian Tern	4	5	5	13
335	Little Tern	0	0	0	1
338	Whiskered Tern	30	76	7	43
339	Whitewinged Tern	4	14	1	5
428	Pied Kingfisher	30	36	31	44
429	Giant Kingfisher	1	3	1	3
431	Malachite Kingfisher	4	12	4	10
	Total	820	1208	742	979
	No. of species		55		

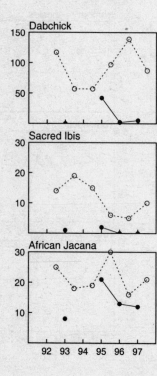
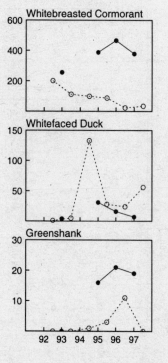
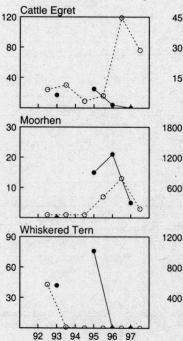
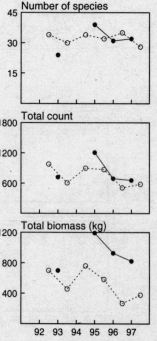

Malandeni Sewage Works, Ladysmith, KwaZulu–Natal
28° 34' S 29° 48' E (2829DB)

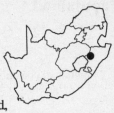

One of the most important palustrine wetland sites in the interior of KwaZulu-Natal. Sewage works adjacent to Klip River: maturation ponds, and extensive reedbeds, sedgebeds and seasonally flooded grassland. Actively managed to maintain and improve bird habitats. Breeding colonies of Sacred Ibis, Reed and Whitebreasted Cormorants and Cattle Egret. The critically endangered Bittern occurs regularly; Little Bittern and Purple Heron resident. An important site for Rallidae: 12 species recorded, including Corncrake, African Crake, Striped Crake and significant population of Baillon's Crake ((breeds); Lesser Gallinule and Lesser Moorhen occur regularly. Nationally significant numbers of Cape Shoveller recorded. Important threats include livestock grazing/trampling, and fishing, hunting/poaching.

		Summer (5)		Winter (5)				Summer (5)		Winter (5)	
		Mean	Max.	Mean	Max.			Mean	Max.	Mean	Max.
008	Dabchick	8	15	22	30	209	Crowned Crane	0	0	0	2
055	Whitebreasted Cormorant	16	26	32	55	210	African Rail	1	4	1	6
058	Reed Cormorant	35	130	113	282	212	African Crake	0	1	0	0
060	Darter	3	7	13	43	213	Black Crake	0	2	1	2
062	Grey Heron	6	22	11	22	215	Baillon's Crake	3	12	0	0
063	Blackheaded Heron	6	16	6	16	217	Redchested Flufftail	0	1	0	0
064	Goliath Heron	0	1	1	1	223	Purple Gallinule	12	18	9	16
065	Purple Heron	3	9	8	14	224	Lesser Gallinule	1	4	0	0
066	Great White Heron	14	42	5	11	226	Moorhen	26	39	35	52
067	Little Egret	2	5	0	1	227	Lesser Moorhen	0	2	0	0
068	Yellowbilled Egret	1	3	0	2	228	Redknobbed Coot	71	161	176	577
071	Cattle Egret	665	1010	199	257	240	African Jacana	0	1	1	3
072	Squacco Heron	3	5	2	4	249	Threebanded Plover	17	36	22	71
076	Blackcrowned Night Heron	14	38	17	34	258	Blacksmith Plover	39	81	35	46
078	Little Bittern	4	7	0	2	260	Wattled Plover	0	0	0	2
081	Hamerkop	7	9	5	15	264	Common Sandpiper	3	6	0	1
091	Sacred Ibis	39	99	64	104	266	Wood Sandpiper	18	24	0	1
093	Glossy Ibis	30	89	30	72	269	Marsh Sandpiper	2	3	0	1
094	Hadeda Ibis	13	18	14	24	270	Greenshank	3	6	0	0
095	African Spoonbill	12	56	7	14	272	Curlew Sandpiper	1	4	0	0
099	Whitefaced Duck	31	46	181	462	274	Little Stint	6	13	0	0
100	Fulvous Duck	4	9	0	0	284	Ruff	162	333	0	1
102	Egyptian Goose	7	13	15	25	286	Ethiopian Snipe	2	8	4	11
103	South African Shelduck	1	4	1	4	295	Blackwinged Stilt	13	53	3	10
104	Yellowbilled Duck	107	210	208	469	298	Water Dikkop	0	2	0	2
105	African Black Duck	5	10	1	3	338	Whiskered Tern	0	1	0	0
106	Cape Teal	0	0	1	3	339	Whitewinged Tern	1	4	0	0
107	Hottentot Teal	39	61	32	63	395	Marsh Owl	0	0	1	3
108	Redbilled Teal	62	148	54	85	428	Pied Kingfisher	5	7	2	5
112	Cape Shoveller	17	50	120	422**	429	Giant Kingfisher	2	3	1	2
113	Southern Pochard	19	52	6	27	431	Malachite Kingfisher	7	12	2	6
115	Knobbilled Duck	0	2	0	0	713	Cape Wagtail	10	27	26	33
116	Spurwinged Goose	2	5	3	9		Total	1583	2418	1495	2712
148	African Fish Eagle	0	0	1	2		No. of species		67		
165	African Marsh Harrier	0	1	0	0						

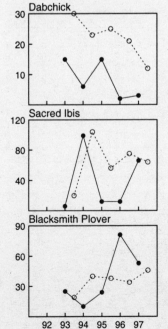

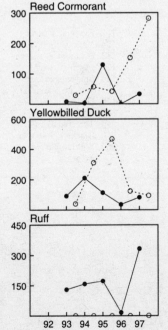

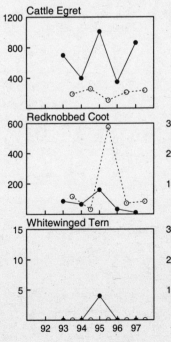

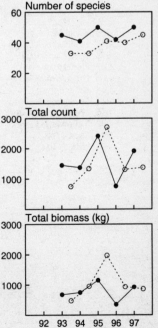

Maputaland Coast, Kwangwanase, KwaZulu–Natal
26° 58' S 32° 53' E (2632DD)

The Maputaland coastline, south from Kosi Mouth for c. 26 km, ending north of Black Rock; predominantly sandy beaches. Only one count is available (Jan. 1996), which produced one of the highest totals of Little Tern recorded during the survey period; it was exceeded only by the maximum counts from Lake St Lucia and the Tugela River mouth. No threats have been identified.

		Summer (1)		Winter (0)				Summer (1)		Winter (0)	
		Mean	Max.	Mean	Max.			Mean	Max.	Mean	Max.
170	Osprey	2	2	–	–	281	Sanderling	87	87	–	–
245	Ringed Plover	3	3	–	–	290	Whimbrel	8	8	–	–
246	Whitefronted Plover	17	17	–	–	324	Swift Tern	74	74	–	–
254	Grey Plover	13	13	–	–	327	Common Tern	129	129	–	–
262	Turnstone	1	1	–	–	335	Little Tern	793*	793*	–	–
264	Common Sandpiper	2	2	–	–		Total	1132	1132	–	–
270	Greenshank	3	3	–	–		No. of species		12		

Mfazana Pans, St Lucia, KwaZulu–Natal
28° 15' S 32° 28' E (2832AD)

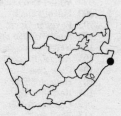

Falls within the St Lucia system Ramsar site. Two seasonal freshwater pans on the Eastern Shores of Lake St Lucia. Only summer and winter counts for 1997 are available; twice as many waterbirds were recorded on the summer count, when numbers of Egyptian Goose and Yellowbilled Duck were particularly high. Numbers of Dabchick, Hadeda Ibis and Whitefaced Duck were relatively high in winter. The bird species diversity is probably typical of pans in this area. No threats have been identified.

		Summer (1)		Winter (1)				Summer (1)		Winter (1)	
		Mean	Max.	Mean	Max.			Mean	Max.	Mean	Max.
008	Dabchick	6	6	11	11	102	Egyptian Goose	26	26	5	5
050	Pinkbacked Pelican	2	2	0	0	104	Yellowbilled Duck	147	147	0	0
058	Reed Cormorant	13	13	6	6	113	Southern Pochard	2	2	0	0
062	Grey Heron	7	7	0	0	114	Pygmy Goose	0	0	2	2
066	Great White Heron	4	4	1	1	116	Spurwinged Goose	16	16	2	2
067	Little Egret	0	0	1	1	165	African Marsh Harrier	0	0	1	1
081	Hamerkop	1	1	0	0	170	Osprey	1	1	0	0
086	Woollynecked Stork	1	1	1	1	240	African Jacana	7	7	7	7
090	Yellowbilled Stork	1	1	0	0	249	Threebanded Plover	0	0	1	1
091	Sacred Ibis	0	0	3	3	258	Blacksmith Plover	2	2	0	0
094	Hadeda Ibis	0	0	37	37	260	Wattled Plover	2	2	0	0
095	African Spoonbill	5	5	0	0		Total	272	272	138	138
099	Whitefaced Duck	29	29	60	60		No. of species		24		

Mavuya Pan, Mtubatuba, KwaZulu–Natal
28° 30' S 32° 12' E (2832AC)

A semi-permanent freshwater pan with fringing and emergent vegetation and variably extensive *Nymphaea* cover; a causeway crosses the pan at its narrowest (central) point. Compared to summer totals, winter counts of the commoner bird species are high, often because of exceptionally good counts in a single winter: Reed Cormorant, African Spoonbill, Grey Heron, Great White Heron, Egyptian Goose and Yellowbilled Stork in 1994; Yellowbilled Egret, Cattle Egret and Spurwinged Goose in 1995 (note high biomass figure due to Spurwing numbers); Whitebacked Duck and Redbilled Teal in 1997. Blackwinged Stilt is recorded only in winter. Variation in African Jacana numbers presumably reflects variations in floating vegetation cover. Potential threats are duck hunting and the replacement of grassland by sugar cane.

		Summer (3)		Winter (4)					Summer (3)		Winter (4)	
		Mean	Max.	Mean	Max.				Mean	Max.	Mean	Max.
008	Dabchick	2	6	9	16		108	Redbilled Teal	0	0	9	22
050	Pinkbacked Pelican	0	1	1	4		113	Southern Pochard	0	0	0	1
055	Whitebreasted Cormorant	1	1	1	3		114	Pygmy Goose	0	1	5	11
058	Reed Cormorant	4	11	23	65		115	Knobbilled Duck	0	0	1	3
060	Darter	0	1	2	8		116	Spurwinged Goose	2	5	81	295
062	Grey Heron	0	0	3	11		148	African Fish Eagle	0	1	1	2
063	Blackheaded Heron	0	1	1	1		165	African Marsh Harrier	1	1	1	1
064	Goliath Heron	1	1	0	1		223	Purple Gallinule	2	6	0	0
065	Purple Heron	0	0	0	1		226	Moorhen	5	14	4	11
066	Great White Heron	1	3	33	119		228	Redknobbed Coot	3	6	63	127
067	Little Egret	0	1	0	1		240	African Jacana	18	45	10	18
068	Yellowbilled Egret	0	0	15	40		241	Lesser Jacana	0	0	0	1
071	Cattle Egret	5	13	43	150		258	Blacksmith Plover	0	0	1	2
081	Hamerkop	0	0	0	1		270	Greenshank	1	4	1	5
086	Woollynecked Stork	0	1	0	0		294	Avocet	1	4	2	6
090	Yellowbilled Stork	0	0	8	31		295	Blackwinged Stilt	0	0	11	25
093	Glossy Ibis	0	0	1	4		322	Caspian Tern	0	0	1	4
095	African Spoonbill	0	0	11	39		324	Swift Tern	0	1	0	0
099	Whitefaced Duck	3	10	5	10		335	Little Tern	0	0	1	3
100	Fulvous Duck	1	4	4	10		339	Whitewinged Tern	1	2	0	0
101	Whitebacked Duck	1	3	22	86		428	Pied Kingfisher	1	3	1	2
102	Egyptian Goose	0	0	7	21		432	Pygmy Kingfisher	0	0	0	1
104	Yellowbilled Duck	9	22	9	20			Total	68	153	391	657
107	Hottentot Teal	3	10	1	4			No. of species			46	

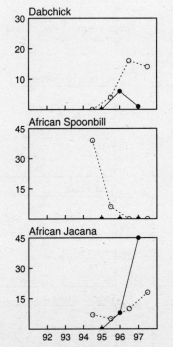

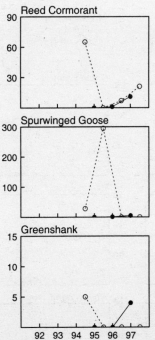

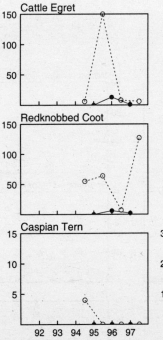

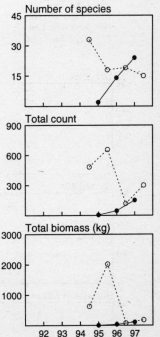

Mbozambo Waste Water Lagoon, Stanger, KwaZulu–Natal
29° 17' S 31° 17' E (2931AD)

Dam receiving treated sewage effluent, and industrial effluent treatment ponds; some fringing reedy vegetation; dam has open water, ponds completely covered with water hyacinth *Eichhornia*. Good selection of bird species recorded, but number of species apparently declining in summer and winter. Counts of Yellowbilled Duck and Egyptian Goose declining in both seasons, and of Whitebreasted Cormorant, Redknobbed Coot and Dabchick in winter. Hadeda and Sacred Ibis increasing in winter. Good numbers of Whitebacked Duck recorded in winter, when numbers of Spurwinged Goose, Cattle Egret and African Jacana also peak. Goliath Heron regular. Threats include encroachment of alien vegetation, agriculture, and domestic sewage and industrial waste pollution.

		Summer (3)		Winter (5)	
		Mean	Max.	Mean	Max.
008	Dabchick	0	0	3	6
049	White Pelican	0	0	3	15
055	Whitebreasted Cormorant	4	9	26	68
056	Cape Cormorant	0	0	0	2
058	Reed Cormorant	12	30	12	20
060	Darter	14	23	7	13
062	Grey Heron	9	19	7	9
063	Blackheaded Heron	6	15	10	23
064	Goliath Heron	3	6	4	6
065	Purple Heron	0	1	0	1
066	Great White Heron	0	0	0	1
067	Little Egret	2	5	1	2
068	Yellowbilled Egret	0	0	1	3
071	Cattle Egret	6	17	62	137
074	Greenbacked Heron	0	0	0	1
076	Blackcrowned Night Heron	1	1	0	1
081	Hamerkop	1	2	1	2
091	Sacred Ibis	96	190	147	261
093	Glossy Ibis	3	8	0	0
094	Hadeda Ibis	5	9	25	74
095	African Spoonbill	0	0	1	4
099	Whitefaced Duck	5	14	61	124
100	Fulvous Duck	1	4	1	4
101	Whitebacked Duck	3	10	15	72
102	Egyptian Goose	26	44	16	29
104	Yellowbilled Duck	18	30	26	31
106	Cape Teal	3	6	1	5
107	Hottentot Teal	7	8	5	14
108	Redbilled Teal	6	18	17	34
112	Cape Shoveller	0	1	4	12
113	Southern Pochard	1	4	1	2
115	Knobbilled Duck	0	0	0	1
116	Spurwinged Goose	12	30	116	195
148	African Fish Eagle	1	2	0	1
165	African Marsh Harrier	0	0	0	1
213	Black Crake	1	2	0	0
223	Purple Gallinule	0	1	4	11
226	Moorhen	3	5	2	4
228	Redknobbed Coot	1	2	10	27
240	African Jacana	5	13	25	39
245	Ringed Plover	0	0	1	4
248	Kittlitz's Plover	1	2	3	7
249	Threebanded Plover	3	6	10	15
258	Blacksmith Plover	19	39	11	19
264	Common Sandpiper	9	20	0	0
266	Wood Sandpiper	3	4	1	3
269	Marsh Sandpiper	4	10	0	0
272	Curlew Sandpiper	2	7	0	2
284	Ruff	10	30	0	0
286	Ethiopian Snipe	0	0	0	1
298	Water Dikkop	0	0	0	2
327	Common Tern	5	14	0	0
338	Whiskered Tern	3	8	7	33
339	Whitewinged Tern	22	61	0	2
428	Pied Kingfisher	1	2	0	0
429	Giant Kingfisher	0	1	0	1
711	African Pied Wagtail	0	1	5	20
713	Cape Wagtail	1	3	15	32
	Total	340	570	666	914
	No. of species			58	

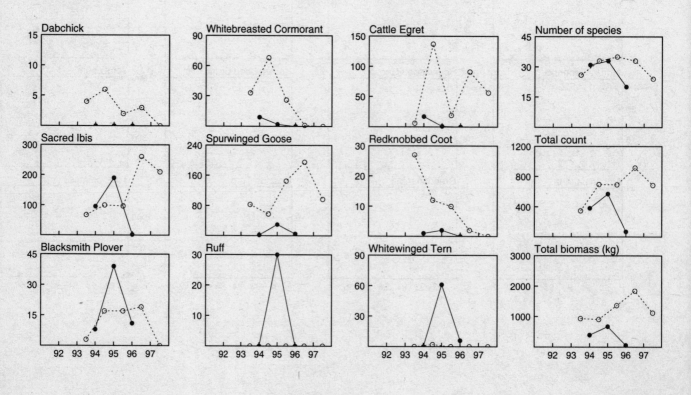

Mfolozi Mouth Area, St Lucia, KwaZulu–Natal
28° 24' S 32° 25' E (2832AD)

The mouth of the Mfolozi River, with open water, open shoreline, mudflats and some mangroves. The only count available (winter 1997) shows a typical bird species diversity for such habitat and includes small numbers of White and Pinkbacked Pelicans. Known threats (siltation, dredging and development) have only slight negative impacts. The Mfolozi swamps, on the alluvial plain of the Lower Mfolozi River, although severely reduced and modified by agricultural development and afforestation, still constitute a significant palustrine wetland system the avifauna of which requires urgent investigation.

		Summer (0) Mean	Summer (0) Max.	Winter (1) Mean	Winter (1) Max.			Summer (0) Mean	Summer (0) Max.	Winter (1) Mean	Winter (1) Max.
049	White Pelican	–	–	17	17	148	African Fish Eagle	–	–	1	1
050	Pinkbacked Pelican	–	–	4	4	246	Whitefronted Plover	–	–	93	93
058	Reed Cormorant	–	–	11	11	258	Blacksmith Plover	–	–	2	2
060	Darter	–	–	2	2	270	Greenshank	–	–	4	4
062	Grey Heron	–	–	5	5	281	Sanderling	–	–	30	30
064	Goliath Heron	–	–	3	3	294	Avocet	–	–	64	64
066	Great White Heron	–	–	13	13	312	Kelp Gull	–	–	2	2
067	Little Egret	–	–	3	3	315	Greyheaded Gull	–	–	48	48
086	Woollynecked Stork	–	–	2	2	322	Caspian Tern	–	–	8	8
091	Sacred Ibis	–	–	10	10	335	Little Tern	–	–	8	8
094	Hadeda Ibis	–	–	4	4	428	Pied Kingfisher	–	–	3	3
095	African Spoonbill	–	–	8	8	429	Giant Kingfisher	–	–	1	1
099	Whitefaced Duck	–	–	122	122		Total	–	–	470	470
102	Egyptian Goose	–	–	2	2		No. of species		26		

Muzi Lake (South), Mbazwane, KwaZulu–Natal
27° 38' S 32° 24' E (2732CB)

A narrow cut-off lake, c. 10 km long, with predominantly bare shorelines but some fringing *Phragmites* mainly at the northern end, and some floating-leaved vegetation, including *Nymphaea*. Only one count is available (June 1992), from the southern end of the lake and adjacent marshes; this produced an unremarkable selection of species, mainly waterfowl but also small numbers of shorebirds including 75 Curlew Sandpiper; 14 African Jacana were also recorded. Black Crake and Purple Gallinule presumably occur. Threats include excessive grazing and trampling by livestock, dam construction, drainage, and hunting/trapping.

		Summer (0) Mean	Summer (0) Max.	Winter (1) Mean	Winter (1) Max.			Summer (0) Mean	Summer (0) Max.	Winter (1) Mean	Winter (1) Max.
008	Dabchick	–	–	1	1	240	African Jacana	–	–	14	14
055	Whitebreasted Cormorant	–	–	1	1	248	Kittlitz's Plover	–	–	5	5
062	Grey Heron	–	–	1	1	249	Threebanded Plover	–	–	2	2
064	Goliath Heron	–	–	1	1	264	Common Sandpiper	–	–	1	1
091	Sacred Ibis	–	–	1	1	269	Marsh Sandpiper	–	–	2	2
093	Glossy Ibis	–	–	20	20	272	Curlew Sandpiper	–	–	75	75
099	Whitefaced Duck	–	–	73	73	274	Little Stint	–	–	2	2
100	Fulvous Duck	–	–	2	2	286	Ethiopian Snipe	–	–	6	6
102	Egyptian Goose	–	–	97	97	295	Blackwinged Stilt	–	–	6	6
108	Redbilled Teal	–	–	5	5	431	Malachite Kingfisher	–	–	1	1
114	Pygmy Goose	–	–	4	4		Total	–	–	393	393
115	Knobbilled Duck	–	–	36	36		No. of species		23		
116	Spurwinged Goose	–	–	37	37						

Mfula Pan, Mbazwane, KwaZulu–Natal
27° 37' S 32° 33' E (2732DA)

A grassy freshwater pan with much *Eleocharis*, some tall *Cyperus* sedges and some *Polygonum*. Counts reflect only small numbers of waterbirds, the commonest species being Whitefaced Duck, Spurwinged Goose (in winter) and Wood Sandpiper. Great fluctuations in water level occur and when full the pan can be excellent for birds. Rufous-bellied Heron, Longtoed Plover and Pinkthroated Longclaw occur. The pan could attract birds such as Baillon's Crake and Painted Snipe if grazing pressure were reduced. Excessive grazing and trampling by cattle have destroyed much of the palustrine wetland habitat. Total counts and total number of species have declined sharply over the analysis period.

		Summer (5)		Winter (6)				Summer (5)		Winter (6)	
		Mean	Max.	Mean	Max.			Mean	Max.	Mean	Max.
008	Dabchick	0	0	1	3	223	Purple Gallinule	0	1	0	0
058	Reed Cormorant	0	0	0	1	240	African Jacana	3	8	4	13
060	Darter	0	0	0	2	241	Lesser Jacana	0	0	0	2
062	Grey Heron	0	0	0	1	245	Ringed Plover	1	5	0	0
063	Blackheaded Heron	0	1	1	4	249	Threebanded Plover	0	2	1	4
064	Goliath Heron	0	0	0	1	258	Blacksmith Plover	4	8	1	3
065	Purple Heron	0	2	0	0	260	Wattled Plover	6	15	6	13
066	Great White Heron	0	1	1	3	261	Longtoed Plover	0	1	0	2
067	Little Egret	0	1	0	0	264	Common Sandpiper	0	1	0	0
068	Yellowbilled Egret	0	0	0	1	266	Wood Sandpiper	13	35	0	0
071	Cattle Egret	5	17	2	12	269	Marsh Sandpiper	1	4	0	0
072	Squacco Heron	0	0	1	4	270	Greenshank	1	2	0	1
075	Rufousbellied Heron	0	1	0	2	274	Little Stint	1	4	0	0
078	Little Bittern	0	0	0	1	284	Ruff	1	5	0	0
081	Hamerkop	0	1	0	1	286	Ethiopian Snipe	0	1	0	1
094	Hadeda Ibis	2	11	8	22	294	Avocet	0	1	0	0
099	Whitefaced Duck	24	69	12	71	304	Redwinged Pratincole	0	0	0	2
100	Fulvous Duck	0	0	1	6	338	Whiskered Tern	0	2	0	1
101	Whitebacked Duck	0	2	0	2	428	Pied Kingfisher	0	0	0	1
105	African Black Duck	0	0	0	2	431	Malachite Kingfisher	0	1	0	0
114	Pygmy Goose	0	0	1	6	713	Cape Wagtail	0	0	2	4
116	Spurwinged Goose	4	6	33	100		Total	70	122	78	232
148	African Fish Eagle	0	0	0	1		No. of species		45		
165	African Marsh Harrier	0	1	0	1						

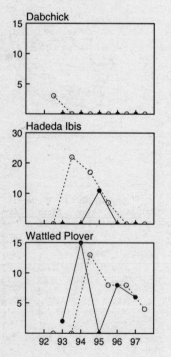

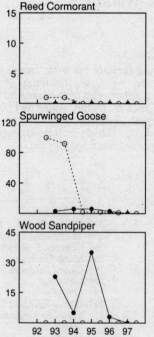

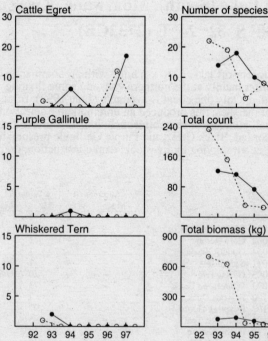

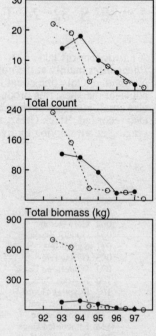

Mhlazi Pan, Mbazwane, KwaZulu–Natal
27° 36' S 32° 39' E (2732DA)

A seasonal pan in the moist coastal grassland between Sodwana Bay and Lake Bhangazi. Such pans on the coastal plain are typically in grassy depressions, with some fringing sedges and *Typha*, and some *Nymphaea* cover. Only small numbers of waterbirds are normally recorded. The great difference between winter and summer figures arises from an exceptional count of 175 birds in winter 1992, when the pan was presumably full; all subsequent counts are low: winter, 0–14 birds; summer, 1–9 birds. No threats have been identified.

		Summer (5)		Winter (6)				Summer (5)		Winter (6)	
		Mean	Max.	Mean	Max.			Mean	Max.	Mean	Max.
008	Dabchick	0	0	1	6	107	Hottentot Teal	0	0	1	4
058	Reed Cormorant	0	0	1	7	108	Redbilled Teal	0	0	1	7
060	Darter	0	0	0	1	114	Pygmy Goose	0	0	0	2
062	Grey Heron	0	0	0	1	240	African Jacana	0	0	2	10
066	Great White Heron	0	0	0	1	241	Lesser Jacana	0	0	1	6
068	Yellowbilled Egret	0	0	1	3	249	Threebanded Plover	0	0	1	4
071	Cattle Egret	0	0	2	10	258	Blacksmith Plover	1	3	1	2
072	Squacco Heron	0	0	1	5	260	Wattled Plover	0	0	1	3
081	Hamerkop	0	0	0	1	266	Wood Sandpiper	1	3	0	1
091	Sacred Ibis	0	0	1	4	270	Greenshank	0	1	0	0
093	Glossy Ibis	0	0	0	2	338	Whiskered Tern	0	0	0	2
095	African Spoonbill	0	0	1	5	713	Cape Wagtail	0	0	0	2
099	Whitefaced Duck	0	1	17	100		Total	3	6	34	175
102	Egyptian Goose	0	0	0	2		No. of species		26		

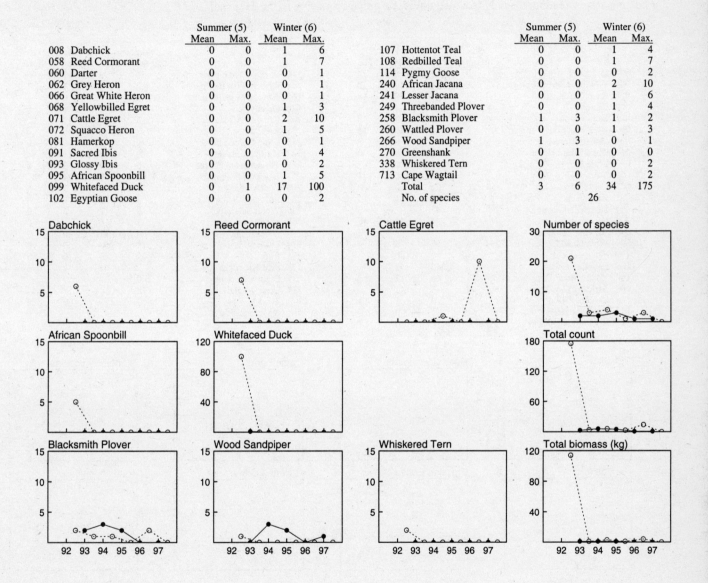

Midmar Dam, Howick, KwaZulu–Natal
29° 31' S 30° 11' E (2930CA)

An IBA. A large water supply dam with open, rather barren and fairly steep shoreline of earth/stones with adjacent grass; marshy patch at one inlet stream, and a little foraging habitat for waders. All three crane species breed. Largest counts of cormorants and Grey Heron in winter 1994, and of Cattle Egret and Sacred Ibis in summer 1994; high biomass totals in summer 1993, and winter 1996 and 1997, due to large counts of Spurwinged and Egyptian Geese. Blacksmith Plover numbers highest in summers of 1993 and 1995; summer 1993 also had highest counts of Little Stint and Ruff. Notable decline in number of species and total counts in recent summers. Used for boating and recreation; the only recorded threat is a proposed raising of the dam wall.

		Summer (5)		Winter (3)					Summer (5)		Winter (3)	
		Mean	Max.	Mean	Max.				Mean	Max.	Mean	Max.
008	Dabchick	0	1	5	14		116	Spurwinged Goose	36	93	127	195
055	Whitebreasted Cormorant	8	16	14	30		148	African Fish Eagle	2	4	1	1
058	Reed Cormorant	4	7	19	48		165	African Marsh Harrier	0	1	0	1
060	Darter	1	4	1	4		170	Osprey	0	1	0	0
062	Grey Heron	2	3	4	10		209	Crowned Crane	5	15	19	22
063	Blackheaded Heron	1	5	6	13		228	Redknobbed Coot	2	6	0	0
064	Goliath Heron	0	1	0	0		246	Whitefronted Plover	0	1	0	0
066	Great White Heron	0	2	0	0		248	Kittlitz's Plover	3	13	11	34
067	Little Egret	0	1	6	17		249	Threebanded Plover	3	9	3	8
068	Yellowbilled Egret	1	3	0	1		258	Blacksmith Plover	65	139	24	41
071	Cattle Egret	26	73	0	0		260	Wattled Plover	6	21	3	5
081	Hamerkop	0	0	1	2		264	Common Sandpiper	5	12	0	0
091	Sacred Ibis	10	43	2	6		266	Wood Sandpiper	5	17	0	0
094	Hadeda Ibis	12	25	25	46		269	Marsh Sandpiper	1	5	0	0
095	African Spoonbill	0	1	1	2		270	Greenshank	4	17	0	0
099	Whitefaced Duck	5	12	0	0		274	Little Stint	19	50	0	0
100	Fulvous Duck	1	3	0	0		284	Ruff	22	80	0	0
102	Egyptian Goose	227	370	157	336		428	Pied Kingfisher	2	4	2	6
104	Yellowbilled Duck	17	46	12	22		429	Giant Kingfisher	0	1	0	1
105	African Black Duck	0	0	2	4		713	Cape Wagtail	6	18	17	45
108	Redbilled Teal	2	8	6	13			Total	503	767	469	520
112	Cape Shoveller	1	2	0	0			No. of species		43		
115	Knobbilled Duck	0	0	0	1							

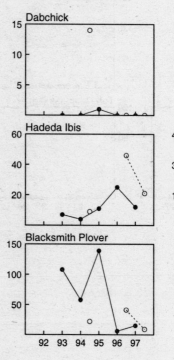

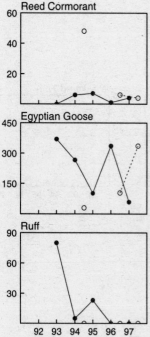

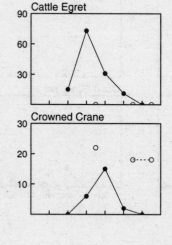

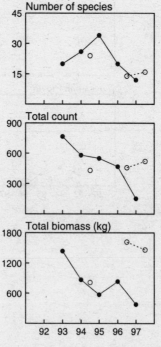

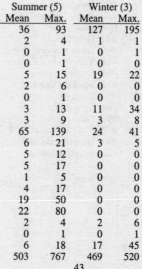

Mlalazi River Estuary, Mtunzini, KwaZulu–Natal
28° 57' S 31° 47' E (2831DD)

The estuary and mouth of the Mlalazi River, with sand beaches, mudflats, saltmarsh, and adjacent mangroves and coastal dune forest. Two winter and two summer counts show a high number of Whitefronted Plover in 1997, and an excellent number of Sanderling in 1996; some Sanderling remain during the austral winter. A number of Sandwich Terns were also recorded in summer 1996. Important threats include pollution by pesticides and fertilizers from sugar cane farms, and a mining threat to the northern side of the dunes.

		Summer (2)		Winter (2)				Summer (2)		Winter (2)	
		Mean	Max.	Mean	Max.			Mean	Max.	Mean	Max.
058	Reed Cormorant	1	2	4	7	270	Greenshank	1	1	0	0
064	Goliath Heron	0	0	2	3	281	Sanderling	159	307	28	55
067	Little Egret	0	0	1	2	284	Ruff	15	29	0	0
074	Greenbacked Heron	1	2	0	0	312	Kelp Gull	3	6	0	0
081	Hamerkop	0	0	1	2	315	Greyheaded Gull	2	3	1	2
086	Woollynecked Stork	1	1	0	0	322	Caspian Tern	1	1	1	1
094	Hadeda Ibis	1	1	0	0	324	Swift Tern	1	1	7	10
099	Whitefaced Duck	2	4	0	0	325	Lesser Crested Tern	3	5	0	0
102	Egyptian Goose	0	0	2	3	326	Sandwich Tern	15	30	0	0
104	Yellowbilled Duck	2	4	3	5	327	Common Tern	7	13	0	0
116	Spurwinged Goose	1	1	1	1	428	Pied Kingfisher	0	0	6	7
148	African Fish Eagle	0	0	1	1	429	Giant Kingfisher	0	0	1	2
246	Whitefronted Plover	6	12	1	2	431	Malachite Kingfisher	0	0	1	1
258	Blacksmith Plover	1	2	0	0		Total	219	366	58	90
264	Common Sandpiper	1	2	2	3		No. of species		28		

Mtunzini Prawn Hatchery, Mtunzini, KwaZulu–Natal
28° 57' S 31° 46' E (2831DD)

Ponds at the Mtunzini Prawn Hatchery. These hold a reasonable selection of waterbirds, including eight Palearctic migrant shorebird species, good counts of which were recorded in summer 1997 when Whitefaced Duck and Reed Cormorant also occurred. Threebanded Plover occurs in good numbers, with relatively high winter counts suggesting seasonal movement, while Woollynecked Stork is apparently more numerous than at most other CWAC sites in the region. Agricultural runoff poses a mild threat.

		Summer (2)		Winter (3)	
		Mean	Max.	Mean	Max.
058	Reed Cormorant	6	11	0	0
062	Grey Heron	5	9	6	10
063	Blackheaded Heron	0	0	1	3
066	Great White Heron	0	0	0	1
067	Little Egret	1	1	3	7
068	Yellowbilled Egret	0	0	0	1
071	Cattle Egret	0	0	1	3
074	Greenbacked Heron	0	0	1	2
081	Hamerkop	2	3	1	3
086	Woollynecked Stork	16	26	19	32
091	Sacred Ibis	0	0	1	3
094	Hadeda Ibis	3	5	1	2
095	African Spoonbill	1	2	4	8
099	Whitefaced Duck	13	25	0	0
102	Egyptian Goose	0	0	1	2
104	Yellowbilled Duck	3	3	3	8
116	Spurwinged Goose	1	1	1	3
245	Ringed Plover	13	24	0	0
246	Whitefronted Plover	3	5	2	4
248	Kittlitz's Plover	11	15	8	13
249	Threebanded Plover	13	23	26	40
258	Blacksmith Plover	8	12	4	7
260	Wattled Plover	2	4	0	0
264	Common Sandpiper	14	19	2	5
266	Wood Sandpiper	22	34	1	3
269	Marsh Sandpiper	2	3	0	0
270	Greenshank	1	2	0	0
272	Curlew Sandpiper	42	83	0	1
274	Little Stint	27	41	0	0
284	Ruff	20	35	0	0
298	Water Dikkop	1	1	1	2
339	Whitewinged Tern	1	1	0	0
428	Pied Kingfisher	2	3	1	2
711	African Pied Wagtail	1	1	0	1
713	Cape Wagtail	3	6	5	8
	Total	227	376	93	107
	No. of species		35		

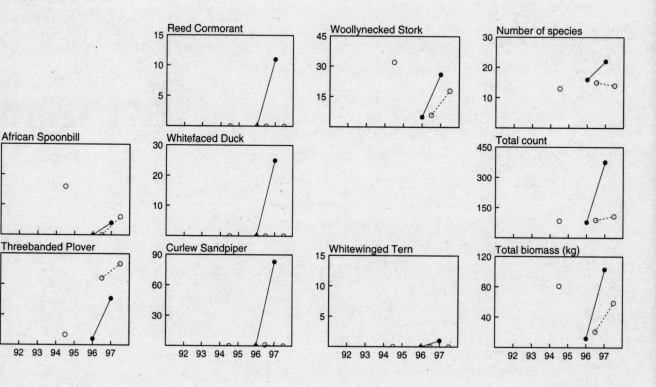

Neshe Pan, Mbazwane, KwaZulu–Natal
27° 39' S 32° 24' E (2732CB)

A shallow natural pan fringed by reeds, grass and some cultivation; floating vegetation can sometimes be extensive. Most waterfowl more numerous in winter, when counts of Whitefaced Duck and Egyptian Goose show recent declines; good for Knobbilled Duck in winter. High winter counts of some waterfowl (including Pygmy Goose), and shorebirds, in only one or two years, and of Curlew Sandpiper in 1992 and Curlew in 1994. Redknobbed Coot recorded only in winter 1992. Important threats are grazing and trampling by livestock, and subsistence agriculture on shorelines; other threats include hunting/trapping, net fishing, and vegetation clearance. Shooting rights recently granted and this may have contributed to the observed decline in the number of species and total counts.

		Summer (5)		Winter (6)	
		Mean	Max.	Mean	Max.
008	Dabchick	0	0	5	14
049	White Pelican	0	1	11	39
050	Pinkbacked Pelican	1	4	1	5
055	Whitebreasted Cormorant	0	0	0	1
058	Reed Cormorant	12	28	5	17
060	Darter	5	15	0	1
062	Grey Heron	1	3	3	6
063	Blackheaded Heron	0	0	4	22
064	Goliath Heron	3	4	1	2
066	Great White Heron	4	7	3	8
067	Little Egret	1	2	3	9
068	Yellowbilled Egret	0	0	0	1
069	Black Egret	0	1	0	0
071	Cattle Egret	25	44	1	2
072	Squacco Heron	5	11	0	1
081	Hamerkop	0	0	0	1
090	Yellowbilled Stork	0	0	0	1
091	Sacred Ibis	0	2	1	1
093	Glossy Ibis	4	19	21	103
095	African Spoonbill	0	0	7	21
096	Greater Flamingo	0	0	0	1
097	Lesser Flamingo	0	0	101	321
099	Whitefaced Duck	21	52	180	416
102	Egyptian Goose	0	1	104	237
104	Yellowbilled Duck	4	20	7	21
107	Hottentot Teal	0	0	3	9
108	Redbilled Teal	0	2	21	109
112	Cape Shoveller	0	0	9	49
114	Pygmy Goose	1	2	17	46
115	Knobbilled Duck	0	0	23	63
116	Spurwinged Goose	6	13	47	227
148	African Fish Eagle	0	1	1	1
165	African Marsh Harrier	0	2	0	1
228	Redknobbed Coot	0	0	23	139
240	African Jacana	33	66	12	28
241	Lesser Jacana	0	1	0	0
242	Painted Snipe	0	0	0	2
248	Kittlitz's Plover	0	1	17	97
249	Threebanded Plover	0	0	1	1
258	Blacksmith Plover	0	0	2	6
260	Wattled Plover	0	0	0	1
264	Common Sandpiper	0	0	1	5
266	Wood Sandpiper	0	1	0	2
269	Marsh Sandpiper	0	0	0	1
270	Greenshank	0	1	2	11
272	Curlew Sandpiper	0	0	40	241
284	Ruff	6	25	0	0
286	Ethiopian Snipe	0	0	1	3
289	Curlew	0	0	18	108
294	Avocet	0	0	6	30
295	Blackwinged Stilt	0	0	29	88
304	Redwinged Pratincole	0	0	1	8
315	Greyheaded Gull	0	0	1	3
322	Caspian Tern	0	1	0	0
335	Little Tern	0	2	3	19
338	Whiskered Tern	5	24	5	18
339	Whitewinged Tern	10	42	3	10
428	Pied Kingfisher	1	3	3	8
431	Malachite Kingfisher	0	0	1	3
711	African Pied Wagtail	0	2	0	0
713	Cape Wagtail	0	0	1	1
	Total	153	226	746	1754
	No. of species		61		

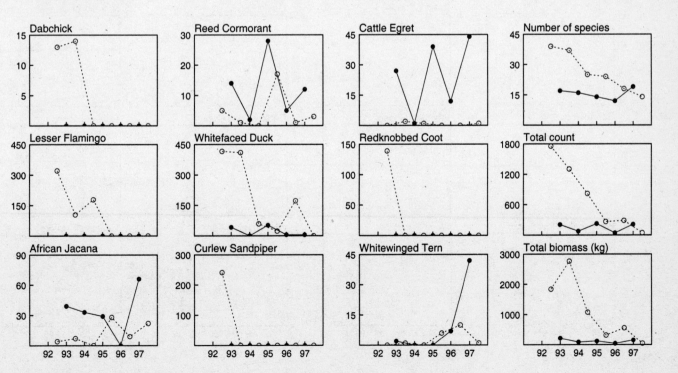

Northern Treatment Works, Durban, KwaZulu–Natal
29° 48' S 31° 00' E (2930DD)

Sewage works with open and reed-fringed ponds, some floating vegetation, reedbeds, and some mud. Holds a good variety of waterbirds, including Greenbacked Heron, Blackcrowned Night Heron, Little Bittern, Black Crake, Purple Gallinule and African Jacana. Waterfowl numbers generally low, except for Egyptian Goose; 35 Black Duck were counted in summer 1995. Cormorant, Cattle Egret and Sacred Ibis numbers are good; all peak in winter. Whiskered and Whitewinged Tern numbers are good in summer, when Common and Little Terns have also occurred. In summer 1997, 272 Wood Sandpiper were recorded. Recent increases in numbers of Whitebreasted Cormorant, Sacred Ibis and Egyptian Goose have contributed to the upward trend shown on total count and biomass graphs. A critical threat is posed by over-trimming of vegetation at pond margins; other threats are alien plant infestation, and the lowering of nutrients following changes in sewage processing methods.

		Summer (5)		Winter (5)				Summer (5)		Winter (5)	
		Mean	Max.	Mean	Max.			Mean	Max.	Mean	Max.
008	Dabchick	1	4	3	5	213	Black Crake	0	0	1	2
049	White Pelican	10	29	1	4	223	Purple Gallinule	0	0	0	1
055	Whitebreasted Cormorant	66	93	40	109	226	Moorhen	0	1	1	3
058	Reed Cormorant	36	54	74	148	228	Redknobbed Coot	7	16	10	23
060	Darter	6	11	13	26	240	African Jacana	6	9	4	7
062	Grey Heron	3	10	5	12	249	Threebanded Plover	5	9	14	30
063	Blackheaded Heron	2	5	0	2	258	Blacksmith Plover	32	48	23	31
065	Purple Heron	0	0	1	2	264	Common Sandpiper	6	11	0	0
067	Little Egret	5	12	4	8	266	Wood Sandpiper	87	272	0	1
071	Cattle Egret	49	223	238	400	269	Marsh Sandpiper	1	3	0	0
072	Squacco Heron	0	0	0	1	270	Greenshank	1	4	0	0
074	Greenbacked Heron	6	7	4	8	272	Curlew Sandpiper	4	22	0	0
076	Blackcrowned Night Heron	0	2	6	12	274	Little Stint	11	41	0	0
078	Little Bittern	0	1	0	0	284	Ruff	80	152	0	0
081	Hamerkop	4	7	6	15	295	Blackwinged Stilt	1	6	2	12
086	Woollynecked Stork	0	0	0	1	298	Water Dikkop	3	4	2	3
091	Sacred Ibis	26	50	120	286	327	Common Tern	1	3	0	0
094	Hadeda Ibis	21	40	7	11	335	Little Tern	0	1	0	0
095	African Spoonbill	2	9	1	7	338	Whiskered Tern	28	140	0	0
099	Whitefaced Duck	10	40	0	0	339	Whitewinged Tern	99	169	0	0
102	Egyptian Goose	460	535	219	408	428	Pied Kingfisher	5	9	4	8
103	South African Shelduck	3	6	1	3	429	Giant Kingfisher	0	1	1	2
104	Yellowbilled Duck	8	17	9	12	431	Malachite Kingfisher	2	3	3	7
105	African Black Duck	7	32	0	0	711	African Pied Wagtail	7	12	8	16
107	Hottentot Teal	1	2	0	0	713	Cape Wagtail	10	12	27	60
112	Cape Shoveller	0	0	0	2	891	Mallard	0	0	0	1
116	Spurwinged Goose	2	4	9	13		Total	1124	1375	866	1170
148	African Fish Eagle	1	2	1	2		No. of species		54		

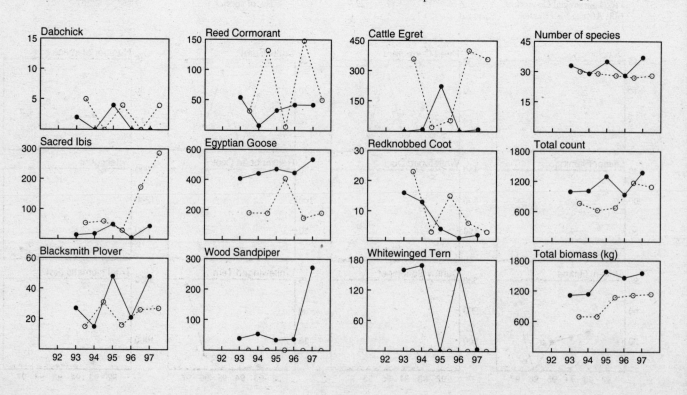

Nsumu Pan, Mkuzi Game Reserve, KwaZulu–Natal

27° 40' S 32° 19' E (2732CB)

Large, permanent, freshwater pan with much fringing *Phragmites*, some marshy areas, variable floating-leaved vegetation (up to 50% *Nymphaea* cover) and variable open shoreline, depending on water level. The only regular breeding site for Pinkbacked Pelican in southern Africa; c. 50 nests in most years. Yellowbilled Stork apparently resident and breeds in most years; some egrets and ibises also breed. Great variation in counts of species such as Spurwinged Goose, African Jacana and some shorebirds may be at least partly explained by variations in water level and vegetation cover. Winter presence of Knot noteworthy. Decline evident in species numbers and count totals, both summer and winter. No threats have been identified.

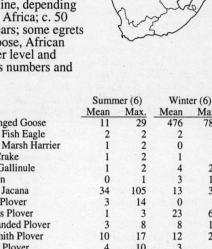

		Summer (6)		Winter (6)				Summer (6)		Winter (6)	
		Mean	Max.	Mean	Max.			Mean	Max.	Mean	Max.
008	Dabchick	0	1	0	0	116	Spurwinged Goose	11	29	476	785
049	White Pelican	2	12	19	81	148	African Fish Eagle	2	2	2	3
050	Pinkbacked Pelican	90	164	4	12	165	African Marsh Harrier	1	2	0	0
055	Whitebreasted Cormorant	0	0	10	58	213	Black Crake	1	2	1	5
058	Reed Cormorant	12	26	1	3	223	Purple Gallinule	1	2	4	21
060	Darter	19	63	0	2	226	Moorhen	0	1	3	16
062	Grey Heron	2	4	3	6	240	African Jacana	34	105	13	35
063	Blackheaded Heron	1	3	5	12	245	Ringed Plover	3	14	0	0
064	Goliath Heron	3	6	0	1	248	Kittlitz's Plover	1	3	23	65
065	Purple Heron	0	1	0	0	249	Threebanded Plover	3	8	8	18
066	Great White Heron	16	64	1	3	258	Blacksmith Plover	10	17	12	21
067	Little Egret	7	28	3	5	260	Wattled Plover	4	10	3	7
068	Yellowbilled Egret	1	4	0	1	264	Common Sandpiper	5	13	1	1
069	Black Egret	3	15	0	0	266	Wood Sandpiper	14	33	0	0
071	Cattle Egret	153	269	180	1000	269	Marsh Sandpiper	9	36	2	8
072	Squacco Heron	27	82	0	1	270	Greenshank	4	15	1	2
074	Greenbacked Heron	4	14	0	0	271	Knot	0	0	16	95
081	Hamerkop	1	2	1	1	272	Curlew Sandpiper	96	421	81	430
086	Woollynecked Stork	1	2	0	0	274	Little Stint	189	702	4	21
087	Openbilled Stork	13	41	2	7	284	Ruff	53	162	0	0
090	Yellowbilled Stork	12	28	7	29	286	Ethiopian Snipe	0	1	0	0
091	Sacred Ibis	13	57	3	8	294	Avocet	0	0	10	33
093	Glossy Ibis	11	53	6	16	295	Blackwinged Stilt	10	23	20	38
094	Hadeda Ibis	2	7	9	50	298	Water Dikkop	6	20	10	28
095	African Spoonbill	16	38	41	84*	315	Greyheaded Gull	0	0	1	3
096	Greater Flamingo	0	0	4	17	322	Caspian Tern	0	0	0	2
097	Lesser Flamingo	0	0	14	56	335	Little Tern	1	6	4	21
099	Whitefaced Duck	63	184	165	488	338	Whiskered Tern	41	179	12	26
100	Fulvous Duck	20	117	0	0	339	Whitewinged Tern	10	41	1	6
102	Egyptian Goose	45	132	38	69	395	Marsh Owl	0	2	0	0
104	Yellowbilled Duck	1	2	2	8	428	Pied Kingfisher	3	8	1	4
107	Hottentot Teal	6	32	1	4	431	Malachite Kingfisher	1	2	0	1
108	Redbilled Teal	0	0	5	22	711	African Pied Wagtail	5	8	2	4
112	Cape Shoveller	0	0	0	1	713	Cape Wagtail	0	1	4	10
113	Southern Pochard	0	0	0	2		Total	1059	1927	1238	2714
114	Pygmy Goose	2	5	1	3		No. of species		71		
115	Knobbilled Duck	0	0	1	5						

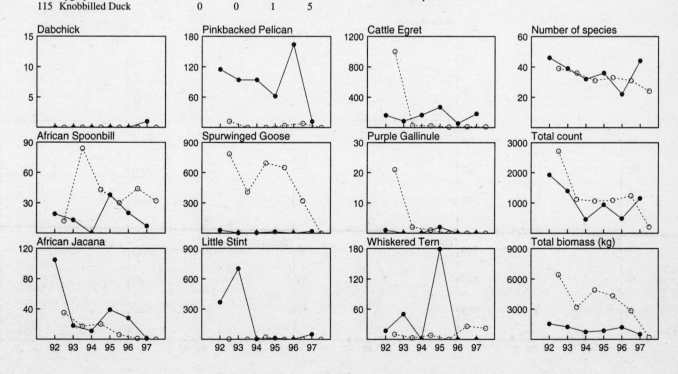

Nyamithi Pan (Ndumo), Ingwavuma, KwaZulu–Natal
26° 53' S 32° 18' E (2632CD)

Large pan fed by Pongola River; because of controlled water release from Pongolapoort Dam, subjected to irregular and unnatural flooding regime in recent years; new water level control just introduced, giving good counts in 1998 (S. Mostert). Fringing grass and *Acacia*; some *Phragmites*; variable exposed muddy substrate. Good numbers of Avocet, Blackwinged Stilt and Water Dikkop sometimes recorded; Slaty Egret regular since 1997; Painted Snipe in 1998. In summer 1995, exceptional counts of Glossy Ibis, Ruff, Fulvous and Whitefaced Duck reflect shallow flooding, probable *Potamogeton* bloom, and muddy foraging areas. High biomass figure in winter 1995 attributable to exceptional count of White Pelicans. Threats include sedimentation, eutrophication, and pollution by pesticides.

		Summer (4)		Winter (5)				Summer (4)		Winter (5)	
		Mean	Max.	Mean	Max.			Mean	Max.	Mean	Max.
049	White Pelican	0	0	34	167	114	Pygmy Goose	0	0	7	33
050	Pinkbacked Pelican	2	6	0	0	116	Spurwinged Goose	2	5	1	5
058	Reed Cormorant	5	17	12	43	148	African Fish Eagle	8	9	5	7
060	Darter	0	1	1	5	213	Black Crake	0	1	1	3
062	Grey Heron	2	5	5	11	223	Purple Gallinule	1	3	1	2
063	Blackheaded Heron	1	2	0	1	226	Moorhen	2	6	0	1
064	Goliath Heron	1	3	1	3	240	African Jacana	0	1	7	25
065	Purple Heron	0	0	0	1	245	Ringed Plover	0	0	0	1
066	Great White Heron	5	7	4	11	248	Kittlitz's Plover	0	0	6	18
067	Little Egret	12	21	4	8	249	Threebanded Plover	9	16	13	24
068	Yellowbilled Egret	1	2	0	0	258	Blacksmith Plover	24	34	17	22
069	Black Egret	1	2	0	0	264	Common Sandpiper	27	50	1	2
071	Cattle Egret	5	19	5	23	266	Wood Sandpiper	1	4	0	1
072	Squacco Heron	0	1	0	2	269	Marsh Sandpiper	32	102	0	1
074	Greenbacked Heron	0	1	0	1	270	Greenshank	3	10	1	4
081	Hamerkop	0	0	1	3	274	Little Stint	18	71	0	0
086	Woollynecked Stork	2	5	1	3	281	Sanderling	0	1	0	0
087	Openbilled Stork	0	1	0	0	284	Ruff	161	621	0	0
088	Saddlebilled Stork	1	2	1	4	294	Avocet	6	23	13	58
090	Yellowbilled Stork	5	13	1	2	295	Blackwinged Stilt	28	93	35	88
091	Sacred Ibis	1	3	1	4	298	Water Dikkop	8	14	6	22
093	Glossy Ibis	96	352	8	33	304	Redwinged Pratincole	0	1	0	0
094	Hadeda Ibis	12	27	1	3	338	Whiskered Tern	6	24	0	0
095	African Spoonbill	10	28	14	46	428	Pied Kingfisher	5	9	16	24
096	Greater Flamingo	0	0	0	1	429	Giant Kingfisher	0	1	0	1
099	Whitefaced Duck	105	369	137	484	431	Malachite Kingfisher	1	2	0	0
100	Fulvous Duck	297	1184	4	20	711	African Pied Wagtail	6	9	8	11
102	Egyptian Goose	180	339	55	108	713	Cape Wagtail	0	1	4	8
107	Hottentot Teal	0	0	0	1		Total	1090	3175	437	983
108	Redbilled Teal	0	0	1	4		No. of species			58	

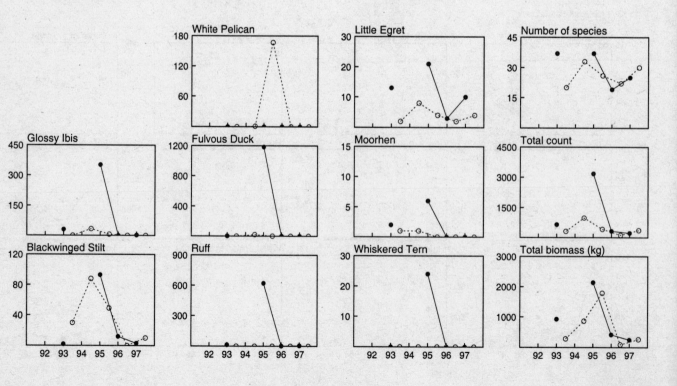

Pongolapoort Dam, Mkuze, KwaZulu–Natal
27° 25' S 31° 58' E (2731BD)

In Pongolapoort Nature Reserve IBA. Large dam on Pongola River; deep water; steep shoreline. When water level was low, had a muddy/rocky shore, so more shorebird habitat; dam now full and shoreline flooded grass and trees, making visibility poor for counts – this may be responsible for recent decline in count totals (D. Johnson). Wide winter and/or summer fluctuations in numbers of some species; no consistent pattern. Whitebreasted Cormorant and Yellowbilled Stork have bred. Numbers of cormorant, ibis and most waterfowl peak in winter; most egrets, Fulvous Duck and Egyptian Goose commoner in summer. Good numbers of Blackheaded Heron and Blackwinged Stilt in winter. High biomass in winter 1995 due to Spurwinged Goose numbers. Threats are eutrophication from fertilizer runoff, and periodic dense growths of blue-green algae.

		Summer (6) Mean	Summer (6) Max.	Winter (6) Mean	Winter (6) Max.			Summer (6) Mean	Summer (6) Max.	Winter (6) Mean	Winter (6) Max.
008	Dabchick	0	0	1	3	115	Knobbilled Duck	0	0	0	2
050	Pinkbacked Pelican	2	10	0	0	116	Spurwinged Goose	22	38	356	1424
055	Whitebreasted Cormorant	0	0	88	144	148	African Fish Eagle	7	13	7	10
058	Reed Cormorant	18	43	95	260	165	African Marsh Harrier	2	5	1	2
060	Darter	1	2	17	36	170	Osprey	2	5	1	2
062	Grey Heron	15	23	12	17	213	Black Crake	0	1	1	3
063	Blackheaded Heron	27	66	69	155	223	Purple Gallinule	0	1	0	0
064	Goliath Heron	7	8	4	9	227	Lesser Moorhen	0	1	0	0
065	Purple Heron	0	1	0	0	228	Redknobbed Coot	0	0	0	1
066	Great White Heron	19	57	11	24	240	African Jacana	17	83	17	54
067	Little Egret	6	14	11	19	245	Ringed Plover	1	4	0	0
068	Yellowbilled Egret	29	172	2	6	248	Kittlitz's Plover	2	10	15	28
069	Black Egret	0	1	0	0	249	Threebanded Plover	1	4	5	9
071	Cattle Egret	594	1582	122	384	258	Blacksmith Plover	7	24	111	214
072	Squacco Heron	1	1	0	0	260	Wattled Plover	10	42	2	3
074	Greenbacked Heron	1	1	1	2	264	Common Sandpiper	9	19	1	4
076	Blackcrowned Night Heron	0	2	0	2	266	Wood Sandpiper	8	29	0	1
081	Hamerkop	0	1	1	2	269	Marsh Sandpiper	0	1	1	4
086	Woollynecked Stork	0	1	4	25	270	Greenshank	11	32	8	31
087	Openbilled Stork	0	0	0	1	272	Curlew Sandpiper	0	1	0	0
090	Yellowbilled Stork	6	15	8	18	274	Little Stint	7	26	0	0
091	Sacred Ibis	18	60	75	308	284	Ruff	1	2	0	0
093	Glossy Ibis	2	7	9	25	294	Avocet	0	0	3	19
094	Hadeda Ibis	9	26	22	41	295	Blackwinged Stilt	1	5	82	212
095	African Spoonbill	5	19	19	38	298	Water Dikkop	3	7	1	5
096	Greater Flamingo	0	0	5	26	339	Whitewinged Tern	0	0	0	1
099	Whitefaced Duck	577	1767	1134	2856	428	Pied Kingfisher	3	5	6	11
100	Fulvous Duck	61	278	1	3	429	Giant Kingfisher	0	0	1	2
102	Egyptian Goose	259	582	182	368	431	Malachite Kingfisher	1	2	1	2
104	Yellowbilled Duck	15	38	11	24	711	African Pied Wagtail	1	7	1	2
107	Hottentot Teal	0	2	3	19	713	Cape Wagtail	0	0	0	2
108	Redbilled Teal	13	58	59	161		Total	1798	4607	2596	5295
112	Cape Shoveller	0	0	14	40		No. of species		65		
113	Southern Pochard	1	8	0	0						

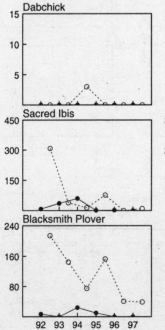

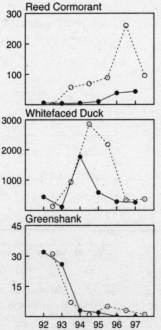

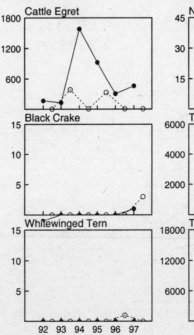

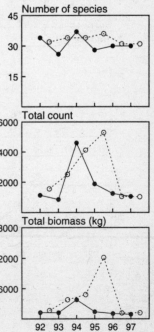

Reichenau Mission Dam, Underberg, KwaZulu–Natal
29° 48' S 29° 38' E (2929DC)

A farm dam with open water, some fringing reeds, some marshy vegetation, and a little exposed mud at low water levels. The commonest waterbirds are Yellowbilled Duck and Redknobbed Coot, both of which show peak numbers in winter. Other waterfowl, and ibises and Dabchick, also peak in winter, but cormorant numbers are higher in summer. Reasonable counts of some shorebirds such as Blacksmith Plover, Curlew Sandpiper and Ruff are recorded in summer. Crowned Crane, African Rail, Purple Gallinule and Halfcollared Kingfisher also occur. Declining Redknobbed Coot numbers contribute significantly to the observed overall decline in total counts during the survey period. Threats include hunting, and adjacent overhead powerlines.

		Summer (5) Mean	Summer (5) Max.	Winter (5) Mean	Winter (5) Max.			Summer (5) Mean	Summer (5) Max.	Winter (5) Mean	Winter (5) Max.
008	Dabchick	16	31	46	80	209 Crowned Crane		4	8	4	6
055	Whitebreasted Cormorant	1	1	0	0	210 African Rail		0	0	0	1
058	Reed Cormorant	13	25	8	18	223 Purple Gallinule		0	1	0	0
060	Darter	2	6	0	0	226 Moorhen		7	17	7	16
062	Grey Heron	1	3	1	3	228 Redknobbed Coot		295	650	612	1010
063	Blackheaded Heron	1	2	5	16	240 African Jacana		0	0	0	1
065	Purple Heron	0	1	0	0	249 Threebanded Plover		1	5	0	0
066	Great White Heron	1	7	0	2	258 Blacksmith Plover		26	48	7	20
068	Yellowbilled Egret	0	1	1	2	264 Common Sandpiper		1	4	0	0
071	Cattle Egret	0	1	1	3	266 Wood Sandpiper		1	2	0	0
081	Hamerkop	0	1	0	1	269 Marsh Sandpiper		0	2	0	0
091	Sacred Ibis	0	2	4	13	272 Curlew Sandpiper		8	40	0	0
094	Hadeda Ibis	4	8	7	21	284 Ruff		10	50	0	0
095	African Spoonbill	1	2	2	3	286 Ethiopian Snipe		0	0	1	3
101	Whitebacked Duck	0	0	2	12	295 Blackwinged Stilt		1	7	2	7
102	Egyptian Goose	27	61	47	67	338 Whiskered Tern		0	0	0	1
103	South African Shelduck	0	0	6	19	428 Pied Kingfisher		1	3	1	4
104	Yellowbilled Duck	64	130	133	350	429 Giant Kingfisher		0	0	0	1
108	Redbilled Teal	1	6	1	4	430 Halfcollared Kingfisher		0	1	0	0
112	Cape Shoveller	2	5	6	10	431 Malachite Kingfisher		1	1	1	3
113	Southern Pochard	1	3	1	3	713 Cape Wagtail		1	4	1	2
116	Spurwinged Goose	8	22	15	60	Total		504	1062	923	1650
165	African Marsh Harrier	1	2	0	1	No. of species			44		

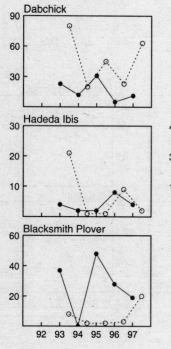

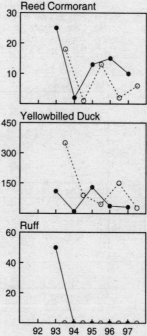

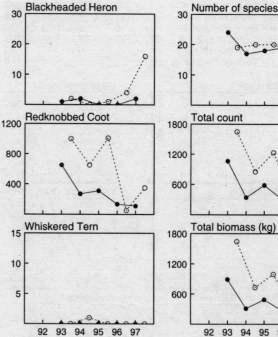

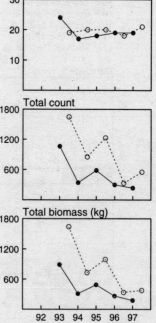

Richards Bay, Richards Bay (town), KwaZulu–Natal
28° 49' S 32° 02' E (2832CC)

An IBA. Richards Bay port area; open estuary (including Mhlatuze Lagoon), permanent marsh and seasonal wetland; Thulazihleka Pan within survey area but is counted separately. Wide variety of birds, but recent decline in number of species; exceptional total count in summer 1996 due to globally significant number of 13 000 Common Tern; same count produced highest numbers of Crested and Little Terns. Good numbers of Reed Cormorant, Woolly-necked Stork and Caspian Tern summer and winter; Whimbrel counts high even in winter. Threats are sedimentation, vegetation cutting, reclamation/drainage, and pollution by industrial waste.

		Summer (5)		Winter (5)				Summer (5)		Winter (5)	
		Mean	Max.	Mean	Max.			Mean	Max.	Mean	Max.
008	Dabchick	7	21	17	20	228	Redknobbed Coot	6	18	12	16
049	White Pelican	54	140	25	74	240	African Jacana	6	13	16	30
050	Pinkbacked Pelican	2	9	14	35	241	Lesser Jacana	0	1	0	1
055	Whitebreasted Cormorant	6	29	19	35	245	Ringed Plover	22	40	0	1
056	Cape Cormorant	0	0	0	2	246	Whitefronted Plover	21	36	55	90
058	Reed Cormorant	91	342	89	332	248	Kittlitz's Plover	0	2	3	12
060	Darter	14	45	13	22	249	Threebanded Plover	1	2	1	5
062	Grey Heron	11	21	10	22	254	Grey Plover	141	260	19	48
063	Blackheaded Heron	1	4	2	7	258	Blacksmith Plover	3	5	3	8
064	Goliath Heron	2	4	2	4	262	Turnstone	3	8	0	0
065	Purple Heron	9	29	3	8	263	Terek Sandpiper	161	410	1	6
066	Great White Heron	5	18	4	11	264	Common Sandpiper	6	11	0	0
067	Little Egret	4	11	21	38	266	Wood Sandpiper	20	57	0	0
068	Yellowbilled Egret	1	3	0	1	269	Marsh Sandpiper	12	33	0	1
071	Cattle Egret	11	54	2	12	270	Greenshank	4	10	1	4
072	Squacco Heron	0	1	0	0	271	Knot	1	1	0	0
074	Greenbacked Heron	0	1	0	0	272	Curlew Sandpiper	180	541	10	50
081	Hamerkop	1	4	0	1	274	Little Stint	116	302	0	0
086	Woollynecked Stork	15	42	35	69	281	Sanderling	13	16	0	0
087	Openbilled Stork	0	0	2	12	284	Ruff	16	64	0	0
090	Yellowbilled Stork	1	6	2	11	288	Bartailed Godwit	3	10	0	0
091	Sacred Ibis	8	22	16	43	289	Curlew	7	13	1	4
093	Glossy Ibis	5	16	1	2	290	Whimbrel	182	356	43	119
094	Hadeda Ibis	5	20	5	12	295	Blackwinged Stilt	7	25	8	29
095	African Spoonbill	5	14	5	10	296	Crab Plover	0	1	0	0
096	Greater Flamingo	2	10	19	97	298	Water Dikkop	1	4	0	0
097	Lesser Flamingo	0	0	0	1	304	Redwinged Pratincole	1	4	3	13
099	Whitefaced Duck	5	13	0	0	312	Kelp Gull	7	17	15	24
101	Whitebacked Duck	7	22	3	7	315	Greyheaded Gull	120	210	72	97
102	Egyptian Goose	2	4	4	10	322	Caspian Tern	19	30	18	32
104	Yellowbilled Duck	46	119	29	83	324	Swift Tern	9	25	47	115
106	Cape Teal	3	11	4	10	325	Lesser Crested Tern	34	80	0	0
107	Hottentot Teal	10	34	7	33	326	Sandwich Tern	48	81	1	2
108	Redbilled Teal	0	0	3	11	327	Common Tern	2866	13000**	3	8
112	Cape Shoveller	1	2	2	6	335	Little Tern	335	700*	0	0
114	Pygmy Goose	0	2	5	13	338	Whiskered Tern	0	1	0	2
116	Spurwinged Goose	4	8	6	14	339	Whitewinged Tern	31	50	0	0
148	African Fish Eagle	3	6	5	8	428	Pied Kingfisher	5	10	10	14
165	African Marsh Harrier	1	2	0	1	429	Giant Kingfisher	1	3	2	6
170	Osprey	3	6	1	2	431	Malachite Kingfisher	1	3	1	4
209	Crowned Crane	2	3	2	4	711	African Pied Wagtail	3	5	2	7
210	African Rail	0	0	1	2	713	Cape Wagtail	6	10	4	12
213	Black Crake	4	11	5	16		Total	4798	14617	768	1382
223	Purple Gallinule	10	30	10	26		No. of species		87		
226	Moorhen	17	39	17	34						

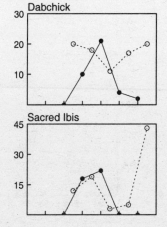

Dabchick

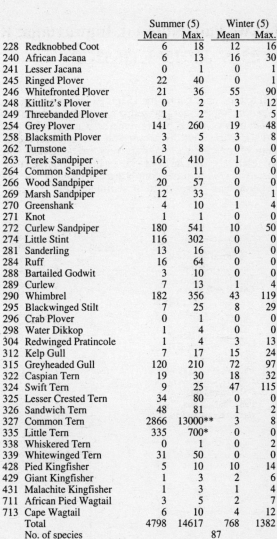

Reed Cormorant — Woollynecked Stork — Number of species

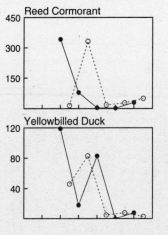

Sacred Ibis

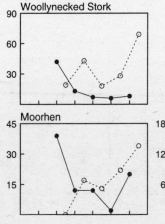

Yellowbilled Duck — Moorhen

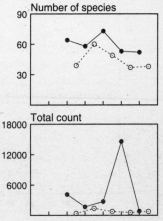

Total count

More graphs on next page.

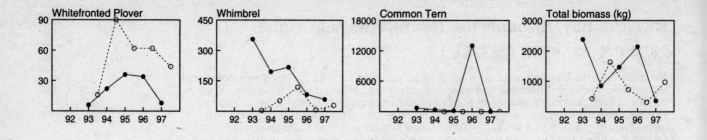

Shokwe Pan (Ndumo), Ingwavuma, KwaZulu–Natal
26° 53' S 32° 13' E (2632CD)

Small oxbow pan, fed by the Usutu River; often dry; water usually very turbid; very little floating vegetation; some emergent sedge and grass, and one *Phragmites* bed; muddy substrate. Deep channel now connects pan to river, so water level depends on river flow – uncontrolled water-level fluctuations are possibly responsible for the observed decline in total counts and species numbers. Counts of individual species are very erratic in both summer and winter, but winter bird numbers were relatively high in 1993–95, owing to to large counts of Whitefaced Duck and Spurwinged Goose, whereas summer counts are consistently low. African Jacana presumably inhabits emergent vegetation here. Threatened by sedimentation.

		Summer (3)		Winter (5)				Summer (3)		Winter (5)	
		Mean	Max.	Mean	Max.			Mean	Max.	Mean	Max.
058	Reed Cormorant	0	0	0	1	099	Whitefaced Duck	4	11	172	549
062	Grey Heron	0	0	2	7	102	Egyptian Goose	7	19	26	75
064	Goliath Heron	0	0	1	2	116	Spurwinged Goose	10	28	193	487
065	Purple Heron	1	2	0	0	148	African Fish Eagle	3	6	0	1
066	Great White Heron	0	0	1	5	213	Black Crake	1	2	0	0
067	Little Egret	0	0	1	2	226	Moorhen	0	0	0	1
071	Cattle Egret	0	0	3	14	240	African Jacana	9	14	9	23
072	Squacco Heron	1	2	0	1	258	Blacksmith Plover	0	0	2	4
074	Greenbacked Heron	1	3	1	4	266	Wood Sandpiper	0	1	0	0
081	Hamerkop	0	1	0	2	295	Blackwinged Stilt	0	0	1	6
086	Woollynecked Stork	1	2	0	2	298	Water Dikkop	5	12	3	14
090	Yellowbilled Stork	0	0	7	31	428	Pied Kingfisher	2	5	1	3
091	Sacred Ibis	0	0	0	1		Total	50	72	434	968
094	Hadeda Ibis	6	12	3	12		No. of species			27	
095	African Spoonbill	0	0	5	13						

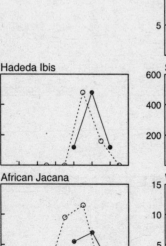

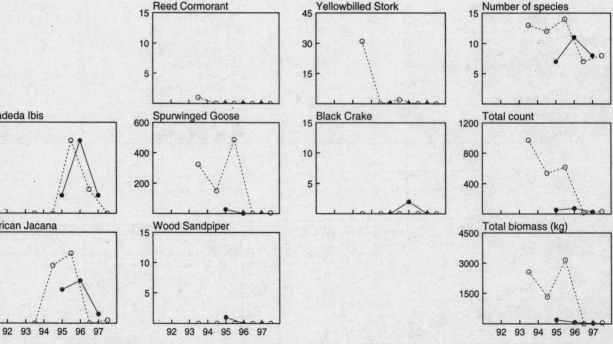

Slangdraai Dam, Ladysmith, KwaZulu–Natal
28° 14' S 29° 45' E (2829BA)

A dam on the Sundays River, constructed for irrigation purposes. Open water with little fringing vegetation. Counts are available for winter 1995 and summer/winter 1996. High numbers of Redknobbed Coot were recorded in winter 1995, when Yellowbilled Duck numbers were also relatively high. In winter 1996, when waterfowl numbers were low, the overall bird count (102) was only 4% of that in winter 1995 (2491). Egyptian and Spurwinged Goose numbers are apparently high in years when grain crops are grown in the vicinity of the dam. No threats have been identified.

	Summer (1)		Winter (2)				Summer (1)		Winter (2)	
	Mean	Max.	Mean	Max.			Mean	Max.	Mean	Max.
008 Dabchick	0	0	4	8	108 Redbilled Teal		4	4	8	12
055 Whitebreasted Cormorant	0	0	1	1	113 Southern Pochard		8	8	4	7
060 Darter	0	0	1	2	115 Knobbilled Duck		0	0	2	3
063 Blackheaded Heron	0	0	1	2	117 Maccoa Duck		0	0	1	2
071 Cattle Egret	35	35	5	10	228 Redknobbed Coot		3	3	1127	2220
094 Hadeda Ibis	0	0	1	2	258 Blacksmith Plover		5	5	10	16
096 Greater Flamingo	0	0	1	2	713 Cape Wagtail		6	6	10	12
102 Egyptian Goose	300	300	75	127	Total		373	373	1297	2491
103 South African Shelduck	0	0	2	4	No. of species				17	

Sodwana Bay to Cape Vidal, St Lucia, KwaZulu–Natal
27° 52' S 32° 36' E (2732DC)

About 68 kms of sandy beach from Sodwana Bay south to Cape Vidal. Three counts are available, two features of these being of particular interest. The relative abundance of Whitefronted Plover in summer may reflect either summer movement to the coast by inland populations (race *mechowi*) from tropical rivers during flooding, or winter local movement of birds away from exposed open coastline. The winter abundance of Greyheaded Gull, a species which normally breeds in winter and spring, may represent nonbreeders (possibly immatures) from the nearest breeding colony, at Lake St Lucia. Disturbance from vehicles is an important threat on such beaches, with other recreational activities having a variable impact, while mild threats are posed by occasional oil pollution and by solid waste materials, including fishing lines.

	Summer (1)		Winter (2)				Summer (1)		Winter (2)	
	Mean	Max.	Mean	Max.			Mean	Max.	Mean	Max.
148 African Fish Eagle	2	2	2	2	322 Caspian Tern		4	4	9	13
170 Osprey	1	1	0	0	324 Swift Tern		0	0	4	8
246 Whitefronted Plover	127	127	66	81	327 Common Tern		21	21	1	1
270 Greenshank	2	2	0	0	335 Little Tern		46	46	0	0
271 Knot	23	23	0	0	713 Cape Wagtail		3	3	0	0
281 Sanderling	28	28	7	14	Total		258	258	171	226
315 Greyheaded Gull	1	1	84	108	No. of species				12	

The Swamp, Underberg, KwaZulu–Natal
29° 46' S 29° 37' E (2929DC)

The Swamp Nature Reserve contains a highly disturbed remnant of a much larger wetland on the Pholela floodplain. Vegetation includes hygrophilous grassland and mixed sedgebeds which are often very fragmented and may be deeply flooded seasonally. Counts were made only in 1993 and summer 1994; subsequently discontinued because of small numbers of birds, difficulty of access, and disturbance from poaching and nearby human activities. Counts reflect nothing of significance, but the site does hold Redchested Flufftail, Wattled and Crowned Cranes, Ethiopian Snipe and Grass Owl.

	Summer (2)		Winter (1)				Summer (2)		Winter (1)	
	Mean	Max.	Mean	Max.			Mean	Max.	Mean	Max.
058 Reed Cormorant	2	3	0	0	209 Crowned Crane		1	2	0	0
063 Blackheaded Heron	2	4	1	1	431 Malachite Kingfisher		1	1	0	0
094 Hadeda Ibis	3	5	0	0	713 Cape Wagtail		1	2	4	4
102 Egyptian Goose	1	2	0	0	Total		18	35	5	5
104 Yellowbilled Duck	5	9	0	0	No. of species				9	

Spioenkop Dam, Winterton, KwaZulu–Natal
28° 41' S 29° 29' E (2829CB)

A large dam within the Spioenkop Nature Reserve IBA. Shoreline mostly steep and rocky, with some more shallowly sloping grassy areas; very little mud. Holds relatively moderate numbers of a reasonable selection of waterbird species. Counts of Dabchick, cormorants, Darter, Cattle Egret, Whitefaced and Yellowbilled Duck, Redbilled Teal, Spurwinged Goose, Redknobbed Coot, and Threebanded and Blacksmith Plovers peak in winter; counts of Egyptian Goose are highest in summer. Adverse conditions caused the summer 1996 count to be abandoned. Grass Owl and Whitebacked Night Heron occur; 1 pair of Goliath Heron breeds. Overall numbers, and species richness, appear to be declining in winter. Boating, fishing and human disturbance may pose mild localized threats; quelea-control measures have adversely affected reedbed birds in the past.

		Summer (4)		Winter (5)				Summer (4)		Winter (5)	
		Mean	Max.	Mean	Max.			Mean	Max.	Mean	Max.
008	Dabchick	0	0	5	7	105	African Black Duck	0	0	1	4
055	Whitebreasted Cormorant	3	10	37	100	108	Redbilled Teal	0	0	6	30
058	Reed Cormorant	2	6	45	86	115	Knobbilled Duck	0	0	0	1
060	Darter	4	8	20	53	116	Spurwinged Goose	6	12	64	194
062	Grey Heron	3	7	3	4	148	African Fish Eagle	1	2	1	2
063	Blackheaded Heron	2	4	1	3	165	African Marsh Harrier	0	0	0	2
064	Goliath Heron	2	5	3	6	226	Moorhen	0	0	1	3
065	Purple Heron	0	0	0	1	228	Redknobbed Coot	0	1	10	41
066	Great White Heron	0	0	0	1	249	Threebanded Plover	2	8	5	19
071	Cattle Egret	5	21	12	40	258	Blacksmith Plover	3	12	9	20
076	Blackcrowned Night Heron	0	0	4	12	264	Common Sandpiper	2	7	0	0
081	Hamerkop	1	3	2	4	270	Greenshank	2	9	1	3
091	Sacred Ibis	0	0	1	5	339	Whitewinged Tern	0	0	0	1
093	Glossy Ibis	0	1	0	0	428	Pied Kingfisher	13	25	11	15
094	Hadeda Ibis	4	13	5	12	429	Giant Kingfisher	0	1	1	2
095	African Spoonbill	0	0	3	12	431	Malachite Kingfisher	3	12	0	1
099	Whitefaced Duck	1	4	47	210	711	African Pied Wagtail	1	2	0	0
102	Egyptian Goose	174	504	72	146	713	Cape Wagtail	16	23	21	30
103	South African Shelduck	3	12	1	2		Total	275	726	683	1459
104	Yellowbilled Duck	21	79	289	615		No. of species			38	

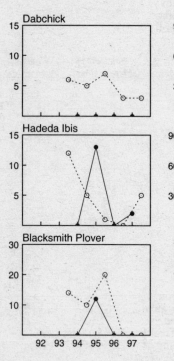
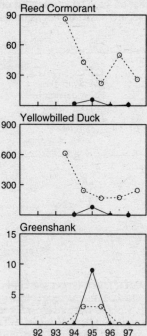
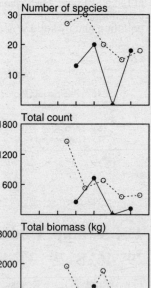
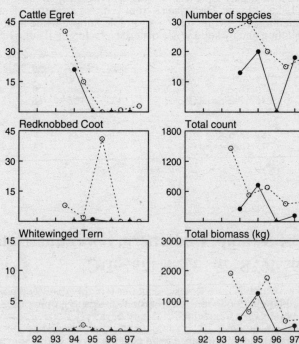

Sundumbili Sewage Works, Mandini, KwaZulu–Natal
29° 11' S 31° 25' E (2931AB)

Sewage works near the Tugela River. Like the nearby Mandini Sewage Works, only two summer and three winter counts are available. These have recorded twice the number of bird species counted at Mandini during the same period, but numbers of most species were low. Purple Heron, Yellowbilled Stork, Fish Eagle, Black Crake, three species of tern and three species of kingfisher are recorded. High counts of African Jacana in summer 1995 and of Common Sandpiper in summer 1996. Whitefaced Duck counts are higher in winter. No threats have been identified.

		Summer (2)		Winter (3)					Summer (2)		Winter (3)	
		Mean	Max.	Mean	Max.				Mean	Max.	Mean	Max.
008	Dabchick	6	10	5	5		108	Redbilled Teal	2	3	1	3
049	White Pelican	0	0	0	1		148	African Fish Eagle	0	0	1	2
050	Pinkbacked Pelican	1	1	3	8		213	Black Crake	0	0	0	1
055	Whitebreasted Cormorant	6	8	0	1		226	Moorhen	1	1	1	2
058	Reed Cormorant	7	11	9	11		229	African Finfoot	1	1	0	0
060	Darter	1	2	0	1		240	African Jacana	12	20	4	7
062	Grey Heron	2	2	4	7		249	Threebanded Plover	1	1	0	0
063	Blackheaded Heron	3	3	0	0		258	Blacksmith Plover	5	5	2	4
065	Purple Heron	1	1	0	0		264	Common Sandpiper	10	16	0	0
066	Great White Heron	1	2	1	2		266	Wood Sandpiper	2	4	0	0
067	Little Egret	0	0	0	1		274	Little Stint	0	0	0	1
068	Yellowbilled Egret	0	0	0	1		327	Common Tern	1	1	0	0
071	Cattle Egret	9	15	2	5		338	Whiskered Tern	1	1	0	0
081	Hamerkop	2	2	1	2		339	Whitewinged Tern	1	1	0	0
090	Yellowbilled Stork	0	0	1	2		428	Pied Kingfisher	2	2	1	2
091	Sacred Ibis	0	0	1	2		429	Giant Kingfisher	0	0	1	1
094	Hadeda Ibis	2	3	0	0		431	Malachite Kingfisher	1	1	1	3
099	Whitefaced Duck	3	6	17	29		713	Cape Wagtail	2	3	2	4
102	Egyptian Goose	2	3	1	2			Total	87	92	65	76
104	Yellowbilled Duck	9	10	5	9			No. of species			38	

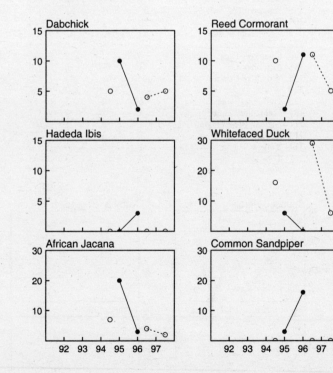
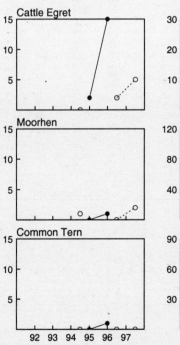
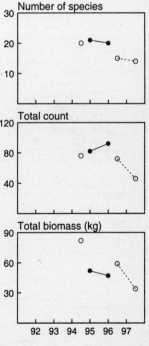

Thulazihleka Pan, Richards Bay, KwaZulu–Natal
28° 47' S 32° 03' E (2832CC)

Shallow pan created by disposal of sludge from harbour construction; nutrient-rich; no inflow/outflow; maintained by rain, seepage and runoff. Much emergent and floating vegetation (*Phragmites, Typha*, sedges, grass, etc.). Varied avifauna, including 7 rail species. Large counts of Dabchick, African Spoonbill, Purple Heron, Whitebacked Duck, Hottentot Teal, Pygmy Goose, Redknobbed Coot, African and Lesser Jacana, and Whitewinged Tern particularly noteworthy. Waterfowl and flamingos peak in winter. Threats: vegetation cutting, water level manipulation, landfill, solid waste, and pollution (gypsum, fluoride, fertilizers).

		Summer (5)		Winter (5)	
		Mean	Max.	Mean	Max.
008	Dabchick	5	13	156	400*
049	White Pelican	36	120	44	108
050	Pinkbacked Pelican	11	27	7	14
055	Whitebreasted Cormorant	19	71	91	158
058	Reed Cormorant	66	152	85	216
060	Darter	58	83	27	82
062	Grey Heron	11	21	12	20
063	Blackheaded Heron	2	4	7	19
064	Goliath Heron	2	4	3	6
065	Purple Heron	11	27	10	24
066	Great White Heron	6	27	4	7
067	Little Egret	12	28	12	33
068	Yellowbilled Egret	1	2	1	1
069	Black Egret	1	2	0	0
071	Cattle Egret	8	38	1	2
072	Squacco Heron	18	33	13	24
074	Greenbacked Heron	0	1	0	0
076	Blackcrowned Night Heron	1	2	0	0
078	Little Bittern	1	2	0	0
081	Hamerkop	0	1	1	2
086	Woollynecked Stork	2	5	0	0
090	Yellowbilled Stork	3	6	1	3
091	Sacred Ibis	6	26	10	28
093	Glossy Ibis	13	58	5	13
094	Hadeda Ibis	1	4	4	17
095	African Spoonbill	31	136*	42	81*
096	Greater Flamingo	24	118	56	134
097	Lesser Flamingo	0	0	55	170
099	Whitefaced Duck	21	68	19	50
100	Fulvous Duck	7	30	5	25
101	Whitebacked Duck	28	118	63	216
102	Egyptian Goose	6	9	11	20
104	Yellowbilled Duck	25	82	68	106
106	Cape Teal	0	0	2	6
107	Hottentot Teal	59	145	29	51
108	Redbilled Teal	1	2	26	58
112	Cape Shoveller	0	0	9	19
113	Southern Pochard	1	3	17	66
114	Pygmy Goose	0	0	42	115
116	Spurwinged Goose	5	9	13	44
148	African Fish Eagle	2	4	3	6
165	African Marsh Harrier	2	3	2	3
170	Osprey	1	1	0	0
210	African Rail	1	4	5	15
213	Black Crake	14	18	14	22
215	Baillon's Crake	0	1	0	0
217	Redchested Flufftail	0	1	0	0
223	Purple Gallinule	17	41	14	21
226	Moorhen	15	47	15	30
228	Redknobbed Coot	102	290	272	500
240	African Jacana	48	104	52	80
241	Lesser Jacana	3	9	4	16
245	Ringed Plover	7	16	0	0
246	Whitefronted Plover	0	1	0	2
248	Kittlitz's Plover	18	55	5	11
249	Threebanded Plover	6	15	5	10
254	Grey Plover	0	0	0	2
258	Blacksmith Plover	1	5	4	7
264	Common Sandpiper	2	8	0	0
266	Wood Sandpiper	40	152	0	1
269	Marsh Sandpiper	31	81	0	1
270	Greenshank	1	3	4	17
272	Curlew Sandpiper	20	58	0	0
274	Little Stint	92	295	0	0
284	Ruff	68	136	1	4
294	Avocet	0	0	16	32
295	Blackwinged Stilt	23	45	21	74
304	Redwinged Pratincole	0	1	4	18
315	Greyheaded Gull	64	280	25	54
322	Caspian Tern	4	14	6	25
327	Common Tern	0	0	2	10
335	Little Tern	4	12	0	0
338	Whiskered Tern	29	100	82	200
339	Whitewinged Tern	1005*	2000**	230	900
428	Pied Kingfisher	6	10	8	14
431	Malachite Kingfisher	4	5	3	7
711	African Pied Wagtail	1	3	1	3
713	Cape Wagtail	1	3	4	13
714	Yellow Wagtail	1	2	0	0
	Total	2130	4415	1753	2653
	No. of species			79	

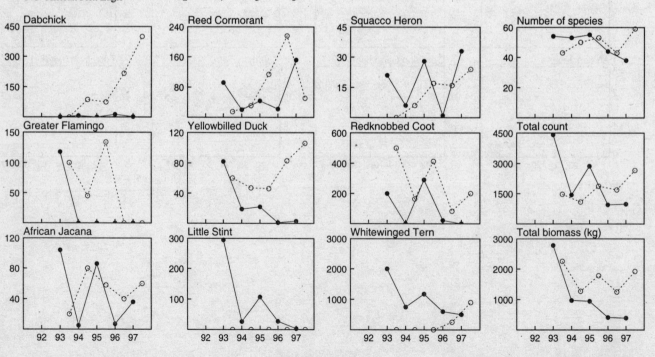

Tshanetshe Pan, Mbazwane, KwaZulu–Natal
27° 40' S 32° 26' E (2732CB)

A floodplain pan with much emergent grass, some *Nymphaea* and discontinuous fringing strips of *Cyperus*. A good selection of wetland birds occurs; most species occur in small numbers, but a globally significant count of Whitebacked Duck was made in winter 1992 ((the only record), and large numbers of Whitefaced Duck and Spurwinged Goose in the winters of 1992–1993 winters, when unusually good counts made of other species (Dabchick, Fulvous Duck and Pygmy Goose in 1992; White Pelican, Knobbilled Duck and Egyptian Goose in 1993); 29 Curlew in winter 1994. Most Squacco Herons occur in summer, when vegetation cover is better. Has good potential for Lesser Moorhen. It lies outside of the Greater St Lucia Wetland Park and suffers from severe bank erosion, grazing and trampling by cattle, and hunting and trapping.

		Summer (5) Mean	Summer (5) Max.	Winter (6) Mean	Winter (6) Max.			Summer (5) Mean	Summer (5) Max.	Winter (6) Mean	Winter (6) Max.
008	Dabchick	0	0	6	34	115	Knobbilled Duck	0	0	10	32
049	White Pelican	0	0	20	80	116	Spurwinged Goose	14	31	65	211
055	Whitebreasted Cormorant	0	0	2	9	148	African Fish Eagle	0	1	1	1
058	Reed Cormorant	6	14	6	16	165	African Marsh Harrier	0	1	0	0
060	Darter	4	14	5	18	213	Black Crake	1	2	0	0
062	Grey Heron	1	1	1	2	223	Purple Gallinule	0	0	0	1
063	Blackheaded Heron	0	0	0	1	240	African Jacana	26	46	23	65
064	Goliath Heron	1	2	1	2	241	Lesser Jacana	0	0	1	3
065	Purple Heron	1	3	0	1	248	Kittlitz's Plover	0	1	2	9
066	Great White Heron	4	11	2	5	249	Threebanded Plover	0	2	1	3
067	Little Egret	1	4	1	5	258	Blacksmith Plover	2	6	1	4
068	Yellowbilled Egret	0	2	0	0	260	Wattled Plover	7	18	6	15
069	Black Egret	0	2	0	0	264	Common Sandpiper	1	2	0	0
071	Cattle Egret	36	54	24	56	266	Wood Sandpiper	4	15	1	5
072	Squacco Heron	7	17	0	1	270	Greenshank	1	2	0	0
081	Hamerkop	1	1	0	0	284	Ruff	2	6	0	0
086	Woollynecked Stork	0	1	0	0	289	Curlew	0	0	5	29
090	Yellowbilled Stork	1	5	1	2	295	Blackwinged Stilt	1	5	6	21
091	Sacred Ibis	7	17	2	9	304	Redwinged Pratincole	0	0	0	1
093	Glossy Ibis	1	5	5	22	315	Greyheaded Gull	0	0	0	1
094	Hadeda Ibis	2	6	1	5	322	Caspian Tern	0	0	0	2
095	African Spoonbill	0	0	5	9	338	Whiskered Tern	2	5	4	10
099	Whitefaced Duck	26	51	295	882	339	Whitewinged Tern	1	5	0	0
100	Fulvous Duck	0	0	6	33	428	Pied Kingfisher	3	6	2	6
101	Whitebacked Duck	0	0	92	550**	429	Giant Kingfisher	0	0	0	2
102	Egyptian Goose	3	9	16	80	431	Malachite Kingfisher	1	3	2	4
104	Yellowbilled Duck	1	4	8	31	713	Cape Wagtail	0	0	1	2
108	Redbilled Teal	0	2	0	0		Total	172	226	645	1814
114	Pygmy Goose	0	2	16	89		No. of species			56	

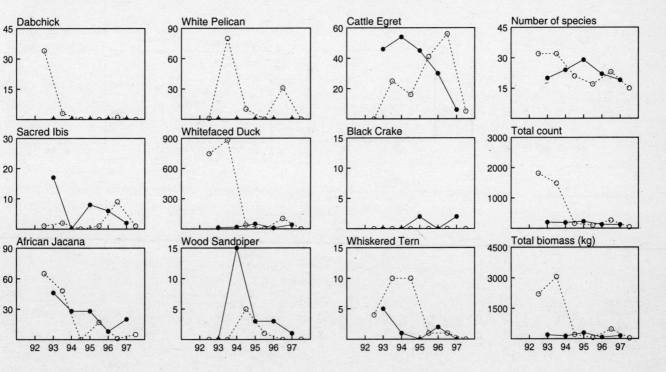

TOTAL CWAC Report 1992–97   KwaZulu-Natal   129

Tugela River Mouth, Mandini, KwaZulu–Natal
29° 13' S 31° 28' E (2931AB)

The open estuary of the Tugela River; it has sand beaches, and little natural fringing vegetation because of the encroachment of sugar cane. Only 3 summer counts are available, reflecting small numbers of shorebirds and Sandwich Tern, but large numbers of Common Tern and the second highest total of Little Tern recorded during the survey period. Threats include siltation, organic pollution, agricultural encroachment, and disturbance from recreational activities, including ski boats and four-wheel-drive vehicles.

		Summer (3)		Winter (0)				Summer (3)		Winter (0)	
		Mean	Max.	Mean	Max.			Mean	Max.	Mean	Max.
049	White Pelican	0	1	–	–	298	Water Dikkop	1	2	–	–
050	Pinkbacked Pelican	0	1	–	–	304	Redwinged Pratincole	0	1	–	–
055	Whitebreasted Cormorant	1	3	–	–	312	Kelp Gull	6	17	–	–
062	Grey Heron	2	3	–	–	315	Greyheaded Gull	2	7	–	–
067	Little Egret	0	1	–	–	322	Caspian Tern	2	6	–	–
086	Woollynecked Stork	1	2	–	–	324	Swift Tern	40	120	–	–
170	Osprey	0	1	–	–	326	Sandwich Tern	31	80	–	–
245	Ringed Plover	9	26	–	–	327	Common Tern	2117	3000	–	–
246	Whitefronted Plover	9	18	–	–	335	Little Tern	280	800*	–	–
249	Threebanded Plover	1	2	–	–	339	Whitewinged Tern	1	3	–	–
262	Turnstone	0	1	–	–	428	Pied Kingfisher	1	2	–	–
264	Common Sandpiper	11	28	–	–	429	Giant Kingfisher	0	1	–	–
270	Greenshank	7	14	–	–	713	Cape Wagtail	9	25	–	–
274	Little Stint	31	60	–	–		Total	2584	3588	–	–
281	Sanderling	19	42	–	–		No. of species		28		

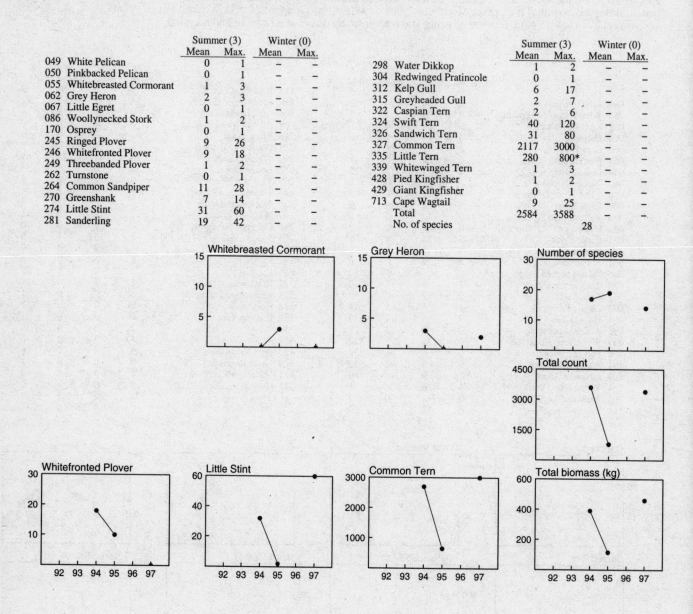

Umgeni River Estuary, Durban, KwaZulu–Natal
29° 49' S 31° 02' E (2931CC)

An open estuary with mud, sandbanks, and some patches of reeds, sedges and grass. A good site for concentrations of shorebirds and terns; the relatively high counts in summer reflect the abundance of these migratory species. Nationally significant numbers of Greyheaded Gull are recorded in summer; Kelp Gull is most numerous in winter. Relatively few waterfowl occur. Numbers of cormorants, ibises and Darter peak in winter; White Pelican is recorded only on summer counts, and Blacksmith Plover and Swift Tern are common in summer and winter. Woollynecked Stork, Whitefronted Plover, African Black Oystercatcher and Caspian Tern are recorded. Boating and water skiing are critical threats, while a severe threat is posed by industrial and domestic pollution; domestic dogs are also a problem.

		Summer (5)		Winter (5)	
		Mean	Max.	Mean	Max.
049	White Pelican	25	53	0	0
050	Pinkbacked Pelican	1	3	10	20
055	Whitebreasted Cormorant	12	23	27	54
056	Cape Cormorant	0	0	3	13
058	Reed Cormorant	1	2	15	37
060	Darter	0	1	3	4
062	Grey Heron	15	19	12	20
063	Blackheaded Heron	1	2	0	2
064	Goliath Heron	1	2	1	2
065	Purple Heron	2	3	1	2
066	Great White Heron	0	0	0	2
067	Little Egret	2	5	8	12
071	Cattle Egret	0	0	5	10
072	Squacco Heron	0	0	0	1
081	Hamerkop	0	1	1	3
086	Woollynecked Stork	2	5	1	3
091	Sacred Ibis	35	119	60	192
094	Hadeda Ibis	1	2	3	10
095	African Spoonbill	1	3	3	13
099	Whitefaced Duck	2	10	3	12
102	Egyptian Goose	24	39	15	34
103	South African Shelduck	0	0	1	3
104	Yellowbilled Duck	4	9	3	11
116	Spurwinged Goose	5	11	3	8
148	African Fish Eagle	1	2	1	4
170	Osprey	0	1	0	0
240	African Jacana	0	0	0	1
244	African Black Oystercatcher	0	0	0	1
245	Ringed Plover	21	31	0	0
246	Whitefronted Plover	4	15	0	1
248	Kittlitz's Plover	0	1	0	0
249	Threebanded Plover	2	4	9	19

		Summer (5)		Winter (5)	
		Mean	Max.	Mean	Max.
254	Grey Plover	1	3	0	0
258	Blacksmith Plover	32	54	51	57
263	Terek Sandpiper	2	4	0	0
264	Common Sandpiper	2	4	0	0
266	Wood Sandpiper	2	6	0	0
269	Marsh Sandpiper	0	1	0	0
270	Greenshank	5	12	1	2
272	Curlew Sandpiper	401	631	0	0
274	Little Stint	107	288	0	0
281	Sanderling	0	1	0	0
284	Ruff	1	6	0	0
290	Whimbrel	10	31	0	1
296	Crab Plover	0	1	0	0
298	Water Dikkop	2	4	9	18
312	Kelp Gull	15	30	46	77
315	Greyheaded Gull	569*	831*	50	158
322	Caspian Tern	1	2	3	5
324	Swift Tern	65	110	79	111
325	Lesser Crested Tern	1	4	0	0
326	Sandwich Tern	4	8	0	0
327	Common Tern	388	650	3	16
328	Arctic Tern	6	30	0	0
335	Little Tern	58	270	0	0
339	Whitewinged Tern	121	235	0	0
428	Pied Kingfisher	1	2	6	11
429	Giant Kingfisher	0	1	1	2
431	Malachite Kingfisher	0	0	1	5
711	African Pied Wagtail	0	1	1	4
713	Cape Wagtail	1	2	2	4
	Total	1959	2157	444	625
	No. of species		61		

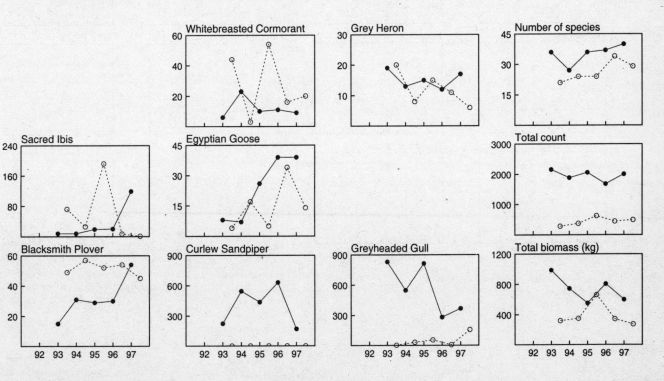

Umhlanga Treatment Works, Umhlanga, KwaZulu–Natal
29° 41' S 31° 05' E (2931CA)

One large and four small maturation ponds with short-grassed banks, some reedbeds, thick fringing vegetation, and trees which held a roost of Little Bittern, Greenbacked Heron, large herons, egrets, ibises, cormorants, etc. Formerly provided varied habitat for a wide range of waterbirds but habitat allowed to degenerate recently: ponds have not been cleaned and have become covered with invasive *Salvinia molesta*; most fish have probably died; thick fringing reeds and bush have been cleared, and roost trees were removed. A very sharp drop in the total count occurred after summer 1993; since then total counts and species numbers have continued to decline. Counts show a summer peak of cormorants, most waterfowl, and Moorhen and Redknobbed Coot; African Jacana is resident and White Pelicans have occurred in summer. Small numbers of waders frequent the pond edges, shallow water and grassy banks. Lesser Jacana has been recorded. Two ponds have been cleared of *Salvinia* so conditions may improve.

		Summer (3)		Winter (5)	
		Mean	Max.	Mean	Max.
008	Dabchick	3	6	1	3
049	White Pelican	26	71	0	0
055	Whitebreasted Cormorant	4	12	0	1
058	Reed Cormorant	4	10	1	4
060	Darter	1	2	1	2
062	Grey Heron	0	1	0	0
063	Blackheaded Heron	1	2	1	2
065	Purple Heron	1	3	0	1
066	Great White Heron	0	1	0	2
067	Little Egret	1	3	0	0
071	Cattle Egret	0	1	0	1
072	Squacco Heron	0	0	0	1
074	Greenbacked Heron	1	4	0	1
078	Little Bittern	1	2	0	1
081	Hamerkop	1	4	1	2
094	Hadeda Ibis	2	4	4	7
095	African Spoonbill	0	1	0	0
099	Whitefaced Duck	8	13	0	0
102	Egyptian Goose	5	10	1	2
104	Yellowbilled Duck	9	19	2	4
107	Hottentot Teal	12	34	0	0
108	Redbilled Teal	1	2	0	2
116	Spurwinged Goose	1	4	3	10
148	African Fish Eagle	1	2	0	1
213	Black Crake	2	5	2	4
223	Purple Gallinule	0	1	1	3
226	Moorhen	6	10	3	7
228	Redknobbed Coot	5	11	2	9
240	African Jacana	10	12	11	15
249	Threebanded Plover	2	5	2	5
258	Blacksmith Plover	2	4	2	5
264	Common Sandpiper	2	3	0	0
266	Wood Sandpiper	8	13	0	0
270	Greenshank	0	1	0	0
284	Ruff	1	2	0	0
428	Pied Kingfisher	1	4	0	0
429	Giant Kingfisher	0	1	0	2
431	Malachite Kingfisher	1	2	0	0
711	African Pied Wagtail	0	0	3	8
713	Cape Wagtail	8	10	4	5
	Total	133	258	49	65
	No. of species		40		

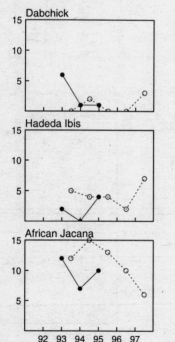

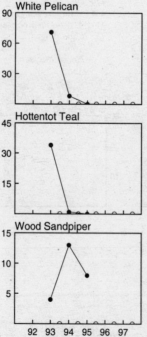

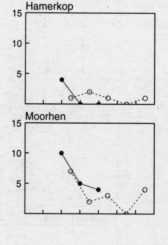

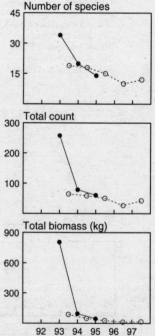

Umvoti River Estuary, Stanger, KwaZulu–Natal
29° 23' S 31° 21' E (2931AD)

An IBA. Open estuary, with sandbanks, tidal mudflats and floodplain; mouth closed during periods of low flow. Some *Phragmites, Typha* and sedgebeds. Regularly has 10 000+ birds; many migrants; major tern roost on sandbanks, with many Common and Little Terns in summer, the latter increasing in numbers. Winter numbers of Swift Tern increasing and of Spurwinged Goose and Kelp Gull decreasing. Redwinged Pratincole breeds; many wader species occur, including Chestnutbanded Plover. Threats include upstream dam building: reduced water flow could lead to frequent mouth closure and deterioration of mudflats. Fishing and bait collection are a problem; boating and all beach vehicles must be banned from the site.

		Summer (3)		Winter (5)					Summer (3)		Winter (5)	
		Mean	Max.	Mean	Max.				Mean	Max.	Mean	Max.
008	Dabchick	0	0	2	7		245	Ringed Plover	31	52	0	2
049	White Pelican	16	24	0	0		246	Whitefronted Plover	22	37	11	17
050	Pinkbacked Pelican	2	6	0	0		248	Kittlitz's Plover	20	33	14	48
055	Whitebreasted Cormorant	15	20	10	29		249	Threebanded Plover	8	13	21	44
056	Cape Cormorant	1	4	0	0		254	Grey Plover	0	1	0	0
058	Reed Cormorant	5	9	20	26		258	Blacksmith Plover	17	20	13	20
060	Darter	5	14	9	17		264	Common Sandpiper	18	39	2	6
062	Grey Heron	15	21	3	5		266	Wood Sandpiper	15	16	0	1
063	Blackheaded Heron	2	3	2	4		269	Marsh Sandpiper	6	10	0	1
064	Goliath Heron	1	2	1	2		270	Greenshank	8	9	3	9
065	Purple Heron	1	2	1	4		271	Knot	1	3	0	0
066	Great White Heron	1	3	3	4		272	Curlew Sandpiper	23	34	4	16
067	Little Egret	9	14	6	11		274	Little Stint	59	62	0	0
068	Yellowbilled Egret	0	0	0	1		281	Sanderling	5	11	0	0
069	Black Egret	1	2	0	0		284	Ruff	42	52	0	2
071	Cattle Egret	9	26	7	14		286	Ethiopian Snipe	0	0	3	9
072	Squacco Heron	0	0	0	1		294	Avocet	0	1	0	2
081	Hamerkop	9	18	4	7		295	Blackwinged Stilt	2	4	1	2
086	Woollynecked Stork	14	20	4	10		298	Water Dikkop	2	3	4	18
091	Sacred Ibis	11	23	7	15		304	Redwinged Pratincole	30	41	0	0
094	Hadeda Ibis	4	7	9	13		312	Kelp Gull	6	12	17	32
095	African Spoonbill	10	16	3	12		315	Greyheaded Gull	3	6	8	24
102	Egyptian Goose	26	60	10	20		322	Caspian Tern	0	0	4	19
104	Yellowbilled Duck	22	42	23	43		324	Swift Tern	5	11	41	80
106	Cape Teal	8	23	7	23		325	Lesser Crested Tern	1	1	0	0
107	Hottentot Teal	20	53	1	3		326	Sandwich Tern	16	31	0	0
108	Redbilled Teal	9	26	9	34		327	Common Tern	1188	1960	2	6
112	Cape Shoveller	2	5	4	14		335	Little Tern	293	650*	3	13
116	Spurwinged Goose	18	40	60	125		338	Whiskered Tern	4	11	0	1
148	African Fish Eagle	2	2	1	2		339	Whitewinged Tern	15	25	0	0
165	African Marsh Harrier	1	2	0	0		428	Pied Kingfisher	6	7	7	12
170	Osprey	0	1	0	0		429	Giant Kingfisher	1	3	1	3
209	Crowned Crane	1	2	0	0		431	Malachite Kingfisher	2	5	2	4
212	African Crake	0	0	0	2		711	African Pied Wagtail	0	0	1	2
213	Black Crake	0	1	1	2		713	Cape Wagtail	12	25	17	22
223	Purple Gallinule	0	0	1	2		714	Yellow Wagtail	2	4	0	0
228	Redknobbed Coot	0	0	1	3			Total	2106	2986	387	407
244	African Black Oystercatcher	0	1	0	0			No. of species		74		

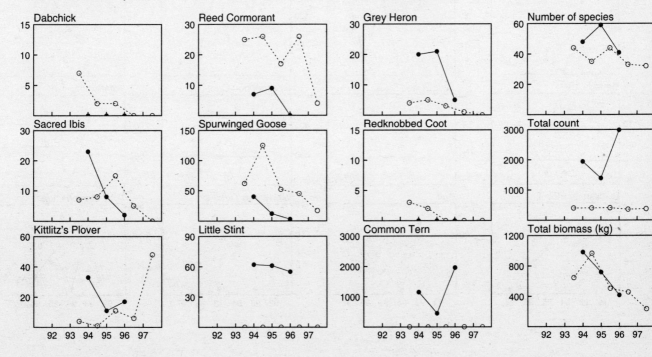

Watermead Dam, Underberg, KwaZulu–Natal
29° 50' S 29° 35' E (2929DC)

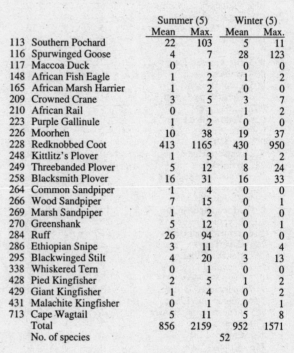

A large farm dam; inlet has some good *Phragmites/Typha* beds and variably extensive sedges and flooded grass, depending on water level. Supports generally small numbers of a good variety of waterbirds; summer 1993 numbers particularly high, with maximum counts of Dabchick, Whitebacked and Yellowbilled Ducks, Cape Shoveller, Southern Pochard, Moorhen, Redknobbed Coot and Ruff. Counts show downward trend in numbers of Yellowbilled Duck, Egyptian Goose and Blacksmith Plover, and an upward trend in Reed Cormorant. Total count and number of species also show some decline. High biomass in winter 1994 due to large count of Spurwinged Goose, plus good number of Yellowbilled Duck. Purple Gallinule resident in marshy areas, where Moorhen is common and Baillon's Crake has occurred. No threats have been identified.

		Summer (5) Mean	Summer (5) Max.	Winter (5) Mean	Winter (5) Max.				Summer (5) Mean	Summer (5) Max.	Winter (5) Mean	Winter (5) Max.
008	Dabchick	54	191	40	61		113	Southern Pochard	22	103	5	11
055	Whitebreasted Cormorant	2	6	3	10		116	Spurwinged Goose	4	7	28	123
058	Reed Cormorant	15	29	8	15		117	Maccoa Duck	0	1	0	0
060	Darter	0	1	0	1		148	African Fish Eagle	1	2	1	2
062	Grey Heron	1	2	0	0		165	African Marsh Harrier	1	2	0	0
063	Blackheaded Heron	1	4	1	3		209	Crowned Crane	3	5	3	7
066	Great White Heron	1	5	0	0		210	African Rail	0	1	1	2
067	Little Egret	0	1	0	0		223	Purple Gallinule	1	2	0	0
068	Yellowbilled Egret	0	1	0	2		226	Moorhen	10	38	19	37
071	Cattle Egret	81	180	1	3		228	Redknobbed Coot	413	1165	430	950
072	Squacco Heron	0	1	0	0		248	Kittlitz's Plover	1	3	1	2
076	Blackcrowned Night Heron	0	2	0	0		249	Threebanded Plover	5	12	8	24
078	Little Bittern	0	2	0	0		258	Blacksmith Plover	16	31	16	33
081	Hamerkop	1	3	0	1		264	Common Sandpiper	1	4	0	0
091	Sacred Ibis	1	5	0	1		266	Wood Sandpiper	7	15	0	1
093	Glossy Ibis	1	3	0	1		269	Marsh Sandpiper	1	2	0	0
094	Hadeda Ibis	3	8	5	10		270	Greenshank	5	12	0	1
095	African Spoonbill	1	3	0	0		284	Ruff	26	94	0	0
099	Whitefaced Duck	0	1	0	0		286	Ethiopian Snipe	3	11	1	4
101	Whitebacked Duck	17	52	0	1		295	Blackwinged Stilt	4	20	3	13
102	Egyptian Goose	39	69	124	188		338	Whiskered Tern	0	1	0	0
103	South African Shelduck	0	1	1	3		428	Pied Kingfisher	2	5	1	2
104	Yellowbilled Duck	84	233	234	430		429	Giant Kingfisher	1	4	0	2
105	African Black Duck	0	0	1	4		431	Malachite Kingfisher	0	1	0	1
107	Hottentot Teal	5	16	2	4		713	Cape Wagtail	5	11	5	8
108	Redbilled Teal	1	6	4	12			Total	856	2159	952	1571
112	Cape Shoveller	13	39	5	14			No. of species		52		

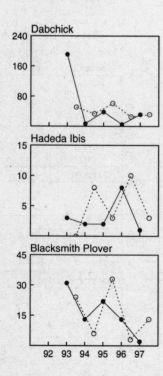
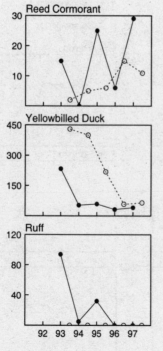
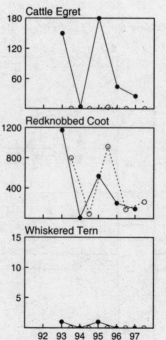
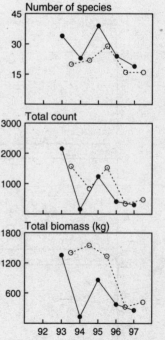

Yengweni Lake, Mbazwane, KwaZulu–Natal
27° 39' S 32° 26' E (2732CB)

A long, narrow cut-off lake, within the Greater St Lucia Wetland Park. Predominantly open water, with few fringing reeds and a little floating *Nymphaea* cover. Winter counts normally much higher than summer counts; numbers of most waterfowl, including Pygmy Goose, peak in winter, when large concentrations of Whitefaced Duck and Spurwinged Goose are recorded. Larger numbers of pelicans, African Spoonbill and African Jacana have also been recorded on winter counts; spoonbill numbers are apparently declining in winter. No serious threats; slight negative impacts are likely from livestock grazing and trampling, and from poaching.

		Summer (5)		Winter (6)				Summer (5)		Winter (6)	
		Mean	Max.	Mean	Max.			Mean	Max.	Mean	Max.
008	Dabchick	0	0	1	5	116	Spurwinged Goose	75	223	338	735
049	White Pelican	2	9	27	133	148	African Fish Eagle	1	3	2	5
050	Pinkbacked Pelican	1	4	4	8	165	African Marsh Harrier	0	0	0	1
055	Whitebreasted Cormorant	0	0	0	2	213	Black Crake	0	2	1	2
058	Reed Cormorant	3	5	3	10	223	Purple Gallinule	0	0	1	4
060	Darter	3	6	3	13	226	Moorhen	0	0	0	1
062	Grey Heron	1	2	1	2	228	Redknobbed Coot	0	0	0	1
064	Goliath Heron	1	2	1	2	240	African Jacana	38	51	49	97
066	Great White Heron	3	6	3	5	241	Lesser Jacana	0	0	0	1
067	Little Egret	2	5	2	3	245	Ringed Plover	1	3	0	0
068	Yellowbilled Egret	0	0	0	1	248	Kittlitz's Plover	1	4	2	10
069	Black Egret	4	11	0	0	249	Threebanded Plover	0	2	2	7
071	Cattle Egret	10	24	14	40	258	Blacksmith Plover	3	7	3	8
072	Squacco Heron	3	8	0	1	260	Wattled Plover	0	1	1	4
074	Greenbacked Heron	0	0	0	2	264	Common Sandpiper	3	15	0	1
076	Blackcrowned Night Heron	0	0	0	1	266	Wood Sandpiper	4	11	0	0
081	Hamerkop	0	2	0	0	269	Marsh Sandpiper	6	14	0	1
086	Woollynecked Stork	1	3	1	5	272	Curlew Sandpiper	6	20	8	45
088	Saddlebilled Stork	0	0	0	1	274	Little Stint	1	4	0	0
090	Yellowbilled Stork	1	3	1	4	284	Ruff	16	38	0	0
091	Sacred Ibis	6	11	2	4	286	Ethiopian Snipe	0	0	0	2
093	Glossy Ibis	6	21	4	10	295	Blackwinged Stilt	4	12	4	11
094	Hadeda Ibis	0	0	1	3	298	Water Dikkop	1	4	0	0
095	African Spoonbill	1	4	13	28	315	Greyheaded Gull	0	0	0	1
099	Whitefaced Duck	58	176	256	836	335	Little Tern	1	6	0	0
100	Fulvous Duck	4	21	18	109	338	Whiskered Tern	8	39	13	18
102	Egyptian Goose	9	28	17	56	339	Whitewinged Tern	27	133	3	16
104	Yellowbilled Duck	4	15	5	24	428	Pied Kingfisher	1	2	3	6
107	Hottentot Teal	4	15	0	2	431	Malachite Kingfisher	1	1	0	0
108	Redbilled Teal	1	4	3	15	713	Cape Wagtail	0	0	1	2
114	Pygmy Goose	1	2	23	58		Total	328	551	840	1407
115	Knobbilled Duck	0	0	7	24		No. of species		62		

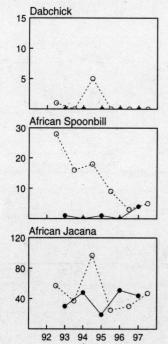

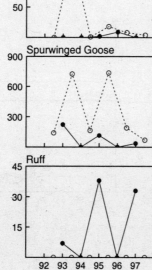

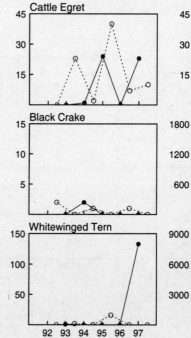

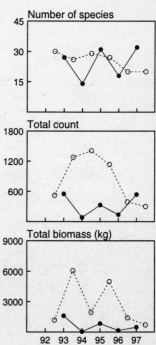

Bar None Saltpans, Port Elizabeth, Eastern Cape
33° 50' S 25° 33' E (3325DC)

Commercial saltpans, near Redhouse and Chatty saltpans. Similar avifauna to those pans, but counts consistently much lower, and exceptionally high totals recorded for few species, including 76 Blacknecked Grebe in winter 1995, 194 Cape Teal in summer 1997 and 273 Greater Flamingo in winter 1997; good numbers of Redbilled Teal in summer, and higher counts of Sacred Ibis and African Spoonbill than at the other sites. As for those sites, Dabchick, cormorant and flamingo numbers peak in winter. High winter count of Kittlitz's Plover in 1995; Blackwinged Stilt particularly numerous in 1997. Very few gulls and terns recorded in comparison to Redhouse and Chatty. Threats include total reclamation, and hunting/trapping.

		Summer (2)		Winter (3)					Summer (2)		Winter (3)	
		Mean	Max.	Mean	Max.				Mean	Max.	Mean	Max.
007	Blacknecked Grebe	0	0	26	76		228	Redknobbed Coot	9	17	0	1
008	Dabchick	2	3	20	59		245	Ringed Plover	43	44	0	0
055	Whitebreasted Cormorant	4	4	59	85		248	Kittlitz's Plover	17	26	56	99
056	Cape Cormorant	0	0	0	1		249	Threebanded Plover	1	1	0	0
058	Reed Cormorant	2	3	1	4		254	Grey Plover	6	11	0	0
062	Grey Heron	19	21	12	20		258	Blacksmith Plover	4	6	9	12
063	Blackheaded Heron	1	1	0	0		262	Turnstone	0	0	1	2
067	Little Egret	3	5	1	1		266	Wood Sandpiper	2	4	0	0
068	Yellowbilled Egret	0	0	0	1		269	Marsh Sandpiper	1	1	0	0
071	Cattle Egret	15	30	2	7		270	Greenshank	12	17	1	1
084	Black Stork	1	1	0	0		272	Curlew Sandpiper	46	70	38	99
091	Sacred Ibis	11	18	1	1		274	Little Stint	288	304	0	1
093	Glossy Ibis	1	1	0	0		284	Ruff	106	200	0	0
095	African Spoonbill	0	0	12	27		290	Whimbrel	1	2	0	0
096	Greater Flamingo	60	118	144	273		294	Avocet	13	22	18	32
097	Lesser Flamingo	0	0	13	39		295	Blackwinged Stilt	23	40	20	35
102	Egyptian Goose	8	13	0	1		312	Kelp Gull	5	6	15	21
103	South African Shelduck	6	7	6	9		315	Greyheaded Gull	0	0	2	4
104	Yellowbilled Duck	48	92	50	77		322	Caspian Tern	1	1	16	21
106	Cape Teal	109	194	56	87		327	Common Tern	4	7	1	3
108	Redbilled Teal	40	50	13	21		713	Cape Wagtail	1	2	9	24
112	Cape Shoveller	5	5	12	32			Total	909	1137	617	877
148	African Fish Eagle	1	1	0	0			No. of species			45	
170	Osprey	1	2	0	0							

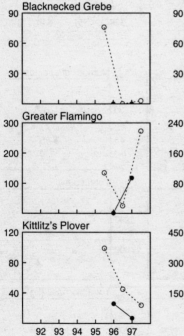

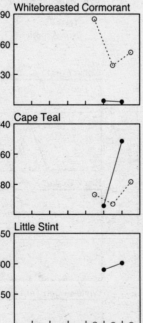

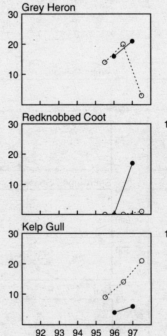

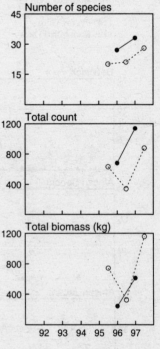

Cape Recife Reclamation Works, Port Elizabeth, Eastern Cape
34° 01' S 25° 41' E (3425BA)

The settling ponds of a sewage works, with reedbeds which hold Little Bittern, Purple Heron, African Rail, Black Crake and Purple Gallinule. Small to moderate numbers of 41 waterbird species are recorded; most species for which reasonable counts exist appear to be commoner in winter, with the exception of Egyptian Goose, Yellowbilled Duck, Cape Shoveller and Greyheaded Gull. Few Palearctic migrants are recorded. Threats include sedimentation and eutrophication.

		Summer (4)		Winter (4)				Summer (4)		Winter (4)	
		Mean	Max.	Mean	Max.			Mean	Max.	Mean	Max.
008	Dabchick	5	10	34	53	213	Black Crake	7	11	9	10
055	Whitebreasted Cormorant	2	4	5	15	223	Purple Gallinule	3	5	4	5
056	Cape Cormorant	0	0	1	2	226	Moorhen	9	15	8	12
058	Reed Cormorant	2	5	10	22	228	Redknobbed Coot	7	12	22	46
060	Darter	0	0	5	17	240	African Jacana	0	0	1	2
062	Grey Heron	2	3	3	8	249	Threebanded Plover	1	3	1	4
065	Purple Heron	0	0	2	5	258	Blacksmith Plover	3	5	4	10
067	Little Egret	2	5	3	7	266	Wood Sandpiper	0	1	0	0
072	Squacco Heron	0	0	0	1	270	Greenshank	0	1	0	0
076	Blackcrowned Night Heron	3	6	3	6	284	Ruff	6	16	0	0
078	Little Bittern	1	4	0	0	298	Water Dikkop	0	0	2	4
094	Hadeda Ibis	0	1	6	22	312	Kelp Gull	1	3	3	6
102	Egyptian Goose	5	13	4	5	315	Greyheaded Gull	9	30	1	1
103	South African Shelduck	0	0	2	2	322	Caspian Tern	0	0	1	3
104	Yellowbilled Duck	68	75	33	46	327	Common Tern	1	1	0	0
107	Hottentot Teal	0	1	1	2	428	Pied Kingfisher	4	5	4	7
108	Redbilled Teal	4	6	4	6	429	Giant Kingfisher	0	0	0	1
112	Cape Shoveller	14	17	8	9	431	Malachite Kingfisher	0	1	0	0
116	Spurwinged Goose	0	1	0	0	713	Cape Wagtail	3	4	3	4
148	African Fish Eagle	0	0	1	2		Total	160	209	184	221
165	African Marsh Harrier	0	1	0	0		No. of species			41	
210	African Rail	0	0	0	1						

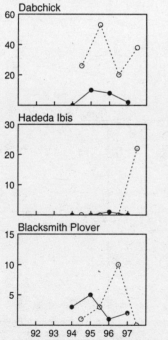

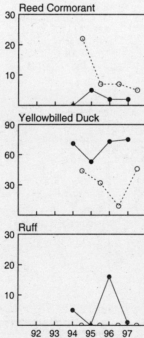

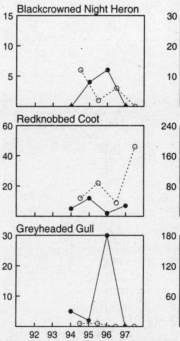

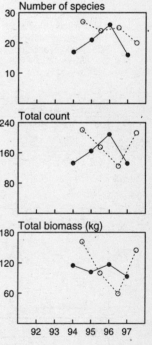

Chatty Saltpans, Port Elizabeth, Eastern Cape
33° 51' S 25° 35' E (3325DC)

Commercial saltpans within Swartkops Estuary IBA. Similar avifauna to nearby Redhouse saltpan, but has held globally significant numbers of Blacknecked Grebe and one nationally significant count of Greater Flamingo (winter 1995). As at Redhouse, Dabchick, cormorant and flamingo numbers peak in winter, but Cape Teal numbers peak in summer. Good summer counts of Grey Plover, Turnstone and Ruff, but few Ringed Plover; good counts of Avocet and Blackwinged Stilt in summer 1996; high winter count of Kittlitz's Plover in 1997. In contrast to Redhouse, few Kelp Gulls recorded but high numbers of Greyheaded Gulls in summer; like nearby Bar None saltpans, maximum counts of Palearctic waders lower than at Redhouse. South African Shelduck not recorded; few Redbilled Teal counted, and only one Yellowbilled Duck. Threats include pollution by domestic sewage and solid waste, hunting/trapping, and overhead powerlines.

		Summer (2) Mean	Max.	Winter (3) Mean	Max.			Summer (2) Mean	Max.	Winter (3) Mean	Max.
007	Blacknecked Grebe	48	89	632**	1249**	246	Whitefronted Plover	2	4	1	1
008	Dabchick	1	1	105	158	247	Chestnutbanded Plover	1	1	0	0
055	Whitebreasted Cormorant	16	26	54	82	248	Kittlitz's Plover	20	24	56	117
056	Cape Cormorant	1	1	33	55	249	Threebanded Plover	0	0	13	24
058	Reed Cormorant	6	10	93	164	254	Grey Plover	106	195	0	0
062	Grey Heron	17	27	9	11	258	Blacksmith Plover	14	16	13	26
063	Blackheaded Heron	1	1	0	0	262	Turnstone	29	43	23	70
066	Great White Heron	1	2	0	0	269	Marsh Sandpiper	63	105	0	1
067	Little Egret	5	5	5	6	270	Greenshank	42	57	2	4
071	Cattle Egret	0	0	0	1	272	Curlew Sandpiper	141	274	84	224
091	Sacred Ibis	1	2	1	1	274	Little Stint	98	120	0	0
095	African Spoonbill	0	0	2	2	284	Ruff	443	572	0	0
096	Greater Flamingo	40	80	353	895*	290	Whimbrel	1	1	0	0
097	Lesser Flamingo	0	0	72	198	294	Avocet	352	490	121	244
099	Whitefaced Duck	0	0	2	7	295	Blackwinged Stilt	99	173	111	185
100	Fulvous Duck	0	0	1	2	312	Kelp Gull	17	26	13	22
102	Egyptian Goose	2	3	1	2	315	Greyheaded Gull	300	363	12	31
104	Yellowbilled Duck	0	0	0	1	322	Caspian Tern	1	2	5	9
106	Cape Teal	220	296	66	102	327	Common Tern	26	38	17	22
108	Redbilled Teal	4	7	2	3	335	Little Tern	2	2	0	0
112	Cape Shoveller	42	45	120	168	339	Whitewinged Tern	69	120	0	1
113	Southern Pochard	2	4	1	3	428	Pied Kingfisher	1	2	0	1
170	Osprey	0	0	0	1	713	Cape Wagtail	12	16	34	71
228	Redknobbed Coot	42	71	27	53		Total	2288	3123	2087	2694
244	African Black Oystercatcher	1	1	0	0		No. of species		49		
245	Ringed Plover	9	10	0	0						

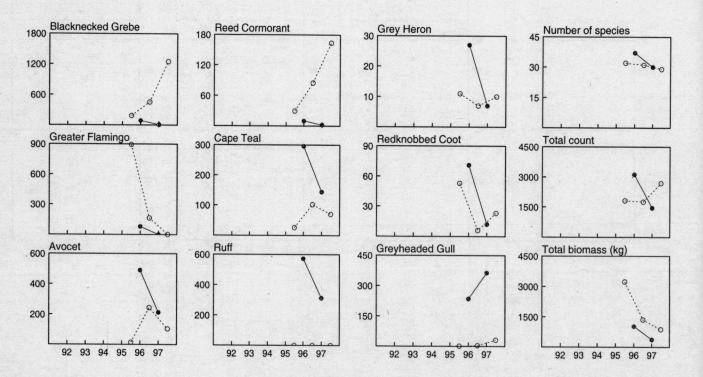

Ghio Pans, Kenton–on–Sea, Eastern Cape
33° 38' S 26° 34' E (3326DA)

Erratically flooded pans, with some reeds (mainly *Phragmites*). A good variety of waterbirds occurs. Large variations in counts of ducks, shorebirds and other species, in summer and winter, reflect variations in water levels due to area's uncertain and erratic rainfall; pans need heavy rain to flood, and most inflow is sheetwash from higher up valley. Formerly, water inflow after dry periods was followed by proliferation of small aquatic crustacea (*Daphnia*); numbers of ducks and shorebirds (especially Blackwinged Stilt) arrived to breed, the young apparently being dependent on the crustacean food supply (A.J. Tree). In 1995 a large population of fish-eating birds occurred after bream entered the system during the 1994–95 flood and bred prolifically. Great recent increases in Ruff numbers possibly associated with increase in Diptera following increased sewage inflow (A.J. Tree). A recent and severe threat is influx of sewage from nearby Ostrich farm paddocks, through which sheetwash flows; high concentrations of *Daphnia* no longer occur and breeding birds are much less numerous.

		Summer (4)		Winter (4)				Summer (4)		Winter (4)	
		Mean	Max.	Mean	Max.			Mean	Max.	Mean	Max.
008	Dabchick	11	33	15	32	148	African Fish Eagle	0	1	0	1
055	Whitebreasted Cormorant	0	0	3	11	226	Moorhen	1	3	0	0
058	Reed Cormorant	1	1	10	38	228	Redknobbed Coot	135	289	120	370
060	Darter	0	0	0	1	245	Ringed Plover	5	13	0	0
062	Grey Heron	5	9	4	12	246	Whitefronted Plover	0	0	0	1
063	Blackheaded Heron	5	9	1	5	248	Kittlitz's Plover	6	16	2	6
065	Purple Heron	0	0	1	2	249	Threebanded Plover	2	4	6	15
066	Great White Heron	0	0	3	10	258	Blacksmith Plover	11	23	2	5
067	Little Egret	2	5	1	4	266	Wood Sandpiper	23	38	0	0
068	Yellowbilled Egret	0	0	0	1	269	Marsh Sandpiper	14	30	1	5
081	Hamerkop	0	1	0	0	270	Greenshank	2	5	0	1
084	Black Stork	2	6	0	1	272	Curlew Sandpiper	1	2	1	2
091	Sacred Ibis	1	4	1	3	274	Little Stint	55	102	0	0
094	Hadeda Ibis	1	2	0	0	284	Ruff	118	230	1	2
095	African Spoonbill	2	3	10	38	286	Ethiopian Snipe	0	0	2	6
099	Whitefaced Duck	1	2	0	0	295	Blackwinged Stilt	24	51	4	10
102	Egyptian Goose	3	7	12	42	312	Kelp Gull	1	2	0	1
103	South African Shelduck	8	19	17	39	322	Caspian Tern	0	0	0	1
104	Yellowbilled Duck	53	75	45	117	327	Common Tern	0	0	0	1
106	Cape Teal	0	0	1	2	428	Pied Kingfisher	0	1	0	0
108	Redbilled Teal	32	70	11	32	713	Cape Wagtail	2	4	4	12
112	Cape Shoveller	24	42	15	36		Total	546	694	289	714
116	Spurwinged Goose	0	1	0	1		No. of species		45		
117	Maccoa Duck	1	2	0	0						

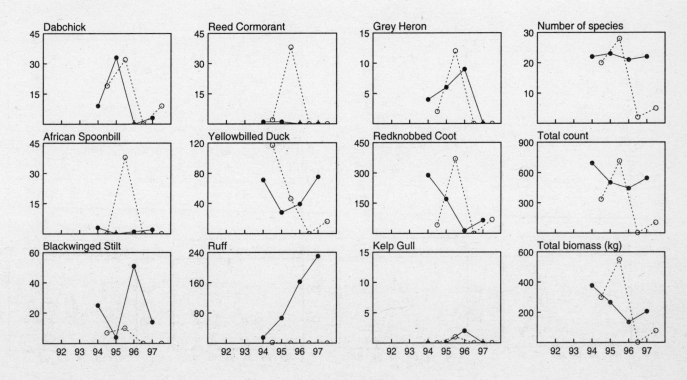

Great Fish River Estuary, Port Alfred, Eastern Cape
33° 29' S 27° 07' E (3327AC)

The estuary of the Great Fish River, with open shoreline and some short fringing vegetation. A good variety of waterbirds occurs, including African Black Oyster-catcher and 15 Palearctic shorebird species. Duck numbers average higher in winter, as do numbers of Whitefronted and Threebanded Plovers, and Blackwinged Stilt; numbers of Whitebreasted Cormorant and Egyptian Goose normally higher in summer. Good numbers of Common Tern occur erratically in summer. Sedimentation, and tourism and recreational activities, are important threats; pollution by fertilizers may also be a problem.

		Summer (4) Mean	Summer (4) Max.	Winter (4) Mean	Winter (4) Max.			Summer (4) Mean	Summer (4) Max.	Winter (4) Mean	Winter (4) Max.
055	Whitebreasted Cormorant	18	24	9	11	254	Grey Plover	4	6	1	3
056	Cape Cormorant	0	1	1	5	258	Blacksmith Plover	17	23	8	12
058	Reed Cormorant	1	2	1	3	262	Turnstone	1	2	1	5
060	Darter	0	0	3	4	263	Terek Sandpiper	3	5	0	0
062	Grey Heron	11	21	7	12	264	Common Sandpiper	13	21	0	1
063	Blackheaded Heron	5	13	0	1	266	Wood Sandpiper	10	24	0	0
064	Goliath Heron	0	1	0	0	269	Marsh Sandpiper	2	3	1	3
067	Little Egret	0	0	1	3	270	Greenshank	38	67	10	11
071	Cattle Egret	18	70	13	32	272	Curlew Sandpiper	1	3	0	0
081	Hamerkop	1	2	0	1	274	Little Stint	34	60	0	0
084	Black Stork	1	2	0	0	281	Sanderling	28	38	12	36
091	Sacred Ibis	2	8	11	23	284	Ruff	43	125	0	0
094	Hadeda Ibis	0	0	3	7	288	Bartailed Godwit	0	1	0	0
095	African Spoonbill	0	0	4	7	289	Curlew	0	1	0	0
102	Egyptian Goose	22	37	12	19	290	Whimbrel	21	29	5	8
103	South African Shelduck	1	3	23	39	294	Avocet	0	0	0	1
104	Yellowbilled Duck	6	9	20	32	295	Blackwinged Stilt	7	16	29	47
105	African Black Duck	1	2	2	4	312	Kelp Gull	18	30	14	23
108	Redbilled Teal	1	3	2	4	322	Caspian Tern	1	2	1	2
112	Cape Shoveller	1	2	5	10	324	Swift Tern	5	9	2	4
148	African Fish Eagle	4	6	2	2	326	Sandwich Tern	8	14	0	0
165	African Marsh Harrier	0	1	0	1	327	Common Tern	169	435	1	3
170	Osprey	0	1	0	0	335	Little Tern	4	9	0	0
226	Moorhen	0	0	0	1	428	Pied Kingfisher	5	8	2	4
244	African Black Oystercatcher	8	13	4	9	429	Giant Kingfisher	1	3	0	0
245	Ringed Plover	29	43	0	0	431	Malachite Kingfisher	1	2	0	1
246	Whitefronted Plover	31	45	41	62	713	Cape Wagtail	9	30	13	40
248	Kittlitz's Plover	1	1	1	2		Total	603	1067	272	334
249	Threebanded Plover	5	9	11	21		No. of species		56		

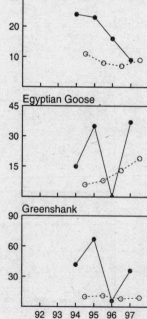

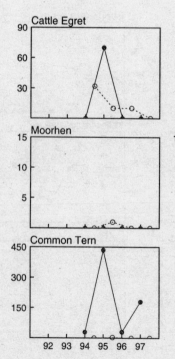

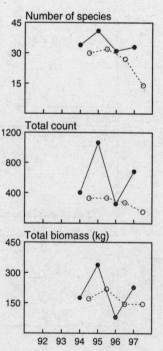

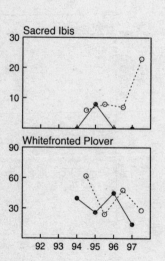

Kabeljous River Estuary, Jeffreys Bay, Eastern Cape
34° 00' S 24° 56' E (3424BB)

The tidal estuary of the Kabeljous River; many new adjacent wetlands also attract birds. The site has a good variety of waterbirds: 20 shorebird species are listed, including 12 Palearctic migrants, two of which (Knot and Whimbrel) are recorded only in winter. Good numbers of Common Terns occurred in summer 1996 (when maximum numbers of several shorebird species were also recorded), and of Arctic Terns in summer 1997; large numbers of Redknobbed Coot and South African Shelduck were present in winter 1995, when peak counts of Dabchick and African Spoonbill were also recorded. Disturbance by 4x4 and other vehicles poses a critical threat around the lagoon, while lesser threats include boating on the lagoon, fishing, bait collecting, and disturbance by livestock.

		Summer (2)		Winter (3)					Summer (2)		Winter (3)	
		Mean	Max.	Mean	Max.				Mean	Max.	Mean	Max.
008	Dabchick	0	0	20	45		248	Kittlitz's Plover	63	122	28	80
055	Whitebreasted Cormorant	8	11	11	27		249	Threebanded Plover	18	36	2	4
056	Cape Cormorant	0	0	1	2		254	Grey Plover	4	8	0	0
058	Reed Cormorant	12	24	59	98		258	Blacksmith Plover	2	3	6	10
060	Darter	2	4	1	2		262	Turnstone	13	25	0	0
062	Grey Heron	6	11	5	6		266	Wood Sandpiper	1	1	0	0
063	Blackheaded Heron	3	6	0	1		269	Marsh Sandpiper	7	13	1	1
065	Purple Heron	1	2	2	7		270	Greenshank	7	13	1	2
067	Little Egret	5	6	4	6		271	Knot	0	0	13	38
091	Sacred Ibis	1	1	3	7		272	Curlew Sandpiper	660	1320	14	42
094	Hadeda Ibis	1	1	0	0		274	Little Stint	222	337	0	0
095	African Spoonbill	1	1	7	21		281	Sanderling	17	24	0	0
096	Greater Flamingo	0	0	1	3		284	Ruff	15	29	0	0
097	Lesser Flamingo	0	0	4	12		290	Whimbrel	0	0	2	5
102	Egyptian Goose	0	0	1	3		294	Avocet	1	1	2	5
103	South African Shelduck	9	18	46	139		295	Blackwinged Stilt	19	38	14	35
104	Yellowbilled Duck	3	6	14	23		298	Water Dikkop	3	5	7	11
106	Cape Teal	5	10	7	13		312	Kelp Gull	28	39	36	60
107	Hottentot Teal	0	0	1	2		322	Caspian Tern	9	16	5	8
108	Redbilled Teal	8	16	14	31		324	Swift Tern	9	13	4	10
112	Cape Shoveller	8	15	7	15		326	Sandwich Tern	13	13	0	0
148	African Fish Eagle	1	2	1	2		327	Common Tern	666	1330	1	2
165	African Marsh Harrier	1	1	0	0		328	Arctic Tern	59	108	0	0
213	Black Crake	0	0	0	1		335	Little Tern	3	6	0	0
226	Moorhen	0	0	1	4		428	Pied Kingfisher	7	12	3	6
228	Redknobbed Coot	132	264	672	2000		431	Malachite Kingfisher	0	0	1	2
244	African Black Oystercatcher	12	14	5	10		713	Cape Wagtail	8	11	9	12
245	Ringed Plover	8	16	0	0			Total	2081	3798	1036	2544
246	Whitefronted Plover	11	11	0	0			No. of species		56		

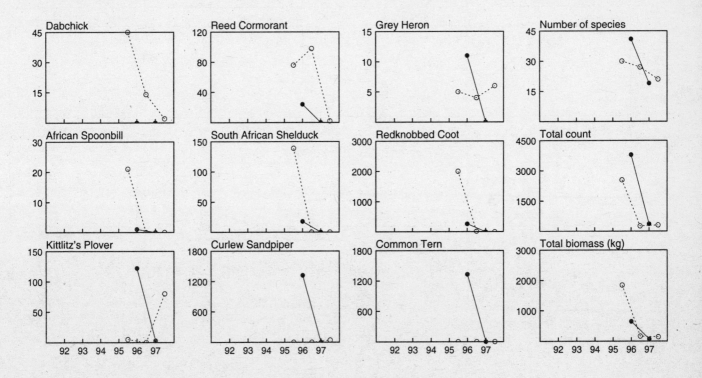

Queenstown Sewage Works, Queenstown, Eastern Cape
31° 55' S 26° 50' E (3126DD)

This site includes open-water dams, sludge ponds and reedbeds. The only summer count was in 1995; winter counts are available 1995–97. Counts have been too few to show well-defined patterns of occurrence, apart from the summer influx of Palearctic shorebirds, but ibises and most waterfowl appear to be more numerous in winter (the exception being South African Shelduck), while Redknobbed Coot is commoner in summer. Avocet and Blacksmith Plover numbers are greater in summer, but Threebanded Plover is more numerous in winter. Good counts of Redbilled Teal and Blacksmith Plover are noteworthy. Pollution by domestic waste, and the encroachment of squatters, are severe threats, while the spread of alien water plants poses an important threat.

		Summer (1)		Winter (3)				Summer (1)		Winter (3)	
		Mean	Max.	Mean	Max.			Mean	Max.	Mean	Max.
008	Dabchick	15	15	5	7	116	Spurwinged Goose	16	16	20	49
055	Whitebreasted Cormorant	4	4	18	55	148	African Fish Eagle	2	2	0	1
058	Reed Cormorant	19	19	1	2	209	Crowned Crane	2	2	0	0
060	Darter	0	0	4	8	226	Moorhen	0	0	2	6
062	Grey Heron	8	8	5	8	228	Redknobbed Coot	54	54	14	19
063	Blackheaded Heron	2	2	14	28	249	Threebanded Plover	7	7	20	27
071	Cattle Egret	19	19	4	8	258	Blacksmith Plover	60	60	34	65
081	Hamerkop	0	0	1	1	264	Common Sandpiper	1	1	0	0
091	Sacred Ibis	0	0	23	36	266	Wood Sandpiper	9	9	0	0
094	Hadeda Ibis	1	1	5	9	270	Greenshank	3	3	0	0
095	African Spoonbill	15	15	0	1	274	Little Stint	57	57	0	0
099	Whitefaced Duck	2	2	33	39	284	Ruff	13	13	0	0
102	Egyptian Goose	8	8	44	128	286	Ethiopian Snipe	1	1	1	2
103	South African Shelduck	44	44	1	2	294	Avocet	26	26	0	0
104	Yellowbilled Duck	62	62	73	104	295	Blackwinged Stilt	3	3	1	4
105	African Black Duck	0	0	1	2	428	Pied Kingfisher	2	2	0	0
106	Cape Teal	0	0	1	2	429	Giant Kingfisher	0	0	0	1
108	Redbilled Teal	83	83	124	246	713	Cape Wagtail	5	5	7	11
112	Cape Shoveller	11	11	10	18		Total	554	554	469	694
113	Southern Pochard	0	0	1	4		No. of species			38	

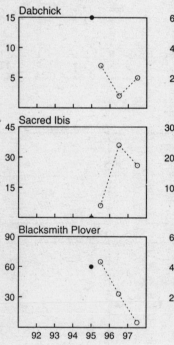

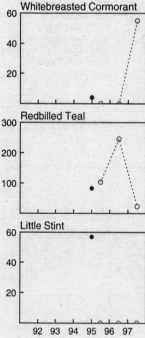

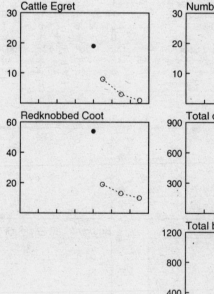

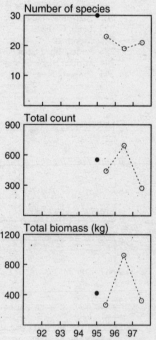

Redhouse Saltpan, Port Elizabeth, Eastern Cape
33° 50' S 25° 35' E (3325DC)

Falls within Swartkops Estuary IBA. A primary concentration saltpan; water salinity varies with summer rainfall, hence large count of Redknobbed Coot in July 1997 after good rains. Duck numbers tend to peak in winter, but nationally significant number of South African Shelduck counted in summer 1996. Good numbers of Dabchick and cormorants, especially in winter; few Blacknecked Grebe recorded (up to 220 have occurred); good numbers of Cape Shoveller and Cape Teal in winter. High counts of Ringed and Grey Plover, Curlew Sandpiper (nationally significant), Little Stint and Ruff in Summer 1994. Kelp Gull and Caspian Tern numbers high; both species breed. Also an important breeding site for Whitebreasted Cormorant, Sacred Ibis and Greyheaded Gull. Four high biomass totals between summer 1994 and winter 1996 reflect presence of many Greater Flamingo. Threats include site modifications and hunting/trapping.

		Summer (4)		Winter (4)				Summer (4)		Winter (4)	
		Mean	Max.	Mean	Max.			Mean	Max.	Mean	Max.
007	Blacknecked Grebe	0	0	2	7	245	Ringed Plover	59	164	0	0
008	Dabchick	3	6	147	168	246	Whitefronted Plover	0	0	1	3
055	Whitebreasted Cormorant	125	183	109	154	248	Kittlitz's Plover	11	13	44	65
056	Cape Cormorant	1	2	62	119	249	Threebanded Plover	0	0	1	2
058	Reed Cormorant	21	37	183	350	254	Grey Plover	132	242	37	149
060	Darter	0	0	3	7	258	Blacksmith Plover	0	0	11	15
062	Grey Heron	26	31	32	37	262	Turnstone	2	7	1	4
063	Blackheaded Heron	4	12	1	3	269	Marsh Sandpiper	24	70	0	1
066	Great White Heron	0	0	2	3	270	Greenshank	48	122	14	41
067	Little Egret	20	50	8	10	272	Curlew Sandpiper	1182	4187*	11	24
071	Cattle Egret	1	2	0	0	274	Little Stint	410	1320	0	0
084	Black Stork	0	1	0	0	284	Ruff	101	208	0	0
091	Sacred Ibis	1	2	0	0	288	Bartailed Godwit	2	8	1	2
095	African Spoonbill	3	10	11	23	290	Whimbrel	8	15	0	0
096	Greater Flamingo	234	487	268	535	294	Avocet	9	33	15	36
097	Lesser Flamingo	2	8	34	68	295	Blackwinged Stilt	7	18	32	47
102	Egyptian Goose	0	0	2	4	312	Kelp Gull	651**	799**	362**	678**
103	South African Shelduck	100	300*	53	122	315	Greyheaded Gull	1	2	36	117
104	Yellowbilled Duck	10	22	14	34	322	Caspian Tern	36	59	25	64
106	Cape Teal	32	50	132	199	327	Common Tern	4	13	10	30
108	Redbilled Teal	15	43	4	13	335	Little Tern	28	50	0	0
112	Cape Shoveller	22	82	53	130	339	Whitewinged Tern	48	193	0	0
148	African Fish Eagle	0	0	1	2	428	Pied Kingfisher	0	1	1	2
170	Osprey	1	1	0	1	713	Cape Wagtail	4	9	14	19
228	Redknobbed Coot	9	34	121	376		Total	3393	7493	1854	2592
244	African Black Oystercatcher	1	3	0	1		No. of species		50		

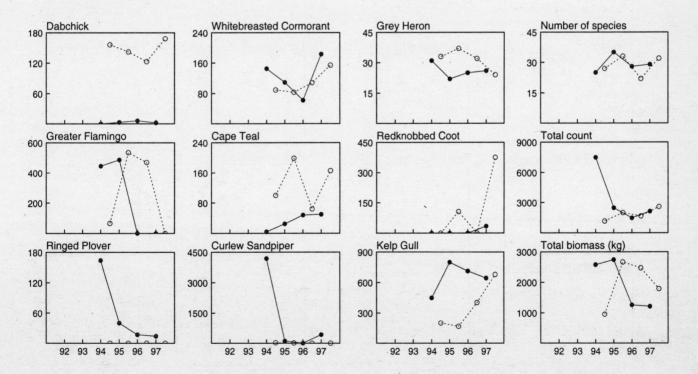

Seekoei River Estuary, Jeffreys Bay, Eastern Cape
34° 05' S 24° 54' E (3424BB)

Open estuary and lagoon, partly within a nature reserve. Dabchick, cormorant and
Greater Flamingo numbers usually greater in winter, with highest count recorded
in winter 1996; numbers of Redknobbed Coot also much higher in winter 1995
and 1996 but declined drastically in 1997; numbers of waterfowl and Kittlitz's
Plover peak in summer. Occurrence of Antarctic Tern noteworthy. Declines shown
in number of species and in total counts, summer and winter. Important threats
are dam building upstream, residential development, and overhead powerlines.

		Summer (2)		Winter (3)				Summer (2)		Winter (3)	
		Mean	Max.	Mean	Max.			Mean	Max.	Mean	Max.
006	Great Crested Grebe	1	1	0	1	245	Ringed Plover	6	10	0	0
008	Dabchick	4	8	31	58	246	Whitefronted Plover	0	0	2	4
055	Whitebreasted Cormorant	20	30	104	252	248	Kittlitz's Plover	42	47	18	44
056	Cape Cormorant	0	0	1	2	249	Threebanded Plover	1	2	5	7
058	Reed Cormorant	69	73	118	166	254	Grey Plover	3	6	0	0
060	Darter	5	5	5	9	258	Blacksmith Plover	11	17	4	7
062	Grey Heron	12	17	11	15	262	Turnstone	0	0	1	2
063	Blackheaded Heron	1	1	1	1	264	Common Sandpiper	0	0	2	5
064	Goliath Heron	0	0	0	1	269	Marsh Sandpiper	9	15	6	19
065	Purple Heron	0	0	2	4	270	Greenshank	5	7	1	4
067	Little Egret	11	18	14	28	272	Curlew Sandpiper	8	11	13	31
071	Cattle Egret	0	0	0	1	274	Little Stint	60	88	0	0
076	Blackcrowned Night Heron	0	0	0	1	284	Ruff	18	35	0	0
091	Sacred Ibis	1	2	6	12	290	Whimbrel	1	2	1	3
094	Hadeda Ibis	0	0	1	2	295	Blackwinged Stilt	11	22	17	28
095	African Spoonbill	5	10	4	10	298	Water Dikkop	1	2	6	15
096	Greater Flamingo	0	0	19	49	312	Kelp Gull	51	58	35	57
101	Whitebacked Duck	1	2	0	0	315	Greyheaded Gull	0	0	1	2
102	Egyptian Goose	162	179	4	7	322	Caspian Tern	8	11	15	30
103	South African Shelduck	86	111	11	23	324	Swift Tern	4	7	1	2
104	Yellowbilled Duck	40	66	34	47	327	Common Tern	52	103	11	24
106	Cape Teal	22	29	16	27	328	Arctic Tern	2	2	7	20
107	Hottentot Teal	0	0	1	3	329	Antarctic Tern	0	0	10	30
108	Redbilled Teal	17	22	5	16	335	Little Tern	0	0	1	3
112	Cape Shoveller	46	55	29	52	428	Pied Kingfisher	1	2	10	18
113	Southern Pochard	0	0	1	3	429	Giant Kingfisher	1	1	2	3
148	African Fish Eagle	2	2	0	1	711	African Pied Wagtail	2	4	0	0
170	Osprey	0	0	0	1	713	Cape Wagtail	11	11	17	22
226	Moorhen	0	0	1	2		Total	1106	1198	1532	2137
228	Redknobbed Coot	302	430	927	1592		No. of species			59	
244	African Black Oystercatcher	0	0	1	3						

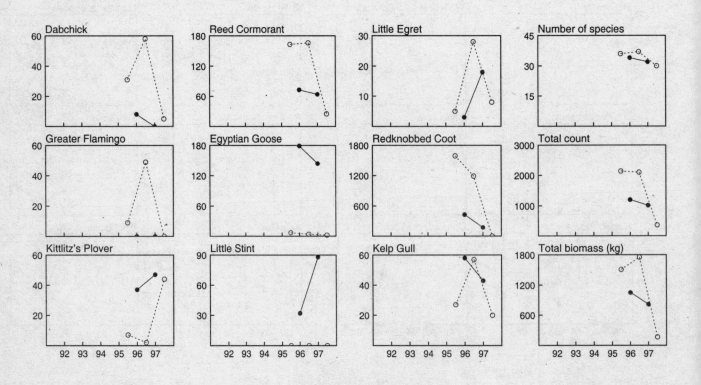

Swartkops River Estuary, Port Elizabeth, Eastern Cape
33° 52' S 25° 38' E (3325DC)

Comprises an IBA with Redhouse and Chatty saltpans. Open estuary; little waterfowl habitat but good foraging and roosting site for shorebirds; large tern roost. Good winter counts of Cape Cormorant and Little Egret in 1994; other cormorants, and Sacred Ibis, African Spoonbill and Cape Teal, also normally peak in winter. Globally significant numbers of Kelp Gull, and nationally significant numbers of African Black Oystercatcher, highest in winter. In summer, high numbers of Palearctic shorebirds, especially Grey Plover, Turnstone, Terek and Curlew Sandpipers, Greenshank, Bartailed Godwit, Curlew and Whimbrel; also good winter counts of several of these species, and of Blackwinged Stilt and Whitefronted Plover. Roseate Tern recorded irregularly. Threats include sedimentation, reclamation, pollution (domestic sewage and solid waste), and overhead powerlines.

		Summer (6) Mean	Max.	Winter (6) Mean	Max.			Summer (6) Mean	Max.	Winter (6) Mean	Max.
007	Blacknecked Grebe	0	1	0	0	258	Blacksmith Plover	6	22	12	21
008	Dabchick	0	0	1	5	262	Turnstone	294*	376**	92	165
055	Whitebreasted Cormorant	11	30	43	67	263	Terek Sandpiper	161*	260**	8	21
056	Cape Cormorant	2	3	291	771	264	Common Sandpiper	7	10	0	2
058	Reed Cormorant	4	12	12	34	269	Marsh Sandpiper	4	11	0	0
060	Darter	0	0	1	3	270	Greenshank	160	237	77	107
062	Grey Heron	13	15	5	10	271	Knot	8	16	0	1
063	Blackheaded Heron	1	2	0	0	272	Curlew Sandpiper	1010	2099	47	137
064	Goliath Heron	0	1	0	0	274	Little Stint	72	168	0	0
065	Purple Heron	0	0	0	1	281	Sanderling	131	182	8	26
066	Great White Heron	0	0	2	3	284	Ruff	1	5	0	0
067	Little Egret	36	53	123	222	288	Bartailed Godwit	50	92	14	32
071	Cattle Egret	2	9	0	0	289	Curlew	62	85	18	27
084	Black Stork	0	1	0	0	290	Whimbrel	577	755	154	194
091	Sacred Ibis	31	94	83	118	295	Blackwinged Stilt	2	6	53	113
093	Glossy Ibis	0	0	0	1	298	Water Dikkop	1	3	0	2
094	Hadeda Ibis	1	8	0	0	312	Kelp Gull	326**	417**	491**	682**
095	African Spoonbill	1	6	33	59	315	Greyheaded Gull	21	34	7	17
102	Egyptian Goose	1	4	0	1	322	Caspian Tern	14	20	11	16
104	Yellowbilled Duck	1	3	1	3	324	Swift Tern	1	3	37	79
106	Cape Teal	9	21	18	39	326	Sandwich Tern	55	123	4	21
108	Redbilled Teal	0	1	0	0	327	Common Tern	1033	1618	53	96
112	Cape Shoveller	1	2	2	7	330	Roseate Tern	3	10	1	4
148	African Fish Eagle	0	0	1	1	335	Little Tern	94	123	0	0
170	Osprey	1	3	0	0	339	Whitewinged Tern	125	472	0	0
244	African Black Oystercatcher	33*	37*	38*	47*	428	Pied Kingfisher	4	12	11	17
245	Ringed Plover	162	301	0	0	429	Giant Kingfisher	0	1	0	1
246	Whitefronted Plover	49	85	117	161	430	Halfcollared Kingfisher	0	0	0	1
247	Chestnutbanded Plover	0	1	0	0	713	Cape Wagtail	6	16	10	20
248	Kittlitz's Plover	9	12	29	72		Total	5216	6210	2034	2721
249	Threebanded Plover	0	2	2	6		No. of species		61		
254	Grey Plover	624	721	126	234						

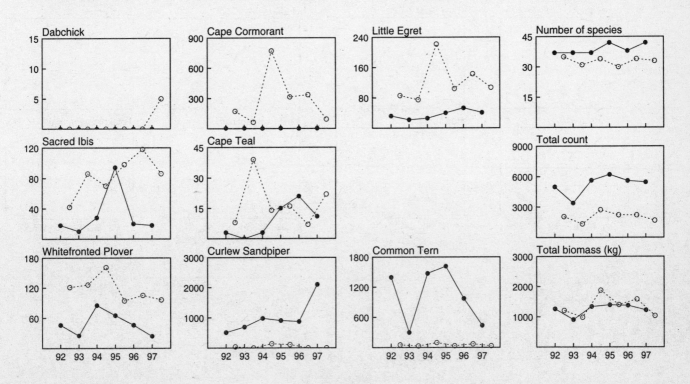

Beaufort West Bird Sanctuary, Beaufort West, Western Cape
32° 22' S 22° 37' E (3222BC)

This sanctuary comprises a sewage works, which holds small to moderate numbers of quite a good variety of waterbirds. Sacred Ibis, Yellowbilled Duck and Redbilled Teal are commoner in winter, while Cape Teal, Cape Shoveller, plovers, Blackwinged Stilt and Greyheaded Gull are commoner in summer. A good count of Avocet was recorded in summer 1995, but there appears to be little habitat suitable for Palearctic shorebirds in summer. The survey figures indicate a marked decline in the total number of species, total count and biomass, in summer ((species involved including Dabchick, South African Shelduck, Cape Teal, Cape Shoveller and Redknobbed Coot). No threats have been identified.

		Summer (5)		Winter (5)				Summer (5)		Winter (5)	
		Mean	Max.	Mean	Max.			Mean	Max.	Mean	Max.
007	Blacknecked Grebe	4	7	4	12	226	Moorhen	0	0	0	2
008	Dabchick	8	25	8	13	228	Redknobbed Coot	39	61	49	66
055	Whitebreasted Cormorant	0	1	1	3	248	Kittlitz's Plover	19	47	12	19
058	Reed Cormorant	1	2	2	8	249	Threebanded Plover	11	22	7	11
062	Grey Heron	1	2	1	3	258	Blacksmith Plover	39	65	30	60
063	Blackheaded Heron	1	2	2	4	264	Common Sandpiper	4	15	0	0
067	Little Egret	0	0	0	2	266	Wood Sandpiper	6	12	0	2
071	Cattle Egret	1	4	0	0	269	Marsh Sandpiper	1	3	0	1
076	Blackcrowned Night Heron	0	0	0	1	270	Greenshank	1	3	0	0
091	Sacred Ibis	10	30	30	52	272	Curlew Sandpiper	3	7	0	1
094	Hadeda Ibis	1	4	0	0	274	Little Stint	17	36	0	0
096	Greater Flamingo	0	0	1	3	284	Ruff	27	70	0	2
099	Whitefaced Duck	0	2	0	1	294	Avocet	10	44	0	0
103	South African Shelduck	12	30	11	14	295	Blackwinged Stilt	11	27	6	25
104	Yellowbilled Duck	11	20	34	64	315	Greyheaded Gull	49	109	34	53
105	African Black Duck	0	1	0	0	339	Whitewinged Tern	134	213	0	0
106	Cape Teal	39	75	15	27	428	Pied Kingfisher	0	1	0	0
108	Redbilled Teal	2	6	16	60	431	Malachite Kingfisher	0	1	0	2
112	Cape Shoveller	25	36	19	37	713	Cape Wagtail	29	38	29	47
113	Southern Pochard	6	14	3	7		Total	524	682	315	354
116	Spurwinged Goose	0	0	0	1		No. of species			41	
117	Maccoa Duck	1	3	0	1						

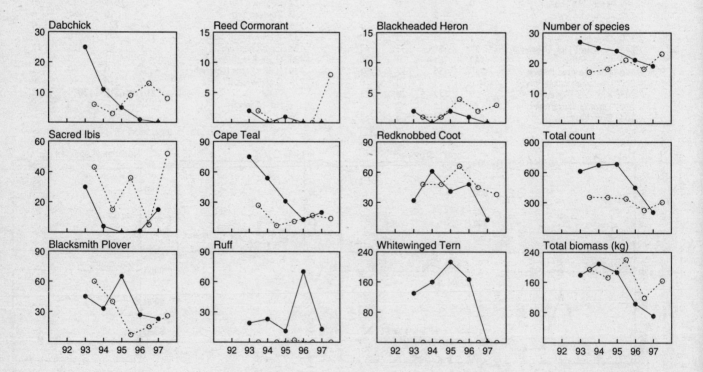

Berg River System, Velddrif, Western Cape
32° 47' S 18° 12' E (3218CA)

An IBA. The lower reaches and mouth of the Berg River, incorporating the open estuary, mudflats and lagoon, various saltpans, permanent marshes and riparian reedbeds, floodplains at Kruispad, Langrietvlei and Kersfontein, the Kliphoek River, and Doornfontein pan. A very important wetland system, with large concentrations of many waterbird species in summer and winter, with globally significant numbers of seven species, nationally significant numbers of six more, and large counts of White Pelican, cormorants, ibises, waterfowl, Blacksmith Plover, Avocet and terns. Saltpans are being enlarged at the expense of mud flats and reedbeds (Kliphoek). Other important threats include boating, water-skiing, dam construction (Kliphoek River), and gill net fishing; there is some pollution and hunting.

		Summer (5)		Winter (4)				Summer (5)		Winter (4)	
		Mean	Max.	Mean	Max.			Mean	Max.	Mean	Max.
006	Great Crested Grebe	14	31*	3	6	246	Whitefronted Plover	7	12	70	182
007	Blacknecked Grebe	9	24	296**	380**	247	Chestnutbanded Plover	34	63	142	224*
008	Dabchick	3	11	28	56	248	Kittlitz's Plover	279	648*	199	297
049	White Pelican	98	227	113	196	249	Threebanded Plover	10	28	16	30
055	Whitebreasted Cormorant	98	146	85	117	254	Grey Plover	224	417	30	68
056	Cape Cormorant	1233	3082*	131	159	258	Blacksmith Plover	142	232	144	192
058	Reed Cormorant	108	273	82	158	262	Turnstone	1	3	8	19
060	Darter	18	34	41	54	263	Terek Sandpiper	0	0	0	1
062	Grey Heron	36	57	23	27	264	Common Sandpiper	2	5	54	204
063	Blackheaded Heron	2	5	4	7	266	Wood Sandpiper	10	26	2	6
065	Purple Heron	6	10	5	6	269	Marsh Sandpiper	60	134	25	66
066	Great White Heron	0	0	2	5	270	Greenshank	268	566	90	147
067	Little Egret	46	64	52	60	271	Knot	1	4	0	1
068	Yellowbilled Egret	3	12	4	6	272	Curlew Sandpiper	4062*	6818*	480	769
071	Cattle Egret	10	52	10	15	274	Little Stint	1060	1575	29	72
076	Blackcrowned Night Heron	0	1	0	1	284	Ruff	147	344	0	1
078	Little Bittern	0	1	0	0	286	Ethiopian Snipe	2	6	0	1
091	Sacred Ibis	133	373	77	121	288	Bartailed Godwit	19	41	6	19
093	Glossy Ibis	9	40	54	142	289	Curlew	12	22	7	13
095	African Spoonbill	76*	211**	82*	115*	290	Whimbrel	36	67	4	11
096	Greater Flamingo	822*	1776**	1093*	1656**	294	Avocet	84	251	205	247
097	Lesser Flamingo	117	446	1129	1634	295	Blackwinged Stilt	159	239	511	751*
102	Egyptian Goose	214	712	253	482	298	Water Dikkop	0	0	3	4
103	South African Shelduck	225*	476**	82	125	312	Kelp Gull	256*	411**	472**	596**
104	Yellowbilled Duck	111	248	160	211	315	Greyheaded Gull	93	443	3	4
105	African Black Duck	0	2	2	4	316	Hartlaub's Gull	327**	585**	419**	672**
106	Cape Teal	344	734	111	226	322	Caspian Tern	34	69	18	29
108	Redbilled Teal	22	93	78	127	324	Swift Tern	12	41	32	121
112	Cape Shoveller	31	84	158	303*	326	Sandwich Tern	70	120	0	0
113	Southern Pochard	1	4	33	62	327	Common Tern	415	1561	1	3
116	Spurwinged Goose	203	640	83	115	335	Little Tern	15	67	0	1
117	Maccoa Duck	0	0	30	119	338	Whiskered Tern	0	0	0	1
148	African Fish Eagle	1	2	1	2	339	Whitewinged Tern	52	132	3	7
165	African Marsh Harrier	2	3	7	11	395	Marsh Owl	0	2	0	0
170	Osprey	0	1	0	0	428	Pied Kingfisher	27	42	39	50
210	African Rail	1	2	2	3	429	Giant Kingfisher	0	0	0	1
223	Purple Gallinule	0	1	0	0	431	Malachite Kingfisher	1	2	1	2
226	Moorhen	2	5	7	15	713	Cape Wagtail	74	135	81	109
228	Redknobbed Coot	211	348	3269*	6614**	891	Mallard	1	3	8	13
242	Painted Snipe	0	1	0	0		Total	12256	17093	10697	14477
244	African Black Oystercatcher	3	13	8	19		No. of species			81	
245	Ringed Plover	49	99	2	4						

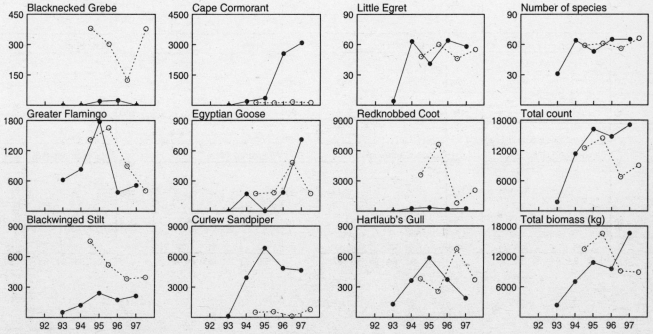

Bitou River, Plettenberg Bay, Western Cape
34° 01' S 23° 23' E (3423AB)

The lower Bitou River, progressing from marsh and floodplain to tidal conditions in the lowest reaches. Includes excellent marsh habitat for rails and other secretive birds; Redchested Flufftail and Baillon's Crake may breed. Moorhen counts peak in winter although recorded numbers are decreasing; winter Dabchick counts are also decreasing. Important for foraging and roosting shorebirds, waterfowl and egrets. Good numbers of South African Shelduck and Yellowbilled Duck recorded in winter 1995; Avocet numbers are high in summer. Species numbers and total counts have decreased over the three years of the survey period. Critical threats include pollution from effluent, pesticides and fertilizers, and damage by livestock; also threatened by siltation, reed encroachment, and residential development.

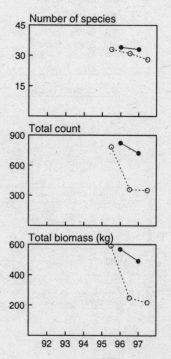

		Summer (2)		Winter (3)	
		Mean	Max.	Mean	Max.
008	Dabchick	11	13	12	22
055	Whitebreasted Cormorant	1	1	1	4
056	Cape Cormorant	0	0	1	2
058	Reed Cormorant	91	120	30	46
060	Darter	0	0	0	1
062	Grey Heron	4	4	2	3
063	Blackheaded Heron	5	9	1	2
065	Purple Heron	1	1	1	2
067	Little Egret	14	27	2	3
068	Yellowbilled Egret	0	0	0	1
071	Cattle Egret	27	54	1	1
078	Little Bittern	0	0	0	1
081	Hamerkop	1	2	0	0
091	Sacred Ibis	9	10	15	19
094	Hadeda Ibis	0	0	5	12
095	African Spoonbill	4	5	4	7
101	Whitebacked Duck	0	0	6	10
102	Egyptian Goose	58	95	11	18
103	South African Shelduck	26	27	18	44
104	Yellowbilled Duck	139	207	175	363
106	Cape Teal	23	32	6	17
107	Hottentot Teal	0	0	7	11
108	Redbilled Teal	33	43	16	27
112	Cape Shoveller	72	72	30	42
113	Southern Pochard	1	1	0	1
116	Spurwinged Goose	5	9	2	5
117	Maccoa Duck	0	0	1	2
148	African Fish Eagle	2	2	1	1

		Summer (2)		Winter (3)	
		Mean	Max.	Mean	Max.
165	African Marsh Harrier	2	3	1	2
223	Purple Gallinule	0	0	1	1
226	Moorhen	10	10	58	78
228	Redknobbed Coot	8	10	12	17
245	Ringed Plover	1	2	0	0
248	Kittlitz's Plover	5	10	0	0
249	Threebanded Plover	1	1	4	11
254	Grey Plover	2	4	0	0
258	Blacksmith Plover	20	27	7	9
266	Wood Sandpiper	24	36	0	0
269	Marsh Sandpiper	1	1	0	0
270	Greenshank	15	26	1	2
272	Curlew Sandpiper	35	70	0	0
284	Ruff	5	10	0	0
290	Whimbrel	7	8	0	1
294	Avocet	45	50	19	26
295	Blackwinged Stilt	38	52	34	42
312	Kelp Gull	6	8	4	5
322	Caspian Tern	0	0	1	2
338	Whiskered Tern	25	33	0	0
428	Pied Kingfisher	4	6	5	7
429	Giant Kingfisher	1	1	1	2
430	Halfcollared Kingfisher	0	0	0	1
431	Malachite Kingfisher	1	1	0	0
713	Cape Wagtail	0	0	2	4
	Total	773	823	498	784
	No. of species			53	

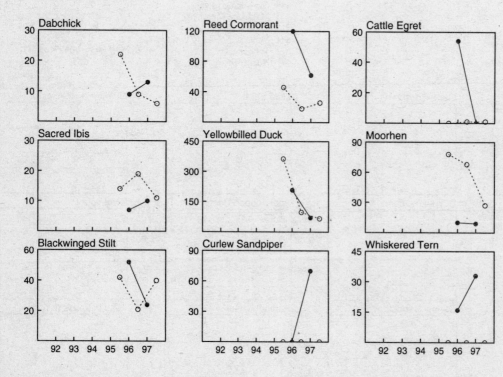

Botriviervlei, Kleinmond, Western Cape
34° 21' S 19° 06' E (3419AC)

Comprises an IBA with Kleinmond Estuary to the west. Closed estuarine lagoon, with sporadic natural or artificial openings; salinity sometimes high. Shore-line open; some adjacent reed- and sedgemarsh (see Kleinmond Estuary). Important for a wide variety of waterbird species; globally significant numbers of Great Crested Grebe, Cape Shoveller, Redknobbed Coot and Swift Tern occur; up to 15 500 coot recorded. Peak counts of gulls, terns, flamingos and small African plovers recorded in summer; coot, Dabchick and Blacknecked Grebe peak in winter. Number of species apparently declining. Threatened by human disturbance, sewage waste, illegal fishing, and a proposed waste dump; management plan urgently needed.

		Summer (4)		Winter (5)				Summer (4)		Winter (5)	
		Mean	Max.	Mean	Max.			Mean	Max.	Mean	Max.
006	Great Crested Grebe	62**	152**	21	50**	244	African Black Oystercatcher	3	4	1	4
007	Blacknecked Grebe	0	0	8	17	245	Ringed Plover	39	78	0	0
008	Dabchick	7	15	50	128	246	Whitefronted Plover	77	210	41	110
049	White Pelican	5	18	0	2	248	Kittlitz's Plover	102	211	16	78
055	Whitebreasted Cormorant	38	58	48	85	249	Threebanded Plover	15	31	4	17
056	Cape Cormorant	44	138	6	10	254	Grey Plover	1	1	0	0
058	Reed Cormorant	180	257	181	336	258	Blacksmith Plover	25	45	23	55
060	Darter	25	61	19	32	262	Turnstone	0	1	0	0
062	Grey Heron	28	38	12	30	264	Common Sandpiper	158	578	0	0
063	Blackheaded Heron	1	2	3	7	269	Marsh Sandpiper	5	17	0	0
065	Purple Heron	2	4	0	1	270	Greenshank	20	38	2	9
066	Great White Heron	1	2	0	1	271	Knot	73	225	0	0
067	Little Egret	22	55	3	7	272	Curlew Sandpiper	584	1000	0	0
068	Yellowbilled Egret	3	10	0	1	274	Little Stint	144	275	0	0
071	Cattle Egret	1	3	3	12	281	Sanderling	3	10	0	0
076	Blackcrowned Night Heron	0	0	0	1	284	Ruff	70	270	0	0
081	Hamerkop	0	1	1	2	286	Ethiopian Snipe	2	4	0	0
091	Sacred Ibis	12	18	3	15	289	Curlew	2	5	0	0
093	Glossy Ibis	4	14	0	0	290	Whimbrel	2	7	0	0
094	Hadeda Ibis	4	14	21	39	294	Avocet	15	48	0	0
095	African Spoonbill	5	19	4	15	295	Blackwinged Stilt	33	52	26	115
096	Greater Flamingo	301	538	110	300	298	Water Dikkop	8	16	2	5
102	Egyptian Goose	73	156	84	114	312	Kelp Gull	116	150*	64	78
103	South African Shelduck	0	0	1	7	315	Greyheaded Gull	1	2	4	20
104	Yellowbilled Duck	461	787	79	125	316	Hartlaub's Gull	93	121	25	48
105	African Black Duck	0	0	1	2	322	Caspian Tern	29	41	10	30
106	Cape Teal	13	31	6	14	324	Swift Tern	193	512**	66	150
107	Hottentot Teal	1	3	0	0	326	Sandwich Tern	246	951*	5	25
108	Redbilled Teal	28	94	40	178	327	Common Tern	553	868	13	56
112	Cape Shoveller	82	197*	86	352**	339	Whitewinged Tern	43	167	1	4
113	Southern Pochard	5	18	2	12	428	Pied Kingfisher	25	48	15	29
116	Spurwinged Goose	27	42	17	30	429	Giant Kingfisher	2	2	1	3
148	African Fish Eagle	6	11	5	6	430	Halfcollared Kingfisher	0	1	0	1
165	African Marsh Harrier	2	4	2	4	431	Malachite Kingfisher	3	10	1	2
170	Osprey	2	3	1	2	713	Cape Wagtail	37	48	18	29
226	Moorhen	3	6	1	2		Total	5140	8028	2873	6764
228	Redknobbed Coot	980	2899*	1716	5339**		No. of species		72		

Great Crested Grebe
Reed Cormorant
Grey Heron
Number of species
Greater Flamingo
Yellowbilled Duck
Redknobbed Coot
Total count
Kittlitz's Plover
Curlew Sandpiper
Common Tern
Total biomass (kg)

De Hoop Vlei, Bredasdorp, Western Cape
34° 26' S 20° 23' E (3420AD)

An IBA and Ramsar site. Coastal lake at mouth of seasonal Sout River; inflow only during winter; salinity fluctuates widely. Sandy and muddy substrates; extensive submergents but little marginal vegetation; *Phragmites, Typha* and sedges at springs and along river. Globally and nationally significant numbers of several waterbirds; maximum counts of which exceed those recorded in survey period and include 1473 Greater and 1715 Lesser Flamingo, 4626 Yellowbilled Duck and 3004 Cape Shoveller (both breed), 2166 Egyptian Goose and 24400 Redknobbed Coot. Large counts of shorebirds and terns in summer. Reeds/ sedges also hold Redchested Flufftail, African Rail and Black Crake. Threats include sedimentation, eutrophication, livestock damage (upper reaches), and pollution (pesticides and fertilizers).

		Summer (5)		Winter (4)				Summer (5)		Winter (4)	
		Mean	Max.	Mean	Max.			Mean	Max.	Mean	Max.
006	Great Crested Grebe	64**	180**	13	50**	116	Spurwinged Goose	54	176	54	100
007	Blacknecked Grebe	1	6	15	42	148	African Fish Eagle	1	3	1	3
008	Dabchick	34	83	20	35	223	Purple Gallinule	0	0	0	1
049	White Pelican	14	36	7	28	226	Moorhen	1	6	1	4
055	Whitebreasted Cormorant	19	38	2	5	228	Redknobbed Coot	2104	6175**	1800	4446*
056	Cape Cormorant	0	2	0	0	245	Ringed Plover	33	140	0	0
058	Reed Cormorant	4	17	13	35	246	Whitefronted Plover	0	1	24	38
060	Darter	2	6	0	1	248	Kittlitz's Plover	0	1	6	13
062	Grey Heron	29	52	9	27	249	Threebanded Plover	0	0	4	14
063	Blackheaded Heron	2	5	6	14	254	Grey Plover	10	45	1	3
066	Great White Heron	6	31	1	3	258	Blacksmith Plover	13	29	15	25
067	Little Egret	27	49	7	16	264	Common Sandpiper	0	0	2	8
068	Yellowbilled Egret	1	6	10	39	270	Greenshank	18	79	3	5
071	Cattle Egret	15	52	24	62	272	Curlew Sandpiper	230	1048	4	15
076	Blackcrowned Night Heron	3	14	2	7	274	Little Stint	145	700	0	1
081	Hamerkop	0	2	1	4	281	Sanderling	51	235	0	0
084	Black Stork	0	0	0	1	284	Ruff	6	28	0	0
091	Sacred Ibis	40	99	3	7	286	Ethiopian Snipe	1	7	0	0
093	Glossy Ibis	7	22	0	0	288	Bartailed Godwit	3	10	0	1
094	Hadeda Ibis	1	3	1	3	294	Avocet	21	102	3	11
095	African Spoonbill	23	70	4	11	295	Blackwinged Stilt	75	226	46	83
096	Greater Flamingo	0	1	24	72	298	Water Dikkop	1	3	0	0
097	Lesser Flamingo	0	0	7	23	312	Kelp Gull	9	16	17	53
099	Whitefaced Duck	2	6	2	8	315	Greyheaded Gull	0	0	0	1
102	Egyptian Goose	934	2117*	123	277	316	Hartlaub's Gull	0	0	0	1
103	South African Shelduck	6	19	41	83	322	Caspian Tern	5	6	1	4
104	Yellowbilled Duck	239	501	242	509	326	Sandwich Tern	2	10	0	0
105	African Black Duck	0	0	20	81	338	Whiskered Tern	166	427	0	0
106	Cape Teal	2	5	58	108	339	Whitewinged Tern	63	316	0	0
108	Redbilled Teal	1	6	32	88	713	Cape Wagtail	1	2	4	15
112	Cape Shoveller	506**	901**	385**	853**		Total	5030	10842	3085	5670
113	Southern Pochard	34	145	28	87		No. of species		62		

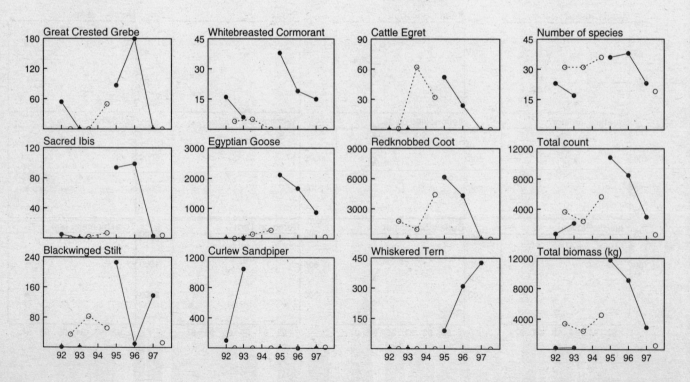

De Mond Estuary, Bredasdorp, Western Cape
34° 43' S 20° 07' E (3420CA)

Ramsar site and IBA. The De Mond State Forest/Heuningnes River Estuary is one of the few breeding sites for the globally near-threatened Damara Tern (total population c. 14450 birds): 5-7 breeding pairs of this African endemic species are recorded. Heuningnes is the most southerly estuary in Africa. Its dune areas and pebble slacks are important nesting sites for birds; it also has breeding African Black Oystercatchers, Caspian Terns and Kelp Gulls. Biomass and total count graphs reflect large numbers of small shorebirds in summer and smaller numbers of large birds in winter. Critical threats include oil pollution and dam building; it is also threatened by human encroachment and chemical pollution.

		Summer (4)		Winter (5)				Summer (4)		Winter (5)	
		Mean	Max.	Mean	Max.			Mean	Max.	Mean	Max.
008	Dabchick	0	0	6	15	258	Blacksmith Plover	18	33	7	13
049	White Pelican	0	0	20	100	263	Terek Sandpiper	1	2	0	0
055	Whitebreasted Cormorant	19	38	38	50	264	Common Sandpiper	2	6	0	0
056	Cape Cormorant	9	21	16	46	269	Marsh Sandpiper	1	2	0	0
058	Reed Cormorant	15	31	11	44	270	Greenshank	15	24	1	3
060	Darter	0	0	4	11	272	Curlew Sandpiper	382	596	1	6
062	Grey Heron	2	2	3	7	274	Little Stint	221	291	0	0
063	Blackheaded Heron	2	5	1	2	281	Sanderling	39	96	1	4
067	Little Egret	4	13	5	9	288	Bartailed Godwit	4	10	0	0
076	Blackcrowned Night Heron	0	1	2	5	289	Curlew	6	13	2	10
091	Sacred Ibis	0	0	2	10	290	Whimbrel	12	14	2	6
095	African Spoonbill	0	0	4	10	295	Blackwinged Stilt	0	0	0	2
096	Greater Flamingo	1	1	0	1	298	Water Dikkop	1	4	6	8
102	Egyptian Goose	0	0	0	2	312	Kelp Gull	36	61	53	119
103	South African Shelduck	0	0	0	2	315	Greyheaded Gull	0	0	2	6
104	Yellowbilled Duck	0	0	5	14	316	Hartlaub's Gull	0	0	1	2
106	Cape Teal	0	0	3	14	322	Caspian Tern	4	7	2	6
112	Cape Shoveller	0	0	10	24	324	Swift Tern	2	5	0	0
116	Spurwinged Goose	0	0	3	11	326	Sandwich Tern	11	36	0	0
148	African Fish Eagle	1	3	1	2	327	Common Tern	19	70	0	0
165	African Marsh Harrier	0	0	0	1	328	Arctic Tern	28	109	0	0
170	Osprey	0	1	0	0	334	Damara Tern	3	10	0	1
228	Redknobbed Coot	0	0	29	146	335	Little Tern	6	21	0	0
244	African Black Oystercatcher	4	5	1	2	428	Pied Kingfisher	4	9	4	8
245	Ringed Plover	227	382	0	0	429	Giant Kingfisher	0	0	1	2
246	Whitefronted Plover	21	34	39	107	713	Cape Wagtail	1	4	9	21
247	Chestnutbanded Plover	0	0	14	68		Total	1192	1646	347	661
248	Kittlitz's Plover	17	41	26	62		No. of species		55		
254	Grey Plover	59	84	8	20						

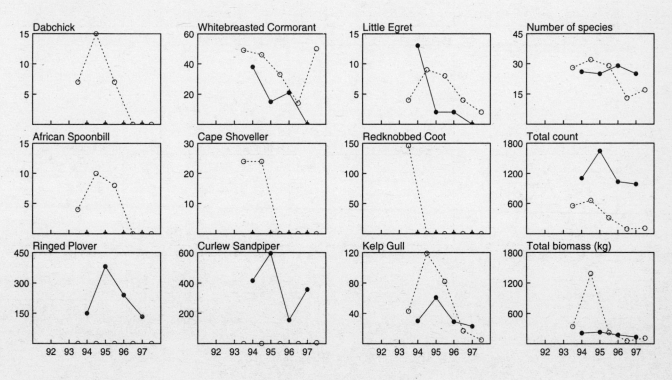

Dick Dent Bird Sanctuary, Somerset West, Western Cape
34° 06' S 18° 49' E (3418BB)

Six ponds of an old sewage works, formerly with open water, fringing reed cover, and shorelines for waders. Reed Cormorant occurs in good numbers and breeds; good counts of Yellowbilled Duck, this and Redbilled Teal being most numerous in summer. More Cape Shoveller recorded than at nearby Paardevlei Dam. Well managed until four years ago, attracting a variety of waterbirds and shorebirds. By 1998, 75% of open water covered by vegetation; no summer shorebirds, and fewer coot, which no longer breed. Total counts and number of species declining, summer and winter. Severe threats include encroachment of reeds, alien grass and waterplants, and lack of proper management by Somerset West Municipality in the last four years.

		Summer (5)		Winter (5)				Summer (5)		Winter (5)	
		Mean	Max.	Mean	Max.			Mean	Max.	Mean	Max.
008	Dabchick	2	4	4	9	106	Cape Teal	0	0	1	3
055	Whitebreasted Cormorant	0	0	1	2	108	Redbilled Teal	7	17	0	1
056	Cape Cormorant	0	0	0	1	112	Cape Shoveller	7	14	8	13
058	Reed Cormorant	34	82	77	150	113	Southern Pochard	0	0	0	1
060	Darter	2	6	5	14	116	Spurwinged Goose	3	8	0	1
062	Grey Heron	2	5	1	3	226	Moorhen	6	13	4	6
063	Blackheaded Heron	1	3	2	6	228	Redknobbed Coot	8	11	9	19
065	Purple Heron	1	2	0	1	249	Threebanded Plover	2	6	0	0
068	Yellowbilled Egret	2	6	0	0	258	Blacksmith Plover	6	12	5	10
071	Cattle Egret	0	2	0	0	266	Wood Sandpiper	1	2	0	0
076	Blackcrowned Night Heron	2	6	4	9	286	Ethiopian Snipe	1	4	0	0
081	Hamerkop	0	1	0	0	316	Hartlaub's Gull	0	0	1	2
091	Sacred Ibis	1	2	0	0	428	Pied Kingfisher	0	1	0	0
093	Glossy Ibis	0	1	0	1	429	Giant Kingfisher	0	1	0	1
094	Hadeda Ibis	0	2	2	5	431	Malachite Kingfisher	0	1	0	0
095	African Spoonbill	0	0	2	6	713	Cape Wagtail	3	10	0	0
102	Egyptian Goose	5	9	7	18	891	Mallard	0	1	0	0
104	Yellowbilled Duck	46	96	17	31		Total	143	213	152	231
105	African Black Duck	0	2	0	1		No. of species			36	

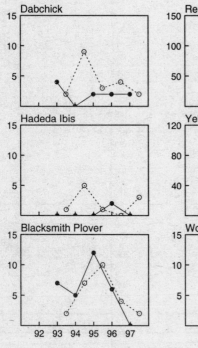

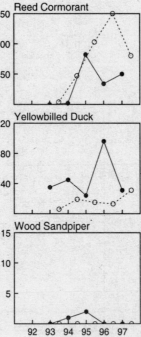

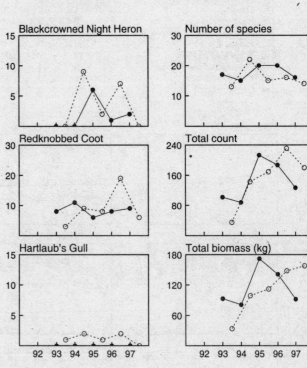

Droëvlei, Klipheuwel, Western Cape
33° 38' S 18° 43' E (3318DA)

A natural vlei, enlarged by an earth dam wall; there are many adjacent seasonal pans. Counts run from winter 1995 to winter 1997. Nationally significant numbers of Egyptian Goose occur in summer, when large numbers of Redbilled Teal, and Kittlitz's and Blacksmith Plovers, are recorded, plus moderate numbers of White Pelican. Cormorants, Yellowbilled Duck, Cape Shoveller and Redknobbed Coot peak in winter. Good numbers of Knot occur in summer, with moderate numbers of other Palearctic shorebirds. Bank erosion is a severe threat; important threats are pollution by waste from a dairy, and livestock grazing/trampling; there is also some pollution by fertilizers.

| | | Summer (2) | | Winter (3) | | | | Summer (2) | | Winter (3) | |
		Mean	Max.	Mean	Max.			Mean	Max.	Mean	Max.
006	Great Crested Grebe	2	3	2	4	116	Spurwinged Goose	7	7	2	2
007	Blacknecked Grebe	0	0	3	9	117	Maccoa Duck	0	0	6	18
008	Dabchick	1	1	9	16	228	Redknobbed Coot	38	38	99	115
049	White Pelican	22	27	5	6	245	Ringed Plover	16	25	0	0
055	Whitebreasted Cormorant	5	6	16	28	248	Kittlitz's Plover	65	74	18	20
058	Reed Cormorant	1	1	6	11	249	Threebanded Plover	0	0	10	12
060	Darter	4	4	5	7	258	Blacksmith Plover	185	197	16	22
062	Grey Heron	3	3	1	2	264	Common Sandpiper	1	2	0	0
063	Blackheaded Heron	1	2	1	3	271	Knot	37	74	0	0
071	Cattle Egret	1	2	1	1	272	Curlew Sandpiper	16	20	10	27
076	Blackcrowned Night Heron	0	0	0	1	274	Little Stint	52	86	2	5
091	Sacred Ibis	7	10	5	6	284	Ruff	78	84	0	0
095	African Spoonbill	6	7	1	1	286	Ethiopian Snipe	4	7	2	5
096	Greater Flamingo	0	0	13	22	294	Avocet	1	1	6	13
102	Egyptian Goose	1992*	2600*	10	13	295	Blackwinged Stilt	7	8	7	9
103	South African Shelduck	3	6	0	0	312	Kelp Gull	4	6	9	15
104	Yellowbilled Duck	10	15	20	29	339	Whitewinged Tern	2	2	0	0
106	Cape Teal	9	10	12	18	713	Cape Wagtail	9	10	13	25
108	Redbilled Teal	51	90	21	48		Total	2641	3318	368	511
112	Cape Shoveller	9	12	39	86		No. of species			38	

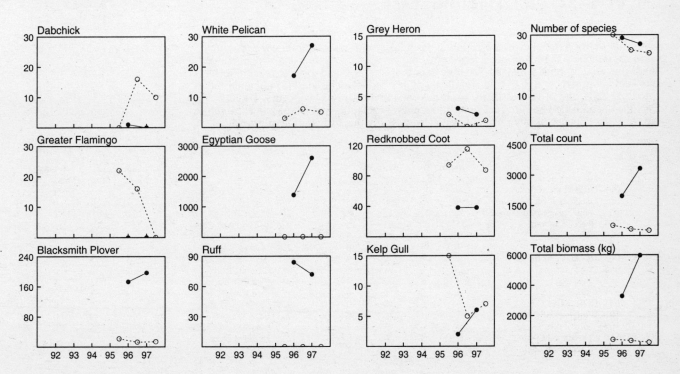

Eikenhof Dam, Grabouw, Western Cape
34° 07' S 19° 02' E (3419AA)

This dam was counted only in winter 1995, when 83 waterbirds of 9 species were recorded. All are common species and numbers are not significant; the only species worthy of note is African Black Duck. Fishing and boating occur, but no threats have been identified.

	Summer (0)		Winter (1)				Summer (0)		Winter (1)	
	Mean	Max.	Mean	Max.			Mean	Max.	Mean	Max.
008 Dabchick	–	–	1	1	258 Blacksmith Plover		–	–	4	4
094 Hadeda Ibis	–	–	2	2	312 Kelp Gull		–	–	1	1
102 Egyptian Goose	–	–	57	57	713 Cape Wagtail		–	–	1	1
104 Yellowbilled Duck	–	–	11	11	Total		–	–	83	83
105 African Black Duck	–	–	4	4	No. of species			9		
228 Redknobbed Coot	–	–	2	2						

Groenvlei, Sedgefield, Western Cape
34° 01' S 22° 52' E (3422BB)

The only South African drowned deflation basin lake, with no stream inflow and with seepage outlets to the sea. Extensive fringing and emergent sedgemarsh and reedmarsh, with surrounding rank grassland. Existing counts are too few and too restricted to reflect the site's importance: it may hold significant numbers of Redchested Flufftail and other secretive rails, and of Little Bittern, while the uncommon Grass Owl occurs. Threats include uncontrolled burning, eutrophication, alien vegetation, and increasing *Phragmites* cover at the expense of other marsh vegetation, possibly due to cessation of grazing.

	Summer (2)		Winter (2)				Summer (2)		Winter (2)	
	Mean	Max.	Mean	Max.			Mean	Max.	Mean	Max.
006 Great Crested Grebe	9	13	4	6	165 African Marsh Harrier		1	1	1	1
008 Dabchick	59	86	130	205	170 Osprey		1	1	0	0
055 Whitebreasted Cormorant	30	32	22	23	226 Moorhen		0	0	2	2
058 Reed Cormorant	75	90	142	175	228 Redknobbed Coot		162	205	256	316
060 Darter	3	3	5	9	258 Blacksmith Plover		3	3	1	2
062 Grey Heron	1	1	0	0	298 Water Dikkop		1	1	0	0
063 Blackheaded Heron	1	1	0	0	312 Kelp Gull		3	3	3	4
065 Purple Heron	2	2	1	1	322 Caspian Tern		2	3	0	0
067 Little Egret	1	1	0	0	327 Common Tern		28	31	4	7
071 Cattle Egret	1	2	0	0	428 Pied Kingfisher		4	8	2	3
094 Hadeda Ibis	3	3	0	0	429 Giant Kingfisher		2	2	0	0
101 Whitebacked Duck	1	1	0	0	713 Cape Wagtail		3	4	0	0
104 Yellowbilled Duck	3	4	7	7	Total		394	488	579	597
116 Spurwinged Goose	1	1	0	0	No. of species			27		
148 African Fish Eagle	2	2	2	2						

Jakkalsvlei, Lambert's Bay, Western Cape
32° 05' S 18° 19' E (3218AB)

A lagoon at the mouth of the Jakkals River. Open water, with very little emergent vegetation; shorelines of sand and mud, with some *Salicornia*; submergent *Myriophyllum* attracts coot. Waterfowl numbers peak in summer, when birds move to such permanent waterbodies from drying seasonal pans in the region. Nationally significant concentrations of Cape Shoveller were recorded in 1997 and 1998. Redknobbed Coot numbers peak in winter. Good numbers of Whitewinged Tern occurred in summer 1997. Variable numbers of Hartlaub's and Kelp Gulls visit the vlei to bathe in fresh water (K. Shaw). The river mouth should be open periodically but has remained closed for some time, largely due to a weir built by Lamberts Bay Municipality to ensure flooding on a more permanent basis (theoretically to attract birds and hence tourists). Even if the weir were removed, the system might not revert to its natural state because of water abstraction upstream and because a harbour wall extension has caused greater deposition of sand at the river mouth. Severe threats are posed by dam construction in the catchment; gravel pits in the river course, a nearby municipal dump, and alien plant infestation all have important effects.

		Summer (1)		Winter (1)				Summer (1)		Winter (1)	
		Mean	Max.	Mean	Max.			Mean	Max.	Mean	Max.
006	Great Crested Grebe	6	6	0	0	249	Threebanded Plover	1	1	0	0
007	Blacknecked Grebe	7	7	35	35	258	Blacksmith Plover	11	11	2	2
008	Dabchick	28	28	54	54	264	Common Sandpiper	1	1	0	0
055	Whitebreasted Cormorant	3	3	6	6	266	Wood Sandpiper	15	15	0	0
058	Reed Cormorant	12	12	0	0	269	Marsh Sandpiper	5	5	0	0
060	Darter	5	5	0	0	270	Greenshank	1	1	0	0
062	Grey Heron	1	1	0	0	272	Curlew Sandpiper	3	3	0	0
067	Little Egret	2	2	1	1	274	Little Stint	66	66	0	0
091	Sacred Ibis	10	10	15	15	284	Ruff	65	65	0	0
093	Glossy Ibis	28	28	0	0	295	Blackwinged Stilt	33	33	0	0
102	Egyptian Goose	63	63	5	5	312	Kelp Gull	91	91	47	47
103	South African Shelduck	37	37	5	5	315	Greyheaded Gull	6	6	0	0
104	Yellowbilled Duck	2	2	0	0	316	Hartlaub's Gull	47	47	75	75
106	Cape Teal	13	13	0	0	322	Caspian Tern	3	3	0	0
112	Cape Shoveller	183*	183*	34	34	324	Swift Tern	51	51	0	0
113	Southern Pochard	9	9	0	0	338	Whiskered Tern	4	4	0	0
117	Maccoa Duck	7	7	12	12	339	Whitewinged Tern	518	518	0	0
228	Redknobbed Coot	296	296	613	613	891	Mallard	1	1	0	0
245	Ringed Plover	2	2	0	0		Total	1637	1637	904	904
248	Kittlitz's Plover	1	1	0	0		No. of species		38		

Keurbooms River Estuary, Plettenberg Bay, Western Cape
34° 02' S 23° 24' E (3423AB)

The open estuary of the Keurbooms River. Two summer and three winter counts indicate good numbers of cormorants (especially in winter), an apparently resident population of Purple Heron, reasonable numbers of Little Egret throughout the year, a good variety of shorebirds (including large concentrations of Grey Plover, Greenshank and Whimbrel) and significant roosts of Kelp Gull (particularly in summer) and Swift Tern. Dabchick have been counted only in the winter and counts are decreasing. Residential development is a critical threat, while boating, fishing, general human disturbance, domestic animals, and bank erosion are also listed as severe threats.

		Summer (2)		Winter (3)				Summer (2)		Winter (3)	
		Mean	Max.	Mean	Max.			Mean	Max.	Mean	Max.
008	Dabchick	0	0	49	77	262	Turnstone	2	4	0	0
055	Whitebreasted Cormorant	20	22	33	38	264	Common Sandpiper	6	6	1	1
056	Cape Cormorant	13	25	62	124	270	Greenshank	92	108	26	35
058	Reed Cormorant	38	39	78	152	271	Knot	4	4	0	0
060	Darter	4	5	3	5	272	Curlew Sandpiper	261	354	24	53
062	Grey Heron	7	9	5	6	274	Little Stint	1	1	0	1
065	Purple Heron	4	5	4	8	288	Bartailed Godwit	4	5	0	1
067	Little Egret	22	24	23	31	290	Whimbrel	129	133	29	35
071	Cattle Egret	0	0	1	2	294	Avocet	0	0	57	170
091	Sacred Ibis	71	106	36	69	295	Blackwinged Stilt	0	0	2	4
094	Hadeda Ibis	1	1	0	0	298	Water Dikkop	4	5	1	4
095	African Spoonbill	0	0	7	11	312	Kelp Gull	544**	628**	238*	385**
096	Greater Flamingo	0	0	12	37	315	Greyheaded Gull	0	0	0	1
102	Egyptian Goose	14	25	10	27	322	Caspian Tern	0	0	2	5
104	Yellowbilled Duck	0	0	3	4	324	Swift Tern	263*	519**	291*	509**
106	Cape Teal	0	0	1	2	326	Sandwich Tern	15	16	0	0
148	African Fish Eagle	0	0	1	1	327	Common Tern	7	14	0	0
244	African Black Oystercatcher	14	14	10	12	428	Pied Kingfisher	8	8	6	9
245	Ringed Plover	56	59	0	0	713	Cape Wagtail	3	4	9	15
246	Whitefronted Plover	44	48	61	76	891	Mallard	6	11	0	0
249	Threebanded Plover	0	0	1	2		Total	1884	2072	1114	1365
254	Grey Plover	223	233	18	25		No. of species			43	
258	Blacksmith Plover	11	15	10	13						

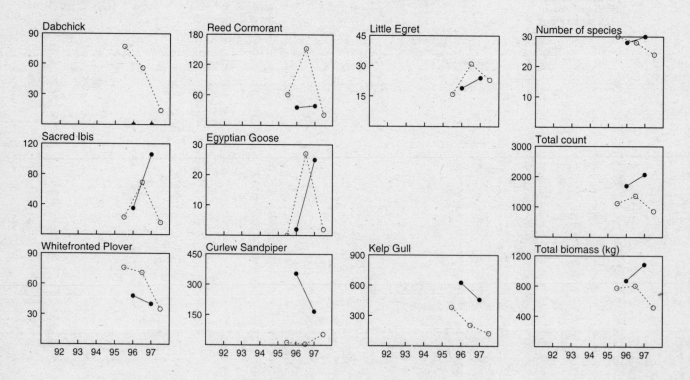

Klavervlei, Somerset West, Western Cape
34° 02' S 18° 45' E (3418BB)

Farm dam with fringing reeds and formerly up to 25% cover of floating alien Parrot-feather *Myriophyllum aquaticum*. Attracts a reasonable selection of waterbird species, none in large numbers; commonest species in summer are Egyptian and Spurwinged Geese, and Blacksmith Plover; in winter Cattle Egret, Yellowbilled Duck and Redknobbed Coot; small numbers of Ethiopian Snipe occur in summer. Decline evident in number of species and total counts; reason suggested (G. Lamont) for this is recent removal of Parrot-feather manually, and of this and other fringing water plants by herbicide. Although Parrot-feather normally considered a threat (e.g. see Paarl Sewage Works), observations at Klavervlei suggest it may attract birds by providing cover and harbouring invertebrate food. African Jacana no longer occurs but was formerly seen on Parrot-feather, as was single Baillon's Crake; Ethiopian Snipe, Black Crake, Purple Gallinule, Moorhen and Redknobbed Coot were probably attracted to it, and any unusually high numbers of Spurwinged and Egyptian Goose and Yellowbilled Duck tended to concentrate among it.

		Summer (3)		Winter (3)					Summer (3)		Winter (3)	
		Mean	Max.	Mean	Max.				Mean	Max.	Mean	Max.
008	Dabchick	0	0	1	2		113	Southern Pochard	0	0	1	2
049	White Pelican	0	0	2	5		116	Spurwinged Goose	47	112	3	5
055	Whitebreasted Cormorant	1	3	1	1		213	Black Crake	1	2	1	2
058	Reed Cormorant	1	3	2	5		223	Purple Gallinule	1	1	2	4
060	Darter	7	10	1	2		226	Moorhen	7	10	10	13
062	Grey Heron	0	1	0	1		228	Redknobbed Coot	7	10	22	40
065	Purple Heron	1	1	0	0		240	African Jacana	0	1	0	0
067	Little Egret	0	0	0	1		258	Blacksmith Plover	14	16	7	10
068	Yellowbilled Egret	0	1	2	2		264	Common Sandpiper	0	1	0	0
071	Cattle Egret	8	16	25	70		286	Ethiopian Snipe	8	15	0	0
076	Blackcrowned Night Heron	1	2	1	3		312	Kelp Gull	0	0	1	2
091	Sacred Ibis	3	7	5	9		316	Hartlaub's Gull	0	0	0	1
093	Glossy Ibis	0	0	3	9		322	Caspian Tern	0	0	0	1
094	Hadeda Ibis	2	5	1	2		428	Pied Kingfisher	1	2	1	2
095	African Spoonbill	0	1	1	3		431	Malachite Kingfisher	0	1	0	1
102	Egyptian Goose	33	79	8	12		713	Cape Wagtail	0	1	1	2
104	Yellowbilled Duck	6	13	14	16			Total	149	283	119	153
108	Redbilled Teal	0	0	0	1			No. of species			35	
112	Cape Shoveller	0	0	4	8							

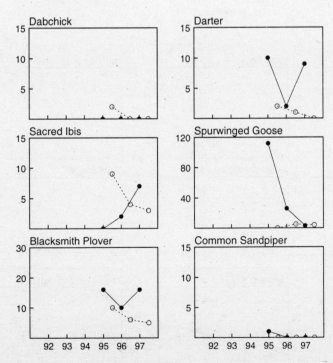

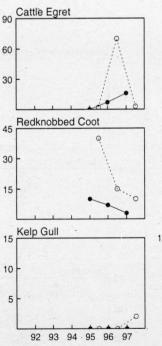

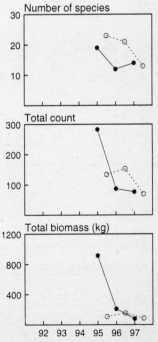

Kleinmond River Estuary, Kleinmond, Western Cape
34° 21' S 19° 05' E (3419AC)

Comprises an IBA with Botriviervlei to the east. Extensively marshy wetland. Large areas of *Phragmites, Typha, Juncus* and sedges (*Scirpus, Schoenoplectus*); also fringing and emergent sparse sedge/grass cover, open water, mud and sand. Habitat for Redchested Flufftail, Black Crake, African Rail and Purple Gallinule, especially at extreme western end (Kleinmond Lagoon); elsewhere has similar avifauna to Botriviervlei, but lower in numbers and species diversity; counts of Sanderling are relatively high. Threats include human disturbance, pollution from fertilizers, stormwater runoff, alien vegetation and poor management.

		Summer (3)		Winter (4)	
		Mean	Max.	Mean	Max.
008	Dabchick	0	0	6	19
055	Whitebreasted Cormorant	1	1	7	22
058	Reed Cormorant	1	3	4	14
060	Darter	1	2	5	18
062	Grey Heron	0	1	2	3
063	Blackheaded Heron	0	0	1	2
065	Purple Heron	1	2	0	1
067	Little Egret	3	5	2	4
068	Yellowbilled Egret	0	0	1	4
071	Cattle Egret	0	0	1	2
091	Sacred Ibis	5	15	0	0
093	Glossy Ibis	0	1	0	0
094	Hadeda Ibis	3	8	1	5
095	African Spoonbill	0	0	0	1
096	Greater Flamingo	0	0	1	2
101	Whitebacked Duck	0	0	1	2
102	Egyptian Goose	2	3	4	7
104	Yellowbilled Duck	17	34	28	50
106	Cape Teal	1	3	0	0
108	Redbilled Teal	1	2	3	7
112	Cape Shoveller	13	30	16	27
116	Spurwinged Goose	2	3	4	7
148	African Fish Eagle	1	1	1	3
165	African Marsh Harrier	1	1	1	2
170	Osprey	0	1	0	0
210	African Rail	0	1	1	4
213	Black Crake	0	0	0	1
223	Purple Gallinule	0	1	0	0

		Summer (3)		Winter (4)	
		Mean	Max.	Mean	Max.
226	Moorhen	0	1	0	1
228	Redknobbed Coot	0	0	41	133
244	African Black Oystercatcher	2	4	0	1
245	Ringed Plover	1	3	0	0
246	Whitefronted Plover	5	8	0	0
247	Chestnutbanded Plover	1	2	0	0
248	Kittlitz's Plover	3	5	0	0
249	Threebanded Plover	5	15	0	0
258	Blacksmith Plover	7	8	5	11
264	Common Sandpiper	19	58	0	0
266	Wood Sandpiper	1	3	0	0
270	Greenshank	7	15	0	0
281	Sanderling	53	160	0	0
286	Ethiopian Snipe	1	3	0	0
295	Blackwinged Stilt	3	8	3	10
312	Kelp Gull	3	4	3	4
315	Greyheaded Gull	3	8	0	0
316	Hartlaub's Gull	7	8	2	2
322	Caspian Tern	1	3	1	3
324	Swift Tern	0	1	0	1
327	Common Tern	0	1	0	1
428	Pied Kingfisher	1	2	1	2
429	Giant Kingfisher	0	0	1	1
431	Malachite Kingfisher	1	2	0	0
713	Cape Wagtail	3	4	1	2
	Total	181	352	146	319
	No. of species		53		

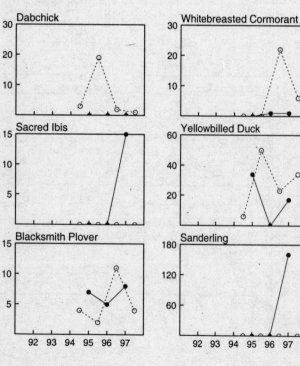

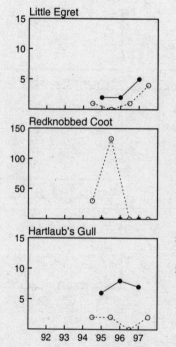

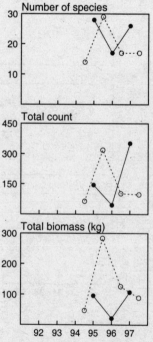

Knysna Lagoon, Knysna, Western Cape
34° 03' S 23° 02' E (3423AA)

Tidal lagoon and open estuary of the Knysna River. Globally significant numbers of the near-threatened African Black Oystercatcher in winter, and nationally significant numbers of this and Cape Shoveller in summer, when good numbers of Yellowbilled Duck also occur in some years. Noteworthy counts of Grey Plover, Greenshank, Curlew Sandpiper and Whimbrel in summer, and of Blackwinged Stilt in winter. Seasonal variation in types of birds using site well shown by biomass and total count graphs: large numbers of small birds (mostly shorebirds) in summer and smaller numbers of large birds (cormorants, egrets, ibises, gulls) in winter. Critically threatened by siltation from local urban development; important threats are bait collection, recreational activities and harassment by dogs.

		Summer (5)		Winter (5)					Summer (5)		Winter (5)	
		Mean	Max.	Mean	Max.				Mean	Max.	Mean	Max.
006	Great Crested Grebe	0	0	0	1		245	Ringed Plover	44	101	0	0
008	Dabchick	0	0	9	27		246	Whitefronted Plover	1	3	11	17
055	Whitebreasted Cormorant	12	23	28	41		248	Kittlitz's Plover	39	69	46	63
056	Cape Cormorant	8	16	317	407		249	Threebanded Plover	4	7	4	8
058	Reed Cormorant	106	136	326	400		254	Grey Plover	441	666	35	66
060	Darter	0	1	5	17		258	Blacksmith Plover	55	81	51	66
062	Grey Heron	49	54	51	70		262	Turnstone	0	1	0	0
063	Blackheaded Heron	2	4	2	4		264	Common Sandpiper	6	13	0	1
065	Purple Heron	0	1	0	0		266	Wood Sandpiper	11	50	0	0
067	Little Egret	72	85	166	217		269	Marsh Sandpiper	44	90	4	21
068	Yellowbilled Egret	0	1	0	0		270	Greenshank	353	499	76	94
071	Cattle Egret	1	5	10	25		272	Curlew Sandpiper	2452	2817	25	99
076	Blackcrowned Night Heron	0	0	3	8		274	Little Stint	7	18	0	0
081	Hamerkop	0	1	0	0		284	Ruff	5	11	0	0
084	Black Stork	0	0	0	1		286	Ethiopian Snipe	2	4	0	0
091	Sacred Ibis	20	36	110	160		288	Bartailed Godwit	0	1	0	0
093	Glossy Ibis	1	5	0	0		289	Curlew	5	7	1	2
094	Hadeda Ibis	2	11	23	55		290	Whimbrel	319	387	31	56
095	African Spoonbill	0	1	20	55		294	Avocet	15	50	53	103
102	Egyptian Goose	30	49	19	38		295	Blackwinged Stilt	54	85	101	184
103	South African Shelduck	0	2	1	3		312	Kelp Gull	338**	437**	511**	580**
104	Yellowbilled Duck	146	237	99	121		315	Greyheaded Gull	0	0	0	2
106	Cape Teal	24	48	22	39		322	Caspian Tern	2	5	4	6
108	Redbilled Teal	1	5	1	4		324	Swift Tern	3	15	22	51
112	Cape Shoveller	122	216*	76	123		326	Sandwich Tern	26	34	0	0
113	Southern Pochard	0	0	0	1		327	Common Tern	106	151	45	123
116	Spurwinged Goose	0	0	2	10		428	Pied Kingfisher	10	21	25	35
148	African Fish Eagle	2	3	2	3		429	Giant Kingfisher	0	0	2	5
170	Osprey	2	2	1	2		430	Halfcollared Kingfisher	0	0	0	1
210	African Rail	1	4	0	0		431	Malachite Kingfisher	0	1	1	1
213	Black Crake	0	0	1	4		713	Cape Wagtail	10	20	14	22
226	Moorhen	1	2	4	10		891	Mallard	0	1	1	2
228	Redknobbed Coot	10	13	7	10			Total	5002	5571	2421	2868
244	African Black Oystercatcher	39*	45*	50**	71**			No. of species		66		

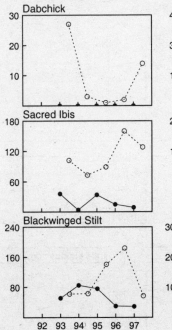

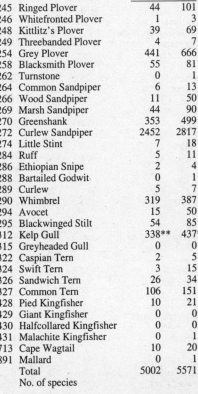

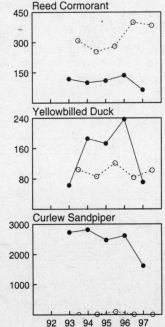

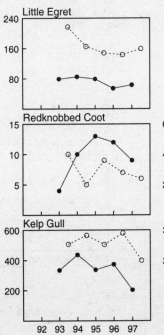

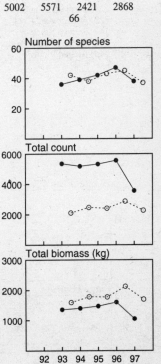

Langebaan Lagoon, Langebaan, Western Cape
33° 09' S 18° 04' E (3318AA)

A Ramsar site and part of the West Coast National Park. The lagoon is a sheltered inlet from Saldanha Bay, 15 km long and averaging 3 km wide. Saltmarsh covers about 600 ha, and there are about 1750 ha of intertidal sandflats. There are no rivers running into the lagoon, but extensive reedbeds and sedge marshes on the western shore depend on freshwater seepage. Saltpans at the southern end are flooded only at the highest spring tides. These diverse habitats support large numbers of Palearctic and intra-African migrants, and resident species. Twice-yearly high-tide counts by the Western Cape Wader Study Group commenced in 1975 and many research studies have taken place here. Currently, the most important threat is the risk of oil and industrial pollution from the harbour and associated developments in Saldanha Bay. Levels of human disturbance in the sensitive southern areas have decreased markedly since the proclamation of the national park.

		Summer (6)		Winter (6)	
		Mean	Max.	Mean	Max.
049	White Pelican	56	108	51	201
055	Whitebreasted Cormorant	22	39	23	42
056	Cape Cormorant	181	379	168	636
058	Reed Cormorant	26	80	9	24
060	Darter	0	1	0	0
062	Grey Heron	22	35	7	16
063	Blackheaded Heron	4	11	3	12
065	Purple Heron	1	1	0	1
066	Great White Heron	1	3	0	0
067	Little Egret	72	103	63	103
068	Yellowbilled Egret	0	1	0	1
071	Cattle Egret	0	1	7	21
091	Sacred Ibis	302	446	344	586
093	Glossy Ibis	0	1	10	54
094	Hadeda Ibis	0	0	0	2
095	African Spoonbill	35	52	24	42
096	Greater Flamingo	619	2520**	2817**	6062**
097	Lesser Flamingo	0	1	595	1606
102	Egyptian Goose	25	46	19	28
103	South African Shelduck	26	68	10	15
104	Yellowbilled Duck	51	87	15	32
106	Cape Teal	4	14	18	40
108	Redbilled Teal	0	0	3	17
112	Cape Shoveller	1	2	4	16
116	Spurwinged Goose	0	0	0	1
148	African Fish Eagle	0	0	0	1
165	African Marsh Harrier	2	5	3	7
170	Osprey	2	5	0	0
210	African Rail	0	1	0	0
213	Black Crake	0	2	0	0
217	Redchested Flufftail	2	8	0	0
223	Purple Gallinule	0	2	0	0
228	Redknobbed Coot	1	2	0	0
242	Painted Snipe	0	0	0	1
244	African Black Oystercatcher	34*	71**	26*	47*
245	Ringed Plover	326	548	0	0

		Summer (6)		Winter (6)	
		Mean	Max.	Mean	Max.
246	Whitefronted Plover	178	215	123	154
247	Chestnutbanded Plover	11	28	15	35
248	Kittlitz's Plover	73	118	103	184
249	Threebanded Plover	2	8	3	6
254	Grey Plover	3126**	4877**	257	540
258	Blacksmith Plover	16	47	25	37
262	Turnstone	2433**	4587**	414**	796**
263	Terek Sandpiper	94**	251**	14**	58**
264	Common Sandpiper	7	34	1	3
269	Marsh Sandpiper	9	22	5	26
270	Greenshank	578	992	200	320
271	Knot	838	2171	21	90
272	Curlew Sandpiper	14564**	18495**	1272	2303
274	Little Stint	406	721	6	19
281	Sanderling	1387*	2260**	41	155
284	Ruff	19	35	0	1
288	Bartailed Godwit	427	620	60	211
289	Curlew	326	1373	82	362
290	Whimbrel	825	1193	219	312
294	Avocet	69	135	65	130
295	Blackwinged Stilt	39	98	74	132
298	Water Dikkop	1	2	0	0
312	Kelp Gull	479**	1106**	359**	611**
316	Hartlaub's Gull	575**	1025**	882**	1550**
322	Caspian Tern	19	24	16	42
324	Swift Tern	28	101	5	21
326	Sandwich Tern	31	57	1	6
327	Common Tern	1150	4078*	13	56
335	Little Tern	6	16	0	1
395	Marsh Owl	0	0	1	5
428	Pied Kingfisher	7	13	7	15
431	Malachite Kingfisher	0	0	0	1
713	Cape Wagtail	91	128	63	114
	Total	29627	35002	8563	12538
	No. of species		69		

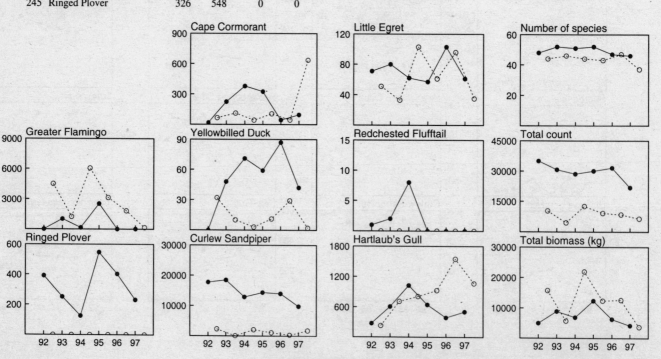

Cape Cormorant

Little Egret

Number of species

Greater Flamingo

Yellowbilled Duck

Redchested Flufftail

Total count

Ringed Plover

Curlew Sandpiper

Hartlaub's Gull

Total biomass (kg)

92 93 94 95 96 97

Mossel Bay Sewage Works, Mossel Bay, Western Cape
34° 07' S 22° 06' E (3422AA)

Three maturation ponds and a small grassy and reedy vlei. A single count in July 1994 yielded small to moderate numbers of 26 waterbird species, in particular Dabchick, Whitebreasted Cormorant, Yellowbilled Duck, Cape Teal, Cape Shoveler (the commonest bird), Moorhen, Threebanded Plover and Kelp Gull. No threats have been identified.

		Summer (0)		Winter (1)				Summer (0)		Winter (1)	
		Mean	Max.	Mean	Max.			Mean	Max.	Mean	Max.
008	Dabchick	–	–	20	20	223	Purple Gallinule	–	–	1	1
055	Whitebreasted Cormorant	–	–	20	20	226	Moorhen	–	–	15	15
058	Reed Cormorant	–	–	6	6	228	Redknobbed Coot	–	–	15	15
060	Darter	–	–	5	5	245	Ringed Plover	–	–	5	5
062	Grey Heron	–	–	3	3	249	Threebanded Plover	–	–	13	13
063	Blackheaded Heron	–	–	2	2	258	Blacksmith Plover	–	–	2	2
065	Purple Heron	–	–	1	1	264	Common Sandpiper	–	–	4	4
081	Hamerkop	–	–	1	1	286	Ethiopian Snipe	–	–	3	3
102	Egyptian Goose	–	–	3	3	290	Whimbrel	–	–	1	1
104	Yellowbilled Duck	–	–	31	31	298	Water Dikkop	–	–	1	1
106	Cape Teal	–	–	15	15	312	Kelp Gull	–	–	16	16
108	Redbilled Teal	–	–	5	5	713	Cape Wagtail	–	–	7	7
112	Cape Shoveller	–	–	50	50		Total	–	–	249	249
213	Black Crake	–	–	4	4		No. of species			26	

Olifants River Mouth (South), Lutzville, Western Cape
31° 42' S 18° 12' E (3118CA)

An IBA. An open estuary with mud and sandbanks. Counts began in summer 1996 and have yielded good numbers of a reasonable variety of waterbirds, including 10 Palearctic shorebird species (high counts of Ringed and Grey Plovers are noteworthy). Counts of White Pelican, cormorants, South African Shelduck, Whitefronted and Kittlitz's Plovers, and Swift Tern, are higher in summer, whereas counts of Sacred Ibis, Lesser Flamingo, most waterfowl, Avocet, Blackwinged Stilt and gulls are higher in winter. Good numbers of Avocet are recorded. Severe threats are dam building and water abstraction by riparian landowners. Disturbance by fishermen in 4x4 vehicles is an important threat, and net fishing by the local community is a mild threat.

		Summer (2)		Winter (1)				Summer (2)		Winter (1)	
		Mean	Max.	Mean	Max.			Mean	Max.	Mean	Max.
049	White Pelican	16	31	0	0	246	Whitefronted Plover	17	34	3	3
055	Whitebreasted Cormorant	37	73	11	11	248	Kittlitz's Plover	5	9	0	0
056	Cape Cormorant	30	60	0	0	249	Threebanded Plover	4	8	0	0
058	Reed Cormorant	0	0	2	2	254	Grey Plover	52	104	4	4
062	Grey Heron	4	6	3	3	258	Blacksmith Plover	1	1	0	0
065	Purple Heron	1	1	0	0	269	Marsh Sandpiper	9	13	0	0
066	Great White Heron	5	8	0	0	270	Greenshank	37	72	2	2
067	Little Egret	8	16	8	8	272	Curlew Sandpiper	406	663	0	0
091	Sacred Ibis	2	2	21	21	274	Little Stint	114	228	0	0
093	Glossy Ibis	1	2	0	0	281	Sanderling	3	5	0	0
095	African Spoonbill	15	29	16	16	284	Ruff	26	48	0	0
097	Lesser Flamingo	35	70	177	177	289	Curlew	3	4	0	0
102	Egyptian Goose	1	1	7	7	290	Whimbrel	3	3	5	5
103	South African Shelduck	52	93	10	10	294	Avocet	11	20	74	74
104	Yellowbilled Duck	0	0	3	3	295	Blackwinged Stilt	8	16	24	24
106	Cape Teal	0	0	10	10	312	Kelp Gull	0	0	80	80
112	Cape Shoveller	1	1	35	35	316	Hartlaub's Gull	11	21	57	57
116	Spurwinged Goose	0	0	43	43	322	Caspian Tern	5	8	0	0
228	Redknobbed Coot	0	0	20	20	324	Swift Tern	71	142	0	0
244	African Black Oystercatcher	17	18	16	16		Total	1113	1659	631	631
245	Ringed Plover	110	205	0	0		No. of species			40	

Paardevlei Dam, Somerset West, Western Cape
34° 05' S 18° 49' E (3418BB)

Dam fed by Lourens River; usually no outlet. Until early 1991, habitat in fairly healthy condition with much submerged vegetation providing food for large numbers (up to 478) of Redknobbed Coot. Subsequent eutrophication resulting from fertilisers in water from river led to death of submergents and departure of coot. Counts show large numbers of Whitebreasted Cormorant, Darter, Egyptian Goose and Blacksmith Plover, especially in summer. Good numbers of Reed Cormorant in summer 1995; very few duck except Yellowbilled. 34 Whitewinged Tern recorded summer 1993; 10 Arctic Tern summer 1996, and 21 Avocet winter 1995. Decline apparent in number of species recorded. Eutrophication a critical threat; recent filling of dam during winter rains, when water's fertiliser content lowest, may, if repeated, help alleviate the problem.

		Summer (5)		Winter (5)					Summer (5)		Winter (5)	
		Mean	Max.	Mean	Max.				Mean	Max.	Mean	Max.
006	Great Crested Grebe	0	0	0	1		228	Redknobbed Coot	1	4	1	4
008	Dabchick	0	2	2	5		248	Kittlitz's Plover	0	0	1	3
055	Whitebreasted Cormorant	128	167	92	110		249	Threebanded Plover	2	4	1	5
058	Reed Cormorant	19	68	12	34		258	Blacksmith Plover	62	88	16	25
060	Darter	69	96	47	86		264	Common Sandpiper	1	2	0	1
062	Grey Heron	0	2	0	1		270	Greenshank	1	4	0	0
063	Blackheaded Heron	0	1	0	0		294	Avocet	0	0	4	21
065	Purple Heron	0	1	0	0		295	Blackwinged Stilt	0	0	0	2
068	Yellowbilled Egret	0	0	0	1		298	Water Dikkop	0	0	0	2
071	Cattle Egret	9	14	12	27		312	Kelp Gull	0	0	0	1
076	Blackcrowned Night Heron	1	5	0	0		316	Hartlaub's Gull	3	6	2	9
081	Hamerkop	0	0	1	2		322	Caspian Tern	0	1	0	0
091	Sacred Ibis	13	42	15	34		327	Common Tern	0	2	0	0
094	Hadeda Ibis	1	3	3	8		328	Arctic Tern	2	10	0	0
095	African Spoonbill	0	0	3	7		338	Whiskered Tern	0	1	0	0
102	Egyptian Goose	843	1534	187	294		339	Whitewinged Tern	7	34	0	0
104	Yellowbilled Duck	8	16	14	26		428	Pied Kingfisher	2	5	1	2
105	African Black Duck	0	1	0	0		429	Giant Kingfisher	0	1	0	1
106	Cape Teal	0	0	1	5		431	Malachite Kingfisher	0	1	0	0
108	Redbilled Teal	1	3	2	9		713	Cape Wagtail	2	7	3	7
112	Cape Shoveller	1	4	1	3		891	Mallard	0	1	0	0
116	Spurwinged Goose	4	8	2	7			Total	1186	1905	426	541
148	African Fish Eagle	1	2	0	1			No. of species		45		
226	Moorhen	2	4	1	2							

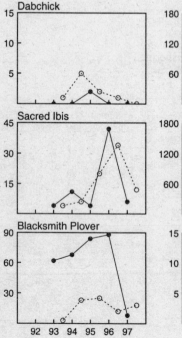

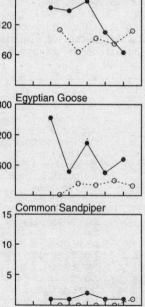

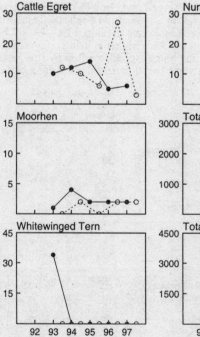

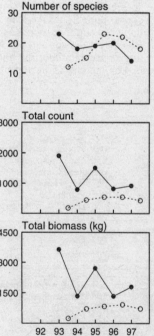

Paarl Bird Sanctuary, Paarl, Western Cape
33° 41' S 18° 58' E (3318DB)

Maturation ponds; small areas of fringing *Typha* and *Phragmites*; some muddy substrate. Good variety of waterbirds; high summer counts of Dabchick, Sacred Ibis, Redbilled Teal, Cape Shoveller (nationally significant), Maccoa Duck (breeds), and Whitewinged Tern (globally significant); high winter counts of Grey Heron, Lesser Flamingo (1993 only), Blackwinged Stilt, and Greyheaded and Hartlaub's Gulls (breed; site globally significant for Hartlaub's). Cormorants, Darter, Little and Cattle Egrets, Grey and Blackheaded Herons, and Blackcrowned Night Heron, all breed. High biomass in winter 1993 due to Lesser Flamingo and gulls. Little habitat for secretive rails, but Baillon's Crake has occurred. Threats include spread of nearby squatter camp, livestock grazing/trampling, and spread of *Myriophyllum aquaticum*.

		Summer (5)		Winter (5)				Summer (5)		Winter (5)	
		Mean	Max.	Mean	Max.			Mean	Max.	Mean	Max.
006	Great Crested Grebe	3	4	1	7	116	Spurwinged Goose	1	4	1	4
007	Blacknecked Grebe	6	20	41	82	117	Maccoa Duck	49	84	7	18
008	Dabchick	118	182	93	118	148	African Fish Eagle	1	2	0	0
049	White Pelican	20	52	23	81	165	African Marsh Harrier	1	2	0	0
055	Whitebreasted Cormorant	24	38	32	55	213	Black Crake	0	1	1	5
058	Reed Cormorant	120	183	22	39	223	Purple Gallinule	1	2	1	3
060	Darter	31	69	5	7	226	Moorhen	50	102	55	71
062	Grey Heron	5	8	11	23	228	Redknobbed Coot	130	211	85	160
063	Blackheaded Heron	1	3	4	12	248	Kittlitz's Plover	2	6	3	15
065	Purple Heron	1	1	1	1	249	Threebanded Plover	13	22	41	85
067	Little Egret	1	1	1	2	258	Blacksmith Plover	64	96	24	39
068	Yellowbilled Egret	1	3	1	2	264	Common Sandpiper	11	33	0	0
071	Cattle Egret	63	85	43	86	266	Wood Sandpiper	0	1	0	0
076	Blackcrowned Night Heron	11	42	12	22	270	Greenshank	1	2	0	0
078	Little Bittern	0	1	0	1	272	Curlew Sandpiper	2	5	0	0
091	Sacred Ibis	163	335	47	86	274	Little Stint	62	105	0	0
093	Glossy Ibis	2	4	3	7	286	Ethiopian Snipe	0	1	0	1
094	Hadeda Ibis	3	7	6	14	294	Avocet	7	33	3	10
095	African Spoonbill	0	0	1	3	295	Blackwinged Stilt	77	141	131	240
096	Greater Flamingo	56	213	6	28	298	Water Dikkop	1	3	2	8
097	Lesser Flamingo	128	320	207	1000	312	Kelp Gull	0	0	8	21
099	Whitefaced Duck	0	2	0	2	315	Greyheaded Gull	23	40	83	272
101	Whitebacked Duck	1	3	0	2	316	Hartlaub's Gull	234*	387**	620**	852**
102	Egyptian Goose	332	453	40	65	339	Whitewinged Tern	2903**	5101**	0	1
103	South African Shelduck	0	2	1	3	428	Pied Kingfisher	0	0	1	2
104	Yellowbilled Duck	27	46	18	36	429	Giant Kingfisher	1	2	1	2
105	African Black Duck	3	6	4	7	431	Malachite Kingfisher	5	13	3	9
106	Cape Teal	13	23	12	22	713	Cape Wagtail	76	85	39	63
108	Redbilled Teal	49	105	43	76		Total	5028	7747	1842	2795
112	Cape Shoveller	125	333*	44	65		No. of species			59	
113	Southern Pochard	6	12	9	19						

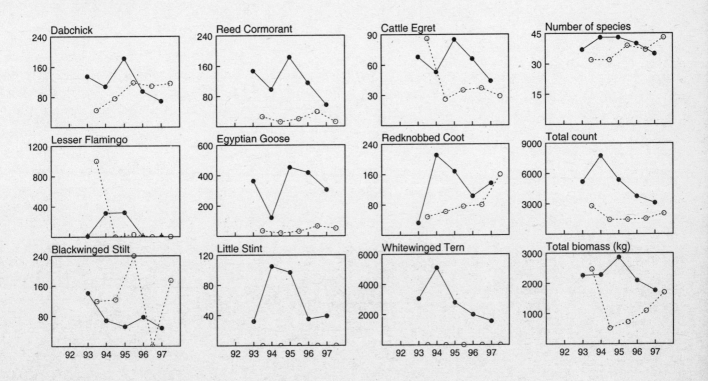

Raapenberg Bird Sanctuary, Cape Town, Western Cape
33° 56' S 18° 28' E (3318CD)

A pan on the floodplain of the Black River; has deeply flooded, dense fringing *Phragmites* and some *Typha*; also some seasonal reedy habitat. Only three counts are available, from summer 1994 to summer 1995. In summer, the site attracts good numbers of Yellowbilled Duck (one high count), Blacksmith Plover, and Kelp and Hartlaub's Gulls; Moorhen is a fairly common resident, and the site also holds Purple Gallinule and Black Crake; Little Bittern should occur. The site is threatened by the proposed widening of the Black River channel, and also by eutrophication, pollution by sewage and industrial waste, hunting and trapping, vegetation cutting, and by the encroachment of alien vegetation.

		Summer (2) Mean	Summer (2) Max.	Winter (1) Mean	Winter (1) Max.			Summer (2) Mean	Summer (2) Max.	Winter (1) Mean	Winter (1) Max.
008	Dabchick	3	4	2	2	223	Purple Gallinule	5	7	1	1
049	White Pelican	0	0	2	2	226	Moorhen	14	20	20	20
055	Whitebreasted Cormorant	2	2	3	3	228	Redknobbed Coot	114	150	84	84
058	Reed Cormorant	16	17	10	10	249	Threebanded Plover	4	7	0	0
060	Darter	7	9	5	5	258	Blacksmith Plover	128	151	24	24
062	Grey Heron	8	8	3	3	266	Wood Sandpiper	5	9	0	0
063	Blackheaded Heron	3	4	1	1	269	Marsh Sandpiper	1	1	0	0
065	Purple Heron	3	4	3	3	270	Greenshank	2	4	0	0
067	Little Egret	8	9	5	5	272	Curlew Sandpiper	2	4	0	0
068	Yellowbilled Egret	3	4	1	1	286	Ethiopian Snipe	5	10	0	0
071	Cattle Egret	12	17	70	70	294	Avocet	2	4	0	0
076	Blackcrowned Night Heron	18	18	15	15	295	Blackwinged Stilt	8	12	0	0
091	Sacred Ibis	11	12	6	6	312	Kelp Gull	65	66	10	10
093	Glossy Ibis	5	7	8	8	315	Greyheaded Gull	0	0	1	1
095	African Spoonbill	0	0	2	2	316	Hartlaub's Gull	160*	213*	34	34
102	Egyptian Goose	2	2	10	10	327	Common Tern	1	2	0	0
104	Yellowbilled Duck	87	165	46	46	428	Pied Kingfisher	2	3	3	3
105	African Black Duck	4	5	2	2	429	Giant Kingfisher	2	3	2	2
106	Cape Teal	1	1	0	0	431	Malachite Kingfisher	1	2	1	1
108	Redbilled Teal	12	22	21	21	713	Cape Wagtail	7	10	1	1
112	Cape Shoveller	6	12	13	13	891	Mallard	4	8	2	2
113	Southern Pochard	0	0	17	17		Total	737	802	428	428
116	Spurwinged Goose	1	1	0	0		No. of species		44		

Radyn Dam, Malmesbury, Western Cape
33° 18' S 18° 45' E (3318BC)

A farm dam with open water and muddy shoreline, a little reed cover and some grassy banks. Good numbers of Dabchick, Blacknecked Grebe, Yellowbilled Duck, Egyptian and Spurwinged Geese, and Redknobbed Coot, especially in summer. Globally significant numbers of South African Shelduck recorded in summer, but counts have declined sharply, as have summer counts of Yellowbilled Duck and Redknobbed Coot. Muddy shorelines attract good numbers of shorebirds in summer, especially Blacksmith Plover, Curlew Sandpiper and Little Stint; largest counts of Blackheaded Heron, Egyptian Goose and Whitewinged Tern in summer 1997. Inflow of fertilizer runoff poses a threat.

		Summer (5)		Winter (4)					Summer (5)		Winter (4)	
		Mean	Max.	Mean	Max.				Mean	Max.	Mean	Max.
006	Great Crested Grebe	8	16	1	2		113	Southern Pochard	7	21	1	3
007	Blacknecked Grebe	23	70	15	42		116	Spurwinged Goose	127	298	6	10
008	Dabchick	89	137	20	69		117	Maccoa Duck	8	20	12	27
049	White Pelican	8	39	0	0		226	Moorhen	0	1	0	0
055	Whitebreasted Cormorant	3	6	3	12		228	Redknobbed Coot	305	630	102	206
056	Cape Cormorant	1	4	0	0		248	Kittlitz's Plover	304	624*	8	24
058	Reed Cormorant	35	136	1	3		249	Threebanded Plover	1	3	2	5
062	Grey Heron	2	3	1	1		258	Blacksmith Plover	167	220	19	36
063	Blackheaded Heron	3	12	2	3		266	Wood Sandpiper	2	3	0	0
067	Little Egret	0	0	0	1		269	Marsh Sandpiper	1	6	0	0
068	Yellowbilled Egret	1	3	0	0		270	Greenshank	2	5	0	0
071	Cattle Egret	1	3	25	48		272	Curlew Sandpiper	61	140	0	0
081	Hamerkop	1	2	0	0		274	Little Stint	138	283	0	0
091	Sacred Ibis	3	8	5	10		284	Ruff	15	62	0	0
093	Glossy Ibis	2	6	0	0		294	Avocet	0	1	0	0
094	Hadeda Ibis	0	0	1	2		295	Blackwinged Stilt	6	16	3	6
095	African Spoonbill	10	16	0	0		312	Kelp Gull	0	0	2	3
096	Greater Flamingo	0	1	0	0		338	Whiskered Tern	1	5	0	0
102	Egyptian Goose	473	886	85	165		339	Whitewinged Tern	104	350	0	0
103	South African Shelduck	817**	1750**	1	3		431	Malachite Kingfisher	0	1	0	0
104	Yellowbilled Duck	195	400	57	146		713	Cape Wagtail	10	14	12	17
106	Cape Teal	0	0	1	2			Total	2986	4687	401	452
108	Redbilled Teal	26	73	5	10			No. of species			45	
112	Cape Shoveller	24	50	12	26							

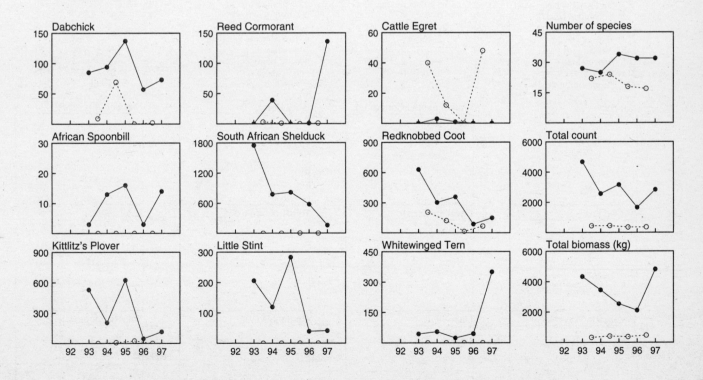

Rietvlei, Milnerton, Western Cape
33° 51' S 18° 29' E (3318CD)

An IBA. Natural pan and excavated vleis; water levels very variable; much emergent sedge plus mud and sand. Also sewage ponds with *Phragmites* and *Typha*. Bird numbers high; globally significant numbers of Cape Shoveller (highest 1995–96), Kelp Gull (1994 and 1995 winters) and Hartlaub's Gull; nationally significant numbers of African Spoonbill, Yellowbilled Duck (winter 1995), African Black Oystercatcher, and Avocet (summer 1993). Highest counts of grebes, pelicans, cormorants, Darter, Redknobbed Coot and Kelp Gull in winter; of geese, Hartlaub's Gull and Cape Wagtail in summer, when shorebird counts also high. Little Bittern resident; African Rail, Baillon's Crake and Painted Snipe occur. Threats include spread of alien vegetation, especially *Paspalum vaginatum*, siltation, eutrophication and urbanisation.

		Summer (5)		Winter (4)				Summer (5)		Winter (4)	
		Mean	Max.	Mean	Max.			Mean	Max.	Mean	Max.
006	Great Crested Grebe	2	3	11	21	226	Moorhen	21	35	23	65
008	Dabchick	9	21	20	27	228	Redknobbed Coot	351	503	851	1417
049	White Pelican	50	166	83	220	242	Painted Snipe	1	4	0	0
055	Whitebreasted Cormorant	65	85	88	112	244	African Black Oystercatcher	15	29*	17	33*
056	Cape Cormorant	0	1	3	6	245	Ringed Plover	43	100	0	0
058	Reed Cormorant	7	11	18	23	246	Whitefronted Plover	1	3	0	0
060	Darter	26	35	44	73	248	Kittlitz's Plover	164	434	14	22
062	Grey Heron	22	41	20	30	249	Threebanded Plover	10	12	8	12
063	Blackheaded Heron	3	7	8	20	258	Blacksmith Plover	286	384	136	183
065	Purple Heron	5	10	4	7	264	Common Sandpiper	1	2	0	0
067	Little Egret	5	7	4	7	266	Wood Sandpiper	22	30	0	0
068	Yellowbilled Egret	7	10	8	14	269	Marsh Sandpiper	78	200	0	0
071	Cattle Egret	13	24	6	13	270	Greenshank	3	7	1	2
076	Blackcrowned Night Heron	5	13	10	18	272	Curlew Sandpiper	387	1435	4	13
078	Little Bittern	0	1	0	0	274	Little Stint	792	1501	0	0
091	Sacred Ibis	45	57	15	21	281	Sanderling	13	40	0	0
093	Glossy Ibis	28	37	31	69	284	Ruff	496	1161	0	1
094	Hadeda Ibis	0	0	1	3	286	Ethiopian Snipe	7	14	1	3
095	African Spoonbill	31	87*	6	11	294	Avocet	166	669*	0	0
096	Greater Flamingo	5	25	0	0	295	Blackwinged Stilt	82	99	69	101
102	Egyptian Goose	853	1378	206	398	298	Water Dikkop	2	6	5	9
103	South African Shelduck	10	35	1	4	312	Kelp Gull	69	160*	224*	420**
104	Yellowbilled Duck	227	763	406	1113*	315	Greyheaded Gull	3	9	0	1
106	Cape Teal	31	84	14	18	316	Hartlaub's Gull	722**	1331**	405**	899**
107	Hottentot Teal	1	5	0	0	322	Caspian Tern	4	8	4	7
108	Redbilled Teal	41	65	251	688	324	Swift Tern	1	2	3	5
112	Cape Shoveller	226*	447**	310*	506**	326	Sandwich Tern	8	17	1	3
113	Southern Pochard	2	6	7	20	327	Common Tern	25	30	79	180
115	Knobbilled Duck	0	0	0	1	339	Whitewinged Tern	372	804	1	2
116	Spurwinged Goose	29	84	7	12	428	Pied Kingfisher	4	9	6	7
117	Maccoa Duck	0	2	0	1	431	Malachite Kingfisher	1	2	1	3
148	African Fish Eagle	0	2	0	0	713	Cape Wagtail	69	121	60	81
165	African Marsh Harrier	1	2	2	3	891	Mallard	6	23	2	6
213	Black Crake	0	0	0	1		Total	5978	8654	3495	5078
223	Purple Gallinule	3	4	3	6		No. of species		68		

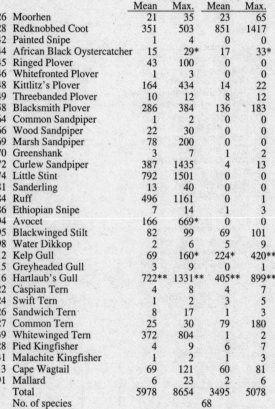

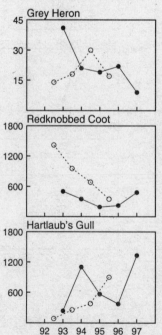

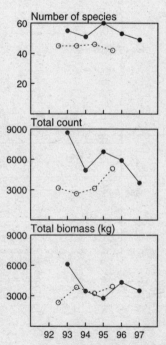

Rocher Pan, Velddrif, Western Cape
32° 36' S 18° 18' E (3218CB)

A nature reserve. Seasonal saline vlei, usually dry March–June; open water and open shoreline, with little palustrine wetland habitat; largest numbers of foraging waterbirds occur when water level falling. Important breeding and moulting site for Cape Shoveller (globally significant numbers); important for breeding Great Crested Grebe (globally significant winter count in 1994) and Dabchick; Sacred Ibis, many waterfowl, Kittlitz's and Blacksmith Plovers, Moorhen, Redknobbed Coot and Hartlaub's Gull breed commonly. In summer, good numbers of Whitebreasted Cormorant, Greater Flamingo (in 1993), many waterfowl, and Palearctic shorebirds; high winter count of Swift Tern and Whitewinged Tern in 1995. Severe threats are pollution by fertilizers and encroachment by emergent plants; other threats include siltation, alien plant infestation in the catchment, and grazing.

		Summer (5)		Winter (6)				Summer (5)		Winter (6)	
		Mean	Max.	Mean	Max.			Mean	Max.	Mean	Max.
006	Great Crested Grebe	3	6	18	102**	228	Redknobbed Coot	745	1811	474	1018
007	Blacknecked Grebe	0	1	60	135*	244	African Black Oystercatcher	3	7	10	21
008	Dabchick	9	15	32	58	245	Ringed Plover	8	19	0	0
049	White Pelican	17	30	1	4	246	Whitefronted Plover	0	0	1	6
055	Whitebreasted Cormorant	371	699	46	111	248	Kittlitz's Plover	41	90	37	141
058	Reed Cormorant	8	20	0	0	249	Threebanded Plover	4	7	1	3
062	Grey Heron	5	10	0	0	258	Blacksmith Plover	34	67	16	32
063	Blackheaded Heron	0	0	0	1	266	Wood Sandpiper	2	6	0	0
065	Purple Heron	0	1	0	0	269	Marsh Sandpiper	54	120	0	0
067	Little Egret	1	5	0	0	270	Greenshank	2	7	0	0
076	Blackcrowned Night Heron	1	3	0	0	272	Curlew Sandpiper	400	1090	0	0
091	Sacred Ibis	40	57	28	146	274	Little Stint	225	396	0	0
093	Glossy Ibis	25	63	0	0	284	Ruff	64	215	0	2
095	African Spoonbill	16	25	0	0	286	Ethiopian Snipe	0	2	0	0
096	Greater Flamingo	254	749*	116	272	294	Avocet	78	145	0	0
102	Egyptian Goose	45	86	14	28	295	Blackwinged Stilt	36	110	23	48
103	South African Shelduck	96	194	7	18	312	Kelp Gull	118	341**	33	114
104	Yellowbilled Duck	90	215	27	39	315	Greyheaded Gull	0	0	0	2
106	Cape Teal	34	98	4	11	316	Hartlaub's Gull	51	81	73	139*
108	Redbilled Teal	70	232	6	27	322	Caspian Tern	4	17	0	0
112	Cape Shoveller	383**	628**	116	207*	324	Swift Tern	0	0	53	206
113	Southern Pochard	0	1	0	2	339	Whitewinged Tern	35	92	52	314
116	Spurwinged Goose	0	2	1	4	713	Cape Wagtail	1	6	11	35
117	Maccoa Duck	3	10	6	14		Total	3383	5481	1268	2300
165	African Marsh Harrier	0	1	0	0		No. of species		49		
226	Moorhen	6	18	2	5						

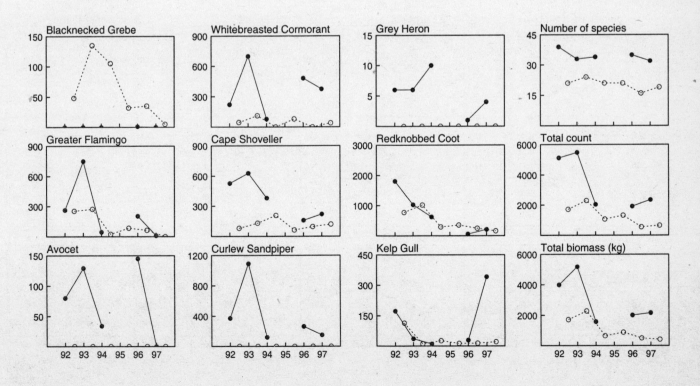

Rondevlei, Cape Flats, Western Cape
34° 04' S 18° 30' E (3418AB)

A nature reserve. Vlei surrounded by low coastal dunes; open water fringed by extensive areas of *Typha*; much emergent *Scirpus littoralis*; some marshy patches with sedges/rushes. Good numbers of Great Crested Grebe, White Pelican, Little Egret, Yellowbilled Egret (summer 1996), Cape Shoveler, Sacred Ibis and Blacksmith Plover recorded irregularly in summer, when peak numbers of most waterbirds occur; however, largest numbers of Grey and Blackheaded Herons, and Blackcrowned Night Heron, recorded in winter. Little Bittern resident; good population of Purple Gallinule; little habitat for small rails and migrant shorebirds. Serious threats include eutrophication and sedimentation, and encroachment of alien vegetation (e.g. *Paspalum vaginatum*); other threats are pollution by domestic sewage and solid waste, illegal access and disturbance, local development, and inflow of storm water.

		Summer (4)		Winter (4)				Summer (4)		Winter (4)	
		Mean	Max.	Mean	Max.			Mean	Max.	Mean	Max.
006	Great Crested Grebe	22	31*	6	10	116	Spurwinged Goose	1	3	0	1
008	Dabchick	15	38	6	8	165	African Marsh Harrier	1	2	1	2
049	White Pelican	84	167	7	27	213	Black Crake	0	1	0	0
055	Whitebreasted Cormorant	20	34	29	46	223	Purple Gallinule	2	4	2	6
056	Cape Cormorant	0	0	0	1	226	Moorhen	11	23	6	12
058	Reed Cormorant	102	197	73	157	228	Redknobbed Coot	42	159	14	22
060	Darter	92	275*	16	25	249	Threebanded Plover	1	3	0	0
062	Grey Heron	16	29	49	77	258	Blacksmith Plover	21	42	4	9
063	Blackheaded Heron	7	14	27	32	272	Curlew Sandpiper	1	3	0	0
065	Purple Heron	4	7	3	6	286	Ethiopian Snipe	1	2	0	0
067	Little Egret	64	164	2	3	294	Avocet	1	3	0	0
068	Yellowbilled Egret	127	255	3	12	295	Blackwinged Stilt	2	6	0	0
071	Cattle Egret	172	550	6	10	312	Kelp Gull	3	8	30	90
076	Blackcrowned Night Heron	6	9	19	75	315	Greyheaded Gull	0	0	0	1
091	Sacred Ibis	293	483	21	60	316	Hartlaub's Gull	25	54	19	45
093	Glossy Ibis	15	24	6	13	322	Caspian Tern	7	10	3	9
094	Hadeda Ibis	1	2	1	2	326	Sandwich Tern	1	4	0	0
095	African Spoonbill	25	66	4	13	327	Common Tern	18	53	0	0
102	Egyptian Goose	41	59	8	18	339	Whitewinged Tern	0	1	0	0
104	Yellowbilled Duck	48	122	12	20	428	Pied Kingfisher	2	3	1	1
106	Cape Teal	2	8	0	0	431	Malachite Kingfisher	0	0	0	1
108	Redbilled Teal	3	7	8	14	713	Cape Wagtail	0	0	0	1
112	Cape Shoveller	39	89	14	41		Total	1336	2555	405	463
113	Southern Pochard	2	6	10	18		No. of species		46		

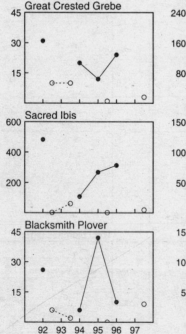

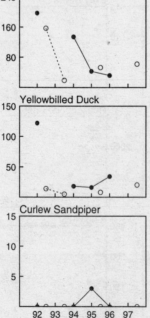

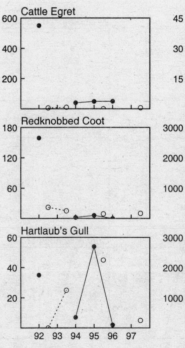

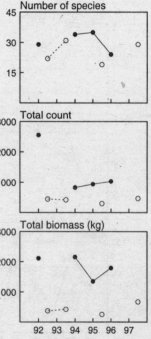

Springfontein Dam, Beaufort West, Western Cape
32° 19' S 22° 38' E (3222BC)

This dam is adjacent to Beaufort West town. Four summer and three winter counts have yielded small to good numbers of a reasonable selection of waterbirds, including good summer counts of shorebirds such as Marsh Sandpiper, Little Stint, Ruff, Avocet and Blackwinged Stilt. Kittlitz's Plover is relatively common in summer and winter, while Threebanded and Blacksmith Plover are more numerous in winter. The dam holds moderate numbers of waterfowl, including South African Shelduck and Cape Teal; waterfowl appear to be marginally more numerous in winter. Good numbers of Cape Wagtail suggest a roost locally. Threats are dam/barrage construction, and solid waste.

		Summer (4)		Winter (3)					Summer (4)		Winter (3)	
		Mean	Max.	Mean	Max.				Mean	Max.	Mean	Max.
007	Blacknecked Grebe	4	10	2	7		228	Redknobbed Coot	41	102	23	69
008	Dabchick	4	15	6	18		248	Kittlitz's Plover	31	80	47	63
062	Grey Heron	0	1	1	2		249	Threebanded Plover	8	17	23	39
063	Blackheaded Heron	1	2	1	1		258	Blacksmith Plover	20	45	47	107
071	Cattle Egret	3	11	0	0		264	Common Sandpiper	0	1	0	0
081	Hamerkop	0	1	0	0		269	Marsh Sandpiper	17	46	0	0
091	Sacred Ibis	1	4	4	11		270	Greenshank	1	2	0	1
093	Glossy Ibis	1	3	0	0		272	Curlew Sandpiper	11	44	0	0
095	African Spoonbill	2	5	1	3		274	Little Stint	93	198	0	0
102	Egyptian Goose	18	39	49	53		284	Ruff	40	80	0	1
103	South African Shelduck	22	41	32	47		294	Avocet	31	81	9	14
104	Yellowbilled Duck	18	37	35	84		295	Blackwinged Stilt	23	62	10	26
106	Cape Teal	7	18	9	26		315	Greyheaded Gull	13	50	11	33
108	Redbilled Teal	15	30	25	42		339	Whitewinged Tern	13	36	0	0
112	Cape Shoveller	6	12	7	19		713	Cape Wagtail	29	40	27	49
113	Southern Pochard	1	5	5	9			Total	474	1067	375	636
115	Knobbilled Duck	1	3	0	0			No. of species			33	
116	Spurwinged Goose	0	0	2	7							

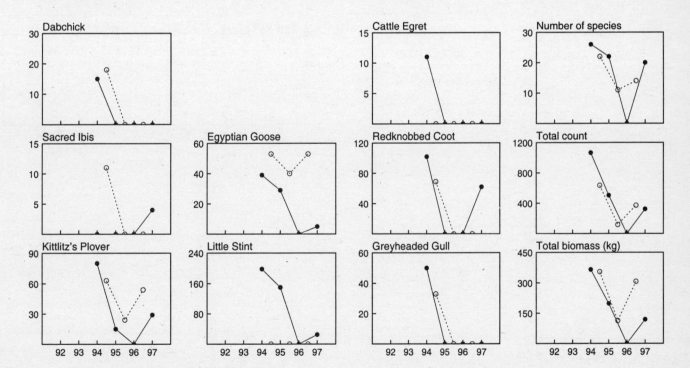

Steenbras Dam, Gordon's Bay, Western Cape
34° 10' S 18° 54' E (3418BB)

A sterile dam with oligotrophic, acid waters and very little food for birds. Kelp Gulls are recorded mainly in July, and they breed on an island in the dam. Egyptian Geese occur mainly in January (possibly moulting) and 2 Reed Cormorant were present in January 1996. No threats have been identified.

		Summer (2)		Winter (3)	
		Mean	Max.	Mean	Max.
058	Reed Cormorant	1	2	0	0
102	Egyptian Goose	50	50	0	1
312	Kelp Gull	27	54	250*	350**

	Summer (2)		Winter (3)	
	Mean	Max.	Mean	Max.
Total	78	104	250	350
No. of species			3	

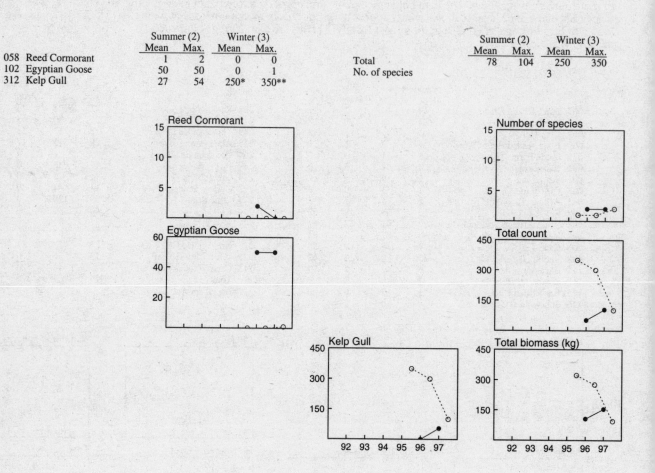

Strandfontein Sewage Works, Muizenberg, Western Cape
34° 05' S 18° 31' E (3418BA)

Regarded as one of the top ten coastal sites for waterbirds in the country. A sewage works on the Cape Flats; important foraging area for birds breeding and roosting at nearby Rondevlei Bird Sanctuary. There is an excellent diversity of waterbird species (72), with globally significant counts of seven species and nationally significant counts of a further three. Good numbers of Palearctic and African waders and terns occur in summer. High summer counts of Grey and Purple Herons, and winter counts of White Pelican, are also noteworthy. Most waterfowl are more numerous in summer, except for South African Shelduck and Southern Pochard. Habitat loss and disturbance will occur if a proposed ring road is built adjacent to sewage works.

		Summer (6) Mean	Summer (6) Max.	Winter (6) Mean	Winter (6) Max.			Summer (6) Mean	Summer (6) Max.	Winter (6) Mean	Winter (6) Max.
006	Great Crested Grebe	5	15	0	1	213	Black Crake	0	0	1	1
007	Blacknecked Grebe	19	46	236*	808**	223	Purple Gallinule	7	11	12	17
008	Dabchick	141	252*	403*	628**	226	Moorhen	32	60	59	92
049	White Pelican	85	161	152	322	228	Redknobbed Coot	758	1676	1129	1716
055	Whitebreasted Cormorant	335	430	129	161	244	African Black Oystercatcher	12	19	6	10
056	Cape Cormorant	8	33	1928	10511**	245	Ringed Plover	21	41	0	0
058	Reed Cormorant	42	88	8	14	248	Kittlitz's Plover	16	55	0	1
060	Darter	30	52	7	18	249	Threebanded Plover	3	5	0	1
062	Grey Heron	19	44	4	11	254	Grey Plover	3	16	0	0
063	Blackheaded Heron	6	10	10	20	258	Blacksmith Plover	99	223	70	122
065	Purple Heron	14	65	3	7	262	Turnstone	0	1	0	0
066	Great White Heron	1	2	0	0	264	Common Sandpiper	1	5	0	1
067	Little Egret	17	27	7	16	266	Wood Sandpiper	8	21	0	0
068	Yellowbilled Egret	6	21	1	3	269	Marsh Sandpiper	9	31	0	0
071	Cattle Egret	169	311	276	685	270	Greenshank	15	21	0	1
076	Blackcrowned Night Heron	5	13	1	7	272	Curlew Sandpiper	90	294	0	0
091	Sacred Ibis	171	309	59	132	274	Little Stint	455	793	0	0
093	Glossy Ibis	112	310	28	108	284	Ruff	133	416	0	0
094	Hadeda Ibis	5	15	1	2	288	Bartailed Godwit	0	2	0	0
095	African Spoonbill	4	14	1	2	294	Avocet	441	649	60	130
096	Greater Flamingo	1594**	2551**	417	1548**	295	Blackwinged Stilt	280	407	104	190
099	Whitefaced Duck	0	0	0	2	298	Water Dikkop	2	5	0	0
100	Fulvous Duck	1	3	0	1	312	Kelp Gull	768**	1067**	551**	1124**
101	Whitebacked Duck	2	4	0	2	315	Greyheaded Gull	5	17	0	1
102	Egyptian Goose	531	1027	80	102	316	Hartlaub's Gull	1186**	1717**	386**	920**
103	South African Shelduck	12	22	21	107	322	Caspian Tern	8	27	0	1
104	Yellowbilled Duck	163	313	42	81	324	Swift Tern	105	263*	43	166
105	African Black Duck	0	2	0	1	326	Sandwich Tern	235	586	0	0
106	Cape Teal	306	421	77	208	327	Common Tern	245	1000	0	0
107	Hottentot Teal	2	9	0	0	338	Whiskered Tern	1	5	0	0
108	Redbilled Teal	102	198	67	143	339	Whitewinged Tern	1154*	1800*	0	1
112	Cape Shoveller	602**	753**	107	232*	428	Pied Kingfisher	2	4	1	2
113	Southern Pochard	90	245	217	427*	429	Giant Kingfisher	0	0	0	2
116	Spurwinged Goose	144	708	11	28	431	Malachite Kingfisher	0	0	0	1
117	Maccoa Duck	14	20	15	64	713	Cape Wagtail	71	149	38	66
148	African Fish Eagle	1	2	0	1		Total	10922	12038	6773	15322
165	African Marsh Harrier	4	6	4	9		No. of species		72		

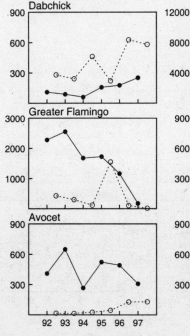

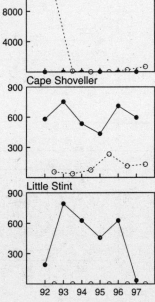

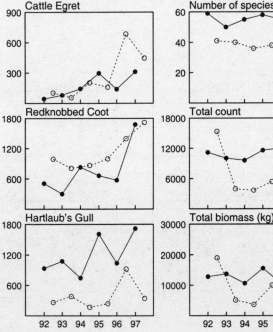

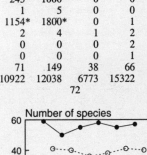

Theewaterskloof Dam, Villiersdorp, Western Cape
34° 02' S 19° 13' E (3419AA)

Large dam; some fringing marshy vegetation; some habitat for shorebirds at low water levels. Globally significant numbers of Darter, and nationally significant numbers of African Spoonbill and Egyptian Goose, recorded. Spurwinged Goose, Redknobbed Coot and Blacksmith Plover normally more numerous in summer, Redbilled Teal and Southern Pochard in winter; Yellowbilled Duck common all year. Good numbers of Purple Heron and African Black Duck. Dead trees in dam are falling down, resulting in fewer nesting sites for cormorants, herons, egrets, African Spoonbill and Sacred Ibis: all these species commoner in summer, but counts of some are declining. Total count and biomass declining in summer, when counts of species such as Egyptian Goose and Blacksmith Plover are falling. Recreational activities are an important threat; pollution by domestic sewage and solid waste is a mild threat.

		Summer (5)		Winter (5)				Summer (5)		Winter (5)	
		Mean	Max.	Mean	Max.			Mean	Max.	Mean	Max.
006	Great Crested Grebe	4	6	6	15	148	African Fish Eagle	3	4	3	5
008	Dabchick	1	5	17	25	165	African Marsh Harrier	0	2	0	1
049	White Pelican	0	0	0	1	170	Osprey	1	3	0	0
055	Whitebreasted Cormorant	88	135	47	76	226	Moorhen	2	4	2	3
058	Reed Cormorant	561	1171	116	304	228	Redknobbed Coot	282	497	124	190
060	Darter	349*	553**	96	193	245	Ringed Plover	1	3	0	0
062	Grey Heron	17	29	4	7	248	Kittlitz's Plover	14	23	0	0
063	Blackheaded Heron	2	3	2	3	249	Threebanded Plover	4	9	0	1
065	Purple Heron	6	19	0	1	258	Blacksmith Plover	57	100	32	60
067	Little Egret	44	77	5	7	264	Common Sandpiper	7	10	0	0
068	Yellowbilled Egret	5	8	7	10	269	Marsh Sandpiper	0	1	0	0
071	Cattle Egret	329	523	65	137	270	Greenshank	0	1	0	0
076	Blackcrowned Night Heron	14	27	3	7	272	Curlew Sandpiper	0	1	0	0
081	Hamerkop	0	1	0	1	274	Little Stint	22	93	0	0
084	Black Stork	0	1	0	0	298	Water Dikkop	2	7	2	4
091	Sacred Ibis	11	22	4	10	312	Kelp Gull	10	16	6	15
093	Glossy Ibis	0	1	0	0	315	Greyheaded Gull	11	26	8	20
094	Hadeda Ibis	14	25	62	90	316	Hartlaub's Gull	0	2	0	0
095	African Spoonbill	63	114*	33	78*	338	Whiskered Tern	0	2	0	0
102	Egyptian Goose	1973*	3070*	515	1072	428	Pied Kingfisher	8	13	3	11
103	South African Shelduck	1	2	0	0	429	Giant Kingfisher	4	7	2	3
104	Yellowbilled Duck	276	517	303	471	431	Malachite Kingfisher	0	1	0	1
105	African Black Duck	14	31	18	23	713	Cape Wagtail	32	58	16	27
108	Redbilled Teal	38	45	66	156	891	Mallard	0	0	1	2
112	Cape Shoveller	16	21	7	13		Total	4394	5597	1676	2221
113	Southern Pochard	5	16	46	114		No. of species			51	
116	Spurwinged Goose	104	190	55	66						

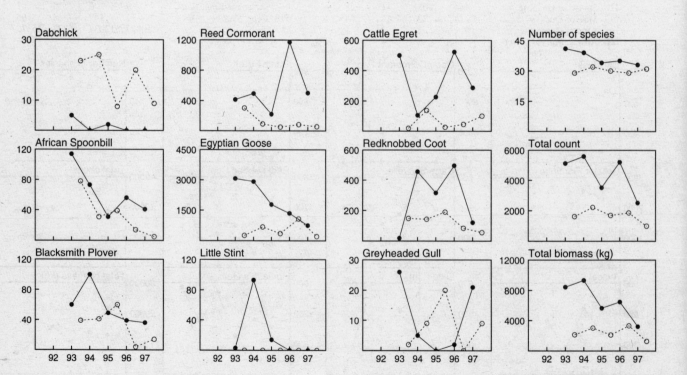

Verlorenvlei, Elandsbaai, Western Cape
32° 20' S 18° 25' E (3218AD)

An IBA and Ramsar site. A freshwater coastal lake, marsh, and closed estuary. Reed-fringed open water in lower reaches, variably extensive *Phragmites, Typha* and sedgebeds upstream to Redelinghuys, with some *Nymphaea* on pools. Globally significant numbers of Great Crested Grebe and South African Shelduck; nationally significant counts of four other species. Pelican, waterfowl and ibis numbers peak in summer. Important for marsh birds: may hold 50 pairs Little Bittern and Purple Gallinule, up to 100 pairs African Rail and Black Crake, and 20 pairs of Redchested Flufftail; Baillon's Crake probably breeds. Up to 200 Ethiopian Snipe and 452 Avocet counted. Total counts declined from 1996. Eutrophication a severe threat; important threats include pollution (pesticides and herbicides), water abstraction and reed encroachment.

		Summer (6)		Winter (5)	
		Mean	Max.	Mean	Max.
006	Great Crested Grebe	53**	87**	58**	123**
007	Blacknecked Grebe	2	6	0	0
008	Dabchick	77	173	78	144
049	White Pelican	177	478	19	37
055	Whitebreasted Cormorant	57	91	113	205
056	Cape Cormorant	0	0	11	56
058	Reed Cormorant	45	60	74	110
060	Darter	58	115	31	51
062	Grey Heron	11	21	6	15
063	Blackheaded Heron	0	1	1	1
065	Purple Heron	4	8	2	4
066	Great White Heron	1	3	1	4
067	Little Egret	17	34	7	10
068	Yellowbilled Egret	1	1	0	2
069	Black Egret	1	3	0	0
091	Sacred Ibis	24	39	4	10
093	Glossy Ibis	13	24	11	33
094	Hadeda Ibis	0	0	0	1
095	African Spoonbill	42	130*	5	9
096	Greater Flamingo	0	0	19	96
102	Egyptian Goose	1223	2041*	303	421
103	South African Shelduck	288*	470**	13	43
104	Yellowbilled Duck	215	642	69	177
106	Cape Teal	7	34	6	25
107	Hottentot Teal	0	0	0	2
108	Redbilled Teal	15	46	18	41
112	Cape Shoveller	91	263*	47	180*
113	Southern Pochard	1	6	1	3
116	Spurwinged Goose	21	59	5	16
148	African Fish Eagle	1	4	1	5
165	African Marsh Harrier	1	2	4	8
213	Black Crake	0	1	0	0
223	Purple Gallinule	3	8	10	14
226	Moorhen	29	141	30	46

		Summer (6)		Winter (5)	
		Mean	Max.	Mean	Max.
228	Redknobbed Coot	1439	3104*	1082	1518
245	Ringed Plover	1	4	0	2
246	Whitefronted Plover	0	1	0	0
248	Kittlitz's Plover	10	16	7	33
249	Threebanded Plover	9	23	15	71
254	Grey Plover	0	0	7	34
258	Blacksmith Plover	61	98	20	45
264	Common Sandpiper	0	2	0	0
266	Wood Sandpiper	0	2	0	0
269	Marsh Sandpiper	2	10	0	0
270	Greenshank	1	5	0	0
272	Curlew Sandpiper	182	530	0	0
274	Little Stint	40	134	0	0
284	Ruff	33	130	0	1
294	Avocet	78	452	3	16
295	Blackwinged Stilt	20	54	23	82
298	Water Dikkop	0	0	0	2
312	Kelp Gull	102	235*	14	30
315	Greyheaded Gull	3	7	2	5
316	Hartlaub's Gull	161*	377**	8	26
322	Caspian Tern	8	16	8	31
324	Swift Tern	1	3	0	0
326	Sandwich Tern	0	1	0	0
327	Common Tern	1	7	0	0
338	Whiskered Tern	4	15	0	0
339	Whitewinged Tern	49	153	10	49
428	Pied Kingfisher	13	20	12	14
429	Giant Kingfisher	1	1	0	1
431	Malachite Kingfisher	1	5	1	2
713	Cape Wagtail	1	4	0	1
891	Mallard	0	0	0	2
	Total	4693	7460	2158	2890
	No. of species		65		

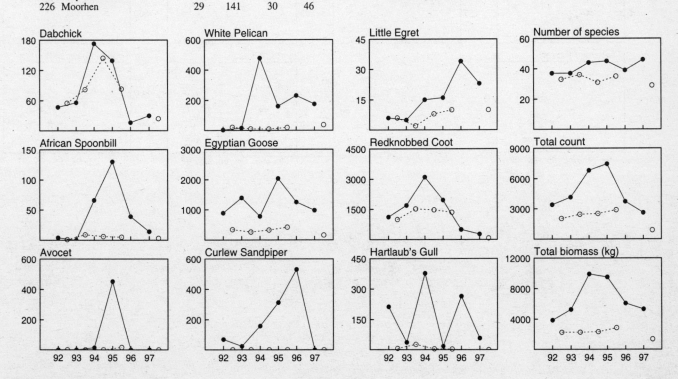

Vermont Salt Pan, Hermanus, Western Cape
34° 25' S 19° 10' E (3419AC)

A 15 ha pan supporting good numbers of a fairly wide selection of species. Cormorants, herons, egrets, ibises, waterfowl and Redknobbed Coot are more numerous in summer. Although the number of species observed has not decreased during the survey period, total count and biomass have declined. Species showing an overall decrease in numbers include Redknobbed Coot (very few recorded after 1994) and Cape Shoveller; counts of Little Egret, Egyptian Goose and Black-winged Stilt are increasing. Threats are alien vegetation, clearing of vegetation, and domestic gardening.

		Summer (5)		Winter (5)	
		Mean	Max.	Mean	Max.
006	Great Crested Grebe	4	12	0	2
008	Dabchick	16	43	18	26
055	Whitebreasted Cormorant	79	117	54	79
058	Reed Cormorant	77	139	44	111
060	Darter	0	2	0	1
062	Grey Heron	7	16	3	6
063	Blackheaded Heron	2	5	2	4
067	Little Egret	8	16	13	30
071	Cattle Egret	67	128	126	231
076	Blackcrowned Night Heron	6	12	2	5
091	Sacred Ibis	6	30	2	11
094	Hadeda Ibis	4	6	6	15
095	African Spoonbill	0	0	0	1
097	Lesser Flamingo	0	0	0	1
101	Whitebacked Duck	0	0	1	4
102	Egyptian Goose	8	14	4	7
104	Yellowbilled Duck	26	43	16	33
106	Cape Teal	9	28	5	13
112	Cape Shoveller	43	61	29	50

		Summer (5)		Winter (5)	
		Mean	Max.	Mean	Max.
113	Southern Pochard	7	32	7	34
116	Spurwinged Goose	1	4	0	0
117	Maccoa Duck	3	9	1	3
213	Black Crake	0	1	1	2
226	Moorhen	6	12	9	19
228	Redknobbed Coot	196	501	91	364
249	Threebanded Plover	1	3	0	2
258	Blacksmith Plover	6	8	4	10
294	Avocet	0	0	0	1
295	Blackwinged Stilt	6	14	2	9
298	Water Dikkop	0	0	0	2
312	Kelp Gull	0	2	0	0
316	Hartlaub's Gull	3	9	1	2
428	Pied Kingfisher	1	4	0	0
429	Giant Kingfisher	0	0	0	1
713	Cape Wagtail	1	3	3	6
891	Mallard	0	1	1	5
	Total	597	896	448	653
	No. of species		36		

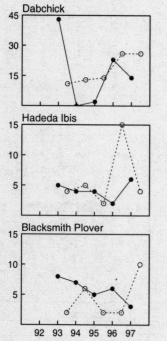

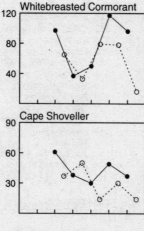

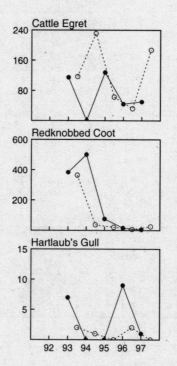

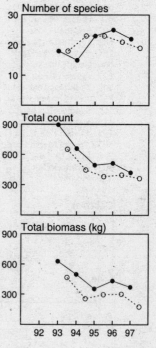

Voëlvlei, Mossel Bay, Western Cape
34° 16' S 21° 49' E (3421BD)

A large pan, fed by the Buffels River, with no outlet. Has held globally significant numbers of African Spoonbill in winter and summer, and nationally significant numbers of Great Crested Grebe (summer 1993), South African Shelduck and Cape Shoveller. Also good summer counts of other grebes (in 1993), herons (especially Grey in 1996), Little Egret and Sacred Ibis (1993), and many Palearctic shorebirds. Good counts of Redknobbed Coot in winter; numbers of Cape and Redbilled Teal, and Kittlitz's and Blacksmith Plovers, high in both seasons. Maccoa Duck and Moorhen recorded in summer 1993, when exceptionally large counts of Blackwinged Stilt ((nationally significant), Greenshank, Little Stint, Ruff and Avocet were made; 280 Whiskered Tern were counted in summer 1997. A threat is agriculture along drying margins.

		Summer (5)		Winter (5)	
		Mean	Max.	Mean	Max.
006	Great Crested Grebe	8	40*	1	4
007	Blacknecked Grebe	10	50	5	16
008	Dabchick	22	100	9	40
055	Whitebreasted Cormorant	50	110	51	92
058	Reed Cormorant	34	90	34	122
060	Darter	1	4	5	10
062	Grey Heron	54	120	21	66
063	Blackheaded Heron	12	60	2	12
065	Purple Heron	0	1	0	0
067	Little Egret	50	200	13	36
068	Yellowbilled Egret	5	10	0	2
071	Cattle Egret	28	110	6	30
076	Blackcrowned Night Heron	6	20	0	0
081	Hamerkop	0	0	1	6
084	Black Stork	1	4	0	1
091	Sacred Ibis	171	400	12	38
093	Glossy Ibis	9	20	3	8
094	Hadeda Ibis	0	0	2	8
095	African Spoonbill	139*	200**	102*	258**
096	Greater Flamingo	0	0	24	120
097	Lesser Flamingo	0	0	5	24
102	Egyptian Goose	32	100	42	180
103	South African Shelduck	140	400*	78	150
104	Yellowbilled Duck	14	40	8	30
106	Cape Teal	20	100	19	34
108	Redbilled Teal	96	250	65	240
112	Cape Shoveller	108	250*	60	114
113	Southern Pochard	8	40	0	0
116	Spurwinged Goose	21	100	4	20
117	Maccoa Duck	6	30	0	0

		Summer (5)		Winter (5)	
		Mean	Max.	Mean	Max.
148	African Fish Eagle	1	4	2	4
165	African Marsh Harrier	0	1	0	0
226	Moorhen	16	80	0	0
228	Redknobbed Coot	264	700	490	2450
245	Ringed Plover	294	560	0	0
246	Whitefronted Plover	0	0	34	140
248	Kittlitz's Plover	232	400	133	400
249	Threebanded Plover	92	260	28	80
258	Blacksmith Plover	57	110	57	136
262	Turnstone	0	1	0	0
266	Wood Sandpiper	18	40	0	0
269	Marsh Sandpiper	10	30	0	0
270	Greenshank	166	700	2	8
272	Curlew Sandpiper	1370	3000	8	40
274	Little Stint	906	2500	28	140
284	Ruff	1160	3000	0	0
286	Ethiopian Snipe	4	20	0	0
294	Avocet	157	600	94	230
295	Blackwinged Stilt	274	800*	127	210
312	Kelp Gull	4	14	3	10
315	Greyheaded Gull	0	0	2	6
316	Hartlaub's Gull	0	2	0	0
322	Caspian Tern	0	1	0	0
338	Whiskered Tern	156	280	2	12
428	Pied Kingfisher	8	20	0	0
711	African Pied Wagtail	0	1	0	0
713	Cape Wagtail	11	20	10	20
	Total	6245	13382	1594	4465
	No. of species		57		

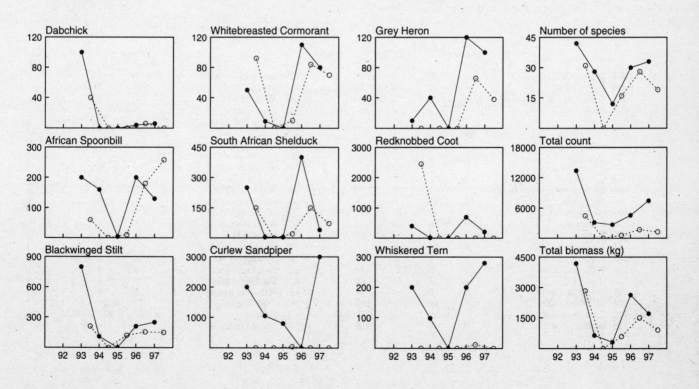

Voëlvlei Dam, Gouda, Western Cape
33° 22' S 19° 03' E (3319AC)

This dam was counted only in the summers of 1995 and 1996. In both years it held nationally significant numbers of Egyptian Goose, and in 1996 there was a globally significant count of South African Shelduck. Counts of these two species make up 96% of the total for the site, which otherwise holds only small numbers of a further 22 waterbird species. Some recreational activity at this site poses a mild threat.

		Summer (2) Mean	Max.	Winter (0) Mean	Max.			Summer (2) Mean	Max.	Winter (0) Mean	Max.
006	Great Crested Grebe	3	5	–	–	249	Threebanded Plover	3	3	–	–
008	Dabchick	1	2	–	–	258	Blacksmith Plover	5	5	–	–
055	Whitebreasted Cormorant	9	18	–	–	264	Common Sandpiper	2	4	–	–
058	Reed Cormorant	8	14	–	–	270	Greenshank	2	2	–	–
060	Darter	4	8	–	–	272	Curlew Sandpiper	16	32	–	–
062	Grey Heron	2	2	–	–	274	Little Stint	5	9	–	–
071	Cattle Egret	1	2	–	–	295	Blackwinged Stilt	1	2	–	–
102	Egyptian Goose	1865*	1873*	–	–	312	Kelp Gull	2	2	–	–
103	South African Shelduck	660**	1085**	–	–	315	Greyheaded Gull	14	19	–	–
104	Yellowbilled Duck	11	15	–	–	428	Pied Kingfisher	1	1	–	–
112	Cape Shoveller	5	9	–	–	713	Cape Wagtail	3	6	–	–
116	Spurwinged Goose	20	26	–	–		Total	2641	3052	–	–
248	Kittlitz's Plover	2	2	–	–		No. of species		24		

Wellington Waste Water Works, Wellington, Western Cape
33° 39' S 18° 58' E (3318DB)

Open ponds; some relatively undisturbed unused ponds have small patches of flooded grass and small *Typha* and *Phragmites* beds interspersed with mud and open patches. Counted first in 1997, when good numbers of ducks and Blackwinged Stilt were found in winter, while in summer good counts of Moorhen and Blacksmith Plover were recorded, and an exceptionally good total of 54 Ethiopian Snipe. Holds possibly 10 pairs of Purple Gallinule, 5–10 pairs of Black Crake; otherwise not significant for rails. Listed threats include eutrophication, the accumulation of solid waste, and hunting and trapping of birds.

		Summer (1) Mean	Max.	Winter (1) Mean	Max.			Summer (1) Mean	Max.	Winter (1) Mean	Max.
007	Blacknecked Grebe	0	0	2	2	116	Spurwinged Goose	7	7	3	3
008	Dabchick	27	27	26	26	117	Maccoa Duck	9	9	9	9
055	Whitebreasted Cormorant	6	6	0	0	148	African Fish Eagle	1	1	2	2
058	Reed Cormorant	7	7	4	4	213	Black Crake	3	3	0	0
060	Darter	1	1	0	0	223	Purple Gallinule	1	1	0	0
062	Grey Heron	0	0	1	1	226	Moorhen	39	39	16	16
063	Blackheaded Heron	1	1	0	0	228	Redknobbed Coot	22	22	22	22
065	Purple Heron	0	0	4	4	249	Threebanded Plover	9	9	0	0
068	Yellowbilled Egret	4	4	2	2	258	Blacksmith Plover	49	49	17	17
071	Cattle Egret	5	5	0	0	264	Common Sandpiper	2	2	0	0
076	Blackcrowned Night Heron	1	1	0	0	266	Wood Sandpiper	3	3	0	0
091	Sacred Ibis	11	11	6	6	286	Ethiopian Snipe	54	54	0	0
093	Glossy Ibis	15	15	13	13	295	Blackwinged Stilt	9	9	39	39
094	Hadeda Ibis	0	0	8	8	298	Water Dikkop	0	0	4	4
099	Whitefaced Duck	2	2	12	12	312	Kelp Gull	0	0	1	1
101	Whitebacked Duck	2	2	4	4	315	Greyheaded Gull	0	0	4	4
102	Egyptian Goose	5	5	8	8	316	Hartlaub's Gull	2	2	9	9
104	Yellowbilled Duck	73	73	280	280	428	Pied Kingfisher	2	2	0	0
106	Cape Teal	11	11	46	46	429	Giant Kingfisher	0	0	1	1
107	Hottentot Teal	0	0	4	4	431	Malachite Kingfisher	1	1	1	1
108	Redbilled Teal	56	56	100	100	713	Cape Wagtail	20	20	2	2
112	Cape Shoveller	7	7	18	18		Total	467	467	674	674
113	Southern Pochard	0	0	6	6		No. of species		44		

Wilderness Lakes – Swartvlei System, Sedgefield, Western Cape
34° 00' S 22° 45' E (3422BB)

Located immediately east of the Touw system, this system comprises Swartvlei (a drowned river valley coastal lake) and its estuary. Swartvlei is saline and is mostly open water, with some fringing and emergent *Phragmites, Typha, Juncus*, sedges and grass. An excellent variety of waterbirds is recorded, including globally significant numbers of Cape Shoveller. The estuary holds a good selection of Palearctic and African shorebirds. Good numbers of Little Bittern, Redchested Flufftail, African Rail, Black Crake and Purple Gallinule are resident at Swartvlei; Baillon's Crake and Grass Owl also occur. Threats include eutrophication, sedimentation, boating, alien vegetation, property development and agriculture.

		Summer (2)		Winter (3)	
		Mean	Max.	Mean	Max.
006	Great Crested Grebe	29*	32*	18	28*
008	Dabchick	18	26	406*	484*
055	Whitebreasted Cormorant	24	27	68	72
056	Cape Cormorant	3	3	7	13
058	Reed Cormorant	136	152	158	218
060	Darter	20	22	11	12
062	Grey Heron	22	30	13	18
063	Blackheaded Heron	3	4	3	6
065	Purple Heron	0	0	0	1
067	Little Egret	9	9	17	23
076	Blackcrowned Night Heron	2	3	3	5
091	Sacred Ibis	2	3	9	15
093	Glossy Ibis	0	0	0	1
094	Hadeda Ibis	3	3	2	4
095	African Spoonbill	1	1	6	12
096	Greater Flamingo	0	0	31	92
101	Whitebacked Duck	0	0	2	5
102	Egyptian Goose	2	4	10	15
104	Yellowbilled Duck	83	102	226	271
106	Cape Teal	1	2	23	26
108	Redbilled Teal	0	0	10	27
112	Cape Shoveller	448**	748**	316*	510**
113	Southern Pochard	2	4	0	0
148	African Fish Eagle	3	4	1	2
165	African Marsh Harrier	1	1	1	3
170	Osprey	1	1	0	1
213	Black Crake	0	0	1	2
223	Purple Gallinule	3	4	4	5

		Summer (2)		Winter (3)	
		Mean	Max.	Mean	Max.
226	Moorhen	5	6	9	16
228	Redknobbed Coot	1896	1991	4310*	7472**
244	African Black Oystercatcher	2	2	0	1
245	Ringed Plover	56	75	0	0
246	Whitefronted Plover	0	0	1	2
248	Kittlitz's Plover	6	10	5	10
254	Grey Plover	7	13	0	0
258	Blacksmith Plover	16	17	14	23
264	Common Sandpiper	1	2	0	0
269	Marsh Sandpiper	79	87	0	0
270	Greenshank	51	83	7	12
272	Curlew Sandpiper	195	254	3	6
274	Little Stint	21	23	0	1
284	Ruff	2	3	0	0
289	Curlew	0	0	0	1
295	Blackwinged Stilt	17	20	83	131
298	Water Dikkop	0	0	5	9
312	Kelp Gull	16	18	20	25
322	Caspian Tern	8	10	1	2
327	Common Tern	10	10	2	5
338	Whiskered Tern	1	1	0	0
428	Pied Kingfisher	4	4	10	13
429	Giant Kingfisher	0	0	1	2
430	Halfcollared Kingfisher	0	0	1	1
431	Malachite Kingfisher	1	1	1	2
713	Cape Wagtail	9	13	7	12
	Total	3207	3631	5827	8808
	No. of species		54		

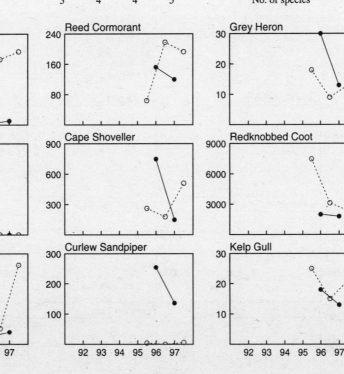

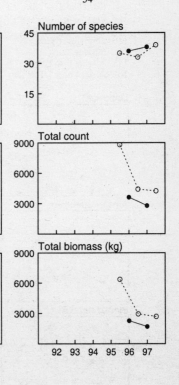

Wilderness Lakes – Touw River System, Sedgefield, Western Cape
33° 59' S 22° 40' E (3322DC)

An IBA, National Park and Ramsar site. The system includes the lagoon and floodplain of the Touw River, with a natural channel (the Serpentine) to the three interconnected lakes: Eilandvlei, Langvlei and Rondevlei. One of the few coastal lake systems in southern Africa, and an important wintering site for waterbirds. Fresh to slightly saline water; extensive fringing emergent vegetation of *Phragmites, Typha, Juncus*, sedges and grass, and much submerged vegetation. Globally significant numbers of Great Crested Grebe, Dabchick, Cape Shoveller and Redknobbed Coot occur, and nationally significant numbers of Blacknecked Grebe and Southern Pochard. There are also good counts of Reed Cormorant, Whitebacked Duck, Yellowbilled Duck Maccoa Duck and Moorhen. Counts of almost all waterbird species (except Palearctic migrants) peak in winter. The lakes hold good numbers of Little Bittern, Redchested Flufftail, African Rail, Black Crake and Purple Gallinule. Threats include increasing sediment and nutrient loadings, leading to eutrophication and associated expansion of *Phragmites* and algal blooms.

		Summer (6)		Winter (6)				Summer (6)		Winter (6)	
		Mean	Max.	Mean	Max.			Mean	Max.	Mean	Max.
006	Great Crested Grebe	91**	206**	125**	274**	170	Osprey	0	1	0	1
007	Blacknecked Grebe	2	11	179*	836**	210	African Rail	1	1	0	1
008	Dabchick	146	184	940**	1819**	213	Black Crake	2	3	6	18
055	Whitebreasted Cormorant	24	38	49	87	223	Purple Gallinule	5	8	9	24
056	Cape Cormorant	0	2	272	1332	226	Moorhen	43	79	217	338
058	Reed Cormorant	67	109	196	330	228	Redknobbed Coot	2642*	4651*	5247**	15277**
060	Darter	3	6	23	55	240	African Jacana	0	1	1	2
062	Grey Heron	3	6	10	14	245	Ringed Plover	2	8	0	0
063	Blackheaded Heron	2	5	6	24	248	Kittlitz's Plover	0	1	9	24
065	Purple Heron	4	7	8	18	249	Threebanded Plover	0	1	8	18
067	Little Egret	17	28	20	35	258	Blacksmith Plover	26	48	23	47
068	Yellowbilled Egret	3	6	1	2	264	Common Sandpiper	1	3	0	0
071	Cattle Egret	6	11	1	4	266	Wood Sandpiper	8	20	0	1
076	Blackcrowned Night Heron	0	0	1	2	269	Marsh Sandpiper	16	39	1	4
078	Little Bittern	1	2	1	2	270	Greenshank	8	13	0	0
081	Hamerkop	0	2	0	0	272	Curlew Sandpiper	62	340	1	3
091	Sacred Ibis	0	1	0	0	274	Little Stint	6	30	0	0
093	Glossy Ibis	0	1	1	4	284	Ruff	115	237	1	2
094	Hadeda Ibis	1	4	2	6	286	Ethiopian Snipe	1	2	0	0
095	African Spoonbill	8	20	4	8	294	Avocet	1	4	5	19
096	Greater Flamingo	0	1	4	14	295	Blackwinged Stilt	24	61	46	106
100	Fulvous Duck	0	0	2	12	298	Water Dikkop	0	1	7	18
101	Whitebacked Duck	4	10	112	254**	312	Kelp Gull	9	16	17	44
102	Egyptian Goose	43	95	58	166	322	Caspian Tern	1	2	1	2
103	South African Shelduck	1	2	0	2	326	Sandwich Tern	0	0	0	1
104	Yellowbilled Duck	655	1059*	660	1509*	327	Common Tern	29	59	24	95
106	Cape Teal	10	17	39	95	338	Whiskered Tern	3	8	0	0
107	Hottentot Teal	1	5	4	9	339	Whitewinged Tern	1	1	0	0
108	Redbilled Teal	6	26	44	164	428	Pied Kingfisher	6	13	11	16
112	Cape Shoveller	1006**	1508**	206*	464**	429	Giant Kingfisher	1	2	1	4
113	Southern Pochard	111	323*	245	962**	430	Halfcollared Kingfisher	0	2	0	1
116	Spurwinged Goose	5	16	1	2	431	Malachite Kingfisher	2	2	2	8
117	Maccoa Duck	6	15	49	93	713	Cape Wagtail	3	9	6	22
148	African Fish Eagle	3	6	2	4		Total	5244	8009	8907	22696
165	African Marsh Harrier	1	4	3	5		No. of species			68	

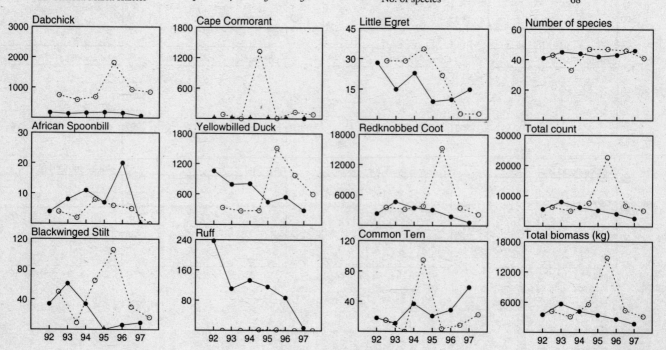

Wildevoëlvlei, Kommetjie, Western Cape
34° 08' S 18° 21' E (3418AB)

A seasonal vlei until 1977, since when treated sewage effluent discharged into the system has made the two interconnected vleis perennial. Has reedbeds, and open water with *Potamogeton* and *Azolla*. Redknobbed Coot and Dabchick breed (numbers of both species peak in April and are lowest in October–November); Blacknecked Grebe and Whiskered Tern have bred. Supports a good variety of waterbirds, with wide fluctuations in numbers; good counts of Whitebacked Duck ((especially in summer), Cape Shoveller (summer), Maccoa Duck (winter) and Moorhen. Total counts declined during analysis period. In 1998, aquatic vegetation died, a severe growth of blue-green algae occurred, and bird numbers crashed; the algae were eliminated by salt-dosing, and it is hoped that the vlei's flora and fauna will recover. Continued eutrophication is a severe threat, industrial and residential development an important threat.

		Summer (6)		Winter (6)	
		Mean	Max.	Mean	Max.
006	Great Crested Grebe	3	8	2	3
007	Blacknecked Grebe	14	71	17	87
008	Dabchick	268*	331*	309*	373*
055	Whitebreasted Cormorant	7	13	23	61
058	Reed Cormorant	40	67	20	41
060	Darter	3	12	3	8
062	Grey Heron	5	9	5	8
063	Blackheaded Heron	2	5	1	2
065	Purple Heron	3	6	3	5
067	Little Egret	6	10	1	1
068	Yellowbilled Egret	5	7	2	7
071	Cattle Egret	12	24	8	10
076	Blackcrowned Night Heron	7	10	3	6
078	Little Bittern	1	3	0	0
081	Hamerkop	0	1	0	0
091	Sacred Ibis	14	35	6	13
093	Glossy Ibis	6	7	5	8
094	Hadeda Ibis	1	3	2	3
095	African Spoonbill	0	0	3	15
101	Whitebacked Duck	37	95	21	35
102	Egyptian Goose	10	23	7	14
104	Yellowbilled Duck	113	208	29	48
106	Cape Teal	4	15	2	5
107	Hottentot Teal	0	2	0	0
108	Redbilled Teal	5	7	2	5
112	Cape Shoveller	110	210*	49	79
113	Southern Pochard	2	5	7	18
116	Spurwinged Goose	1	2	1	3

		Summer (6)		Winter (6)	
		Mean	Max.	Mean	Max.
117	Maccoa Duck	2	3	19	42
148	African Fish Eagle	1	2	1	2
165	African Marsh Harrier	0	1	1	1
213	Black Crake	0	1	1	3
223	Purple Gallinule	1	2	1	3
226	Moorhen	35	57	41	69
228	Redknobbed Coot	753	1038	712	940
240	African Jacana	0	0	0	1
249	Threebanded Plover	0	1	0	2
258	Blacksmith Plover	18	27	11	18
266	Wood Sandpiper	0	2	0	0
270	Greenshank	30	71	0	0
286	Ethiopian Snipe	1	1	0	0
295	Blackwinged Stilt	16	34	1	5
298	Water Dikkop	1	2	6	10
312	Kelp Gull	6	12	1	4
316	Hartlaub's Gull	47	75	56	85
322	Caspian Tern	1	1	1	1
327	Common Tern	2	7	0	0
338	Whiskered Tern	29	71	0	0
339	Whitewinged Tern	1	4	0	0
428	Pied Kingfisher	3	7	2	4
429	Giant Kingfisher	0	1	0	1
431	Malachite Kingfisher	0	1	1	1
713	Cape Wagtail	2	8	1	3
891	Mallard	0	2	3	8
	Total	1626	1981	1386	1701
	No. of species		54		

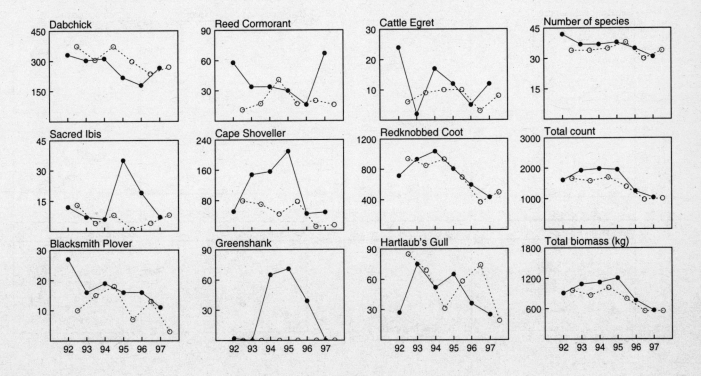

Zandvlei, Muizenberg, Western Cape
34° 06' S 18° 28' E (3418AB)

An open estuary, with some reedbeds and other emergent vegetation. Holds a good variety of birds, including Purple Heron, Little Bittern and Purple Gallinule. Cormorant counts peak in winter; numbers of Darter, Cape Teal, Redknobbed Coot, Blackwinged Stilt and Hartlaub's Gull show no definite seasonal peak. There were unusually large counts of Blacksmith Plover in summer 1993, of Cape Shoveller in the 1994–1996 summers, of Sacred Ibis in summer 1994, and of Egyptian Goose in winter 1997. Numbers of Darter show some overall increase but Cape Teal appear to be declining. Severe threats are posed by invasive alien plants (*Paspalum* grass and *Eichhornia*); important threats include eutrophication, and pollution by solid waste. Hunting, fishing, domestic dogs and cats, and residential development, are also problems. Mallard pose some hybridization threat.

		Summer (5)		Winter (5)	
		Mean	Max.	Mean	Max.
006	Great Crested Grebe	3	5	6	12
008	Dabchick	1	4	2	4
049	White Pelican	1	2	8	17
055	Whitebreasted Cormorant	3	7	26	55
056	Cape Cormorant	0	0	1	3
058	Reed Cormorant	5	9	7	18
060	Darter	19	32	20	32
062	Grey Heron	1	1	1	2
063	Blackheaded Heron	1	2	1	2
065	Purple Heron	1	1	1	4
067	Little Egret	2	4	1	1
068	Yellowbilled Egret	0	1	0	1
071	Cattle Egret	1	3	3	9
076	Blackcrowned Night Heron	2	4	3	4
078	Little Bittern	1	1	0	1
091	Sacred Ibis	13	62	5	17
093	Glossy Ibis	2	5	0	0
094	Hadeda Ibis	0	0	1	2
095	African Spoonbill	1	1	1	1
102	Egyptian Goose	14	18	23	40
104	Yellowbilled Duck	3	9	5	13
106	Cape Teal	21	32	14	40
108	Redbilled Teal	2	8	0	0
112	Cape Shoveller	19	30	9	13
113	Southern Pochard	0	2	0	2
116	Spurwinged Goose	0	0	2	11

		Summer (5)		Winter (5)	
		Mean	Max.	Mean	Max.
165	African Marsh Harrier	0	1	1	1
223	Purple Gallinule	1	2	3	5
226	Moorhen	7	11	14	25
228	Redknobbed Coot	104	169	62	127
249	Threebanded Plover	1	2	0	1
258	Blacksmith Plover	45	112	10	12
264	Common Sandpiper	0	1	0	0
266	Wood Sandpiper	0	1	0	0
269	Marsh Sandpiper	0	1	0	0
294	Avocet	4	9	1	3
295	Blackwinged Stilt	17	35	18	31
298	Water Dikkop	1	4	2	7
312	Kelp Gull	9	27	19	32
315	Greyheaded Gull	0	0	0	1
316	Hartlaub's Gull	24	47	25	28
322	Caspian Tern	2	4	1	2
327	Common Tern	1	3	0	0
339	Whitewinged Tern	3	11	0	0
428	Pied Kingfisher	6	8	2	6
429	Giant Kingfisher	0	1	1	2
431	Malachite Kingfisher	2	3	1	2
713	Cape Wagtail	2	6	3	11
891	Mallard	1	3	9	27
	Total	348	455	312	424
	No. of species		49		

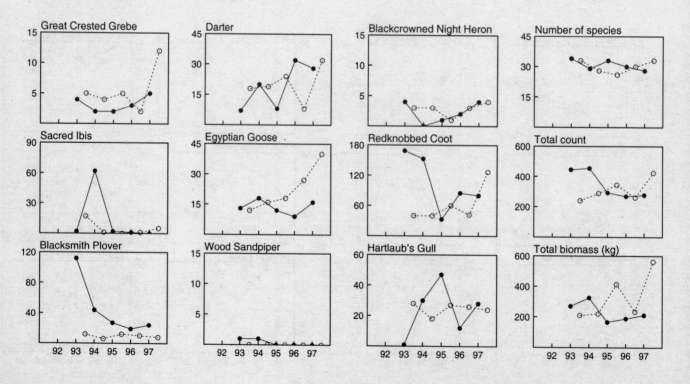

Species accounts

Texts by P.B. Taylor

Graphics by R.A. Navarro

006 Great Crested Grebe *Podiceps cristatus*

All major concentrations fall within known centres of distribution in Western Cape, former Transvaal and extreme northeastern Northern Cape; good winter numbers also at Kalkfontein-dam, western Free State. High winter numbers at some sites in northeastern region, and high summer counts at some Western Cape sites, may reflect some seasonal movements, but many sites hold birds all year. Large numbers at Stan Madden Bird Sanctuary and Barberspan in 1993 occurred during widespread drought in that region. Normally occurs mainly on clean, permanent waters, avoiding shallow pans; some impoundments hold significant numbers.

		Summer			Winter		
		Mean	Max.	N	Mean	Max.	N
3359S 2240E	Wilderness Lakes – Touw River System, Sedgefield, Western Cape	91**	206**	6	125**	274**	6
3220S 1825E	Verlorenvlei, Elandsbaai, Western Cape	53**	87**	6	58**	123**	5
2804S 2433E	Spitskop Dam, Spitskop, Northern Cape	8	9	2	99**	134**	2
2635S 2535E	Barberspan, Delareyville, North West	29*	101**	4	62**	115**	2
3421S 1906E	Botriviervlei, Kleinmond, Western Cape	62**	152**	4	21	50**	5
3426S 2023E	De Hoop Vlei, Bredasdorp, Western Cape	64**	180**	5	13	50**	4
2510S 2751E	Klipvoor Dam, Brits, North West	2	3	4	46*	63**	3
3400S 2245E	Wilderness Lakes – Swartvlei System, Sedgefield, Western Cape	29*	32*	2	18	28*	3
3404S 1830E	Rondevlei, Cape Flats, Western Cape	22	31*	4	6	10	4
2553S 2817E	Rietvlei Dam, Pretoria, Gauteng	17	17	1	9	9	1
2932S 2515E	Kalkfontein Dam, Koffiefontein, Free State	4	10	6	20	52**	6
2614S 2819E	Leeupan, Benoni, Gauteng	19	42*	5	2	8	6
3236S 1818E	Rocher Pan, Velddrif, Western Cape	3	6	5	18	102**	6
2624S 2828E	Stan Madden Bird Sanctuary, Nigel, Gauteng	17	49*	5	2	6	5
2635S 2857E	Leeuwpan, Secunda, Mpumalanga	14	23	3	5	10	4

Wilderness Lakes – Touw River System

Kalkfontein Dam

Verlorenvlei

Leeupan

007 Blacknecked Grebe *Podiceps nigricollis*

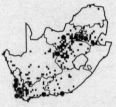

A nomadic species; many sites have irregular large concentrations of birds. Significant counts were made in two widely separated regions: the largest winter concentrations were along Cape coasts, where nonbreeding birds congregate at shallow permanent wetlands (sometimes for several years in drought periods), and panveld regions of the central high-veld, where birds breed at pans after flood events and concentrations therefore tend to occur in summer. At Kamfersdam birds occurred only in 1997, when many bred. Some coastal sewage works and saltpans provide important refuges for nonbreeders.

		Summer			Winter		
		Mean	Max.	N	Mean	Max.	N
3351S 2535E	Chatty Saltpans, Port Elizabeth, Eastern Cape	48	89	2	632**	1249**	3
3247S 1812E	Berg River System, Velddrif, Western Cape	9	24	5	296**	380**	4
3405S 1831E	Strandfontein Sewage Works, Muizenberg, Western Cape	19	46	6	236*	808**	6
3359S 2240E	Wilderness Lakes – Touw River System, Sedgefield, Western Cape	2	11	6	179*	836**	6
2840S 2446E	Kamfers Dam, Kimberley, Northern Cape	32	95	3	94	282**	3
2839S 2437E	Platfontein Pans, Kimberley, Northern Cape	52	52	1	32	32	1
2632S 2536E	Leeupan, Delareyville, North West	68	204*	3	0	0	1
3236S 1818E	Rocher Pan, Velddrif, Western Cape	0	1	5	60	135*	6
2629S 2828E	Blesbokspruit, Nigel, Gauteng	0	0	1	51	51	1
3341S 1858E	Paarl Bird Sanctuary, Paarl, Western Cape	6	20	5	41	82	5
3205S 1819E	Jakkalsvlei, Lambert's Bay, Western Cape	7	7	1	35	35	1
2622S 2810E	Vlakplaas Water Treatment Works, Germiston, Gauteng	21	68	4	21	36	4
3318S 1845E	Radyn Dam, Malmesbury, Western Cape	23	70	5	15	42	4
2635S 2857E	Leeuwpan, Secunda, Mpumalanga	11	33	3	23	45	4
3408S 1821E	Wildevoëlvlei, Kommetjie, Western Cape	14	71	6	17	87	6

Strandfontein Sewage Works

Wilderness Lakes – Touw River System

Wildevoëlvlei

Rocher Pan

008 Dabchick *Tachybaptus ruficollis*

Recorded from most sites. Breeds at seasonal and ephemeral waters as well as larger permanent sites, and has at least local movements, concentrating at large waterbodies in nonbreeding season when small breeding sites dry out, thus well-marked winter peaks recorded at CWAC sites in many areas. Globally significant numbers occur in winter at four Western Cape sites (also in summer at three) and at two in the North West. Consistent summer peaks only at Radyn Dam, Western Cape, where it breeds. Has benefited from artificially created waters; good counts from dams, sewage works and salt pans, especially in winter.

			Summer			Winter		
			Mean	Max.	N	Mean	Max.	N
3359S 2240E	Wilderness Lakes – Touw River System, Sedgefield, Western Cape		146	184	6	940**	1819**	6
3408S 1821E	Wildevoëlvlei, Kommetjie, Western Cape		268*	331*	6	309*	373*	6
2804S 2433E	Spitskop Dam, Spitskop, Northern Cape		12	23	2	543**	949**	2
3405S 1831E	Strandfontein Sewage Works, Muizenberg, Western Cape		141	252*	6	403*	628**	6
3400S 2245E	Wilderness Lakes – Swartvlei System, Sedgefield, Western Cape		18	26	2	406*	484*	3
3341S 1858E	Paarl Bird Sanctuary, Paarl, Western Cape		118	182	5	93	118	5
3401S 2252E	Groenvlei, Sedgefield, Western Cape		59	86	2	130	205	2
2629S 2828E	Blesbokspruit, Nigel, Gauteng		12	12	1	152	152	1
2847S 3203E	Thulazihleka Pan, Richards Bay, KwaZulu–Natal		5	13	5	156	400*	5
2741S 2540E	Bloemhof Dam, Bloemhof, Free State		1	5	6	159	540**	6
2702S 3030E	Heyshope Dam, Piet Retief, Mpumalanga		–	–	–	159	159	1
2807S 2455E	Vaalharts Weir, Warrenton, Northern Cape		3	5	2	153	166	2
2553S 2817E	Rietvlei Dam, Pretoria, Gauteng		24	24	1	131	131	1
3220S 1825E	Verlorenvlei, Elandsbaai, Western Cape		77	173	6	78	144	5
2915S 2941E	Hlatikulu Vlei, Hlatikulu, KwaZulu–Natal		71	107	2	80	80	1

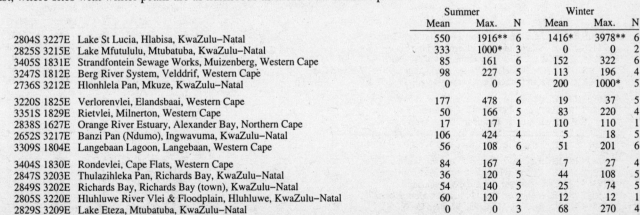

049 White Pelican *Pelecanus onocrotalus*

In RSA largely confined to coastal KwaZulu-Natal and Western Cape, whence come almost all large CWAC counts; very few inland records. Occurs at fresh, alkaline or saline waters, including lakes, pans, floodplains, estuaries, lagoons and tidal inlets; also sometimes at sewage works and dams. Usually breeds after peak rains; St Lucia an important breeding site, with globally significant numbers. Moves in response to changing water levels; favours drying sites where fish concentrate. CWAC data show no seasonal pattern of occurrence on coast, where sites with winter peaks are as numerous as those with summer peaks.

			Summer			Winter		
			Mean	Max.	N	Mean	Max.	N
2804S 3227E	Lake St Lucia, Hlabisa, KwaZulu–Natal		550	1916**	6	1416*	3978**	6
2825S 3215E	Lake Mfutululu, Mtubatuba, KwaZulu–Natal		333	1000*	3	0	0	2
3405S 1831E	Strandfontein Sewage Works, Muizenberg, Western Cape		85	161	6	152	322	6
3247S 1812E	Berg River System, Velddrif, Western Cape		98	227	5	113	196	4
2736S 3212E	Hlonhlela Pan, Mkuze, KwaZulu–Natal		0	0	5	200	1000*	5
3220S 1825E	Verlorenvlei, Elandsbaai, Western Cape		177	478	6	19	37	5
3351S 1829E	Rietvlei, Milnerton, Western Cape		50	166	5	83	220	4
2838S 1627E	Orange River Estuary, Alexander Bay, Northern Cape		17	17	1	110	110	1
2652S 3217E	Banzi Pan (Ndumo), Ingwavuma, KwaZulu–Natal		106	424	4	5	18	5
3309S 1804E	Langebaan Lagoon, Langebaan, Western Cape		56	108	6	51	201	6
3404S 1830E	Rondevlei, Cape Flats, Western Cape		84	167	4	7	27	4
2847S 3203E	Thulazihleka Pan, Richards Bay, KwaZulu–Natal		36	120	5	44	108	5
2849S 3202E	Richards Bay, Richards Bay (town), KwaZulu–Natal		54	140	5	25	74	5
2805S 3220E	Hluhluwe River Vlei & Floodplain, Hluhluwe, KwaZulu–Natal		60	120	2	12	12	1
2829S 3209E	Lake Eteza, Mtubatuba, KwaZulu–Natal		0	0	3	68	270	4

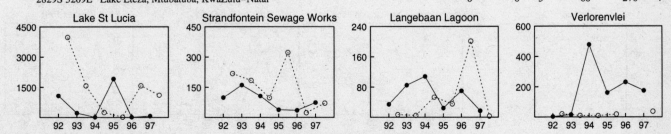

050 Pinkbacked Pelican *Pelecanus rufescens*

CWAC counts confirm this uncommon bird's known distribution and status. There is a small population on the KwaZulu-Natal coast, where birds breed at Nsumo Pan and wander north into Mozambique and south as far as the Durban area; this colony came from the Hluhluwe River mouth, and the species also bred at Pongolapoort Nature Reserve in 1975 and 1986. There are also records, mainly of small numbers in summer, from three sites in North West Province and two in the Free State; these birds are assumed to have dispersed south from the Okavango-Linyanti-Chobe population, which breeds in winter.

		Summer			Winter		
		Mean	Max.	N	Mean	Max.	N
2740S 3219E	Nsumu Pan, Mkuzi Game Reserve, KwaZulu–Natal	90	164	6	4	12	6
2804S 3227E	Lake St Lucia, Hlabisa, KwaZulu–Natal	24	41	6	57	125	6
2804S 2433E	Spitskop Dam, Spitskop, Northern Cape	39	41	2	0	0	2
2847S 3203E	Thulazihleka Pan, Richards Bay, KwaZulu–Natal	11	27	5	7	14	5
2635S 2535E	Barberspan, Delareyville, North West	17	38	4	0	0	2
2849S 3202E	Richards Bay, Richards Bay (town), KwaZulu–Natal	2	9	5	14	35	5
2949S 3102E	Umgeni River Estuary, Durban, KwaZulu–Natal	1	3	5	10	20	5
2741S 2540E	Bloemhof Dam, Bloemhof, Free State	8	21	6	0	0	6
2739S 3226E	Yengweni Lake, Mbazwane, KwaZulu–Natal	1	4	5	4	8	6
2824S 3225E	Mfolozi Mouth Area, St Lucia, KwaZulu–Natal	–	–	–	4	4	1
2911S 3125E	Sundumbili Sewage Works, Mandini, KwaZulu–Natal	1	1	2	3	8	3
2953S 3101E	Durban Bayhead, Durban, KwaZulu–Natal	0	2	5	3	10	5
2739S 3224E	Neshe Pan, Mbazwane, KwaZulu–Natal	1	4	5	1	5	6
2923S 3121E	Umvoti River Estuary, Stanger, KwaZulu–Natal	2	6	3	0	0	5
2815S 3228E	Mfazana Pans, St Lucia, KwaZulu–Natal	2	2	1	0	0	1

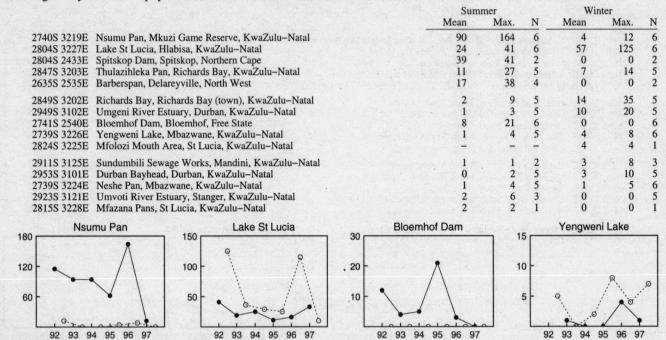

055 Whitebreasted Cormorant *Phalacrocorax carbo*

Common; frequently recorded along coasts and at many inland waterbodies. Although no counts of global or national significance are recorded, many are large; some of the highest are from impoundments, the construction of which has benefited this species considerably. No regular movements are described, but seasonal differences evident at over 50 CWAC sites, patterns being difficult to detect; numbers may peak at inland breeding sites in winter or summer, but winter peaks are commoner at coastal localities (especially lakes and estuaries) and summer peaks at inland sites (e.g. Free State and former Transvaal).

		Summer			Winter		
		Mean	Max.	N	Mean	Max.	N
2804S 2433E	Spitskop Dam, Spitskop, Northern Cape	457	780	2	644	701	2
2741S 2540E	Bloemhof Dam, Bloemhof, Free State	267	504	6	206	640	6
2721S 3240E	Lake Sibaya, Ubombo, KwaZulu–Natal	372	466	4	92	201	6
3405S 1831E	Strandfontein Sewage Works, Muizenberg, Western Cape	335	430	6	129	161	6
2932S 2515E	Kalkfontein Dam, Koffiefontein, Free State	261	615	6	180	601	6
2635S 2535E	Barberspan, Delareyville, North West	335	457	4	90	179	2
3236S 1818E	Rocher Pan, Velddrif, Western Cape	371	699	5	46	111	6
2510S 2751E	Klipvoor Dam, Brits, North West	38	56	4	203	477	3
3350S 2535E	Redhouse Saltpan, Port Elizabeth, Eastern Cape	125	183	4	109	154	4
3405S 1849E	Paardevlei Dam, Somerset West, Western Cape	128	167	5	92	110	5
3247S 1812E	Berg River System, Velddrif, Western Cape	98	146	5	85	117	4
3220S 1825E	Verlorenvlei, Elandsbaai, Western Cape	57	91	6	113	205	5
2635S 2857E	Leeuwpan, Secunda, Mpumalanga	145	181	3	23	32	4
2506S 2855E	Mkhombo Dam, Libangeni, Mpumalanga	32	94	3	122	250	3
3351S 1829E	Rietvlei, Milnerton, Western Cape	65	85	5	88	112	4

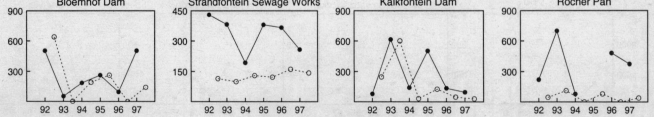

056 Cape Cormorant *Phalacrocorax capensis*

Much commoner on west coast than on east coast; almost all birds breed (mostly in summer) west of Cape Agulhas; some move east to KwaZulu-Natal coast in winter. CWAC counts peak in summer on west coast, from Orange River Estuary south to Kleinmond, and in winter to the east, from Wilderness Lakes/Knysna area to KwaZulu-Natal (where counts normally small and irregular). In winter 1994, large counts made at Kosi Bay and Lake St Lucia, and isolated records also at six sites from Verlorenvlei (Western Cape) to Richards Bay (KwaZulu-Natal). A globally significant total at Strandfontein Sewage Works in winter 1992 is noteworthy.

		Summer			Winter		
		Mean	Max.	N	Mean	Max.	N
3405S 1831E	Strandfontein Sewage Works, Muizenberg, Western Cape	8	33	6	1928	10511**	6
3247S 1812E	Berg River System, Velddrif, Western Cape	1233	3082*	5	131	159	4
3309S 1804E	Langebaan Lagoon, Langebaan, Western Cape	181	379	6	168	636	6
3403S 2302E	Knysna Lagoon, Knysna, Western Cape	8	16	5	317	407	5
3352S 2538E	Swartkops River Estuary, Port Elizabeth, Eastern Cape	2	3	6	291	771	6
3359S 2240E	Wilderness Lakes – Touw River System, Sedgefield, Western Cape	0	2	6	272	1332	6
2658S 3250E	Kosi Bay Nature Reserve, Manguzi, KwaZulu–Natal	0	0	5	117	700	6
3402S 2324E	Keurbooms River Estuary, Plettenberg Bay, Western Cape	13	25	2	62	124	3
3350S 2535E	Redhouse Saltpan, Port Elizabeth, Eastern Cape	1	2	4	62	119	4
3421S 1906E	Botriviervlei, Kleinmond, Western Cape	44	138	4	6	10	5
3351S 2535E	Chatty Saltpans, Port Elizabeth, Eastern Cape	1	1	2	33	55	3
3142S 1812E	Olifants River Mouth (South), Lutzville, Western Cape	30	60	2	0	0	1
2838S 1627E	Orange River Estuary, Alexander Bay, Northern Cape	0	0	1	29	29	1
2804S 3227E	Lake St Lucia, Hlabisa, KwaZulu–Natal	0	0	6	27	149	6
3443S 2007E	De Mond Estuary, Bredasdorp, Western Cape	9	21	4	16	46	5

(Graphs: Strandfontein Sewage Works; Wilderness Lakes – Touw River System; Langebaan Lagoon; Swartkops River Estuary)

058 Reed Cormorant *Phalacrocorax africanus*

Common; range similar to that of Whitebreasted Cormorant but somewhat more widespread, except on west coast. CWAC results closely parallel those for Whitebreasted. Many large counts recorded but none of global or national significance; high counts from some dams reflect the importance of impoundments. Thought to be a partial migrant; large-scale movements suggested. Seasonal differences apparent at over 60 CWAC sites; patterns difficult to detect. Winter peaks commoner at coastal sites and summer peaks at inland sites (e.g. on the central highveld); numbers may peak at breeding sites in either season.

		Summer			Winter		
		Mean	Max.	N	Mean	Max.	N
2804S 2433E	Spitskop Dam, Spitskop, Northern Cape	248	393	2	890	1168	2
3402S 1913E	Theewaterskloof Dam, Villiersdorp, Western Cape	561	1171	5	116	304	5
3403S 2302E	Knysna Lagoon, Knysna, Western Cape	106	136	5	326	400	5
2721S 3240E	Lake Sibaya, Ubombo, KwaZulu–Natal	153	283	4	237	382	6
3421S 1906E	Botriviervlei, Kleinmond, Western Cape	180	257	4	181	336	5
3400S 2245E	Wilderness Lakes – Swartvlei System, Sedgefield, Western Cape	136	152	2	158	218	3
3359S 2240E	Wilderness Lakes – Touw River System, Sedgefield, Western Cape	67	109	6	196	330	6
2741S 2540E	Bloemhof Dam, Bloemhof, Free State	205	456	6	39	112	6
2755S 2446E	Ganspan Pans & Vlei, Jan Kempdorp, Northern Cape	29	54	2	204	209	2
3401S 2252E	Groenvlei, Sedgefield, Western Cape	75	90	2	142	175	2
3350S 2535E	Redhouse Saltpan, Port Elizabeth, Eastern Cape	21	37	4	183	350	4
3247S 1812E	Berg River System, Velddrif, Western Cape	108	273	5	82	158	4
3405S 2454E	Seekoei River Estuary, Jeffreys Bay, Eastern Cape	69	73	2	118	166	3
2849S 3202E	Richards Bay, Richards Bay (town), KwaZulu–Natal	91	342	5	89	332	5
3404S 1830E	Rondevlei, Cape Flats, Western Cape	102	197	4	73	157	4

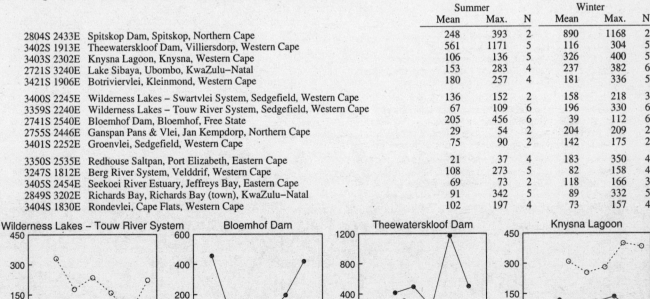

(Graphs: Wilderness Lakes – Touw River System; Bloemhof Dam; Theewaterskloof Dam; Knysna Lagoon)

060 Darter *Anhinga melanogaster*

Locally common; range very similar to that of Whitebreasted Cormorant, but slightly less widespread, and absent from northwest coast; globally significant counts in Western Cape and North West. Frequents many freshwater wetlands; makes good use of dams (whence come highest counts) and sewage works. Breeds mainly in summer, even in winter-rainfall region. Suggested winter movements to coast when seasonal wetlands of interior dry out (ASAB1). CWAC data show winter peaks at several permanent KwaZulu-Natal coastal sites; summer peaks at most Free State sites, no recognizable pattern elsewhere in interior.

		Summer			Winter		
		Mean	Max.	N	Mean	Max.	N
2804S 2433E	Spitskop Dam, Spitskop, Northern Cape	306*	346*	2	522**	569**	2
3402S 1913E	Theewaterskloof Dam, Villiersdorp, Western Cape	349*	553**	5	96	193	5
2741S 2540E	Bloemhof Dam, Bloemhof, Free State	228	610**	6	117	280*	6
3010S 2455E	Vanderkloof Dam, Vanderkloof, Northern Cape	112	112	1	50	50	1
2852S 2600E	Krugersdrift Dam, Bloemfontein, Free State	106	339*	6	49	178	6
2757S 2957E	Chelmsford Dam, Newcastle, KwaZulu-Natal	113	225	2	20	22	3
3405S 1849E	Paardevlei Dam, Somerset West, Western Cape	69	96	5	47	86	5
3404S 1830E	Rondevlei, Cape Flats, Western Cape	92	275*	4	16	25	4
2715S 2741E	Koppies Dam, Koppies, Free State	66	205	6	41	102	6
3220S 1825E	Verlorenvlei, Elandsbaai, Western Cape	58	115	6	31	51	5
2847S 3203E	Thulazihleka Pan, Richards Bay, KwaZulu-Natal	58	83	5	27	82	5
2838S 1627E	Orange River Estuary, Alexander Bay, Northern Cape	1	1	1	79	79	1
2553S 2918E	Witbank Dam, Witbank, Mpumalanga	38	66	4	38	101	5
3351S 1829E	Rietvlei, Milnerton, Western Cape	26	35	5	44	73	4
2918S 2637E	Rusfontein Dam, Thaba Nchu, Free State	17	36	6	53	93	6

Bloemhof Dam

Krugersdrift Dam

Koppies Dam

Rusfontein Dam

062 Grey Heron *Ardea cinerea*

Widespread and locally common, most numerous in moist eastern and southern areas; in dry areas mainly at coasts and major rivers. Frequents shallow open water at rivers, lakes, dams, marshes, estuaries, lagoons and intertidal zones; also pans, sewage works and saltpans. Usually nests and roosts in tall trees; breeding peaks late winter/spring. Assumed resident, but marked summer peaks at some CWAC sites (possibly associated with breeding) and winter peaks at others (postbreeding dispersal?); proportion of summer peaks highest at dams. Without knowing location of breeding colonies, interpretation of these data is difficult.

		Summer			Winter		
		Mean	Max.	N	Mean	Max.	N
3403S 2302E	Knysna Lagoon, Knysna, Western Cape	49	54	5	51	70	5
2804S 3227E	Lake St Lucia, Hlabisa, KwaZulu-Natal	36	53	6	58	94	6
3416S 2149E	Voëlvlei, Mossel Bay, Western Cape	54	120	5	26	66	4
2932S 2515E	Kalkfontein Dam, Koffiefontein, Free State	44	69	6	27	65	6
3404S 1830E	Rondevlei, Cape Flats, Western Cape	16	29	4	49	77	4
2741S 2540E	Bloemhof Dam, Bloemhof, Free State	57	95	6	7	12	6
3037S 2537E	Gariep Dam (West), Gariep Dam (town), Free State	48	84	6	16	62	6
2852S 2600E	Krugersdrift Dam, Bloemfontein, Free State	45	95	6	15	36	6
3247S 1812E	Berg River System, Velddrif, Western Cape	36	57	5	23	27	4
3350S 2535E	Redhouse Saltpan, Port Elizabeth, Eastern Cape	26	31	4	32	37	4
2520S 2728E	Vaalkop Dam, Brits, North West	11	18	4	42	69	5
2506S 2855E	Mkhombo Dam, Libangeni, Mpumalanga	4	10	3	38	84	3
3351S 1829E	Rietvlei, Milnerton, Western Cape	22	41	5	20	30	4
3421S 1906E	Botriviervlei, Kleinmond, Western Cape	28	38	4	12	30	5
3426S 2023E	De Hoop Vlei, Bredasdorp, Western Cape	29	52	5	9	27	4

Lake St Lucia

Kalkfontein Dam

Bloemhof Dam

Gariep Dam (West)

063 Blackheaded Heron *Ardea melanocephala*

Widespread and common; feeds mostly in terrestrial habitats but prefers moist areas, often occurring near water, and commonest in high-rainfall areas. Assumed resident, perhaps with seasonal local movements associated with changes in food availability; CWAC data show marked winter peaks at numerous sites (dams vleis, pans, sewage works, etc.). Nests colonially; breeds all year, with spring peak. Range has expanded, and breeding colonies increased, with creation of pastures, cultivation, artificial waterbodies, and alien trees for nesting. CWAC data indicate that dams are important sites, especially for winter concentrations.

			Summer			Winter		
			Mean	Max.	N	Mean	Max.	N
2725S 3158E	Pongolapoort Dam, Mkuze, KwaZulu–Natal		27	66	6	69	155	6
2915S 2941E	Hlatikulu Vlei, Hlatikulu, KwaZulu–Natal		23	30	2	30	30	1
2609S 2821E	Rynfield Dam, Benoni, Gauteng		19	36	4	34	66	5
2635S 2535E	Barberspan, Delareyville, North West		27	64	4	16	20	2
3404S 1830E	Rondevlei, Cape Flats, Western Cape		7	14	4	27	32	4
2611S 2818E	Korsman Bird Sanctuary, Benoni, Gauteng		10	14	3	20	44	3
2520S 2728E	Vaalkop Dam, Brits, North West		4	8	4	23	66	5
2506S 2855E	Mkhombo Dam, Libangeni, Mpumalanga		1	3	3	23	64	3
2629S 2828E	Blesbokspruit, Nigel, Gauteng		13	13	1	8	8	1
2714S 3002E	Fickland Pan, Wakkerstroom, Mpumalanga		1	1	1	20	20	1
2917S 3117E	Mbozambo Waste Water Lagoon, Stanger, KwaZulu–Natal		6	15	3	10	23	5
3155S 2650E	Queenstown Sewage Works, Queenstown, Eastern Cape		2	2	1	14	28	3
3405S 1831E	Strandfontein Sewage Works, Muizenberg, Western Cape		6	10	6	10	20	6
2611S 2819E	Homestead, Benoni & Middle Lakes, Benoni, Gauteng		6	7	2	9	15	2
3416S 2149E	Voëlvlei, Mossel Bay, Western Cape		12	60	5	3	12	4

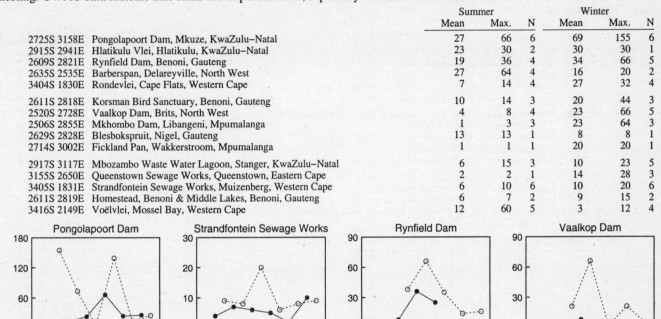

064 Goliath Heron *Ardea goliath*

Widespread, usually in small numbers at open waters, e.g. lakes, rivers, estuaries, and large and small dams; absent from driest regions. Mainly resident; also dispersive and nomadic, moving when water levels change. CWAC data show marked summer peaks at many sites of regular occurrence (see table). Breeds all year. Range is extending westwards (ASAB1). Has benefited from construction of large dams; 30 (42%) of 72 CWAC sites are dams; large dams yield majority of high counts (nationally significant at Bloemhof Dam) and provide breeding sites. CWAC counts indicate declining numbers at several sites (see graphs).

			Summer			Winter		
			Mean	Max.	N	Mean	Max.	N
2804S 3227E	Lake St Lucia, Hlabisa, KwaZulu–Natal		76	107	6	56	93	6
2741S 2540E	Bloemhof Dam, Bloemhof, Free State		76	168*	6	37	79	6
2804S 2433E	Spitskop Dam, Spitskop, Northern Cape		27	41	2	22	35	2
2932S 2515E	Kalkfontein Dam, Koffiefontein, Free State		28	38	6	19	36	6
2852S 2600E	Krugersdrift Dam, Bloemfontein, Free State		24	34	6	11	25	6
2818S 2712E	Allemanskraal Dam, Ventersburg, Free State		28	42	6	6	12	6
3037S 2537E	Gariep Dam (West), Gariep Dam (town), Free State		21	29	6	9	14	6
3010S 2455E	Vanderkloof Dam, Vanderkloof, Northern Cape		20	20	1	5	5	1
2715S 2741E	Koppies Dam, Koppies, Free State		15	18	6	7	10	6
2834S 2650E	Erfenis Dam, Winburg, Free State		15	20	6	5	9	6
2918S 2637E	Rusfontein Dam, Thaba Nchu, Free State		12	19	6	8	11	6
2635S 2535E	Barberspan, Delareyville, North West		6	9	4	9	12	2
2553S 2918E	Witbank Dam, Witbank, Mpumalanga		8	10	4	6	10	5
2629S 2828E	Blesbokspruit, Nigel, Gauteng		9	9	1	3	3	1
2725S 3158E	Pongolapoort Dam, Mkuze, KwaZulu–Natal		7	8	6	4	9	6

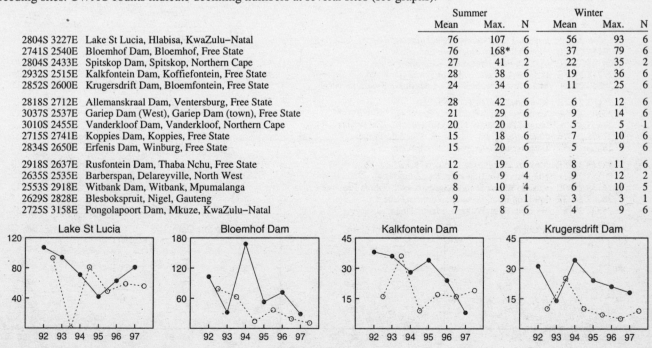

065 Purple Heron *Ardea purpurea*

Widespread; absent from driest regions. Usually solitary and shy, inhabiting dense reedbeds in shallow fresh or estuarine waters; under-recorded by CWAC, but noted at 100 sites. Resident; also nomadic, using seasonal sites. Changes in behaviour and habitat may affect visibility seasonally, but SABAP data indicate summer influx in the north; CWAC data show good summer peaks at widely scattered sites (see table) and winter peaks at Ladysmith and Sedgefield; most are permanent residents. Good counts at natural sites; isolated summer and winter records often at pans; also uses artificial sites: recorded at 12 sewage works, and 25 large and small dams.

		Summer			Winter		
		Mean	Max.	N	Mean	Max.	N
2847S 3203E	Thulazihleka Pan, Richards Bay, KwaZulu–Natal	11	27	5	10	24	5
2629S 2828E	Blesbokspruit, Nigel, Gauteng	12	12	1	8	8	1
2721S 3240E	Lake Sibaya, Ubombo, KwaZulu–Natal	18	40	4	2	4	6
3405S 1831E	Strandfontein Sewage Works, Muizenberg, Western Cape	14	65	6	3	7	6
2849S 3202E	Richards Bay, Richards Bay (town), KwaZulu–Natal	9	29	5	3	8	5
3359S 2240E	Wilderness Lakes – Touw River System, Sedgefield, Western Cape	4	7	6	8	18	6
3247S 1812E	Berg River System, Velddrif, Western Cape	6	10	5	5	6	4
2834S 2948E	Malandeni Sewage Works, Ladysmith, KwaZulu–Natal	3	9	5	8	14	5
3351S 1829E	Rietvlei, Milnerton, Western Cape	5	10	5	4	7	4
3402S 2324E	Keurbooms River Estuary, Plettenberg Bay, Western Cape	4	5	2	4	8	3
2616S 2830E	Grootvaly, Springs, Gauteng	3	4	3	5	12	4
2804S 3227E	Lake St Lucia, Hlabisa, KwaZulu–Natal	3	8	6	5	15	6
2750S 3035E	Blood River Vlei, Vryheid, KwaZulu–Natal	7	7	1	0	0	1
2805S 3220E	Hluhluwe River Vlei & Floodplain, Hluhluwe, KwaZulu–Natal	1	2	2	6	6	1
3404S 1830E	Rondevlei, Cape Flats, Western Cape	4	7	4	3	6	4

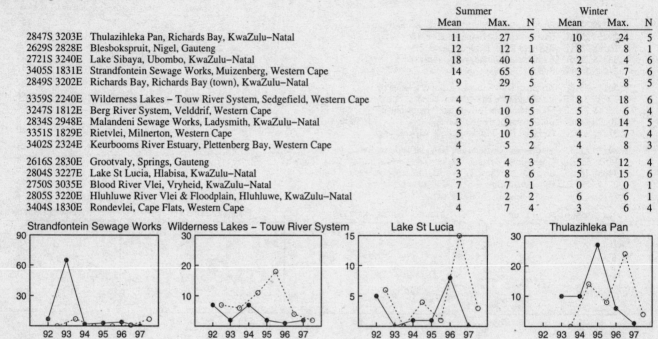

066 Great White Heron *Egretta alba*

RSA distribution largely in moist eastern regions; smaller numbers along south coast to southwestern Cape (confirmed by CWAC). Frequents shallow, open water at lakes, rivers, marshes, floodplains, flooded grass, saltpans, estuaries, dams and sewage works. SABAP data indicate regular movements: peaks from midwinter to early summer in east, possibly of non-breeding birds from East/Central Africa. CWAC data show summer peaks at 26 sites and isolated records at 14 more; winter peaks at 4 sites, isolated records at 8 more. Mainly a summer visitor to the Western Cape; CWAC data include winter records from 4 of 6 sites there.

		Summer			Winter		
		Mean	Max.	N	Mean	Max.	N
2804S 3227E	Lake St Lucia, Hlabisa, KwaZulu–Natal	102	223	6	68	118	6
2741S 2540E	Bloemhof Dam, Bloemhof, Free State	38	109	6	0	2	6
2830S 3212E	Mavuya Pan, Mtubatuba, KwaZulu–Natal	1	3	3	33	119	4
2725S 3158E	Pongolapoort Dam, Mkuze, KwaZulu–Natal	19	57	6	11	24	6
2834S 2948E	Malandeni Sewage Works, Ladysmith, KwaZulu–Natal	14	42	5	5	11	5
2510S 2751E	Klipvoor Dam, Brits, North West	8	15	4	10	18	3
2520S 2728E	Vaalkop Dam, Brits, North West	9	20	4	9	19	5
2740S 3219E	Nsumu Pan, Mkuzi Game Reserve, KwaZulu–Natal	16	64	6	1	3	6
2757S 2957E	Chelmsford Dam, Newcastle, KwaZulu–Natal	2	4	2	15	32	3
2635S 2535E	Barberspan, Delareyville, North West	17	32	4	0	0	2
2824S 3225E	Mfolozi Mouth Area, St Lucia, KwaZulu–Natal	–	–	–	13	13	1
2915S 2941E	Hlatikulu Vlei, Hlatikulu, KwaZulu–Natal	8	9	2	5	5	1
2513S 2830E	Rust de Winter Dam, Pienaarsrivier, Northern Province	4	8	2	8	15	2
2804S 2433E	Spitskop Dam, Spitskop, Northern Cape	9	17	2	3	5	2
2553S 2918E	Witbank Dam, Witbank, Mpumalanga	10	11	4	1	3	5

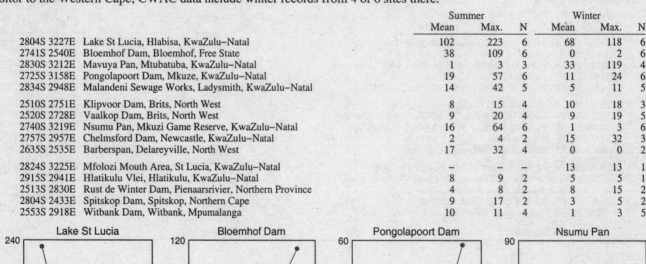

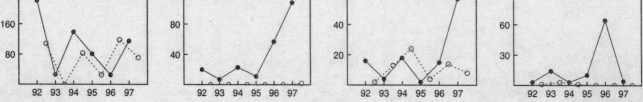

067 Little Egret *Egretta garzetta*

Occurs throughout, except in driest regions; commonest along coast and in northeast. Singly or in small flocks at open, shallow water of lakes, pans, dams, rivers, marshes, irrigation, sewage works, saltpans, estuaries mangroves and open coastline; makes good use of artificial wetlands. Often resident, but also nomadic to seasonal wetlands, and regular movements also noted: summer peaks evident at inland sites and in Western Cape (amply confirmed by CWAC data); winter peaks at eastern and southern Cape coasts (confirmed by CWAC), and often at KwaZulu-Natal coastal sites (CWAC). Breeds mainly October–February.

		Summer			Winter		
		Mean	Max.	N	Mean	Max.	N
3403S 2302E	Knysna Lagoon, Knysna, Western Cape	72	85	5	166	217	5
3352S 2538E	Swartkops River Estuary, Port Elizabeth, Eastern Cape	36	53	6	123	222	6
2804S 3227E	Lake St Lucia, Hlabisa, KwaZulu–Natal	103	280	6	53	119	6
3309S 1804E	Langebaan Lagoon, Langebaan, Western Cape	72	103	6	63	103	6
3247S 1812E	Berg River System, Velddrif, Western Cape	46	64	5	52	60	4
3416S 2149E	Voëlvlei, Mossel Bay, Western Cape	50	200	5	17	36	4
3404S 1830E	Rondevlei, Cape Flats, Western Cape	64	164	4	2	3	4
3402S 1913E	Theewaterskloof Dam, Villiersdorp, Western Cape	44	77	5	5	7	5
3402S 2324E	Keurbooms River Estuary, Plettenberg Bay, Western Cape	22	24	2	23	31	3
2838S 1627E	Orange River Estuary, Alexander Bay, Northern Cape	10	10	1	32	32	1
2735S 2935E	Seekoeivlei, Memel, Free State	19	55	5	23	87	5
3359S 2240E	Wilderness Lakes – Touw River System, Sedgefield, Western Cape	17	28	6	20	35	6
2721S 3240E	Lake Sibaya, Ubombo, KwaZulu–Natal	17	46	4	20	34	6
3426S 2023E	De Hoop Vlei, Bredasdorp, Western Cape	27	49	5	7	16	4
3350S 2535E	Redhouse Saltpan, Port Elizabeth, Eastern Cape	20	50	4	8	10	4

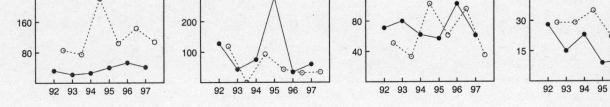

068 Yellowbilled Egret *Egretta intermedia*

Uncommon to locally common in RSA, most numerous in Western Cape, north-eastern highveld and northern coastal KwaZulu-Natal, with highest CWAC counts from those regions. Frequents shallow water at lakes, rivers, saltpans, estuaries, lagoons and (CWAC) sewage ponds; also flooded grass, and marshes with short emergent vegetation; favours seasonal sites. May be resident at permanent sites but moves in response to rain; SABAP data suggest summer influx to northeast, largely supported by CWAC data. CWAC shows winter peaks at some Western Cape and coastal KwaZulu-Natal sites.

		Summer			Winter		
		Mean	Max.	N	Mean	Max.	N
3404S 1830E	Rondevlei, Cape Flats, Western Cape	127	255	4	3	12	4
2725S 3158E	Pongolapoort Dam, Mkuze, KwaZulu–Natal	29	172	6	2	6	6
2715S 3007E	Clarens' Pan, Wakkerstroom, Mpumalanga	23	23	1	–	–	–
2735S 2935E	Seekoeivlei, Memel, Free State	12	18	5	3	8	5
3351S 1829E	Rietvlei, Milnerton, Western Cape	7	10	5	8	14	4
2830S 3212E	Mavuya Pan, Mtubatuba, KwaZulu–Natal	0	0	3	15	40	4
3402S 1913E	Theewaterskloof Dam, Villiersdorp, Western Cape	5	8	5	7	10	5
3426S 2023E	De Hoop Vlei, Bredasdorp, Western Cape	1	6	5	10	39	4
2629S 2828E	Blesbokspruit, Nigel, Gauteng	9	9	1	1	1	1
3408S 1821E	Wildevoëlvlei, Kommetjie, Western Cape	5	7	6	2	7	6
3247S 1812E	Berg River System, Velddrif, Western Cape	3	12	5	4	6	4
3405S 1831E	Strandfontein Sewage Works, Muizenberg, Western Cape	6	21	6	1	3	6
3339S 1858E	Wellington Waste Water Works, Wellington, Western Cape	4	4	1	2	2	1
3416S 2149E	Voëlvlei, Mossel Bay, Western Cape	5	10	5	1	2	4
2553S 2918E	Witbank Dam, Witbank, Mpumalanga	4	8	4	1	4	5

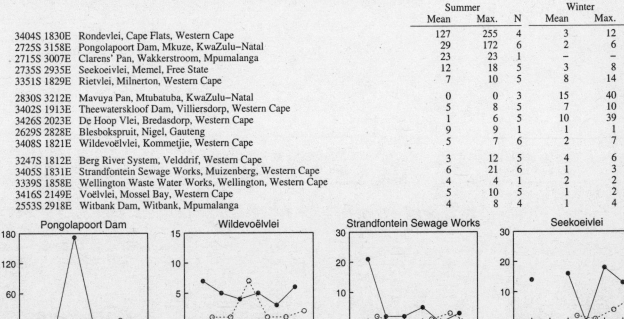

069 Black Egret *Egretta ardesiaca*

In RSA largely confined to northeast; extends southwest to Free State and extreme eastern Northern Cape, and south to northern KwaZulu-Natal; vagrant in south and west (two CWAC summer records at Verloren Vlei, Western Cape). CWAC data show occurrence of small numbers (up to 28 birds) at 37 sites within normal range (30 sites in Gauteng, North West and KwaZulu-Natal), and confirm SABAP finding that occurrences are mostly in summer: 1–3 (once 13) birds were recorded at only 10 sites during July counts. Numbers fluctuate widely from summer to summer at regular sites. Breeds infrequently; most birds breed to the north (ASAB1).

		Summer			Winter		
		Mean	Max.	N	Mean	Max.	N
2611S 2818E	Korsman Bird Sanctuary, Benoni, Gauteng	7	12	3	5	13	3
2804S 2433E	Spitskop Dam, Spitskop, Northern Cape	10	12	2	0	0	2
2645S 2706E	Prozesky Bird Sanctuary, Potchefstroom, North West	7	12	3	0	1	3
2804S 3227E	Lake St Lucia, Hlabisa, KwaZulu–Natal	7	23	6	0	0	6
2616S 2830E	Grootvaly, Springs, Gauteng	6	13	3	0	0	4
2629S 2828E	Blesbokspruit, Nigel, Gauteng	5	5	1	0	0	1
2741S 2540E	Bloemhof Dam, Bloemhof, Free State	5	28	6	0	1	6
2739S 3226E	Yengweni Lake, Mbazwane, KwaZulu–Natal	4	11	5	0	0	6
2520S 2728E	Vaalkop Dam, Brits, North West	3	8	4	0	0	5
2554S 2842E	Bronkhorstspruit Dam, Bronkhorstspruit, Gauteng	3	6	4	0	0	4
2740S 3219E	Nsumu Pan, Mkuzi Game Reserve, KwaZulu–Natal	3	15	6	0	0	6
2621S 2830E	Marievale Bird Sanctuary, Nigel, Gauteng	2	7	5	0	0	5
2825S 3215E	Lake Mfutululu, Mtubatuba, KwaZulu–Natal	2	5	3	1	1	2
2510S 2751E	Klipvoor Dam, Brits, North West	2	8	4	0	0	3
2545S 2752E	Hartbeespoort Dam, Hartbeespoort, North West	2	2	1	–	–	–

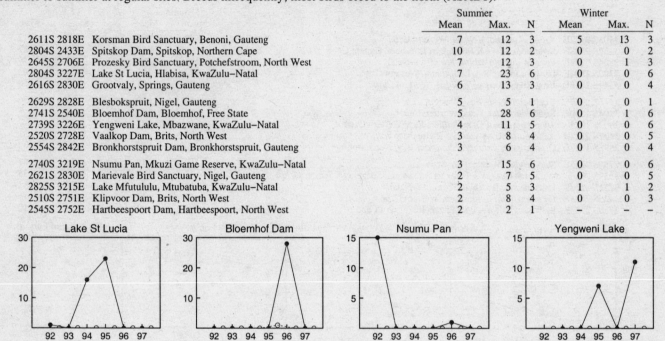

070 Slaty Egret *Egretta vinaceigula*

Rare: recorded twice at Nylsvley (bred 1996), once at Vaalkop Dam (CWAC), and at Nyamithi Pan since 1997.

071 Cattle Egret *Bubulcus ibis*

Widespread and locally abundant, particularly in the east and south (largest CWAC totals from northeast – see table). Although feeding at dryland sites it roosts at waterbodies and sometimes breeds in reedbeds. Not usually in coastal, marine, forested or high mountain environments. Nomadic in response to seasonal rains; also very dispersive. SABAP data show marked reduction in numbers in winter, mainly from inland areas; this is amply confirmed by CWAC data. Seven sites in Western Cape, and 15 in coastal KwaZulu-Natal, show winter peaks. Breeds mainly September–March; extent of breeding at CWAC sites not clear.

		Summer			Winter		
		Mean	Max.	N	Mean	Max.	N
2818S 2712E	Allemanskraal Dam, Ventersburg, Free State	1733	5400*	6	3	14	6
2735S 2935E	Seekoeivlei, Memel, Free State	1338	5000*	5	5	21	5
2645S 2706E	Prozesky Bird Sanctuary, Potchefstroom, North West	1165	2363	3	83	242	3
2852S 2600E	Krugersdrift Dam, Bloemfontein, Free State	1230	5102*	6	0	0	6
2741S 2540E	Bloemhof Dam, Bloemhof, Free State	1217	6233*	6	0	1	6
2757S 2957E	Chelmsford Dam, Newcastle, KwaZulu–Natal	1171	2342	2	25	32	3
2834S 2948E	Malandeni Sewage Works, Ladysmith, KwaZulu–Natal	665	1010	5	199	257	5
2725S 3158E	Pongolapoort Dam, Mkuze, KwaZulu–Natal	594	1582	6	122	384	6
2804S 2433E	Spitskop Dam, Spitskop, Northern Cape	606	1000	2	0	0	2
2658S 3250E	Kosi Bay Nature Reserve, Manguzi, KwaZulu–Natal	22	50	5	520	903	6
2620S 2817E	Rietspruit (Rooikraal), Boksburg, Gauteng	432	908	3	52	202	4
3405S 1831E	Strandfontein Sewage Works, Muizenberg, Western Cape	169	311	6	276	685	6
3402S 1913E	Theewaterskloof Dam, Villiersdorp, Western Cape	329	523	5	65	137	5
2740S 3219E	Nsumu Pan, Mkuzi Game Reserve, KwaZulu–Natal	153	269	6	180	1000	6
2609S 2821E	Rynfield Dam, Benoni, Gauteng	308	967	4	15	58	5

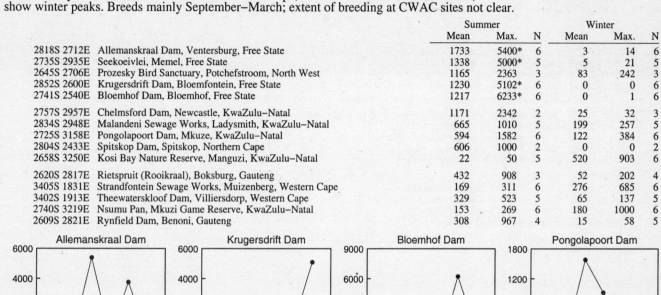

072 Squacco Heron *Ardeola ralloides*

In RSA occurs predominantly in the east, distribution centred on northeastern highveld and KwaZulu-Natal; vagrant in south and west (one CWAC record from Cape Recife). SABAP data show great winter decrease, confirmed by CWAC data: 62 CWAC sites are within the normal range; numbers are higher (or isolated occurrences recorded) at 38 (61%) of these in summer, but only 14 (23%) in winter. Summer increases may reflect influx of both Palearctic and Afrotropical birds (see SABAP). Inhabits natural reed-fringed freshwater sites (ponds, rivers, pans); also dams and sewage works.

		Summer			Winter		
		Mean	Max.	N	Mean	Max.	N
2804S 2433E	Spitskop Dam, Spitskop, Northern Cape	31	57	2	3	5	2
2847S 3203E	Thulazihleka Pan, Richards Bay, KwaZulu–Natal	18	33	5	13	24	5
2740S 3219E	Nsumu Pan, Mkuzi Game Reserve, KwaZulu–Natal	27	82	6	0	1	6
2807S 2455E	Vaalharts Weir, Warrenton, Northern Cape	9	14	2	11	20	2
2611S 2818E	Korsman Bird Sanctuary, Benoni, Gauteng	12	23	3	7	21	3
2629S 2828E	Blesbokspruit, Nigel, Gauteng	18	18	1	0	0	1
2616S 2830E	Grootvaly, Springs, Gauteng	14	18	3	2	7	4
2621S 2830E	Marievale Bird Sanctuary, Nigel, Gauteng	11	33	5	1	4	5
2534S 2814E	Rooiwal Sewage Works, Pretoria, Gauteng	7	8	4	2	4	5
2721S 3240E	Lake Sibaya, Ubombo, KwaZulu–Natal	4	12	4	5	7	6
2740S 3226E	Tshanetshe Pan, Mbazwane, KwaZulu–Natal	7	17	5	0	1	6
2645S 2706E	Prozesky Bird Sanctuary, Potchefstroom, North West	6	16	3	0	1	3
2750S 3035E	Blood River Vlei, Vryheid, KwaZulu–Natal	6	6	1	0	0	1
2739S 3224E	Neshe Pan, Mbazwane, KwaZulu–Natal	5	11	5	0	1	6
2834S 2948E	Malandeni Sewage Works, Ladysmith, KwaZulu–Natal	3	5	5	2	4	5

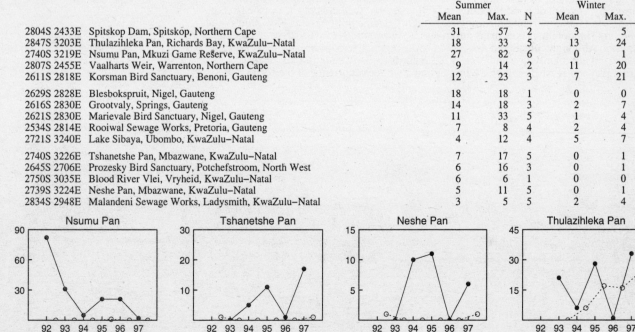

074 Greenbacked Heron *Butorides striatus*

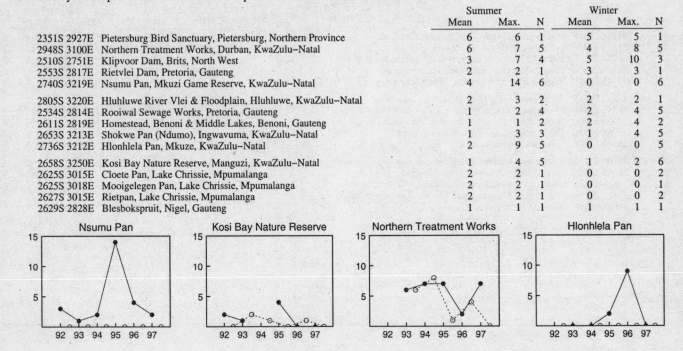

In RSA mostly in the northeast, extending to scattered sites in Free State and Eastern Cape; CWAC records from 33 sites, 20 in KwaZulu-Natal, others in Gauteng, Mpumalanga and North West. Occurs in trees and underbrush at rivers, streams, estuaries, mangroves, swamps, lakes and ponds; also mudflats, intertidal zones, and sewage works. Solitary and retiring; recorded counts small. May breed in loose small colonies; breeds all year, mostly in rains. Usually sedentary, but moves locally in response to rains, e.g. seasonal visitor to Nyl floodplain. No overall seasonal pattern evident from CWAC data.

		Summer			Winter		
		Mean	Max.	N	Mean	Max.	N
2351S 2927E	Pietersburg Bird Sanctuary, Pietersburg, Northern Province	6	6	1	5	5	1
2948S 3100E	Northern Treatment Works, Durban, KwaZulu–Natal	6	7	5	4	8	5
2510S 2751E	Klipvoor Dam, Brits, North West	3	7	4	5	10	3
2553S 2817E	Rietvlei Dam, Pretoria, Gauteng	2	2	1	3	3	1
2740S 3219E	Nsumu Pan, Mkuzi Game Reserve, KwaZulu–Natal	4	14	6	0	0	6
2805S 3220E	Hluhluwe River Vlei & Floodplain, Hluhluwe, KwaZulu–Natal	2	3	2	2	2	1
2534S 2814E	Rooiwal Sewage Works, Pretoria, Gauteng	1	2	4	2	4	5
2611S 2819E	Homestead, Benoni & Middle Lakes, Benoni, Gauteng	1	1	2	2	4	2
2653S 3213E	Shokwe Pan (Ndumo), Ingwavuma, KwaZulu–Natal	1	3	3	1	4	5
2736S 3212E	Hlonhlela Pan, Mkuze, KwaZulu–Natal	2	9	5	0	0	5
2658S 3250E	Kosi Bay Nature Reserve, Manguzi, KwaZulu–Natal	1	4	5	1	2	6
2625S 3015E	Cloete Pan, Lake Chrissie, Mpumalanga	2	2	1	0	0	2
2625S 3018E	Mooigelegen Pan, Lake Chrissie, Mpumalanga	2	2	1	0	0	1
2627S 3015E	Rietpan, Lake Chrissie, Mpumalanga	2	2	1	0	0	2
2629S 2828E	Blesbokspruit, Nigel, Gauteng	1	1	1	1	1	1

075 Rufousbellied Heron *Butorides rufiventris*

Endemic to southern and central Africa; rare in southern Africa. In RSA it occurs erratically in years of good flooding, in well vegetated wetlands of the northeast, e.g. at Nylsvley (an important breeding area) and in extreme northeastern KwaZulu-Natal. It prefers floodplains, lakes, pans and rivers, with aquatic grasses, sedges, reeds and papyrus. Although considered resident in some regions, occurrences in RSA and Swaziland are mainly in summer. CWAC records came from only two localities, Mfula pan and Kosi Bay, with a summer and a winter occurrence at the former site.

076 Blackcrowned Night Heron *Nycticorax nycticorax*

Widespread in dense vegetation of marshes, swamps, floodplains, lakes, pans, estuaries, mangroves and slow-flowing rivers, largely in wetter eastern and southern regions; also sewage works and many dams. Crepuscular and nocturnal, but more conspicuous in breeding season (October–February); certainly under-recorded by CWAC. Highest CWAC numbers in Western Cape and northeastern interior. Nomadic, dispersing in response to rains; also partial migrant, commonest in breeding season (ASAB1). CWAC counts higher, and isolated occurrences more frequent, over much of range in summer, but often in winter in Western Cape.

		Summer			Winter		
		Mean	Max.	N	Mean	Max.	N
3356S 1828E	Raapenberg Bird Sanctuary, Cape Town, Western Cape	18	18	2	15	15	1
2834S 2948E	Malandeni Sewage Works, Ladysmith, KwaZulu–Natal	14	38	5	17	34	5
3404S 1830E	Rondevlei, Cape Flats, Western Cape	6	9	4	19	75	4
2838S 1627E	Orange River Estuary, Alexander Bay, Northern Cape	0	0	1	24	24	1
3341S 1858E	Paarl Bird Sanctuary, Paarl, Western Cape	11	42	5	12	22	5
3402S 1913E	Theewaterskloof Dam, Villiersdorp, Western Cape	14	27	5	3	7	5
3351S 1829E	Rietvlei, Milnerton, Western Cape	5	13	5	10	18	4
2611S 2818E	Korsman Bird Sanctuary, Benoni, Gauteng	8	17	3	4	13	3
2616S 2830E	Grootvaly, Springs, Gauteng	10	28	3	1	3	4
3408S 1821E	Wildevoëlvlei, Kommetjie, Western Cape	7	10	6	3	6	6
2804S 2433E	Spitskop Dam, Spitskop, Northern Cape	9	17	2	0	0	2
3425S 1910E	Vermont Salt Pan, Hermanus, Western Cape	6	12	5	2	5	5
2613S 2828E	Springs Bird Sanctuary, Springs, Gauteng	5	12	5	2	11	5
2948S 3100E	Northern Treatment Works, Durban, KwaZulu–Natal	0	2	5	6	12	5
3416S 2149E	Voëlvlei, Mossel Bay, Western Cape	6	20	5	0	0	4

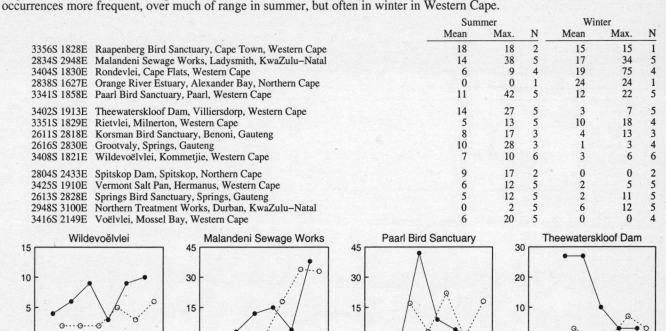

078 Little Bittern *Ixobrychus minutus*

Regarded as uncommon, and recorded only in small numbers from reedbeds at 37 CWAC sites. Two races occur: the Palearctic nominate race which occurs in southern Africa from December to early April, and the African endemic *payesii*, to which winter records are presumably referable. Although the relatively large number of summer records reflects the presence of Palearctic birds, *payesii* is also a migrant in the former Transvaal, present December–April. Recent studies suggest that *payesii* may be fairly common in suitable large reedbeds in the Western Cape, Free State, KwaZulu-Natal and former Transvaal.

		Summer			Winter		
		Mean	Max.	N	Mean	Max.	N
2611S 2818E	Korsman Bird Sanctuary, Benoni, Gauteng	6	10	3	2	5	3
2834S 2948E	Malandeni Sewage Works, Ladysmith, KwaZulu–Natal	4	7	5	0	2	5
2629S 2828E	Blesbokspruit, Nigel, Gauteng	4	4	1	0	0	1
2622S 2810E	Vlakplaas Water Treatment Works, Germiston, Gauteng	3	11	4	0	0	4
2804S 2433E	Spitskop Dam, Spitskop, Northern Cape	3	5	2	0	0	2
3150S 2208E	Sakrivierspoort Wetlands, Loxton, Northern Cape	2	3	3	0	0	2
2557S 2800E	Diepsloot Nature Reserve, Johannesburg, Gauteng	2	4	4	1	4	5
2613S 2828E	Springs Bird Sanctuary, Springs, Gauteng	2	7	5	0	1	5
2621S 2830E	Marievale Bird Sanctuary, Nigel, Gauteng	2	4	5	0	1	5
3359S 2240E	Wilderness Lakes – Touw River System, Sedgefield, Western Cape	1	2	6	1	2	6
2554S 2842E	Bronkhorstspruit Dam, Bronkhorstspruit, Gauteng	1	3	4	1	1	4
3401S 2541E	Cape Recife Reclamation Works, Port Elizabeth, Eastern Cape	1	4	4	0	0	4
2941S 3105E	Umhlanga Treatment Works, Umhlanga, KwaZulu–Natal	1	2	3	0	1	5
2616S 2830E	Grootvaly, Springs, Gauteng	0	1	3	1	2	4
2750S 3035E	Blood River Vlei, Vryheid, KwaZulu–Natal	1	1	1	0	0	1

079 Dwarf Bittern *Ixobrychus sturmii*

A summer breeding migrant to southern Africa, mainly present from November to April;
occurs erratically in northeastern South Africa, west to c. 24°E and south to c. 30°S (ASAB1).
Normally uncommon to rare, but sometimes locally common in breeding areas, e.g. at Nyl
River floodplain. Favours seasonal freshwater pans, pools and floodplains with dense
fringing cover of trees, bushes, reeds, etc. Solitary or in pairs; forages mainly at night,
therefore easily overlooked. Recorded at only three CWAC sites, including two in Free
State (Koppies and Welbedacht Dams).

		Summer			Winter		
		Mean	Max.	N	Mean	Max.	N
2952S 2653E	Welbedacht Dam, Wepener, Free State	1	5	6	0	0	6
2658S 3250E	Kosi Bay Nature Reserve, Manguzi, KwaZulu–Natal	0	1	5	0	0	6
2715S 2741E	Koppies Dam, Koppies, Free State	0	1	6	0	0	6

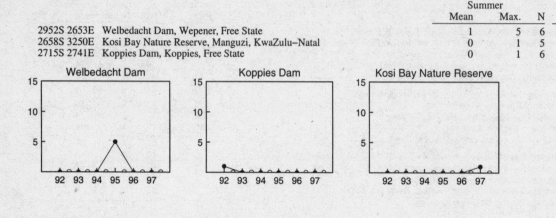

080 Bittern *Botaurus stellaris*

A poorly known bird of tall, dense reedbeds and sedgebeds (including papyrus) at
large wetlands; also in ricefields and flooded grass. Solitary, secretive and crepuscular;
overlooked but undoubtedly rare. In South Africa has undergone a catastrophic range
reduction and decline in numbers this century, apparently because of wetland degradation.
Now recorded regularly only at Nyl River floodplain (ASAB1), where it is a rains visitor,
but also regular at wetlands on the Mzintlava River, East Griqualand (B. Taylor), and
recorded occasionally in northern and central KwaZulu-Natal, whence come the
only two CWAC records, from Pongolapoort Dam and Hlatikulu Vlei.

081 Hamerkop *Scopus umbretta*

Widespread, and fairly common in the eastern part of the country, from which region come the largest counts. It occurs at many aquatic habitats, and is recorded from a wide variety of wetland types, including small to large waterbodies, rivers, vleis, floodplains, pans (more rarely) and sewage works. Some of the highest counts come from man-made habitats, which have enabled it to expand its overall range, particularly in arid areas. Nomadic movements, and some wet-season dispersal to ephemeral waterbodies, are suggested; CWAC data do not show any easily recognisable seasonal differences in occurrence.

		Summer			Winter		
		Mean	Max.	N	Mean	Max.	N
2507S 3028E	Lydenburg Fisheries, Lydenburg, Mpumalanga	6	6	1	8	8	1
2923S 3121E	Umvoti River Estuary, Stanger, KwaZulu–Natal	9	18	3	4	7	5
2834S 2948E	Malandeni Sewage Works, Ladysmith, KwaZulu–Natal	7	9	5	5	15	5
2948S 3100E	Northern Treatment Works, Durban, KwaZulu–Natal	4	7	5	6	15	5
2735S 2935E	Seekoeivlei, Memel, Free State	4	5	5	2	4	5
2838S 1627E	Orange River Estuary, Alexander Bay, Northern Cape	1	1	1	4	4	1
2721S 3240E	Lake Sibaya, Ubombo, KwaZulu–Natal	4	7	4	1	2	6
2534S 2814E	Rooiwal Sewage Works, Pretoria, Gauteng	3	6	4	1	3	5
2510S 2751E	Klipvoor Dam, Brits, North West	1	2	4	3	7	3
2520S 2728E	Vaalkop Dam, Brits, North West	1	2	4	2	5	5
2804S 3227E	Lake St Lucia, Hlabisa, KwaZulu–Natal	2	5	6	1	3	6
2557S 2800E	Diepsloot Nature Reserve, Johannesburg, Gauteng	1	2	4	2	4	5
2645S 2706E	Prozesky Bird Sanctuary, Potchefstroom, North West	1	2	3	2	5	3
2911S 3125E	Sundumbili Sewage Works, Mandini, KwaZulu–Natal	2	2	2	1	2	3
2841S 2929E	Spioenkop Dam, Winterton, KwaZulu–Natal	1	3	4	2	4	5

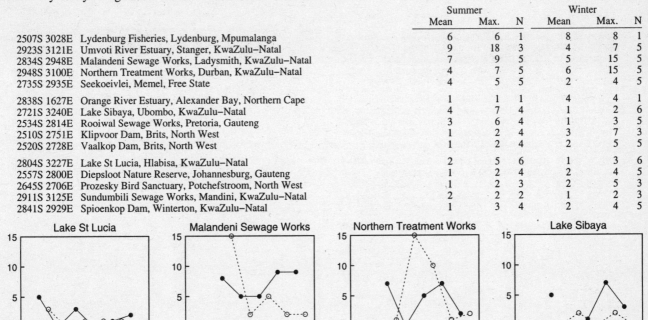

084 Black Stork *Ciconia nigra*

Widespread, but rare and infrequently recorded; feeds in wetlands; breeds on cliffs in winter. It is regarded as largely resident, though nonbreeders wander widely, and there may be a January–April influx into the Western Cape (ASAB1); CWAC data show a preponderance of records in summer but are too few to allow conclusions to be drawn. As well as records from the eight sites shown, there are single summer records from Northern Cape (1 site), Eastern Cape (2) and Western Cape (1) and single winter records from Eastern Cape and Western Cape. A summer 1995 count of 11 birds at Lake Mfutululu, KwaZulu-Natal, is noteworthy.

		Summer			Winter		
		Mean	Max.	N	Mean	Max.	N
2825S 3215E	Lake Mfutululu, Mtubatuba, KwaZulu–Natal	4	11	3	0	0	2
3010S 2455E	Vanderkloof Dam, Vanderkloof, Northern Cape	0	0	1	2	2	1
3338S 2634E	Ghio Pans, Kenton–on–Sea, Eastern Cape	2	6	4	0	1	4
3416S 2149E	Voëlvlei, Mossel Bay, Western Cape	1	4	5	0	1	4
2611S 2819E	Homestead, Benoni & Middle Lakes, Benoni, Gauteng	1	1	2	0	0	2
2826S 3210E	Collin's Lake, Mtubatuba, KwaZulu–Natal	0	0	3	1	1	2
3329S 2707E	Great Fish River Estuary, Port Alfred, Eastern Cape	1	2	4	0	0	4
3350S 2533E	Bar None Saltpans, Port Elizabeth, Eastern Cape	1	1	2	0	0	3
3150S 2208E	Sakrivierspoort Wetlands, Loxton, Northern Cape	0	1	3	0	0	2
3350S 2535E	Redhouse Saltpan, Port Elizabeth, Eastern Cape	0	1	4	0	0	4
3426S 2023E	De Hoop Vlei, Bredasdorp, Western Cape	0	0	5	0	1	4
3402S 1913E	Theewaterskloof Dam, Villiersdorp, Western Cape	0	1	5	0	0	5
3403S 2302E	Knysna Lagoon, Knysna, Western Cape	0	0	5	0	1	5
3352S 2538E	Swartkops River Estuary, Port Elizabeth, Eastern Cape	0	1	6	0	0	6

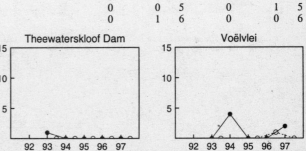

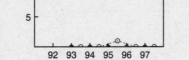

086 Woollynecked Stork *Ciconia episcopus*

In the region, restricted to the extreme northeast (eastern lowveld), Swaziland and KwaZulu-Natal. Recorded from 24 CWAC sites in coastal KwaZulu-Natal, south to Durban. Frequents short grass near water; occurs at floodplains, rivers, pans, mangrove swamps, swamp forest, estuaries, dams and tidal mudflats; sometimes at sewage works, golf courses and flooded roads. RSA birds are regarded as resident, with some southward movement along KwaZulu-Natal coast during rains; CWAC data show only that numbers at Richards Bay are normally higher in winter, and that isolated occurrences are more numerous in summer.

		Summer			Winter		
		Mean	Max.	N	Mean	Max.	N
2849S 3202E	Richards Bay, Richards Bay (town), KwaZulu–Natal	15	42	5	35	69	5
2857S 3146E	Mtunzini Prawn Hatchery, Mtunzini, KwaZulu–Natal	16	26	2	19	32	3
2804S 3227E	Lake St Lucia, Hlabisa, KwaZulu–Natal	12	33	6	6	17	6
2923S 3121E	Umvoti River Estuary, Stanger, KwaZulu–Natal	14	20	3	4	10	5
2725S 3158E	Pongolapoort Dam, Mkuze, KwaZulu–Natal	0	1	6	4	25	6
2825S 3215E	Lake Mfutululu, Mtubatuba, KwaZulu–Natal	2	6	3	2	4	2
2653S 3218E	Nyamithi Pan (Ndumo), Ingwavuma, KwaZulu–Natal	2	5	4	1	3	5
2847S 3203E	Thulazihleka Pan, Richards Bay, KwaZulu–Natal	2	5	5	0	0	5
2949S 3102E	Umgeni River Estuary, Durban, KwaZulu–Natal	2	5	5	1	3	5
2953S 3101E	Durban Bayhead, Durban, KwaZulu–Natal	1	5	5	1	5	5
2652S 3217E	Banzi Pan (Ndumo), Ingwavuma, KwaZulu–Natal	2	9	4	0	0	5
2815S 3228E	Mfazana Pans, St Lucia, KwaZulu–Natal	1	1	1	1	1	1
2824S 3225E	Mfolozi Mouth Area, St Lucia, KwaZulu–Natal	–	–	–	2	2	1
2739S 3226E	Yengweni Lake, Mbazwane, KwaZulu–Natal	1	3	5	1	5	6
2721S 3240E	Lake Sibaya, Ubombo, KwaZulu–Natal	2	4	4	0	0	6

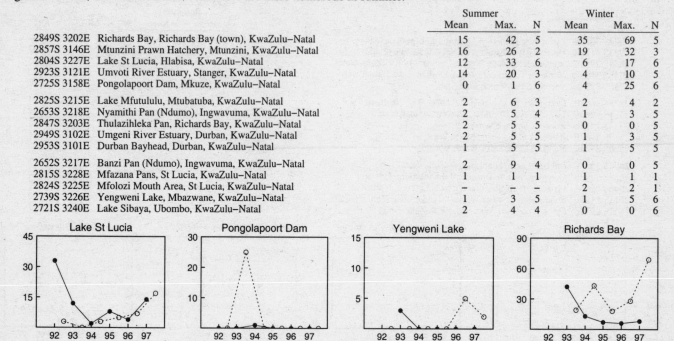

087 Openbilled Stork *Anastomus lamelligerus*

In RSA confined to extreme northeastern KwaZulu-Natal (whence come all CWAC records, from six sites), northeastern lowveld of Mpumalanga and Northern Province, and eastern Swaziland. Inhabits large, open, wet areas: swamps, floodplains, lake and river shallows, rice fields, and pans. Locally common; has regular trans-equatorial movements, breeding south of equator during and after rains; RSA birds apparently present all year, with local movements. CWAC records erratic, presumably dependent on habitat availability, e.g. large count at Bhanzi Pan in 1995 due to low water level and good feeding habitat.

		Summer			Winter		
		Mean	Max.	N	Mean	Max.	N
2652S 3217E	Banzi Pan (Ndumo), Ingwavuma, KwaZulu–Natal	68	270	4	1	6	5
2740S 3219E	Nsumu Pan, Mkuzi Game Reserve, KwaZulu–Natal	13	41	6	2	7	6
2849S 3202E	Richards Bay, Richards Bay (town), KwaZulu–Natal	0	0	5	2	12	5
2736S 3212E	Hlonhlela Pan, Mkuze, KwaZulu–Natal	1	2	5	0	0	5
2653S 3218E	Nyamithi Pan (Ndumo), Ingwavuma, KwaZulu–Natal	0	1	4	0	0	5
2725S 3158E	Pongolapoort Dam, Mkuze, KwaZulu–Natal	0	0	6	0	1	6

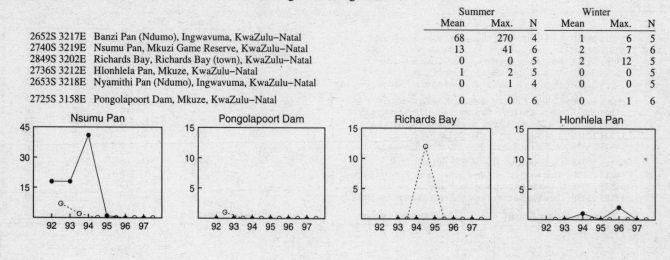

088 Saddlebilled Stork *Ephippiorhynchus senegalensis*

In RSA confined to northeastern lowveld of Mpumalanga and Northern Province, eastern Swaziland and northeastern KwaZulu-Natal; total population c. 50–100 pairs. Occurs at rivers, freshwater and alkaline lakes, marshes, floodplains and pans. All CWAC records are from northern coastal KwaZulu-Natal, where it was regular in very small numbers at three sites and recorded occasionally at four more. Although it is largely resident, there may be some dispersal to ephemeral pans; CWAC data are too few to indicate any seasonal fluctuations. It is threatened by the loss of its extensive wetland habitats.

		Summer			Winter		
		Mean	Max.	N	Mean	Max.	N
2804S 3227E	Lake St Lucia, Hlabisa, KwaZulu-Natal	1	3	6	3	4	6
2653S 3218E	Nyamithi Pan (Ndumo), Ingwavuma, KwaZulu-Natal	1	2	4	1	4	5
2658S 3250E	Kosi Bay Nature Reserve, Manguzi, KwaZulu-Natal	1	2	5	1	2	6
2805S 3218E	Bushlands Pan, Hluhluwe, KwaZulu-Natal	1	1	2	0	0	1
2652S 3217E	Banzi Pan (Ndumo), Ingwavuma, KwaZulu-Natal	0	0	4	0	1	5
2742S 3237E	kuNdlebeni Pan, Mbazwane, KwaZulu-Natal	0	1	5	0	0	6
2739S 3226E	Yengweni Lake, Mbazwane, KwaZulu-Natal	0	0	5	0	1	6

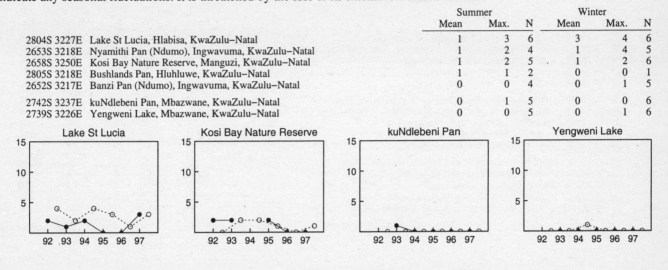

090 Yellowbilled Stork *Mycteria ibis*

CWAC data confirm that this stork occurs regularly, often in small numbers, at perennial and large ephemeral wetlands (including large dams) in eastern RSA. Recorded from 42 CWAC sites, 18 of these in northern KwaZulu-Natal, six in North West Province and seven in the Free State; all good counts and regular occurrences came from sites in these three provinces. Regarded as largely a nonbreeding summer visitor, also nomadic, breeding occasionally (June–September); most CWAC sites showed a summer peak, with occasional high winter counts in KwaZulu-Natal. Isolated occurrences were predominantly in summer.

		Summer			Winter		
		Mean	Max.	N	Mean	Max.	N
2804S 3227E	Lake St Lucia, Hlabisa, KwaZulu-Natal	78	139	6	8	21	6
2741S 2540E	Bloemhof Dam, Bloemhof, Free State	38	94	6	0	1	6
2510S 2751E	Klipvoor Dam, Brits, North West	37	106	4	0	1	3
2804S 2433E	Spitskop Dam, Spitskop, Northern Cape	34	34	2	0	0	2
2852S 2600E	Krugersdrift Dam, Bloemfontein, Free State	22	46	6	0	0	6
2740S 3219E	Nsumu Pan, Mkuzi Game Reserve, KwaZulu-Natal	12	28	6	7	29	6
2825S 3215E	Lake Mfutululu, Mtubatuba, KwaZulu-Natal	15	46	3	0	0	2
2725S 3158E	Pongolapoort Dam, Mkuze, KwaZulu-Natal	6	15	6	8	18	6
2805S 3220E	Hluhluwe River Vlei & Floodplain, Hluhluwe, KwaZulu-Natal	5	9	2	9	9	1
2932S 2515E	Kalkfontein Dam, Koffiefontein, Free State	12	41	6	0	0	6
2829S 3209E	Lake Eteza, Mtubatuba, KwaZulu-Natal	0	0	3	12	47	4
2635S 2535E	Barberspan, Delareyville, North West	10	24	4	0	0	2
2652S 3217E	Banzi Pan (Ndumo), Ingwavuma, KwaZulu-Natal	9	31	4	0	2	5
2818S 2712E	Allemanskraal Dam, Ventersburg, Free State	8	33	6	0	0	6
2830S 3212E	Mavuya Pan, Mtubatuba, KwaZulu-Natal	0	0	3	8	31	4

091 Sacred Ibis *Threskiornis aethiopicus*

Widespread, and common to abundant, except in arid west, extreme northeast and Lesotho. Associated with grassland habitats; usually occurs near inland waterbodies, especially marshes, and also at estuaries and saltmarshes. Often uses artificial habitats such as dams, sewage works, rubbish dumps and cultivated fields. Breeds in spring (winter-rainfall region) and summer. Partly nomadic or migratory; many probably move north to perennial wetlands in winter (ASAB1). CWAC data show equal number of winter and summer peaks overall, but more summer peaks in the Western Cape and Free State, and more winter peaks in KwaZulu-Natal.

		Summer			Winter		
		Mean	Max.	N	Mean	Max.	N
3309S 1804E	Langebaan Lagoon, Langebaan, Western Cape	302	446	6	344	586	6
2351S 2927E	Pietersburg Bird Sanctuary, Pietersburg, Northern Province	420	420	1	7	7	1
3404S 1830E	Rondevlei, Cape Flats, Western Cape	293	483	4	21	60	4
2612S 2817E	Steward's Pan, Benoni, Gauteng	63	120	2	201	201	1
2610S 2813E	Rolfe's Pan, Kempton Park, Gauteng	81	222	3	169	511	5
2917S 3117E	Mbozambo Waste Water Lagoon, Stanger, KwaZulu-Natal	96	190	3	147	261	5
3405S 1831E	Strandfontein Sewage Works, Muizenberg, Western Cape	171	309	6	59	132	6
3341S 1858E	Paarl Bird Sanctuary, Paarl, Western Cape	163	335	5	47	86	5
3247S 1812E	Berg River System, Velddrif, Western Cape	133	373	5	77	121	4
3416S 2149E	Voëlvlei, Mossel Bay, Western Cape	171	400	5	15	38	4
2948S 3100E	Northern Treatment Works, Durban, KwaZulu-Natal	26	50	5	120	286	5
2557S 2800E	Diepsloot Nature Reserve, Johannesburg, Gauteng	136	322	4	10	16	5
2735S 2935E	Seekoeivlei, Memel, Free State	57	152	5	85	356	5
3403S 2302E	Knysna Lagoon, Knysna, Western Cape	20	36	5	110	160	5
2611S 2818E	Korsman Bird Sanctuary, Benoni, Gauteng	93	115	3	36	87	3

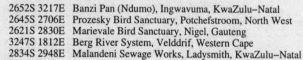

093 Glossy Ibis *Plegadis falcinellus*

Distribution centred in the central highveld, northern KwaZulu-Natal and Western Cape. Favours shallow freshwater wetlands in grassy areas: marshes, seasonal pans, lake edges, flooded grassland, irrigation, and sewage works; also dams. Regular sites may show occasional large summer peaks (e.g. at Banzi and Nyamithi Pans, and Lake Mfutululu, in KwaZulu-Natal), reflecting low water and good feeding habitat. Breeds in summer, mainly in highveld and Western Cape. Seasonal movement to tropics suspected; marked decrease in winter numbers at most CWAC sites. Increasing due to use of artificial habitat.

		Summer			Winter		
		Mean	Max.	N	Mean	Max.	N
2616S 2830E	Grootvaly, Springs, Gauteng	185	332	3	125	481	4
2839S 2437E	Platfontein Pans, Kimberley, Northern Cape	243	243	1	28	28	1
2735S 2935E	Seekoeivlei, Memel, Free State	183	560	5	9	24	5
3405S 1831E	Strandfontein Sewage Works, Muizenberg, Western Cape	112	310	6	28	108	6
2629S 2828E	Blesbokspruit, Nigel, Gauteng	134	134	1	0	0	1
2715S 3007E	Clarens' Pan, Wakkerstroom, Mpumalanga	104	104	1	–	–	–
2653S 3218E	Nyamithi Pan (Ndumo), Ingwavuma, KwaZulu-Natal	96	352	4	8	33	5
2622S 2810E	Vlakplaas Water Treatment Works, Germiston, Gauteng	97	131	4	0	0	4
2804S 3227E	Lake St Lucia, Hlabisa, KwaZulu-Natal	73	391	6	19	78	6
2620S 2817E	Rietspruit (Rooikraal), Boksburg, Gauteng	87	155	3	3	11	4
2652S 3217E	Banzi Pan (Ndumo), Ingwavuma, KwaZulu-Natal	83	332	4	0	2	5
2645S 2706E	Prozesky Bird Sanctuary, Potchefstroom, North West	77	203	3	0	1	3
2621S 2830E	Marievale Bird Sanctuary, Nigel, Gauteng	40	173	5	23	109	5
3247S 1812E	Berg River System, Velddrif, Western Cape	9	40	5	54	142	4
2834S 2948E	Malandeni Sewage Works, Ladysmith, KwaZulu-Natal	30	89	5	30	72	5

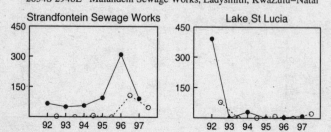
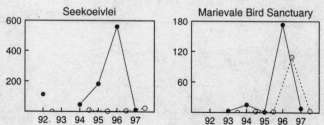

094 Hadeda Ibis *Bostrychia hagedash*

Widespread except in arid west. Inhabits moist grassland and savanna, especially at wooded river courses; also marshes, flooded grassland, lake edges, irrigation, garden lawns, and pans, sewage works and (less commonly) lagoons and estuaries. Usually in pairs; forms nonbreeding flocks and roosts communally. Nests solitarily in trees, usually near water, in midsummer. Mainly sedentary, but probably some regional movement in response to localized rainfall (ASAB1); winter CWAC peaks at many permanent wetlands reflect widespread occurrence of nonbreeding flocks at such sites. Range has expanded dramatically in the 20th century.

		Summer			Winter		
		Mean	Max.	N	Mean	Max.	N
2557S 2800E	Diepsloot Nature Reserve, Johannesburg, Gauteng	104	237	4	302	432	5
2750S 3035E	Blood River Vlei, Vryheid, KwaZulu–Natal	14	14	1	89	89	1
3402S 1913E	Theewaterskloof Dam, Villiersdorp, Western Cape	14	25	5	62	90	5
2735S 2935E	Seekoeivlei, Memel, Free State	41	83	5	22	32	5
2915S 2941E	Hlatikulu Vlei, Hlatikulu, KwaZulu–Natal	26	26	2	23	23	1
2629S 2828E	Blesbokspruit, Nigel, Gauteng	0	0	1	46	46	1
2931S 3011E	Midmar Dam, Howick, KwaZulu–Natal	12	25	5	25	46	3
2815S 3228E	Mfazana Pans, St Lucia, KwaZulu–Natal	0	0	1	37	37	1
2757S 2957E	Chelmsford Dam, Newcastle, KwaZulu–Natal	1	2	2	35	98	3
2609S 2821E	Rynfield Dam, Benoni, Gauteng	10	30	4	24	67	5
2926S 3024E	Albert Falls Dam, Pietermaritzburg, KwaZulu–Natal	20	55	4	12	21	4
2725S 3158E	Pongolapoort Dam, Mkuze, KwaZulu–Natal	9	26	6	22	41	6
2917S 3117E	Mbozambo Waste Water Lagoon, Stanger, KwaZulu–Natal	5	9	3	25	74	5
2948S 3100E	Northern Treatment Works, Durban, KwaZulu–Natal	21	40	5	7	11	5
2834S 2948E	Malandeni Sewage Works, Ladysmith, KwaZulu–Natal	13	18	5	14	24	5

Pongolapoort Dam Theewaterskloof Dam Seekoeivlei Northern Treatment Works

095 African Spoonbill *Platalea alba*

Widespread except in arid and very high areas; globally significant counts in Western Cape, North West, Free State and KwaZulu-Natal. Mainly at shallow freshwater sites: marshes, pans, dams, floodplains, rivers, flooded grass and sewage ponds; also estuaries, lagoons and saltpans. Breeds spring–summer in winter-rainfall region, winter elsewhere. CWAC data show it is more widespread and numerous in breeding season in coastal KwaZulu-Natal (winter) and Western Cape (summer); locally commoner in summer in northeastern interior (habitat more extensive?). No migration known; nomadic in response to habitat changes and rain.

		Summer			Winter		
		Mean	Max.	N	Mean	Max.	N
3416S 2149E	Voëlvlei, Mossel Bay, Western Cape	139*	200**	5	127*	258**	4
2804S 2433E	Spitskop Dam, Spitskop, Northern Cape	186**	257**	2	43	44	2
2804S 3227E	Lake St Lucia, Hlabisa, KwaZulu–Natal	92*	163**	6	93*	158**	6
3247S 1812E	Berg River System, Velddrif, Western Cape	76*	211**	5	82*	115*	4
3402S 1913E	Theewaterskloof Dam, Villiersdorp, Western Cape	63	114*	5	33	78*	5
2847S 3203E	Thulazihleka Pan, Richards Bay, KwaZulu–Natal	31	136*	5	42	81*	5
2741S 2540E	Bloemhof Dam, Bloemhof, Free State	63	193**	6	9	20	6
2838S 1627E	Orange River Estuary, Alexander Bay, Northern Cape	5	5	1	66	66	1
2611S 2818E	Korsman Bird Sanctuary, Benoni, Gauteng	31	50	3	39	63	3
2635S 2535E	Barberspan, Delareyville, North West	60	87*	4	8	15	2
2932S 2515E	Kalkfontein Dam, Koffiefontein, Free State	62	191**	6	4	14	6
3309S 1804E	Langebaan Lagoon, Langebaan, Western Cape	35	52	6	24	42	6
2740S 3219E	Nsumu Pan, Mkuzi Game Reserve, KwaZulu–Natal	16	38	6	41	84*	6
2952S 2653E	Welbedacht Dam, Wepener, Free State	48	147*	6	8	28	6
2829S 3209E	Lake Eteza, Mtubatuba, KwaZulu–Natal	0	0	3	52	206**	4

Lake St Lucia Bloemhof Dam Kalkfontein Dam Langebaan Lagoon

096 Greater Flamingo *Phoenicopterus ruber*

Widespread along coast; interior distribution follows that of shallow saline/alkaline waters. Also at estuaries and lagoons; dams and saltpans can hold good numbers (CWAC). Significant counts in Northern Cape (Kimberley area), western North West Province, Western Cape coastal sites, and St Lucia. Most breed at Etosha Pan, Namibia, and Sua Pan, Botswana, in summer. Many inland sites dry in winter, forcing movement to coastal wetlands where birds may spend summer in poor rainfall years. CWAC data show winter peaks at 33 coastal and inland sites and summer peaks at 14, and good counts in summer at many permanent wetlands.

		Summer			Winter		
		Mean	Max.	N	Mean	Max.	N
2804S 3227E	Lake St Lucia, Hlabisa, KwaZulu–Natal	1314**	3095**	6	3535**	13173**	6
3309S 1804E	Langebaan Lagoon, Langebaan, Western Cape	619	2520**	6	2817**	6062**	6
2632S 2536E	Leeupan, Delareyville, North West	266	799*	3	1825**	1825**	1
3405S 1831E	Strandfontein Sewage Works, Muizenberg, Western Cape	1594**	2551**	6	417	1548**	6
3247S 1812E	Berg River System, Velddrif, Western Cape	822*	1776**	5	1093*	1656**	4
2840S 2446E	Kamfers Dam, Kimberley, Northern Cape	1032*	1467**	3	463	823*	3
2839S 2437E	Platfontein Pans, Kimberley, Northern Cape	788*	788*	1	691*	691*	1
2741S 2540E	Bloemhof Dam, Bloemhof, Free State	119	489	6	507	1632**	6
3350S 2535E	Redhouse Saltpan, Port Elizabeth, Eastern Cape	234	487	4	268	535	4
2629S 2828E	Blesbokspruit, Nigel, Gauteng	78	78	1	341	341	1
3421S 1906E	Botriviervlei, Kleinmond, Western Cape	301	538	4	110	300	5
3351S 2535E	Chatty Saltpans, Port Elizabeth, Eastern Cape	40	80	2	353	895*	3
2624S 2828E	Stan Madden Bird Sanctuary, Nigel, Gauteng	207	388	5	179	480	5
3236S 1818E	Rocher Pan, Velddrif, Western Cape	254	749*	5	116	272	6
2804S 2433E	Spitskop Dam, Spitskop, Northern Cape	113	210	2	244	357	2

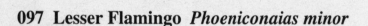

097 Lesser Flamingo *Phoeniconaias minor*

Overall distribution and breeding areas as for Greater Flamingo, but less widespread at inland RSA sites than its larger congener (ASAB1). It occurs at shallow, alkaline or saline lakes and pans, and also at estuaries, lagoons, saltpans and sewage works; some eutrophic dams may also hold good numbers (CWAC). Particularly good CWAC totals from Kamfersdam (Northern Cape), several sites in Western Cape, Lake St Lucia and Blesbokspruit. Movements as for Greater Flamingo. CWAC data show winter peaks at 39 sites (22 inland, 17 coastal) and summer peaks at only 4 minor sites (all inland).

		Summer			Winter		
		Mean	Max.	N	Mean	Max.	N
2840S 2446E	Kamfers Dam, Kimberley, Northern Cape	1875	2820	3	2034	3668	3
2804S 3227E	Lake St Lucia, Hlabisa, KwaZulu–Natal	346	1000	6	2275	5758	6
3247S 1812E	Berg River System, Velddrif, Western Cape	117	446	5	1129	1634	4
2804S 2433E	Spitskop Dam, Spitskop, Northern Cape	55	110	2	819	919	2
3309S 1804E	Langebaan Lagoon, Langebaan, Western Cape	0	1	6	595	1606	6
2632S 2536E	Leeupan, Delareyville, North West	55	164	3	532	532	1
2624S 2828E	Stan Madden Bird Sanctuary, Nigel, Gauteng	69	283	5	338	1625	5
2619S 3013E	Lake Chrissie Pan, Lake Chrissie, Mpumalanga	350	700	2	0	0	2
3341S 1858E	Paarl Bird Sanctuary, Paarl, Western Cape	128	320	5	207	1000	5
2805S 3220E	Hluhluwe River Vlei & Floodplain, Hluhluwe, KwaZulu–Natal	0	0	2	300	300	1
2755S 2446E	Ganspan Pans & Vlei, Jan Kempdorp, Northern Cape	0	0	2	274	483	2
2838S 1627E	Orange River Estuary, Alexander Bay, Northern Cape	0	0	1	259	259	1
3142S 1812E	Olifants River Mouth (South), Lutzville, Western Cape	35	70	2	177	177	1
2741S 2540E	Bloemhof Dam, Bloemhof, Free State	17	79	6	158	707	6
2635S 2535E	Barberspan, Delareyville, North West	110	267	4	48	95	2

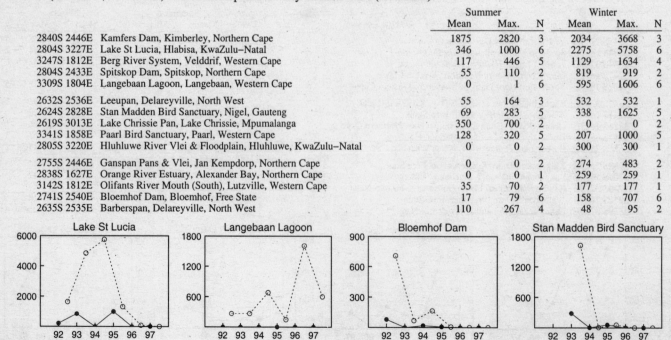

099 Whitefaced Duck *Dendrocygna viduata*

Locally common in the east; expanding range in Free State (no CWAC evidence); rare non-breeding visitor to Western Cape (2–12 birds at three CWAC sites). Nonbreeding flocks prefer large shallow waters, breeding birds small ephemeral pans with emergent vegetation; breeding peaks December–March. Seasonal movements to lowveld in winter; moult migrations to large waters in Free State (January–February and June–July); movements out of southern Africa in winter suggested (ASAB1). For 56 CWAC sites throughout main range, peak numbers are in winter at 41 (nonbreeders; many very large counts), in summer at 13 (one large count).

		Summer			Winter		
		Mean	Max.	N	Mean	Max.	N
2725S 3158E	Pongolapoort Dam, Mkuze, KwaZulu–Natal	577	1767	6	1134	2856	6
2534S 2814E	Rooiwal Sewage Works, Pretoria, Gauteng	32	57	4	354	1215	5
2506S 2855E	Mkhombo Dam, Libangeni, Mpumalanga	17	50	3	353	761	3
2740S 3226E	Tshanetshe Pan, Mbazwane, KwaZulu–Natal	26	51	5	295	882	6
2739S 3226E	Yengweni Lake, Mbazwane, KwaZulu–Natal	58	176	5	256	836	6
2741S 2540E	Bloemhof Dam, Bloemhof, Free State	4	23	6	291	714	6
2653S 3218E	Nyamithi Pan (Ndumo), Ingwavuma, KwaZulu–Natal	105	369	4	137	484	5
2652S 3217E	Banzi Pan (Ndumo), Ingwavuma, KwaZulu–Natal	56	222	4	182	577	5
2622S 2810E	Vlakplaas Water Treatment Works, Germiston, Gauteng	18	59	4	210	473	4
2740S 3219E	Nsumu Pan, Mkuzi Game Reserve, KwaZulu–Natal	63	184	6	165	488	6
2834S 2948E	Malandeni Sewage Works, Ladysmith, KwaZulu–Natal	31	46	5	181	462	5
2840S 2446E	Kamfers Dam, Kimberley, Northern Cape	51	83	3	151	241	3
2739S 3224E	Neshe Pan, Mbazwane, KwaZulu–Natal	21	52	5	180	416	6
2839S 2437E	Platfontein Pans, Kimberley, Northern Cape	22	22	1	177	177	1
2557S 2800E	Diepsloot Nature Reserve, Johannesburg, Gauteng	23	48	4	170	672	5

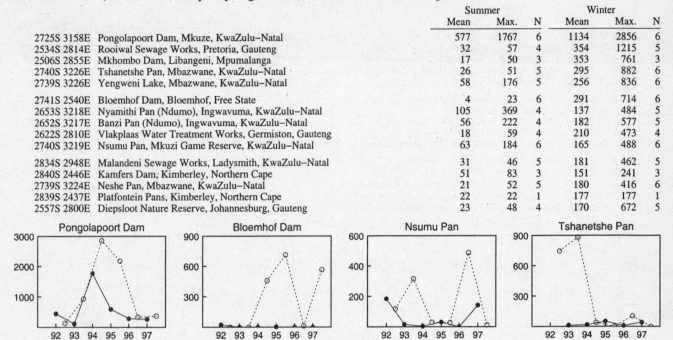

100 Fulvous Duck *Dendrocygna bicolor*

Uncommon and sparse in northern and eastern RSA, mainly northern Free State, Witwatersrand and northeastern KwaZulu-Natal (see table). Scarce in southern and Western Cape; 1–3 birds at Chatty Saltpans and Strandfontein Sewage Works (CWAC). Occurs mainly at large inland waters; prefers quiet sites with surface vegetation; CWAC records also at pans, lakes, dams, sewage works and saltpans. Breeds mainly December–March. Nomadic; also summer breeding migrant to southern Africa. CWAC data show summer peaks at 19 of 30 sites; of the 7 with winter peaks, Banzi Pan and Lake Eteza had large count only in 1994 when habitat was unusually good.

		Summer			Winter		
		Mean	Max.	N	Mean	Max.	N
2653S 3218E	Nyamithi Pan (Ndumo), Ingwavuma, KwaZulu–Natal	297	1184	4	4	20	5
2652S 3217E	Banzi Pan (Ndumo), Ingwavuma, KwaZulu–Natal	13	50	4	157	720	5
2829S 3209E	Lake Eteza, Mtubatuba, KwaZulu–Natal	0	0	3	137	536	4
2825S 3215E	Lake Mfutululu, Mtubatuba, KwaZulu–Natal	117	350	3	0	0	2
2629S 2828E	Blesbokspruit, Nigel, Gauteng	96	96	1	0	0	1
2741S 2540E	Bloemhof Dam, Bloemhof, Free State	11	49	6	69	294	6
2725S 3158E	Pongolapoort Dam, Mkuze, KwaZulu–Natal	61	278	6	1	3	6
2613S 2828E	Springs Bird Sanctuary, Springs, Gauteng	56	222	5	0	0	5
2645S 2706E	Prozesky Bird Sanctuary, Potchefstroom, North West	51	136	3	0	1	3
2715S 2741E	Koppies Dam, Koppies, Free State	47	208	6	0	0	6
2616S 2830E	Grootvaly, Springs, Gauteng	42	88	3	1	5	4
2622S 2810E	Vlakplaas Water Treatment Works, Germiston, Gauteng	19	41	4	22	63	4
2804S 3227E	Lake St Lucia, Hlabisa, KwaZulu–Natal	31	181	6	0	0	6
2739S 3226E	Yengweni Lake, Mbazwane, KwaZulu–Natal	4	21	5	18	109	6
2740S 3219E	Nsumu Pan, Mkuzi Game Reserve, KwaZulu–Natal	20	117	6	0	0	6

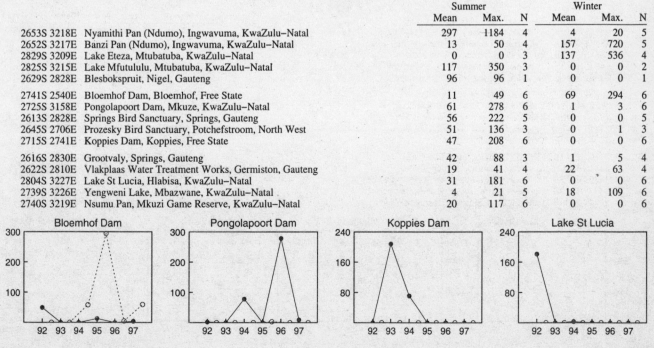

101 Whitebacked Duck *Thalassornis leuconotus*

In RSA largely confined to the east, extending along coastal region to Western Cape.
Noted at 37 CWAC sites; most numerous in KwaZulu-Natal and Western Cape. Inhabits quiet,
clear, permanent or seasonal inland waters with floating and emergent vegetation, including
pans, dams, lakes, marshes and swamps; adapts well to small farm dams and sewage works.
Breeds January–May in winter-rainfall region, March–September elsewhere. Nomadic, moving
from temporary to permanent waters in dry periods. CWAC data record maximum numbers
in winter at 19 sites and in summer at 13 sites; no overall movement pattern discernible.

		Summer			Winter		
		Mean	Max.	N	Mean	Max.	N
3359S 2240E	Wilderness Lakes – Touw River System, Sedgefield, Western Cape	4	10	6	112	254**	6
2740S 3226E	Tshanetshe Pan, Mbazwane, KwaZulu–Natal	0	0	5	92	550**	6
2847S 3203E	Thulazihleka Pan, Richards Bay, KwaZulu–Natal	28	118	5	63	216	5
3408S 1821E	Wildevoëlvlei, Kommetjie, Western Cape	37	95	6	21	35	6
2825S 3215E	Lake Mfutululu, Mtubatuba, KwaZulu–Natal	0	0	3	37	63	2
2702S 3030E	Heyshope Dam, Piet Retief, Mpumalanga	–	–	–	33	33	1
2614S 2819E	Leeupan, Benoni, Gauteng	27	132	5	1	8	6
2830S 3212E	Mavuya Pan, Mtubatuba, KwaZulu–Natal	1	3	3	22	86	4
2625S 3018E	Mooigelegen Pan, Lake Chrissie, Mpumalanga	0	0	1	19	19	1
2620S 3021E	Lake Banagher West, Lake Chrissie, Mpumalanga	3	5	2	16	31	2
2917S 3117E	Mbozambo Waste Water Lagoon, Stanger, KwaZulu–Natal	3	10	3	15	72	5
2950S 2935E	Watermead Dam, Underberg, KwaZulu–Natal	17	52	5	0	1	5
2849S 3202E	Richards Bay, Richards Bay (town), KwaZulu–Natal	7	22	5	3	7	5
2710S 3004E	Wim Rabe Pan, Wakkerstroom, Mpumalanga	10	10	1	–	–	–
3339S 1858E	Wellington Waste Water Works, Wellington, Western Cape	2	2	1	4	4	1

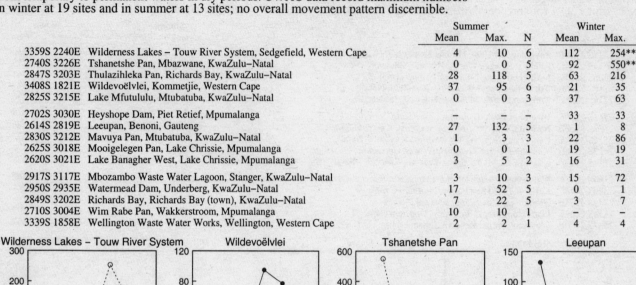

102 Egyptian Goose *Alopochen aegyptiacus*

Widespread and abundant, except in Lesotho and the waterless Kalahari; most abundant waterfowl in CWAC surveys; largest numbers from Western Cape, Free State and North West.
Occurs at almost any inland water; prefers sites with some exposed shoreline; also at estuaries.
Breeding peaks July–December. Nomadic in dry areas; winter influx to Eastern and Western
Cape suggested, but mostly summer peaks there (CWAC). After breeding, concentrations may
occur on large waters (ASAB1); evident at some CWAC sites in Free State and North West,
where birds may join SA Shelduck to moult. Has benefited from dam construction and grain crops.

		Summer			Winter		
		Mean	Max.	N	Mean	Max.	N
2818S 2712E	Allemanskraal Dam, Ventersburg, Free State	1970*	4481**	6	1900*	3851**	6
2852S 2600E	Krugersdrift Dam, Bloemfontein, Free State	713	1254	6	2109*	4196**	6
2834S 2650E	Erfenis Dam, Winburg, Free State	815	1378	6	1691	3152*	6
3402S 1913E	Theewaterskloof Dam, Villiersdorp, Western Cape	1973*	3070*	5	515	1072	5
3338S 1843E	Droëvlei, Klipheuwel, Western Cape	1992*	2600*	2	10	13	3
2635S 2535E	Barberspan, Delareyville, North West	194	325	4	1690	2117*	2
3322S 1903E	Voëlvlei Dam, Gouda, Western Cape	1865*	1873*	2	–	–	–
2932S 2515E	Kalkfontein Dam, Koffiefontein, Free State	875	1638	6	916	1816*	6
2741S 2540E	Bloemhof Dam, Bloemhof, Free State	300	767	6	1481	2543*	6
3220S 1825E	Verlorenvlei, Elandsbaai, Western Cape	1223	2041*	6	303	421	5
2715S 2741E	Koppies Dam, Koppies, Free State	794	1574	6	501	703	6
3351S 1829E	Rietvlei, Milnerton, Western Cape	853	1378	5	206	398	4
3426S 2023E	De Hoop Vlei, Bredasdorp, Western Cape	934	2117*	5	123	277	4
3405S 1849E	Paardevlei Dam, Somerset West, Western Cape	843	1534	5	187	294	5
2804S 2433E	Spitskop Dam, Spitskop, Northern Cape	693	854	2	335	447	2

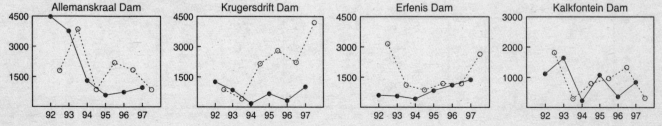

103 South African Shelduck *Tadorna cana*

Southern African endemic, common to locally abundant except in northeast and KwaZulu-Natal. Inhabits shallow, stagnant, temporary waters, often brackish; in Western Cape at farm dams, estuaries and lagoons; also uses sewage works and saltpans (CWAC). Breeds April–September; in summer makes moult migrations to large impoundments (most in Free State). CWAC data show large, often globally significant, January numbers at dams and at some estuaries and coastal lakes. Very few winter peaks – small numbers at widely scattered sites, including some in KwaZulu-Natal. Range has increased dramatically with dam construction.

		Summer			Winter		
		Mean	Max.	N	Mean	Max.	N
2932S 2515E	Kalkfontein Dam, Koffiefontein, Free State	1316**	2721**	6	121	208	6
2804S 2433E	Spitskop Dam, Spitskop, Northern Cape	745**	1184**	2	84	137	2
3318S 1845E	Radyn Dam, Malmesbury, Western Cape	817**	1750**	5	1	3	4
3322S 1903E	Voëlvlei Dam, Gouda, Western Cape	660**	1085**	2	–	–	–
2852S 2600E	Krugersdrift Dam, Bloemfontein, Free State	450**	1156**	6	50	128	6
2838S 1627E	Orange River Estuary, Alexander Bay, Northern Cape	51	51	1	341*	341*	1
3037S 2537E	Gariep Dam (West), Gariep Dam (town), Free State	368*	1287**	6	14	57	6
2839S 2437E	Platfontein Pans, Kimberley, Northern Cape	237*	237*	1	124	124	1
3247S 1812E	Berg River System, Velddrif, Western Cape	225*	476**	5	82	125	4
3220S 1825E	Verlorenvlei, Elandsbaai, Western Cape	288*	470**	6	13	43	5
3416S 2149E	Voëlvlei, Mossel Bay, Western Cape	140	400*	5	98	150	4
2918S 2637E	Rusfontein Dam, Thaba Nchu, Free State	145	234*	6	62	205	6
2741S 2540E	Bloemhof, Bloemhof, Free State	106	348*	6	77	400*	6
2818S 2712E	Allemanskraal Dam, Ventersburg, Free State	165	332*	6	13	35	6
3350S 2535E	Redhouse Saltpan, Port Elizabeth, Eastern Cape	100	300*	4	53	122	4

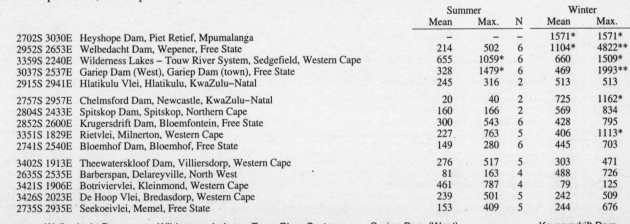

104 Yellowbilled Duck *Anas undulata*

Common and widespread except in very arid regions; most abundant on central plateau (excluding Lesotho). Inhabits most inland waters, also estuaries with marginal vegetation; tolerates brackish water; avoids saline pans and fast-running water. Occurs at all CWAC sites except a few sedge pans, salt pans, open pans (Zululand coastal plain), estuaries, shorelines, saltworks, and sterile dams. Towards end of the dry season it concentrates at permanent waters; disperses to breed in rains: CWAC data show summer peaks at many Western Cape waters, winter peaks elsewhere. Has benefited much from dam construction.

		Summer			Winter		
		Mean	Max.	N	Mean	Max.	N
2702S 3030E	Heyshope Dam, Piet Retief, Mpumalanga	–	–	–	1571*	1571*	1
2952S 2653E	Welbedacht Dam, Wepener, Free State	214	502	6	1104*	4822**	6
3359S 2240E	Wilderness Lakes – Touw River System, Sedgefield, Western Cape	655	1059*	6	660	1509*	6
3037S 2537E	Gariep Dam (West), Gariep Dam (town), Free State	328	1479*	6	469	1993**	6
2915S 2941E	Hlatikulu Vlei, Hlatikulu, KwaZulu–Natal	245	316	2	513	513	1
2757S 2957E	Chelmsford Dam, Newcastle, KwaZulu–Natal	20	40	2	725	1162*	3
2804S 2433E	Spitskop Dam, Spitskop, Northern Cape	160	166	2	569	834	2
2852S 2600E	Krugersdrift Dam, Bloemfontein, Free State	300	543	6	428	795	6
3351S 1829E	Rietvlei, Milnerton, Western Cape	227	763	5	406	1113*	4
2741S 2540E	Bloemhof Dam, Bloemhof, Free State	149	280	6	445	703	6
3402S 1913E	Theewaterskloof Dam, Villiersdorp, Western Cape	276	517	5	303	471	5
2635S 2535E	Barberspan, Delareyville, North West	81	163	4	488	726	2
3421S 1906E	Botriviervlei, Kleinmond, Western Cape	461	787	4	79	125	5
3426S 2023E	De Hoop Vlei, Bredasdorp, Western Cape	239	501	5	242	509	4
2735S 2935E	Seekoeivlei, Memel, Free State	153	409	5	244	676	5

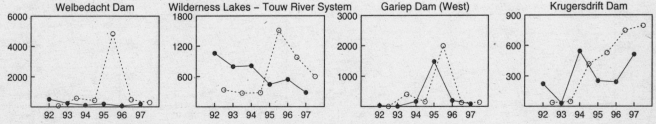

105 African Black Duck *Anas sparsa*

Widespread and locally fairly common but numbers usually small; distribution similar to
that of Yellowbilled Duck, but commoner at high altitudes (e.g. in Lesotho). Occurs mainly
on streams and rivers, sometimes at highland sponges, sandy estuaries, dams, shallow pools
and sewage works. Sedentary and territorial; some, mainly non-territorial, birds roost at night
on farm dams. Breeds June–January. CWAC records are from a wide range of open waters
(no counts at bird's riverine habitats); some of which may be purely roosting sites; some
seasonal variation in numbers but no obvious pattern of movements.

		Summer			Winter		
		Mean	Max.	N	Mean	Max.	N
3402S 1913E	Theewaterskloof Dam, Villiersdorp, Western Cape	14	31	5	18	23	5
3426S 2023E	De Hoop Vlei, Bredasdorp, Western Cape	0	0	5	20	81	4
2952S 2653E	Welbedacht Dam, Wepener, Free State	2	9	6	14	40	6
2735S 2935E	Seekoeivlei, Memel, Free State	3	8	5	9	34	5
2838S 1627E	Orange River Estuary, Alexander Bay, Northern Cape	0	0	1	8	8	1
2948S 3100E	Northern Treatment Works, Durban, KwaZulu–Natal	7	32	5	0	0	5
3341S 1858E	Paarl Bird Sanctuary, Paarl, Western Cape	3	6	5	4	7	5
2557S 2800E	Diepsloot Nature Reserve, Johannesburg, Gauteng	3	7	4	4	10	5
2834S 2650E	Erfenis Dam, Winburg, Free State	3	11	6	3	9	6
2834S 2948E	Malandeni Sewage Works, Ladysmith, KwaZulu–Natal	5	10	5	1	3	5
3356S 1828E	Raapenberg Bird Sanctuary, Cape Town, Western Cape	4	5	2	2	2	1
3150S 2208E	Sakrivierspoort Wetlands, Loxton, Northern Cape	3	5	3	2	2	2
2946S 2653E	Knellpoort Dam, Wepener, Free State	1	3	6	3	16	6
2553S 2918E	Witbank Dam, Witbank, Mpumalanga	3	10	4	1	4	5
2507S 3028E	Lydenburg Fisheries, Lydenburg, Mpumalanga	2	2	1	2	2	1

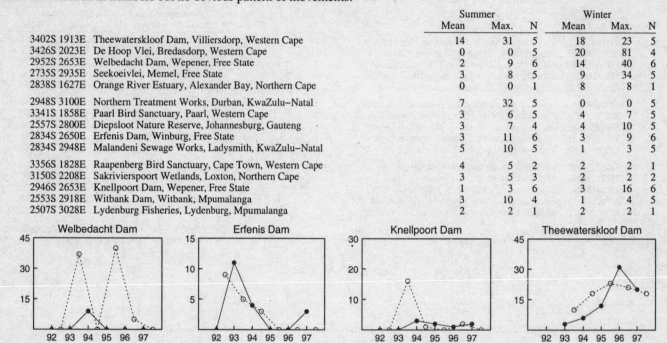

106 Cape Teal *Anas capensis*

Widespread, especially in drier regions; occurs inland at brackish or saline pans and dams,
and shallow vleis; also saltpans, estuaries, coastal lagoons and sewage works. Commonest in
the Western Cape, western Free State and adjacent Northern Cape; large CWAC totals also at
some Eastern Cape estuaries and saltpans. Breeds mainly winter–spring. Ringing recoveries
suggest long-distance movements, patterns unclear; gathers at some waters to moult. CWAC
data show both summer and winter peaks in Western and Eastern Cape, and some summer peaks in
Free State; small winter peaks in Gauteng/North West region.

		Summer			Winter		
		Mean	Max.	N	Mean	Max.	N
3247S 1812E	Berg River System, Velddrif, Western Cape	344	734	5	111	226	4
3405S 1831E	Strandfontein Sewage Works, Muizenberg, Western Cape	306	421	6	77	208	6
2838S 1627E	Orange River Estuary, Alexander Bay, Northern Cape	0	0	1	297	297	1
3351S 2535E	Chatty Saltpans, Port Elizabeth, Eastern Cape	220	296	2	66	102	3
3350S 2533E	Bar None Saltpans, Port Elizabeth, Eastern Cape	109	194	2	56	87	3
3350S 2535E	Redhouse Saltpan, Port Elizabeth, Eastern Cape	32	50	4	132	199	4
2839S 2437E	Platfontein Pans, Kimberley, Northern Cape	69	69	1	64	64	1
2932S 2515E	Kalkfontein Dam, Koffiefontein, Free State	53	169	6	55	89	6
2940S 1753E	Springbok Sewage Works, Springbok, Northern Cape	37	47	2	42	52	2
2840S 2446E	Kamfers Dam, Kimberley, Northern Cape	34	99	3	43	75	3
3426S 2023E	De Hoop Vlei, Bredasdorp, Western Cape	2	5	5	58	108	4
3339S 1858E	Wellington Waste Water Works, Wellington, Western Cape	11	11	1	46	46	1
2741S 2540E	Bloemhof Dam, Bloemhof, Free State	25	68	6	30	55	6
3222S 2237E	Beaufort West Bird Sanctuary, Beaufort West, Western Cape	39	75	5	15	27	5
3359S 2240E	Wilderness Lakes – Touw River System, Sedgefield, Western Cape	10	17	6	39	95	6

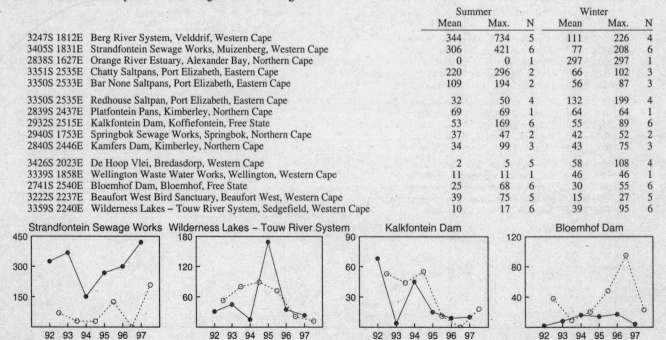

107 Hottentot Teal *Anas hottentota*

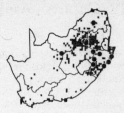

CWAC data confirm that this duck is generally uncommon and localized, occurring mainly in the northeast and KwaZulu-Natal; largest counts are from Gauteng and KwaZulu-Natal. Sparse to rare elsewhere, with 1–11 birds counted at 9 Western and 2 Eastern Cape sites. Prefers quiet freshwater marshes with emergent vegetation (especially *Typha*): lakes, dams, ponds, pans, marshes, floodplains, vleis and sewage ponds. Breeds all year, peak December–June. Sedentary, with some local movements. No seasonal pattern in CWAC data: summer and winter peaks at almost equal numbers of sites; also for inland and coastal regions.

		Summer			Winter		
		Mean	Max.	N	Mean	Max.	N
2629S 2828E	Blesbokspruit, Nigel, Gauteng	61	61	1	97	97	1
2613S 2828E	Springs Bird Sanctuary, Springs, Gauteng	53	83	5	59	86	5
2847S 3203E	Thulazihleka Pan, Richards Bay, KwaZulu–Natal	59	145	5	29	51	5
2834S 2948E	Malandeni Sewage Works, Ladysmith, KwaZulu–Natal	39	61	5	32	63	5
2621S 2830E	Marievale Bird Sanctuary, Nigel, Gauteng	15	37	5	35	62	5
2616S 2830E	Grootvaly, Springs, Gauteng	23	38	3	26	36	4
2735S 2935E	Seekoeivlei, Memel, Free State	19	53	5	28	81	5
2804S 3227E	Lake St Lucia, Hlabisa, KwaZulu–Natal	31	134	6	2	12	6
2750S 3035E	Blood River Vlei, Vryheid, KwaZulu–Natal	16	16	1	17	17	1
2755S 2446E	Ganspan Pans & Vlei, Jan Kempdorp, Northern Cape	6	12	2	21	35	2
2923S 3121E	Umvoti River Estuary, Stanger, KwaZulu–Natal	20	53	3	1	3	5
2351S 2927E	Pietersburg Bird Sanctuary, Pietersburg, Northern Province	16	16	1	4	4	1
2618S 2812E	Rondebult Bird Sanctuary, Germiston, Gauteng	13	25	4	5	14	4
2849S 3202E	Richards Bay, Richards Bay (town), KwaZulu–Natal	10	34	5	7	33	5
2915S 2941E	Hlatikulu Vlei, Hlatikulu, KwaZulu–Natal	5	7	2	10	10	1

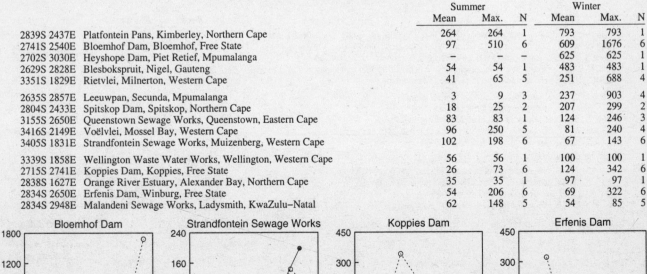

108 Redbilled Teal *Anas erythrorhyncha*

CWAC data confirm this duck is common and widespread except in very arid areas and at very high altitudes, and is most numerous in the highveld and the Western Cape. Prefers shallow, eutrophic fresh waters with much submerged, floating and peripheral vegetation. Breeding peaks in December–April, but in August–October in winter-rainfall region. Exploits temporary waters, and large flocks gather at permanent sites in dry season. While Western and Eastern Cape sites together have approximately equal number of summer peaks and winter peaks, 46 sites elsewhere show definite winter peaks, only 12 have a summer peak.

		Summer			Winter		
		Mean	Max.	N	Mean	Max.	N
2839S 2437E	Platfontein Pans, Kimberley, Northern Cape	264	264	1	793	793	1
2741S 2540E	Bloemhof Dam, Bloemhof, Free State	97	510	6	609	1676	6
2702S 3030E	Heyshope Dam, Piet Retief, Mpumalanga	–	–	–	625	625	1
2629S 2828E	Blesbokspruit, Nigel, Gauteng	54	54	1	483	483	1
3351S 1829E	Rietvlei, Milnerton, Western Cape	41	65	5	251	688	4
2635S 2857E	Leeuwpan, Secunda, Mpumalanga	3	9	3	237	903	4
2804S 2433E	Spitskop Dam, Spitskop, Northern Cape	18	25	2	207	299	2
3155S 2650E	Queenstown Sewage Works, Queenstown, Eastern Cape	83	83	1	124	246	3
3416S 2149E	Voëlvlei, Mossel Bay, Western Cape	96	250	5	81	240	4
3405S 1831E	Strandfontein Sewage Works, Muizenberg, Western Cape	102	198	6	67	143	6
3339S 1858E	Wellington Waste Water Works, Wellington, Western Cape	56	56	1	100	100	1
2715S 2741E	Koppies Dam, Koppies, Free State	26	73	6	124	342	6
2838S 1627E	Orange River Estuary, Alexander Bay, Northern Cape	35	35	1	97	97	1
2834S 2650E	Erfenis Dam, Winburg, Free State	54	206	6	69	322	6
2834S 2948E	Malandeni Sewage Works, Ladysmith, KwaZulu–Natal	62	148	5	54	85	5

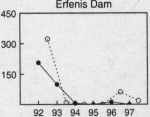

112 Cape Shoveller *Anas smithii*

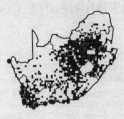

Widespread; most abundant in Western Cape (where globally significant counts at 6 CWAC sites) and highveld. Prefers shallow, plankton-rich waters: pans (often saline), dams, estuaries and lagoons. Breeds all year (highveld), or winter (Western Cape). Often resident, but moves between Western Cape and highveld, where large numbers occur after good rains. Large summer (postbreeding) peaks at most major Western Cape sites; some smaller sites on southern/southwestern Cape coast have winter peaks. Winter peaks predominate on highveld, and in KwaZulu-Natal coastal region (counts small); some Free State dams have summer peaks.

		Summer			Winter		
		Mean	Max.	N	Mean	Max.	N
3359S 2240E	Wilderness Lakes – Touw River System, Sedgefield, Western Cape	1006**	1508**	6	206*	464**	6
3426S 2023E	De Hoop Vlei, Bredasdorp, Western Cape	506**	901**	5	385**	853**	4
3400S 2245E	Wilderness Lakes – Swartvlei System, Sedgefield, Western Cape	448**	748**	2	316*	510**	3
3405S 1831E	Strandfontein Sewage Works, Muizenberg, Western Cape	602**	753**	6	107	232*	6
3351S 1829E	Rietvlei, Milnerton, Western Cape	226*	447**	5	310*	506**	4
3236S 1818E	Rocher Pan, Velddrif, Western Cape	383**	628**	5	116	207*	6
2804S 2433E	Spitskop Dam, Spitskop, Northern Cape	232*	292*	2	151	160	2
2702S 3030E	Heyshope Dam, Piet Retief, Mpumalanga	–	–	–	272*	272*	1
2838S 1627E	Orange River Estuary, Alexander Bay, Northern Cape	0	0	1	269*	269*	1
2839S 2437E	Platfontein Pans, Kimberley, Northern Cape	101	101	1	167	167	1
3205S 1819E	Jakkalsvlei, Lambert's Bay, Western Cape	183*	183*	1	34	34	1
3403S 2302E	Knysna Lagoon, Knysna, Western Cape	122	216*	5	76	123	5
2741S 2540E	Bloemhof Dam, Bloemhof, Free State	35	153	6	156	490**	6
3247S 1812E	Berg River System, Velddrif, Western Cape	31	84	5	158	303*	4
3416S 2149E	Voëlvlei, Mossel Bay, Western Cape	108	250*	5	75	114	4

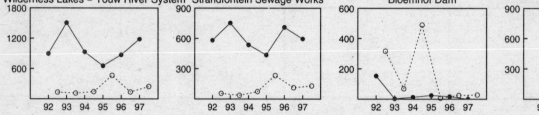

113 Southern Pochard *Netta erythrophthalma*

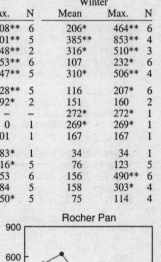

Most widespread and numerous on highveld and in Western Cape, whence come all large CWAC totals; small counts at scattered KwaZulu-Natal sites, mostly inland; hardly any from Eastern Cape. Inhabits permanent or seasonal fresh waters: pans, vleis, dams, sewage ponds and floodplains. Breeds July–December in winter-rainfall region, December–June elsewhere. Moves to Western Cape in winter to moult; summer peak evident in highveld (ASAB1). CWAC data show large concentrations in Western Cape in winter, and in highveld in summer; some Western Cape sites with small numbers have summer peak, many in highveld have winter peak.

		Summer			Winter		
		Mean	Max.	N	Mean	Max.	N
3359S 2240E	Wilderness Lakes – Touw River System, Sedgefield, Western Cape	111	323*	6	245	962**	6
2839S 2437E	Platfontein Pans, Kimberley, Northern Cape	280*	280*	1	31	31	1
3405S 1831E	Strandfontein Sewage Works, Muizenberg, Western Cape	90	245	6	217	427*	6
2622S 2810E	Vlakplaas Water Treatment Works, Germiston, Gauteng	185	476*	4	79	133	4
2702S 3030E	Heyshope Dam, Piet Retief, Mpumalanga	–	–	–	166	166	1
2635S 2857E	Leeuwpan, Secunda, Mpumalanga	61	136	3	60	133	4
2715S 2741E	Koppies Dam, Koppies, Free State	110	508**	6	1	3	6
2613S 2828E	Springs Bird Sanctuary, Springs, Gauteng	74	287*	5	14	29	5
2620S 3021E	Lake Banagher West, Lake Chrissie, Mpumalanga	35	70	2	30	60	2
3426S 2023E	De Hoop Vlei, Bredasdorp, Western Cape	34	145	5	28	87	4
2625S 3018E	Mooigelegen Pan, Lake Chrissie, Mpumalanga	61	61	1	0	0	1
3402S 1913E	Theewaterskloof Dam, Villiersdorp, Western Cape	5	16	5	46	114	5
2852S 2600E	Krugersdrift Dam, Bloemfontein, Free State	5	14	6	46	230	6
2635S 2535E	Barberspan, Delareyville, North West	37	122	4	8	14	2
2741S 2540E	Bloemhof Dam, Bloemhof, Free State	0	0	6	42	175	6

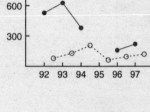

114 Pygmy Goose *Nettapus auritus*

Uncommon to rare in Northern Province, Mpumalanga and Swaziland; more widespread and numerous in lowland and coastal KwaZulu-Natal, where large flocks sometimes recorded. Prefers clear water with *Nymphaea* (eats seeds), *Potamogeton* and emergents; occupies permanent or seasonal pans and pools, and lake margins. Recorded at 24 CWAC sites, 23 in KwaZulu-Natal (Richards Bay to Ndumo), once at Mkhombo Dam, Mpumalanga. Breeds December–February; moves in response to *Nymphaea* growth; uses temporary waters. Many occur July–October; CWAC shows much larger numbers and wider distribution in winter, particularly in 1992 and 1995.

		Summer			Winter		
		Mean	Max.	N	Mean	Max.	N
2825S 3215E	Lake Mfutululu, Mtubatuba, KwaZulu-Natal	0	0	3	103	200	2
2652S 3217E	Banzi Pan (Ndumo), Ingwavuma, KwaZulu-Natal	0	0	4	73	320	5
2847S 3203E	Thulazihleka Pan, Richards Bay, KwaZulu-Natal	0	0	5	42	115	5
2658S 3250E	Kosi Bay Nature Reserve, Manguzi, KwaZulu-Natal	5	21	5	36	181	6
2721S 3240E	Lake Sibaya, Ubombo, KwaZulu-Natal	4	10	4	25	74	6
2739S 3226E	Yengweni Lake, Mbazwane, KwaZulu-Natal	1	2	5	23	58	6
2739S 3224E	Neshe Pan, Mbazwane, KwaZulu-Natal	1	2	5	17	46	6
2740S 3226E	Tshanetshe Pan, Mbazwane, KwaZulu-Natal	0	2	5	16	89	6
2653S 3218E	Nyamithi Pan (Ndumo), Ingwavuma, KwaZulu-Natal	0	0	4	7	33	5
2829S 3209E	Lake Eteza, Mtubatuba, KwaZulu-Natal	2	6	3	4	15	4
2736S 3212E	Hlonhlela Pan, Mkuze, KwaZulu-Natal	4	13	5	2	9	5
2849S 3202E	Richards Bay, Richards Bay (town), KwaZulu-Natal	0	2	5	5	13	5
2830S 3212E	Mavuya Pan, Mtubatuba, KwaZulu-Natal	0	1	3	5	11	4
2826S 3210E	Collin's Lake, Mtubatuba, KwaZulu-Natal	1	2	3	4	8	2
2738S 3224E	Muzi Lake (South), Mbazwane, KwaZulu-Natal	–	–	–	4	4	1

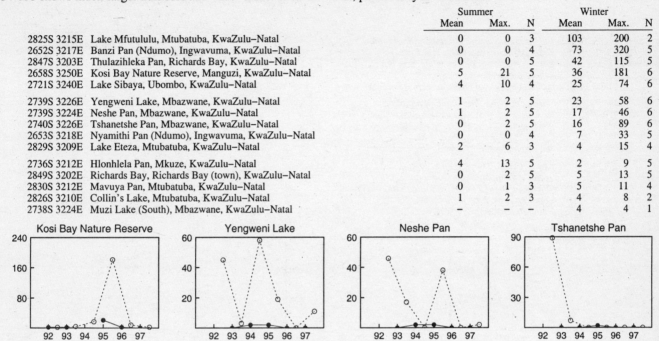

115 Knobbilled Duck *Sarkidiornis melanotos*

In RSA it occurs mainly in northeast, south to Free State and KwaZulu-Natal (ASAB1); widespread and locally common at lower altitudes, mainly December–July. Breeds January–April, at seasonally flooded pans and vleis; nonbreeders also at artificial sites, especially small, shallow grassy dams. Large-scale movements out of southern Africa in winter (ASAB1), but CWAC data show opposite trend: at sites where 3+ birds recorded, almost all occurrences are in July; no January records in KwaZulu-Natal (which has 12 of 31 CWAC sites and majority of birds). This suggests that this population moves north in Africa to breed.

		Summer			Winter		
		Mean	Max.	N	Mean	Max.	N
2738S 3224E	Muzi Lake (South), Mbazwane, KwaZulu-Natal	–	–	–	36	36	1
2739S 3224E	Neshe Pan, Mbazwane, KwaZulu-Natal	0	0	5	23	63	6
2351S 2927E	Pietersburg Bird Sanctuary, Pietersburg, Northern Province	18	18	1	0	0	1
2741S 2540E	Bloemhof Dam, Bloemhof, Free State	0	1	6	17	79	6
2757S 2957E	Chelmsford Dam, Newcastle, KwaZulu-Natal	0	0	2	15	31	3
2506S 2855E	Mkhombo Dam, Libangeni, Mpumalanga	2	7	3	10	20	3
2829S 3209E	Lake Eteza, Mtubatuba, KwaZulu-Natal	0	0	3	11	41	4
2740S 3226E	Tshanetshe Pan, Mbazwane, KwaZulu-Natal	0	0	5	10	32	6
2739S 3226E	Yengweni Lake, Mbazwane, KwaZulu-Natal	0	0	5	7	24	6
2534S 2814E	Rooiwal Sewage Works, Pretoria, Gauteng	0	0	4	7	31	5
2520S 2728E	Vaalkop Dam, Brits, North West	0	1	4	3	8	5
2557S 2800E	Diepsloot Nature Reserve, Johannesburg, Gauteng	0	0	4	2	10	5
2510S 2751E	Klipvoor Dam, Brits, North West	1	4	4	1	2	3
2513S 2830E	Rust de Winter Dam, Pienaarsrivier, Northern Province	0	0	2	2	3	2
2611S 2819E	Homestead, Benoni & Middle Lakes, Benoni, Gauteng	2	3	2	0	0	2

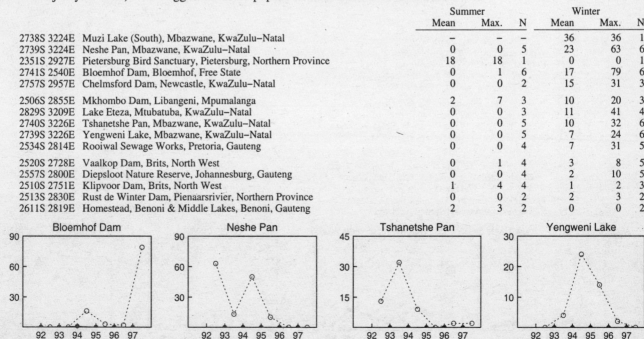

116 Spurwinged Goose *Plectropterus gambensis*

Widespread; generally common, but absent from arid regions, extreme northeast, and Lesotho. At any inland water but prefers large sites for moulting. Breeds August–April (peak December–March). Has winter moult migration to Barberspan and to waters in Free State and KwaZulu-Natal: CWAC data show large winter numbers at many waters, mainly in KwaZulu-Natal (most in northeast lowlands) and Free State, but also in North West; smaller winter concentrations widespread North West, Gauteng and Mpumalanga. Good January counts recorded at several sites in Western Cape, e.g. 708 at Strandfontein and 638 at Berg River.

			Summer			Winter		
			Mean	Max.	N	Mean	Max.	N
2818S 2712E	Allemanskraal Dam, Ventersburg, Free State		17	51	6	885	2654*	6
2741S 2540E	Bloemhof Dam, Bloemhof, Free State		63	163	6	653	1580	6
2852S 2600E	Krugersdrift Dam, Bloemfontein, Free State		137	370	6	551	1667	6
2735S 2935E	Seekoeivlei, Memel, Free State		137	520	5	457	1308	5
2740S 3219E	Nsumu Pan, Mkuzi Game Reserve, KwaZulu–Natal		11	29	6	476	785	6
2757S 2957E	Chelmsford Dam, Newcastle, KwaZulu–Natal		10	19	2	458	669	3
2739S 3226E	Yengweni Lake, Mbazwane, KwaZulu–Natal		75	223	5	338	735	6
2725S 3158E	Pongolapoort Dam, Mkuze, KwaZulu–Natal		22	38	6	356	1424	6
2834S 2650E	Erfenis Dam, Winburg, Free State		19	41	6	326	994	6
3247S 1812E	Berg River System, Velddrif, Western Cape		203	640	5	83	115	4
2715S 2741E	Koppies Dam, Koppies, Free State		53	126	6	227	647	6
2804S 2433E	Spitskop Dam, Spitskop, Northern Cape		1	1	2	275	299	2
2755S 3035E	Klipspruit Dam Complex, Vryheid, KwaZulu–Natal		–	–	–	263	263	1
2829S 3209E	Lake Eteza, Mtubatuba, KwaZulu–Natal		1	2	3	215	821	4
2750S 3035E	Blood River Vlei, Vryheid, KwaZulu–Natal		0	0	1	207	207	1

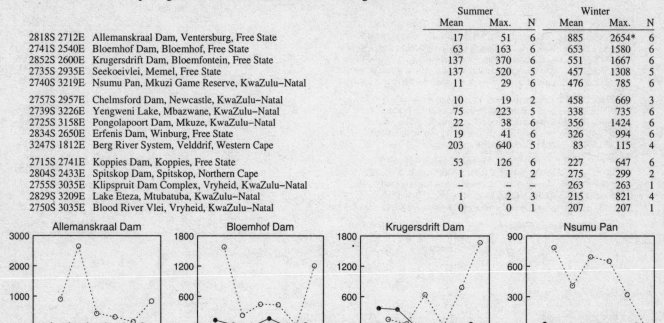

117 Maccoa Duck *Oxyura maccoa*

CWAC data confirm that it is sparsely distributed, usually in small numbers, but sometimes locally common in the Western Cape, whence come the largest CWAC totals; the survey produced only small numbers from another principal area, the highveld; there were a few Northern Cape records, and two records from KwaZulu-Natal, where it is scarce. Breeds August–January in Western Cape, mostly September–April in northeast. May move to Western Cape in spring and early summer (ASAB1); CWAC data show peak numbers at most sites there in winter. Elsewhere, the few counts show both winter and summer peaks in the northeast.

			Summer			Winter		
			Mean	Max.	N	Mean	Max.	N
3341S 1858E	Paarl Bird Sanctuary, Paarl, Western Cape		49	84	5	7	18	5
3359S 2240E	Wilderness Lakes – Touw River System, Sedgefield, Western Cape		6	15	6	49	93	6
3247S 1812E	Berg River System, Velddrif, Western Cape		0	0	5	30	119	4
3405S 1831E	Strandfontein Sewage Works, Muizenberg, Western Cape		14	20	6	15	64	6
3318S 1845E	Radyn Dam, Malmesbury, Western Cape		8	20	5	12	27	4
3408S 1821E	Wildevoëlvlei, Kommetjie, Western Cape		2	3	6	19	42	6
3205S 1819E	Jakkalsvlei, Lambert's Bay, Western Cape		7	7	1	12	12	1
3339S 1858E	Wellington Waste Water Works, Wellington, Western Cape		9	9	1	9	9	1
2839S 2437E	Platfontein Pans, Kimberley, Northern Cape		2	2	1	14	14	1
2714S 3002E	Fickland Pan, Wakkerstroom, Mpumalanga		0	0	1	14	14	1
2622S 2810E	Vlakplaas Water Treatment Works, Germiston, Gauteng		10	34	4	1	4	4
2620S 3021E	Lake Banagher West, Lake Chrissie, Mpumalanga		2	4	2	9	17	2
2710S 3004E	Wim Rabe Pan, Wakkerstroom, Mpumalanga		9	9	1	–	–	–
2838S 1627E	Orange River Estuary, Alexander Bay, Northern Cape		0	0	1	9	9	1
2613S 2828E	Springs Bird Sanctuary, Springs, Gauteng		3	12	5	6	13	5

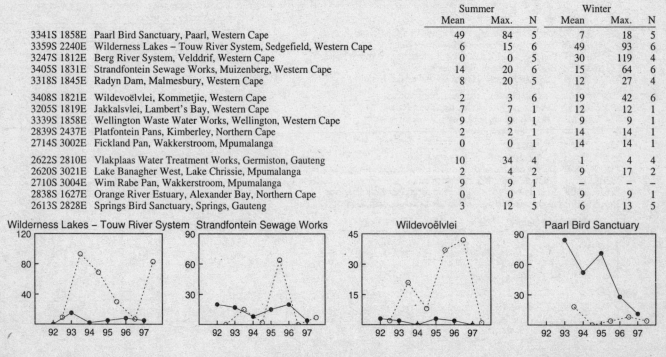

891 Mallard *Anas platyrhynchos*

A localized feral resident, occurring mainly in the Western Cape and also on the Witwatersrand. Recorded from 19 CWAC sites, including coastal Northern Cape (Orange River estuary), and KwaZulu-Natal (Klipspruit and Albert Falls dams, and Durban's Northern Treatment Works). Numbers said to be increasing, but CWAC counts generally small, not approaching largest published totals for sites such as Zandvlei. Summer peaks apparent at 3 Western Cape sites, winter peaks at 3 others; no consistent pattern emerges. Hybridization with Yellowbilled Duck threatens the genetic integrity of that species; hybrids recorded at Sandvlei, Raapenberg and elsewhere.

		Summer			Winter		
		Mean	Max.	N	Mean	Max.	N
3406S 1828E	Zandvlei, Muizenberg, Western Cape	1	3	5	9	27	5
3247S 1812E	Berg River System, Velddrif, Western Cape	1	3	5	8	13	4
3351S 1829E	Rietvlei, Milnerton, Western Cape	6	23	5	2	6	4
3356S 1828E	Raapenberg Bird Sanctuary, Cape Town, Western Cape	4	8	2	2	2	1
3402S 2324E	Keurbooms River Estuary, Plettenberg Bay, Western Cape	6	11	2	0	0	3
2553S 2817E	Rietvlei Dam, Pretoria, Gauteng	0	0	1	3	3	1
2755S 3035E	Klipspruit Dam Complex, Vryheid, KwaZulu-Natal	–	–	–	3	3	1
3408S 1821E	Wildevoëlvlei, Kommetjie, Western Cape	0	2	6	3	8	6
3425S 1910E	Vermont Salt Pan, Hermanus, Western Cape	0	1	5	1	5	5
3403S 2302E	Knysna Lagoon, Knysna, Western Cape	0	1	5	1	2	5
2838S 1627E	Orange River Estuary, Alexander Bay, Northern Cape	0	0	1	1	1	1
3205S 1819E	Jakkalsvlei, Lambert's Bay, Western Cape	1	1	1	0	0	1
3402S 1913E	Theewaterskloof Dam, Villiersdorp, Western Cape	0	0	5	1	2	5
2926S 3024E	Albert Falls Dam, Pietermaritzburg, KwaZulu-Natal	0	0	4	1	3	4
2611S 2818E	Korsman Bird Sanctuary, Benoni, Gauteng	1	2	3	0	0	3

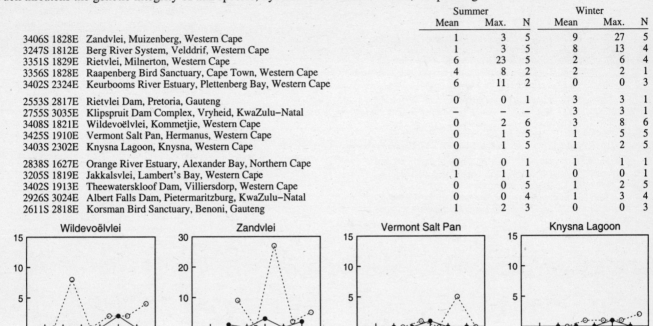

148 African Fish Eagle *Haliaeetus vocifer*

Widespread at suitable open waters; most frequently recorded at coastal sites, large rivers and flood-plains. Recorded at 97 CWAC sites: 33 (34%) dams (breeds at some sites), 12 (12%) sewage works, 4 (4%) vleis and saltpans, 18 (19%) natural pans and 30 (31%) coastal lakes, lagoons and estuaries. Increases in reporting rates in breeding season (in South Africa, peak egg-laying May–October), when the birds are conspicuous (ASAB1); CWAC data show slightly higher means in summer. Some habitat lost through wetland degradation, but has benefited from construction of artificial impoundments (confirmed by CWAC).

		Summer			Winter		
		Mean	Max.	N	Mean	Max.	N
2804S 3227E	Lake St Lucia, Hlabisa, KwaZulu-Natal	72	88	6	63	79	6
2721S 3240E	Lake Sibaya, Ubombo, KwaZulu-Natal	13	18	4	11	13	6
3037S 2537E	Gariep Dam (West), Gariep Dam (town), Free State	13	20	6	11	22	6
3010S 2455E	Vanderkloof Dam, Vanderkloof, Northern Cape	8	8	1	8	8	1
2510S 2751E	Klipvoor Dam, Brits, North West	8	14	4	8	9	3
2725S 3158E	Pongolapoort Dam, Mkuze, KwaZulu-Natal	7	13	6	7	10	6
2653S 3218E	Nyamithi Pan (Ndumo), Ingwavuma, KwaZulu-Natal	8	9	4	5	7	5
2932S 2515E	Kalkfontein Dam, Koffiefontein, Free State	4	10	6	7	10	6
3421S 1906E	Botriviervlei, Kleinmond, Western Cape	6	11	4	5	6	5
2741S 2540E	Bloemhof Dam, Bloemhof, Free State	6	13	6	4	7	6
2658S 3250E	Kosi Bay Nature Reserve, Manguzi, KwaZulu-Natal	4	8	5	6	10	6
2849S 3202E	Richards Bay, Richards Bay (town), KwaZulu-Natal	3	6	5	5	8	5
3402S 1913E	Theewaterskloof Dam, Villiersdorp, Western Cape	3	4	5	3	5	5
2926S 3024E	Albert Falls Dam, Pietermaritzburg, KwaZulu-Natal	3	5	4	3	4	4
3359S 2240E	Wilderness Lakes – Touw River System, Sedgefield, Western Cape	3	6	6	2	4	6

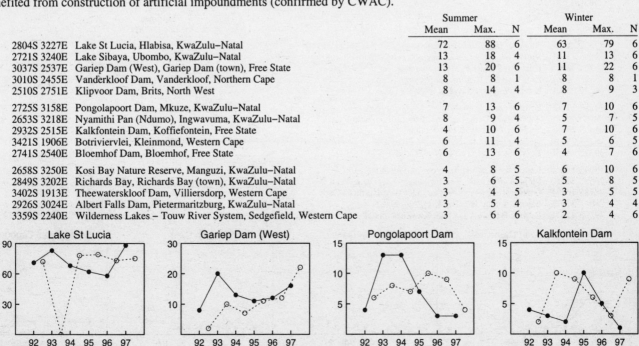

165 African Marsh Harrier *Circus ranivorus*

Thinly distributed, locally not uncommon; usually nests (August–November) in extensive reedbeds; forages over vleis, water margins, floodplains, grassland and cultivation. Record-ed at 63 CWAC sites: 17 (27%) dams, 7 (11%) sewage works, 9 (14.5%) vleis, 13 (20.5%) natural pans and 17 (27%) coastal lakes, reedbeds and estuaries. Threatened by wetland destruction; uses dams, but many impoundments must have drowned suitable marshes. Some seasonal changes in reporting rates recorded (ASAB1); CWAC data (totals small) show higher winter means at Western Cape and KwaZulu-Natal sites (greater visibility/presence of immatures?).

		Summer			Winter		
		Mean	Max.	N	Mean	Max.	N
3247S 1812E	Berg River System, Velddrif, Western Cape	2	3	5	7	11	4
3405S 1831E	Strandfontein Sewage Works, Muizenberg, Western Cape	4	6	6	4	9	6
2750S 3035E	Blood River Vlei, Vryheid, KwaZulu-Natal	2	2	1	3	3	1
2805S 3220E	Hluhluwe River Vlei & Floodplain, Hluhluwe, KwaZulu-Natal	1	2	2	4	4	1
3220S 1825E	Verlorenvlei, Elandsbaai, Western Cape	1	2	6	4	8	5
3309S 1804E	Langebaan Lagoon, Langebaan, Western Cape	2	5	6	3	7	6
3359S 2240E	Wilderness Lakes – Touw River System, Sedgefield, Western Cape	1	4	6	3	5	6
3421S 1906E	Botriviervlei, Kleinmond, Western Cape	2	4	4	2	4	5
2804S 3227E	Lake St Lucia, Hlabisa, KwaZulu-Natal	1	2	6	3	7	6
2847S 3203E	Thulazihleka Pan, Richards Bay, KwaZulu-Natal	2	3	5	2	3	5
2915S 2941E	Hlatikulu Vlei, Hlatikulu, KwaZulu-Natal	2	4	2	1	1	1
3401S 2323E	Bitou River, Plettenberg Bay, Western Cape	2	3	2	1	2	3
3351S 1829E	Rietvlei, Milnerton, Western Cape	1	2	5	2	3	4
2725S 3158E	Pongolapoort Dam, Mkuze, KwaZulu-Natal	2	5	6	1	2	6
2629S 2828E	Blesbokspruit, Nigel, Gauteng	2	2	1	0	0	1

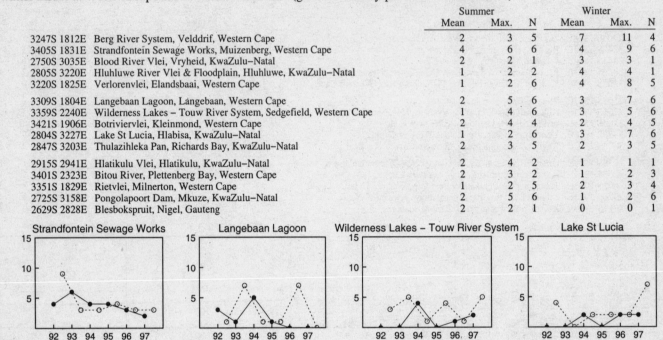

170 Osprey *Pandion haliaetus*

A Palearctic migrant, occurring throughout RSA at natural and artificial waters, including lakes, pans, dams, rivers, coastal marshes and estuaries; occasionally at small ponds and also at saltpans and sewage works. Its distribution is patchy and it normally occurs singly; SABAP reporting rates are low. Most arrivals are in October and departures in March; some individuals, mostly first-year birds, remain during the austral winter and there is a wide scattering of winter CWAC records. It favours coastal sites; some inland records may be of birds migrating to and from coastal areas.

		Summer			Winter		
		Mean	Max.	N	Mean	Max.	N
2849S 3202E	Richards Bay, Richards Bay (town), KwaZulu-Natal	3	6	5	1	2	5
3010S 2455E	Vanderkloof Dam, Vanderkloof, Northern Cape	3	3	1	1	1	1
2658S 3250E	Kosi Bay Nature Reserve, Manguzi, KwaZulu-Natal	3	4	5	1	2	6
3421S 1906E	Botriviervlei, Kleinmond, Western Cape	2	3	4	1	2	5
3403S 2302E	Knysna Lagoon, Knysna, Western Cape	2	2	5	1	2	5
2725S 3158E	Pongolapoort Dam, Mkuze, KwaZulu-Natal	2	5	6	1	2	6
2926S 3024E	Albert Falls Dam, Pietermaritzburg, KwaZulu-Natal	2	3	4	1	2	4
2553S 2918E	Witbank Dam, Witbank, Mpumalanga	2	4	4	1	1	5
2826S 2901E	Sterkfontein Dam, Harrismith, Free State	2	4	6	1	1	6
2932S 2515E	Kalkfontein Dam, Koffiefontein, Free State	2	4	6	1	1	6
3309S 1804E	Langebaan Lagoon, Langebaan, Western Cape	2	5	6	0	0	6
2658S 3253E	Maputaland Coast, Kwangwanase, KwaZulu-Natal	2	2	1	–	–	–
2838S 1627E	Orange River Estuary, Alexander Bay, Northern Cape	1	1	1	1	1	1
2804S 3227E	Lake St Lucia, Hlabisa, KwaZulu-Natal	1	2	6	1	2	6
2953S 3101E	Durban Bayhead, Durban, KwaZulu-Natal	1	1	5	1	2	5

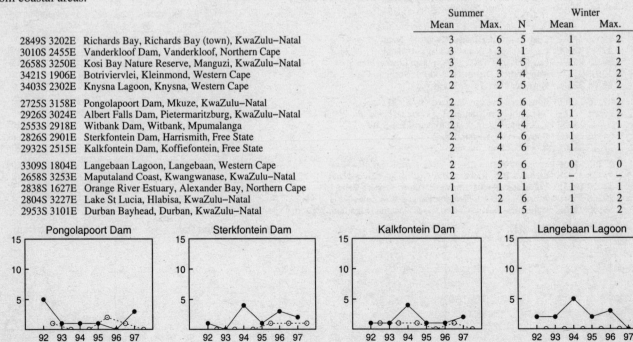

164 European Marsh Harrier *Circus aeruginosus*

Palearctic migrant; regarded as rare, but overlooked and perhaps more regular
than records indicate. One CWAC record from Blesbokspruit.

207 Wattled Crane *Bugeranus carunculatus*

Restricted to Ethiopia, and southern and central Africa; in RSA it is resident at permanently
inundated high-altitude marshes in high-rainfall sour grassland regions. Most sites of
breeding and regular occurrence are not covered by CWAC. During survey period, recorded
from two CWAC sites, at one of which (Seekoeivlei) attempted breeding is known; no
records from some CWAC sites where it is known to occur. Local movements and dispersal
known; noteworthy count at Seekoeivlei in summer 1996. Globally vulnerable (endangered
in RSA); threatened by wetland degradation, disturbance and poisoning.

		Summer			Winter		
		Mean	Max.	N	Mean	Max.	N
2735S 2935E	Seekoeivlei, Memel, Free State	5	24	5	1	2	5
2915S 2941E	Hlatikulu Vlei, Hlatikulu, KwaZulu–Natal	0	0	2	6	6	1

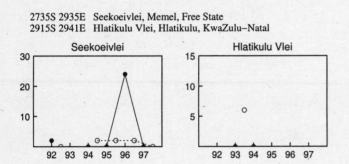

209 Crowned Crane *Balearica regulorum*

In RSA confined to moister eastern regions, total population probably c. 2500 birds. Inhabits
relatively high-altitude, temperate wetlands; breeds (October–March) in wet grass/sedges/
reedbeds; feeds in wetlands and nearby dry habitats (grassland, open savanna, ploughed
fields, etc.). Recorded at 22 CWAC sites. Nonbreeding flocks move widely; CWAC data
show winter increases at some sites; large winter 1996 count at Seekoeivlei noteworthy.
Not listed as globally threatened, but recent evidence of large-scale decreases suggest
it is threatened in South Africa by poisoning, wetland degradation and disturbance.

		Summer			Winter		
		Mean	Max.	N	Mean	Max.	N
2735S 2935E	Seekoeivlei, Memel, Free State	12	31	5	74	180	5
2931S 3011E	Midmar Dam, Howick, KwaZulu–Natal	5	15	5	19	22	3
2750S 3035E	Blood River Vlei, Vryheid, KwaZulu–Natal	5	5	1	7	7	1
2926S 3024E	Albert Falls Dam, Pietermaritzburg, KwaZulu–Natal	5	18	4	7	26	4
2948S 2938E	Reichenau Mission Dam, Underberg, KwaZulu–Natal	4	8	5	4	6	5
2950S 2935E	Watermead Dam, Underberg, KwaZulu–Natal	3	5	5	3	7	5
2757S 2957E	Chelmsford Dam, Newcastle, KwaZulu–Natal	0	0	2	5	9	3
2915S 2941E	Hlatikulu Vlei, Hlatikulu, KwaZulu–Natal	3	6	2	2	2	1
2849S 3202E	Richards Bay, Richards Bay (town), KwaZulu–Natal	2	3	5	2	4	5
2714S 3002E	Fickland Pan, Wakkerstroom, Mpumalanga	2	2	1	1	1	1
2702S 3030E	Heyshope Dam, Piet Retief, Mpumalanga	–	–	–	2	2	1
2748S 3048E	Klipfontein Bird Sanctuary, Vryheid, KwaZulu–Natal	2	2	1	0	0	1
3155S 2650E	Queenstown Sewage Works, Queenstown, Eastern Cape	2	2	1	0	0	3
2826S 2901E	Sterkfontein Dam, Harrismith, Free State	1	6	6	0	0	6
2946S 2937E	The Swamp, Underberg, KwaZulu–Natal	1	2	2	0	0	1

210 African Rail *Rallus caerulescens*

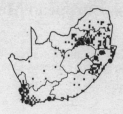

Locally distributed in marshes and in dense cover fringing open waters. No regular movements known, but occurrence in regions such as Northern Cape may be seasonal and erratic in response to variations in habitat availability. Recording rate often higher in summer, when birds call most, but some CWAC counts show high numbers in winter, when birds usually call less. High winter counts at Klipfontein and Blood River result from habitat being easier to penetrate (low water levels), so that more birds are flushed; at the Blesbokspruit system birds are easier to see in winter, when they are out of cover more often.

		Summer Mean	Max.	N	Winter Mean	Max.	N
2629S 2828E	Blesbokspruit, Nigel, Gauteng	9	9	1	22	22	1
2750S 3035E	Blood River Vlei, Vryheid, KwaZulu–Natal	10	10	1	19	19	1
2748S 3048E	Klipfontein Bird Sanctuary, Vryheid, KwaZulu–Natal	6	6	1	13	13	1
2621S 2830E	Marievale Bird Sanctuary, Nigel, Gauteng	5	8	5	7	15	5
2613S 2828E	Springs Bird Sanctuary, Springs, Gauteng	1	2	5	6	9	5
2847S 3203E	Thulazihleka Pan, Richards Bay, KwaZulu–Natal	1	4	5	5	15	5
2616S 2830E	Grootvaly, Springs, Gauteng	1	2	3	3	8	4
2834S 2948E	Malandeni Sewage Works, Ladysmith, KwaZulu–Natal	1	4	5	1	6	5
2620S 2817E	Rietspruit (Rooikraal), Boksburg, Gauteng	1	3	3	1	3	4
3247S 1812E	Berg River System, Velddrif, Western Cape	1	2	5	2	3	4
2645S 2706E	Prozesky Bird Sanctuary, Potchefstroom, North West	1	3	3	1	2	3
2611S 2818E	Korsman Bird Sanctuary, Benoni, Gauteng	1	4	3	0	0	3
3421S 1905E	Kleinmond River Estuary, Kleinmond, Western Cape	0	1	3	1	4	4
3359S 2240E	Wilderness Lakes – Touw River System, Sedgefield, Western Cape	1	1	6	0	1	6
2849S 3202E	Richards Bay, Richards Bay (town), KwaZulu–Natal	0	0	5	1	2	5

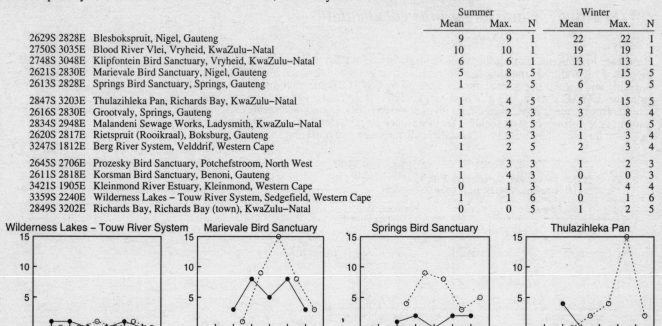

212 African Crake *Crex egregia*

Widespread but local, occurrence unpredictable, in eastern South Africa west to c. 23°E. Largely a rains breeding visitor to grasslands (often seasonally moist) in October–March; most habitat becomes unsuitable in dry season. Secretive and under-recorded; noted at only three CWAC sites, at two in winter (including 5 birds at Benoni Lakes in 1993), when presumably attracted by persistence of moist conditions at wetland edges; not clear if these birds passing through or temporarily resident. At Malandeni Sewage Works, Ladysmith, small numbers breed each summer, in moist to shallowly flooded grass and herbage (K. Gordon).

213 Black Crake *Amaurornis flavirostris*

Widespread and locally common in many types of wetland with moderate cover and some permanent flooding; under-recorded by CWAC. Locally migratory in drier parts of range, in response to seasonal availability of habitat; largely sedentary in South Africa but seasonal influxes noted at Hlonhlela Pan (CWAC), and at Nyl floodplain. Often easier to locate in summer, when birds call most, but more visible in winter at Blesbokspruit system, resulting in high winter counts (as for African Rail). Relatively easy to see when birds accustomed to human presence; some high counts from reserves and bird sanctuaries.

		Summer			Winter		
		Mean	Max.	N	Mean	Max.	N
2629S 2828E	Blesbokspruit, Nigel, Gauteng	9	9	1	22	22	1
2847S 3203E	Thulazihleka Pan, Richards Bay, KwaZulu–Natal	14	18	5	14	22	5
2621S 2830E	Marievale Bird Sanctuary, Nigel, Gauteng	13	20	5	10	19	5
2616S 2830E	Grootvaly, Springs, Gauteng	5	10	3	11	24	4
3401S 2541E	Cape Recife Reclamation Works, Port Elizabeth, Eastern Cape	7	11	4	9	10	4
2557S 2800E	Diepsloot Nature Reserve, Johannesburg, Gauteng	6	10	4	9	12	5
2613S 2828E	Springs Bird Sanctuary, Springs, Gauteng	2	4	5	11	17	5
2611S 2819E	Homestead, Benoni & Middle Lakes, Benoni, Gauteng	7	12	2	6	11	2
2351S 2927E	Pietersburg Bird Sanctuary, Pietersburg, Northern Province	6	6	1	6	6	1
2849S 3202E	Richards Bay, Richards Bay (town), KwaZulu–Natal	4	11	5	5	16	5
2611S 2818E	Korsman Bird Sanctuary, Benoni, Gauteng	6	11	3	2	7	3
2721S 3240E	Lake Sibaya, Ubombo, KwaZulu–Natal	3	5	4	5	16	6
3359S 2240E	Wilderness Lakes – Touw River System, Sedgefield, Western Cape	2	3	6	6	18	6
2645S 2706E	Prozesky Bird Sanctuary, Potchefstroom, North West	2	3	3	5	6	3
2620S 2817E	Rietspruit (Rooikraal), Boksburg, Gauteng	2	6	3	3	5	4

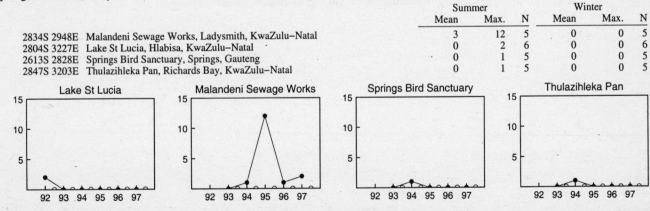

215 Baillon's Crake *Porzana pusilla*

A secretive species of dense marsh vegetation, greatly overlooked and rarely recorded. Recent studies show that it occurs widely but often irregularly, in habitat which may be only seasonal in some areas. On CWAC counts, regularly recorded only at Malandeni Sewage Works, Ladysmith, where good numbers occur throughout the year and birds breed regularly; occurrence of this species emphasizes the importance of this site for rails and other secretive waterbirds. Otherwise, only 3 CWAC records, all in summer, from Springs Bird Sanctuary (1 bird in 1994), Lake St Lucia (2 in 1992) and Thulazihleka (1 in 1994).

		Summer			Winter		
		Mean	Max.	N	Mean	Max.	N
2834S 2948E	Malandeni Sewage Works, Ladysmith, KwaZulu–Natal	3	12	5	0	0	5
2804S 3227E	Lake St Lucia, Hlabisa, KwaZulu–Natal	0	2	6	0	0	6
2613S 2828E	Springs Bird Sanctuary, Springs, Gauteng	0	1	5	0	0	5
2847S 3203E	Thulazihleka Pan, Richards Bay, KwaZulu–Natal	0	1	5	0	0	5

217 Redchested Flufftail *Sarothrura rufa*

A secretive species, greatly under-recorded; it is much more widespread and numerous in, e.g., KwaZulu-Natal and the eastern Free State than is suggested by SABAP and CWAC data. It inhabits many types of dense, seasonally to permanently flooded marshy vegetation, including grass and sedges which dry out in the nonbreeding season. Apart from local movements after habitat destruction (e.g. by fire), and the dispersal of immatures, it is sedentary. The preponderance of summer records at CWAC sites presumably reflects the relative ease with which the species is found in the breeding season, when it calls frequently.

		Summer			Winter		
		Mean	Max.	N	Mean	Max.	N
2748S 3048E	Klipfontein Bird Sanctuary, Vryheid, KwaZulu–Natal	5	5	1	4	4	1
2750S 3035E	Blood River Vlei, Vryheid, KwaZulu–Natal	4	4	1	0	0	1
2629S 2828E	Blesbokspruit, Nigel, Gauteng	3	3	1	0	0	1
3309S 1804E	Langebaan Lagoon, Langebaan, Western Cape	2	8	6	0	0	6
2915S 2941E	Hlatikulu Vlei, Hlatikulu, KwaZulu–Natal	2	3	2	0	0	1
2537S 3002E	Lakenvlei Wetland, Belfast, Mpumalanga	–	–	–	1	1	1
2620S 2817E	Rietspruit (Rooikraal), Boksburg, Gauteng	0	0	3	0	1	4
2557S 2800E	Diepsloot Nature Reserve, Johannesburg, Gauteng	0	0	4	0	1	5
2621S 2830E	Marievale Bird Sanctuary, Nigel, Gauteng	0	1	5	0	0	5
2834S 2948E	Malandeni Sewage Works, Ladysmith, KwaZulu–Natal	0	1	5	0	0	5
2847S 3203E	Thulazihleka Pan, Richards Bay, KwaZulu–Natal	0	1	5	0	0	5

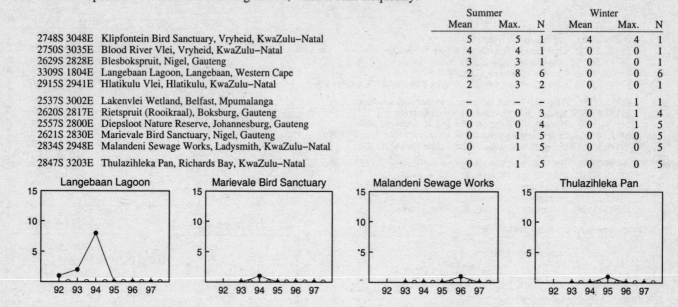

222 Whitewinged Flufftail *Sarothrura ayresi*

Endangered; largely confined to densely vegetated marshes at higher altitudes in the east. No CWAC records available.

223 Purple Gallinule *Porphyrio porphyrio*

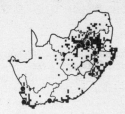

In RSA occurs mainly in wetter regions; locally common in reedbeds and other dense wetland vegetation. Main centres of distribution are KwaZulu-Natal and central highveld; smaller numbers in Western and coastal Eastern Cape. Like Moorhen, normally regarded as sedentary but has at least local seasonal movements and breeds at seasonal and temporary sites. Unlike Moorhen, little significant seasonal variation in CWAC counts; winter peaks at Blesbokspruit system due to birds' greater visibility at this time. Frequents natural and artificially created habitats; some good counts from dams and sewage works.

		Summer			Winter		
		Mean	Max.	N	Mean	Max.	N
2629S 2828E	Blesbokspruit, Nigel, Gauteng	16	16	1	36	36	1
2735S 2935E	Seekoeivlei, Memel, Free State	27	84*	5	22	47	5
2847S 3203E	Thulazihleka Pan, Richards Bay, KwaZulu–Natal	17	41	5	14	21	5
2609S 2821E	Rynfield Dam, Benoni, Gauteng	15	30	4	11	28	5
2611S 2818E	Korsman Bird Sanctuary, Benoni, Gauteng	11	19	3	13	22	3
2621S 2830E	Marievale Bird Sanctuary, Nigel, Gauteng	9	21	5	13	32	5
2613S 2828E	Springs Bird Sanctuary, Springs, Gauteng	6	14	5	16	36	5
2834S 2948E	Malandeni Sewage Works, Ladysmith, KwaZulu–Natal	12	18	5	9	16	5
2849S 3202E	Richards Bay, Richards Bay (town), KwaZulu–Natal	10	30	5	10	26	5
3405S 1831E	Strandfontein Sewage Works, Muizenberg, Western Cape	7	11	6	12	17	6
2611S 2819E	Homestead, Benoni & Middle Lakes, Benoni, Gauteng	9	14	2	9	18	2
2645S 2706E	Prozesky Bird Sanctuary, Potchefstroom, North West	8	14	3	8	11	3
3359S 2240E	Wilderness Lakes – Touw River System, Sedgefield, Western Cape	5	8	6	9	24	6
2616S 2830E	Grootvaly, Springs, Gauteng	4	10	3	9	14	4
3220S 1825E	Verlorenvlei, Elandsbaai, Western Cape	3	8	6	10	14	5

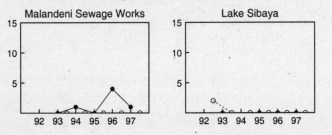

Strandfontein Sewage Works   Wilderness Lakes – Touw River System   Verlorenvlei   Seekoeivlei

224 Lesser Gallinule *Porphyrula alleni*

Inhabits dense, mixed emergent and floating-leaved vegetation; habitat often seasonally flooded; most RSA records December–May. Some birds may remain during dry season if habitat suitable. Locally common, depending on rainfall; Nyl River floodplain has held c. 5000 breeding pairs. Most CWAC records are from Malandeni Sewage Works, a very important site for secretive marsh birds; here it is regular in summer in small numbers, breeds at least occasionally and was recorded in winter 1998. Also single records from Kosi Bay (summer) and Lake Sibaya (winter); must occur regularly on this coastal plain.

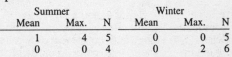

		Summer			Winter		
		Mean	Max.	N	Mean	Max.	N
2834S 2948E	Malandeni Sewage Works, Ladysmith, KwaZulu–Natal	1	4	5	0	0	5
2721S 3240E	Lake Sibaya, Ubombo, KwaZulu–Natal	0	0	4	0	2	6

Malandeni Sewage Works   Lake Sibaya

226 Moorhen *Gallinula chloropus*

Widespread and common in freshwater wetlands with fringing and emergent vegetation. The African race *meridionalis* is normally regarded as sedentary, but seasonal local movements are widely reported. Although known to breed at seasonal and temporary wetlands in southern Africa, movements are not shown by SABAP data, and it is resident at many CWAC sites. However, CWAC counts at 14 permanent waterbodies, from the Western Cape to the Free State, Mpumalanga and KwaZulu-Natal, show a great winter increase in numbers, suggesting regular winter influxes of birds which have bred elsewhere in seasonal habitat.

		Summer			Winter		
		Mean	Max.	N	Mean	Max.	N
3359S 2240E	Wilderness Lakes – Touw River System, Sedgefield, Western Cape	43	79	6	217	338	6
2629S 2828E	Blesbokspruit, Nigel, Gauteng	40	40	1	105	105	1
3341S 1858E	Paarl Bird Sanctuary, Paarl, Western Cape	50	102	5	55	71	5
3405S 1831E	Strandfontein Sewage Works, Muizenberg, Western Cape	32	60	6	59	92	6
2735S 2935E	Seekoeivlei, Memel, Free State	25	64	5	64	235	5
3408S 1821E	Wildevoëlvlei, Kommetjie, Western Cape	35	57	6	41	69	6
2621S 2830E	Marievale Bird Sanctuary, Nigel, Gauteng	41	93	5	31	54	5
2613S 2828E	Springs Bird Sanctuary, Springs, Gauteng	16	27	5	57	119	5
3401S 2323E	Bitou River, Plettenberg Bay, Western Cape	10	10	2	58	78	3
2840S 2446E	Kamfers Dam, Kimberley, Northern Cape	16	24	3	46	111	3
2834S 2948E	Malandeni Sewage Works, Ladysmith, KwaZulu–Natal	26	39	5	35	52	5
2612S 3012E	Tevrede se Pan, Lake Chrissie, Mpumalanga	19	19	1	41	41	1
2755S 2446E	Ganspan Pans & Vlei, Jan Kempdorp, Northern Cape	17	24	2	43	50	2
3220S 1825E	Verlorenvlei, Elandsbaai, Western Cape	29	141	6	30	46	5
2807S 2455E	Vaalharts Weir, Warrenton, Northern Cape	6	8	2	51	68	2

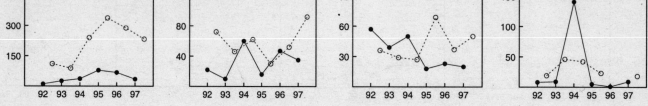

227 Lesser Moorhen *Gallinula angulata*

A secretive inhabitant of emergent vegetation in freshwater wetlands; largely a summer rains breeding visitor to southern Africa. Quite widespread in northeast South Africa; occurs erratically; locally rare to abundant, ranging uncommonly to Swaziland and northern KwaZulu-Natal; also along south coast west to Swellendam. Under-recorded; undoubtedly more widespread than currently known; recently recorded from northeastern Northern Cape, southern Gauteng, northeastern Free State and East Griqualand (B. Taylor). Recorded at three CWAC sites; at Malandeni Sewage Works small numbers regular in flooded *Leersia* grass, Pongola Poort Dam, and Klipvoor Dam.

228 Redknobbed Coot *Fulica cristata*

Widespread, and often extremely abundant at large waterbodies; globally significant counts recorded from 7 sites in North West, Free State, Northern Cape and Western Cape. Breeds all year; peak July–January in all areas (ASAB1). Disperses to small and temporary waters in rains and concentrates at large permanent waters in dry months. CWAC shows peaks at Western Cape waters in both July and January, but more in July during winter rains. From eastern Northern Cape to Mpumalanga, summer and winter peaks also occur, with the majority falling in winter (dry period); in KwaZulu-Natal, all significant peaks are in the dry winter period.

		Summer			Winter		
		Mean	Max.	N	Mean	Max.	N
2804S 2433E	Spitskop Dam, Spitskop, Northern Cape	4868*	6279**	2	5961**	6497**	2
2635S 2535E	Barberspan, Delareyville, North West	5729**	14826**	4	2167	2883*	2
3359S 2240E	Wilderness Lakes – Touw River System, Sedgefield, Western Cape	2642*	4651*	6	5247**	15277**	6
3400S 2245E	Wilderness Lakes – Swartvlei System, Sedgefield, Western Cape	1896	1991	2	4310*	7472**	3
2932S 2515E	Kalkfontein Dam, Koffiefontein, Free State	2852*	7666**	6	1853	3116*	6
3426S 2023E	De Hoop Vlei, Bredasdorp, Western Cape	2104	6175**	5	1800	4446*	4
3247S 1812E	Berg River System, Velddrif, Western Cape	211	348	5	3269*	6614**	4
2839S 2437E	Platfontein Pans, Kimberley, Northern Cape	2224	2224	1	1235	1235	1
2852S 2600E	Krugersdrift Dam, Bloemfontein, Free State	900	3147*	6	2536*	10486**	6
3421S 1906E	Botriviervlei, Kleinmond, Western Cape	980	2899*	4	1716	5339**	5
2635S 2857E	Leeuwpan, Secunda, Mpumalanga	1158	1694	3	1507	2975*	4
3220S 1825E	Verlorenvlei, Elandsbaai, Western Cape	1439	3104*	6	1082	1518	5
2741S 2540E	Bloemhof Dam, Bloemhof, Free State	347	1576	6	1817	3854*	6
2918S 2637E	Rusfontein Dam, Thaba Nchu, Free State	1020	2406	6	975	2709*	6
3405S 1831E	Strandfontein Sewage Works, Muizenberg, Western Cape	758	1676	6	1129	1716	6

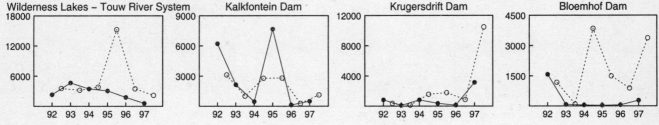

229 African Finfoot *Podica senegalensis*

In South Africa only in northeast (south to c. 27°S) and in coastal regions from KwaZulu-Natal to Mossel Bay. Inhabits perennial streams and rivers with dense overhanging and fringing trees, shrubs and reedbeds (few CWAC sites have this habitat); avoids both stagnant and fast-flowing water. Occasionally at dams (one CWAC record from Klipvoor Dam); once at Sundumbili Sewage Works, KwaZulu-Natal. Under-recorded because of secretive and often crepuscular habits; recorded at five CWAC sites (regular only at Kosi Bay). Vulnerable to habitat loss, e.g. via water flow reduction, siltation, and degradation of riverine vegetation.

		Summer			Winter		
		Mean	Max.	N	Mean	Max.	N
2658S 3250E	Kosi Bay Nature Reserve, Manguzi, KwaZulu–Natal	0	1	5	1	1	6
2911S 3125E	Sundumbili Sewage Works, Mandini, KwaZulu–Natal	1	1	2	0	0	3
2611S 2818E	Korsman Bird Sanctuary, Benoni, Gauteng	0	1	3	0	0	3
2510S 2751E	Klipvoor Dam, Brits, North West	0	1	4	0	0	3
2923S 3121E	Umvoti River, Stanger, KwaZulu–Natal	0	0	3	0	1	5

240 African Jacana *Actophilornis africanus*

Commonest in coastal KwaZulu-Natal (whence come all large CWAC totals), and eastern Mpumalanga, Northern Province and Swaziland; also along Vaal River, and scattered localities elsewhere (ASAB1). Typically at seasonal pans, floodplains, and the edges of meandering rivers, foraging on floating vegetation. Ephemeral nature of habitat causes much local movement and vagrancy; no regular migrations known. Breeds all year, mostly in summer. CWAC data indicate residence at some KwaZulu-Natal sites; otherwise more peaks in winter than summer overall, presumably reflecting winter movements from ephemeral to permanent waters.

		Summer			Winter		
		Mean	Max.	N	Mean	Max.	N
2847S 3203E	Thulazihleka Pan, Richards Bay, KwaZulu-Natal	48	104	5	52	80	5
2739S 3226E	Yengweni Lake, Mbazwane, KwaZulu-Natal	38	51	5	49	97	6
2740S 3226E	Tshanetshe Pan, Mbazwane, KwaZulu-Natal	26	46	5	23	65	6
2740S 3219E	Nsumu Pan, Mkuzi Game Reserve, KwaZulu-Natal	34	105	6	13	35	6
2739S 3224E	Neshe Pan, Mbazwane, KwaZulu-Natal	33	66	5	12	28	6
2721S 3240E	Lake Sibaya, Ubombo, KwaZulu-Natal	14	21	4	22	30	6
2725S 3158E	Pongolapoort Dam, Mkuze, KwaZulu-Natal	17	83	6	17	54	6
2917S 3117E	Mbozambo Waste Water Lagoon, Stanger, KwaZulu-Natal	5	13	3	25	39	5
2830S 3212E	Mavuya Pan, Mtubatuba, KwaZulu-Natal	18	45	3	10	18	4
2849S 3202E	Richards Bay, Richards Bay (town), KwaZulu-Natal	6	13	5	16	30	5
2941S 3105E	Umhlanga Treatment Works, Umhlanga, KwaZulu-Natal	10	12	3	11	15	5
2506S 2855E	Mkhombo Dam, Libangeni, Mpumalanga	1	2	3	20	52	3
2829S 3209E	Lake Eteza, Mtubatuba, KwaZulu-Natal	9	14	3	11	21	4
2652S 3217E	Banzi Pan (Ndumo), Ingwavuma, KwaZulu-Natal	4	10	4	16	38	5
2653S 3213E	Shokwe Pan (Ndumo), Ingwavuma, KwaZulu-Natal	9	14	3	9	23	5

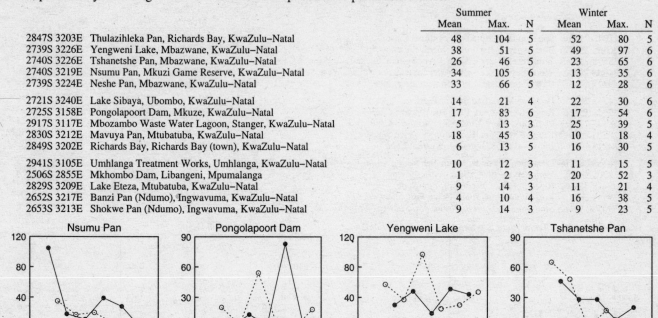

241 Lesser Jacana *Microparra capensis*

In RSA mainly in northern KwaZulu-Natal (where 12 of 13 CWAC sites located); breeds November–May. At shallow waterbodies, often seasonally/erratically flooded, with low emergent/floating vegetation; most CWAC records at pans and lakes; occurrence irregular because of ephemeral habitat. Seasonal movements not known; more birds in winter during survey period, especially during 1992 drought, presumably reflect movement from seasonal to permanent waters. Occasional records in interior of KwaZulu-Natal (e.g. Blood River Vlei), Northern and Mpumalanga Provinces, and Swaziland, probably of nonbreeding visitors (ASAB1).

		Summer			Winter		
		Mean	Max.	N	Mean	Max.	N
2847S 3203E	Thulazihleka Pan, Richards Bay, KwaZulu-Natal	3	9	5	4	16	5
2736S 3259E	Mhlazi Pan, Mbazwane, KwaZulu-Natal	0	0	5	1	6	5
2721S 3240E	Lake Sibaya, Ubombo, KwaZulu-Natal	0	1	4	1	3	6
2750S 3035E	Blood River Vlei, Vryheid, KwaZulu-Natal	0	0	1	1	1	1
2740S 3226E	Tshanetshe Pan, Mbazwane, KwaZulu-Natal	0	0	5	1	3	6
2742S 3237E	kuNdlebeni Pan, Mbazwane, KwaZulu-Natal	0	0	5	1	5	6
2849S 3202E	Richards Bay, Richards Bay (town), KwaZulu-Natal	0	1	5	0	1	5
2658S 3250E	Kosi Bay Nature Reserve, Manguzi, KwaZulu-Natal	0	2	5	0	0	6
2737S 3233E	Mfula Pan, Mbazwane, KwaZulu-Natal	0	0	5	0	2	6
2830S 3212E	Mavuya Pan, Mtubatuba, KwaZulu-Natal	0	0	3	0	1	4
2739S 3224E	Neshe Pan, Mbazwane, KwaZulu-Natal	0	1	5	0	0	6
2739S 3226E	Yengweni Lake, Mbazwane, KwaZulu-Natal	0	0	5	0	1	6

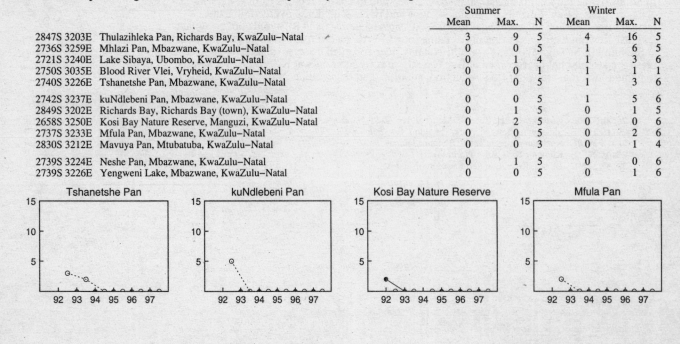

242 Painted Snipe *Rostratula benghalensis*

A widespread but generally uncommon resident, nomad or migrant, with poorly understood movements which are related to the availability of suitable habitat. Normally seen on mud at the edges of dense cover at marshes, swamps, flooded grass, irrigation, lake margins, river banks, ditches and sewage ponds; occurs at both inland and coastal freshwater sites. Greatly under-recorded by CWAC, because of generally secretive behaviour and often crepuscular activity. Normally solitary, or in pairs or family groups; observations in South Africa (B. Taylor) indicate occurrence in small flocks after breeding.

		Summer			Winter		
		Mean	Max.	N	Mean	Max.	N
2510S 2751E	Klipvoor Dam, Brits, North West	1	4	4	0	0	3
3351S 1829E	Rietvlei, Milnerton, Western Cape	1	4	5	0	0	4
2915S 2941E	Hlatikulu Vlei, Hlatikulu, KwaZulu–Natal	1	1	2	0	0	1
2739S 3224E	Neshe Pan, Mbazwane, KwaZulu–Natal	0	0	5	0	2	6
2614S 2819E	Leeupan, Benoni, Gauteng	0	1	5	0	0	6
3247S 1812E	Berg River System, Velddrif, Western Cape	0	1	5	0	0	4
3309S 1804E	Langebaan Lagoon, Langebaan, Western Cape	0	0	6	0	1	6

244 African Black Oystercatcher *Haematopus moquini*

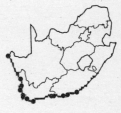

Near-threatened; endemic to coastal southern Africa; total population <5000 birds. Frequents rocky and sandy shorelines, and estuaries; breeds in summer (October–April) on offshore islands and sandy shores east to Mazeppa Bay (Eastern Cape). Largely sedentary, but juveniles disperse widely. Apart from three records at Redhouse and Chatty Saltpans, Eastern Cape, and single KwaZulu-Natal occurrences at Umvoti River mouth (summer) and Umgeni Estuary (winter), all CWAC records are from estuaries, coastal lagoons and pans, and one sewage works. Winter increases at some sites reflect influxes of postbreeding birds.

		Summer			Winter		
		Mean	Max.	N	Mean	Max.	N
3403S 2302E	Knysna Lagoon, Knysna, Western Cape	39*	45*	5	50**	71**	5
3352S 2538E	Swartkops River Estuary, Port Elizabeth, Eastern Cape	33*	37*	6	38*	47*	6
3309S 1804E	Langebaan Lagoon, Langebaan, Western Cape	34*	71**	6	26*	47*	6
3142S 1812E	Olifants River Mouth (South), Lutzville, Western Cape	17	18	2	16	16	1
3351S 1829E	Rietvlei, Milnerton, Western Cape	15	29*	5	17	33*	4
3402S 2324E	Keurbooms River Estuary, Plettenberg Bay, Western Cape	14	14	2	10	12	3
3405S 1831E	Strandfontein Sewage Works, Muizenberg, Western Cape	12	19	6	6	10	6
3400S 2456E	Kabeljous River Estuary, Jeffreys Bay, Eastern Cape	12	14	2	5	10	3
3236S 1818E	Rocher Pan, Velddrif, Western Cape	3	7	5	10	21	6
3329S 2707E	Great Fish River Estuary, Port Alfred, Eastern Cape	8	13	4	4	9	4
3247S 1812E	Berg River System, Velddrif, Western Cape	3	13	5	8	19	4
2838S 1627E	Orange River Estuary, Alexander Bay, Northern Cape	0	0	1	9	9	1
3443S 2007E	De Mond Estuary, Bredasdorp, Western Cape	4	5	4	1	2	5
3421S 1906E	Botriviervlei, Kleinmond, Western Cape	3	4	4	1	4	5
3421S 1905E	Kleinmond River Estuary, Kleinmond, Western Cape	2	4	3	0	1	4

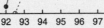

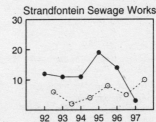

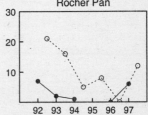

245 Ringed Plover *Charadrius hiaticula*

Palearctic migrant, common on coastlines; prefers tidal mud- and sandflats but also on rocky and stony shores, and at lagoons and saltmarshes. Widespread but local in small numbers (mainly during migration) at inland waters with gently sloping shorelines and mud, sand or gravel substrate. Also occurs at sewage works and saltpans; occasional on dry open ground during migration. All large counts are from coastal sites, especially in Western Cape. Arrivals are from early September; CWAC data confirm that very few remain in austral winter. Numbers declining along much of South African coast due to habitat destruction.

		Summer			Winter		
		Mean	Max.	N	Mean	Max.	N
3309S 1804E	Langebaan Lagoon, Langebaan, Western Cape	326	548	6	0	0	6
3416S 2149E	Voëlvlei, Mossel Bay, Western Cape	294	560	5	0	0	4
3443S 2007E	De Mond Estuary, Bredasdorp, Western Cape	227	382	4	0	0	5
3352S 2538E	Swartkops River Estuary, Port Elizabeth, Eastern Cape	162	301	6	0	0	6
2804S 3227E	Lake St Lucia, Hlabisa, KwaZulu–Natal	147	502	6	1	6	6
3142S 1812E	Olifants River Mouth (South), Lutzville, Western Cape	110	205	2	0	0	1
3350S 2535E	Redhouse Saltpan, Port Elizabeth, Eastern Cape	59	164	4	0	0	4
3400S 2245E	Wilderness Lakes – Swartvlei System, Sedgefield, Western Cape	56	75	2	0	0	3
3402S 2324E	Keurbooms River Estuary, Plettenberg Bay, Western Cape	56	59	2	0	0	3
3247S 1812E	Berg River System, Velddrif, Western Cape	49	99	5	2	4	4
2953S 3101E	Durban Bayhead, Durban, KwaZulu–Natal	49	87	5	0	0	5
3403S 2302E	Knysna Lagoon, Knysna, Western Cape	44	101	5	0	0	5
3351S 1829E	Rietvlei, Milnerton, Western Cape	43	100	5	0	0	4
3350S 2533E	Bar None Saltpans, Port Elizabeth, Eastern Cape	43	44	2	0	0	3
3421S 1906E	Botriviervlei, Kleinmond, Western Cape	39	78	4	0	0	5

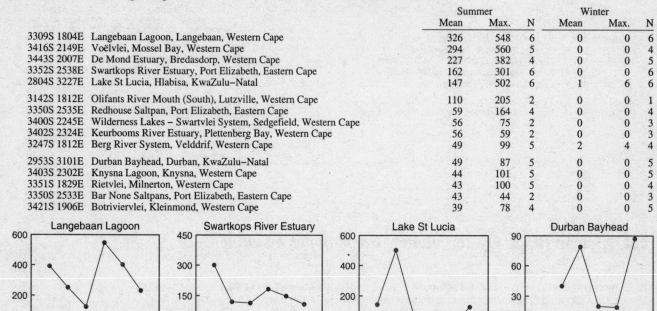

246 Whitefronted Plover *Charadrius marginatus*

Distribution largely coastal in RSA; most numerous on sandy beaches (often with rocks) and on mud and sand at estuaries, etc. Coastal birds largely sedentary; breeding occurs all year but peaks August–February. Inland populations, of sandbanks on tropical rivers, migrate to east coast in summer, as far south as Port Alfred. CWAC counts show no clear overall pattern of occurrence at coastal sites: winter peaks evident at eight major sites and summer peaks at four. Winter peaks may reflect dispersal of immatures, and local post-breeding movements of adults in response to bad weather on exposed shores.

		Summer			Winter		
		Mean	Max.	N	Mean	Max.	N
3309S 1804E	Langebaan Lagoon, Langebaan, Western Cape	178	215	6	123	154	6
2752S 3236E	Sodwana Bay to Cape Vidal, St Lucia, KwaZulu–Natal	127	127	1	66	81	2
3352S 2538E	Swartkops River Estuary, Port Elizabeth, Eastern Cape	49	85	6	117	161	6
3421S 1906E	Botriviervlei, Kleinmond, Western Cape	77	210	4	41	110	5
2838S 1627E	Orange River Estuary, Alexander Bay, Northern Cape	0	0	1	113	113	1
3402S 2324E	Keurbooms River Estuary, Plettenberg Bay, Western Cape	44	48	2	61	76	3
2824S 3225E	Mfolozi Mouth Area, St Lucia, KwaZulu–Natal	–	–	–	93	93	1
3247S 1812E	Berg River System, Velddrif, Western Cape	7	12	5	70	182	4
2849S 3202E	Richards Bay, Richards Bay (town), KwaZulu–Natal	21	36	5	55	90	5
3329S 2707E	Great Fish River Estuary, Port Alfred, Eastern Cape	31	45	4	41	62	4
3443S 2007E	De Mond Estuary, Bredasdorp, Western Cape	21	34	4	39	107	5
3416S 2149E	Voëlvlei, Mossel Bay, Western Cape	0	0	5	43	140	4
2923S 3121E	Umvoti River Estuary, Stanger, KwaZulu–Natal	22	37	3	11	17	5
3426S 2023E	De Hoop Vlei, Bredasdorp, Western Cape	0	1	5	24	38	4
3142S 1812E	Olifants River Mouth (South), Lutzville, Western Cape	17	34	2	3	3	1

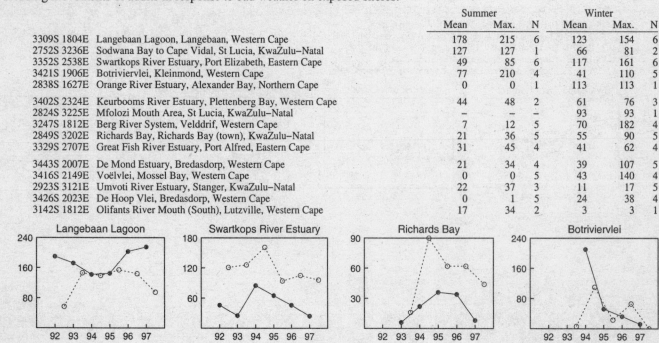

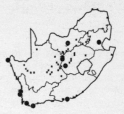

247 Chestnutbanded Plover *Charadrius pallidus*

The nominate race is endemic to southern Africa (population 6000–7000 birds), occurring mainly along the west coast and at widely scattered localities in the interior. Frequents natural and artificial saltpans, and lagoons. Breeding opportunistic, occurring throughout the year; populations breeding at pans in the interior move, mostly to west coast, when pans dry out; coastal breeding populations largely sedentary. CWAC data reflect known distribution, habitat preferences and movement patterns, with erratic inland occurrences, largest concentrations on west coast, and no clear overall seasonal pattern of movement.

		Summer			Winter		
		Mean	Max.	N	Mean	Max.	N
3247S 1812E	Berg River System, Velddrif, Western Cape	34	63	5	142	224*	4
2838S 1627E	Orange River Estuary, Alexander Bay, Northern Cape	0	0	1	61	61	1
3309S 1804E	Langebaan Lagoon, Langebaan, Western Cape	11	28	6	15	35	6
2840S 2446E	Kamfers Dam, Kimberley, Northern Cape	5	8	3	11	18	3
2829S 2446E	Nantwich Saltpan, Kimberley, Northern Cape	7	8	2	8	9	2
3443S 2007E	De Mond Estuary, Bredasdorp, Western Cape	0	0	4	14	68	5
2632S 2536E	Leeupan, Delareyville, North West	2	5	3	12	12	1
2620S 3020E	Blinkpan (Lothair), Lake Chrissie, Mpumalanga	3	4	2	4	6	2
2635S 2535E	Barberspan, Delareyville, North West	0	0	4	7	11	2
2932S 2515E	Kalkfontein Dam, Koffiefontein, Free State	0	2	6	3	11	6
3421S 1905E	Kleinmond River Estuary, Kleinmond, Western Cape	1	2	3	0	0	4
3351S 2535E	Chatty Saltpans, Port Elizabeth, Eastern Cape	1	1	2	0	0	3
3352S 2538E	Swartkops River Estuary, Port Elizabeth, Eastern Cape	0	1	6	0	0	6

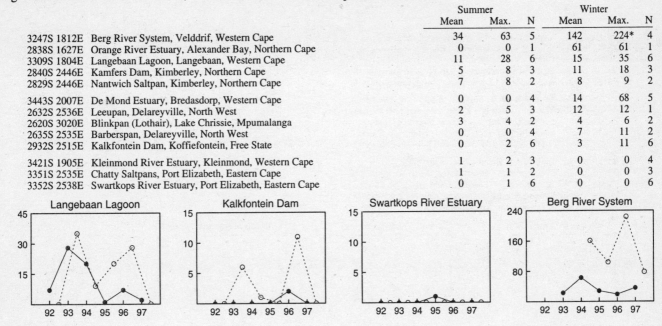

248 Kittlitz's Plover *Charadrius pecuarius*

Widespread and locally common, occurring on dry ground with very short grass, or dried mud, usually near water; at edges of dams, lakes and rivers, natural pans, and tidal mudflats and dry saltflats. CWAC data confirm wide use of artificial habitat at dams. Breeds mainly September–March in winter-rainfall region, mainly July–October elsewhere. Movements complex and poorly understood; regulated by seasonal rainfall. May be a partial migrant with birds moving into South Africa, especially to Western Cape, after breeding; CWAC data show summer peaks at many Western Cape sites, and good winter peaks in other regions.

		Summer			Winter		
		Mean	Max.	N	Mean	Max.	N
3247S 1812E	Berg River System, Velddrif, Western Cape	279	648*	5	199	297	4
3416S 2149E	Voëlvlei, Mossel Bay, Western Cape	232	400	5	166	400	4
2635S 2535E	Barberspan, Delareyville, North West	136	329	4	183	224	2
3318S 1845E	Radyn Dam, Malmesbury, Western Cape	304	624*	5	8	24	4
2838S 1627E	Orange River Estuary, Alexander Bay, Northern Cape	0	0	1	190	190	1
3351S 1829E	Rietvlei, Milnerton, Western Cape	164	434	5	14	22	4
2932S 2515E	Kalkfontein Dam, Koffiefontein, Free State	21	88	6	156	331	6
3309S 1804E	Langebaan Lagoon, Langebaan, Western Cape	73	118	6	103	184	6
2839S 2437E	Platfontein Pans, Kimberley, Northern Cape	20	20	1	115	115	1
3421S 1906E	Botriviervlei, Kleinmond, Western Cape	102	211	4	16	78	5
3400S 2456E	Kabeljous River Estuary, Jeffreys Bay, Eastern Cape	63	122	2	28	80	3
3403S 2302E	Knysna Lagoon, Knysna, Western Cape	39	69	5	46	63	5
3338S 1843E	Droëvlei, Klipheuwel, Western Cape	65	74	2	18	20	3
3219S 2238E	Springfontein Dam, Beaufort West, Western Cape	31	80	4	47	63	3
3236S 1818E	Rocher Pan, Velddrif, Western Cape	41	90	5	37	141	6

249 Threebanded Plover *Charadrius tricollaris*

Very widespread, occupying the widest range of habitats of any shorebird in southern Africa; frequents any freshwater habitat with open shoreline. Normally in small numbers, but large roosts occur in winter. As confirmed by CWAC, makes good use of artificial habitats e.g. dams (all sizes) and sewage works; has benefited greatly from construction of these. Breeds mainly July–January, earliest in north, latest in southwest. Movements complex; in winter may be commoner in northeast and many move from Karoo to south coast; these patterns apparent in CWAC data, with many more winter peaks than summer peaks in all regions.

		Summer Mean	Max.	N	Winter Mean	Max.	N
3416S 2149E	Voëlvlei, Mossel Bay, Western Cape	92	260	5	35	80	4
2553S 2918E	Witbank Dam, Witbank, Mpumalanga	25	95	4	67	193	5
2805S 3218E	Bushlands Pan, Hluhluwe, KwaZulu–Natal	0	0	2	75	75	1
3341S 1858E	Paarl Bird Sanctuary, Paarl, Western Cape	13	22	5	41	85	5
2818S 2712E	Allemanskraal Dam, Ventersburg, Free State	45	227	6	7	13	6
2838S 1627E	Orange River Estuary, Alexander Bay, Northern Cape	0	0	1	49	49	1
2834S 2948E	Malandeni Sewage Works, Ladysmith, KwaZulu–Natal	17	36	5	22	71	5
2839S 2437E	Platfontein Pans, Kimberley, Northern Cape	16	16	1	23	23	1
2857S 3146E	Mtunzini Prawn Hatchery, Mtunzini, KwaZulu–Natal	13	23	2	26	40	3
3150S 2208E	Sakrivierspoort Wetlands, Loxton, Northern Cape	21	28	3	13	14	2
2635S 2535E	Barberspan, Delareyville, North West	3	11	4	29	46	2
3219S 2238E	Springfontein Dam, Beaufort West, Western Cape	8	17	4	23	39	3
2554S 2842E	Bronkhorstspruit Dam, Bronkhorstspruit, Gauteng	7	14	4	23	53	4
2923S 3121E	Umvoti River Estuary, Stanger, KwaZulu–Natal	8	13	3	21	44	5
2629S 2828E	Blesbokspruit, Nigel, Gauteng	4	4	1	24	24	1

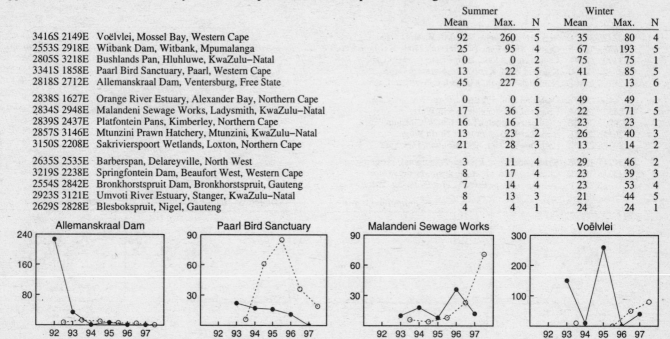

254 Grey Plover *Pluvialis squatarola*

Palearctic migrant; predominantly coastal; widespread and locally abundant; largest concentrations at Cape coasts, including regular globally significant numbers at Langebaan (CWAC shows decreasing numbers). Commonest at estuaries and lagoons; also at saltmarshes, saltpans (CWAC) and on sheltered sandy beaches, sometimes with rocks. Also at scattered inland waters, usually with sandy beaches or mud; most records are of first-year birds on passage. Arrives September. CWAC data confirm that proportion of birds remaining in austral winter high, and that such overwintering birds occur at many coastal localities.

		Summer Mean	Max.	N	Winter Mean	Max.	N
3309S 1804E	Langebaan Lagoon, Langebaan, Western Cape	3126**	4877**	6	257	540	6
3352S 2538E	Swartkops River Estuary, Port Elizabeth, Eastern Cape	624	721	6	126	234	6
3403S 2302E	Knysna Lagoon, Knysna, Western Cape	441	666	5	35	66	5
3247S 1812E	Berg River System, Velddrif, Western Cape	224	417	5	30	68	4
3402S 2324E	Keurbooms River Estuary, Plettenberg Bay, Western Cape	223	233	2	18	25	3
3350S 2535E	Redhouse Saltpan, Port Elizabeth, Eastern Cape	132	242	4	37	149	4
2849S 3202E	Richards Bay, Richards Bay (town), KwaZulu–Natal	141	260	5	19	48	5
3351S 2535E	Chatty Saltpans, Port Elizabeth, Eastern Cape	106	195	2	0	0	3
3443S 2007E	De Mond Estuary, Bredasdorp, Western Cape	59	84	4	8	20	5
2953S 3101E	Durban Bayhead, Durban, KwaZulu–Natal	59	87	5	6	15	5
3142S 1812E	Olifants River Mouth (South), Lutzville, Western Cape	52	104	2	4	4	1
2658S 3253E	Maputaland Coast, Kwangwanase, KwaZulu–Natal	13	13	1	–	–	–
3426S 2023E	De Hoop Vlei, Bredasdorp, Western Cape	10	45	5	1	3	4
2804S 3227E	Lake St Lucia, Hlabisa, KwaZulu–Natal	10	53	6	1	5	6
3220S 1825E	Verlorenvlei, Elandsbaai, Western Cape	0	0	6	7	34	5

258 Blacksmith Plover *Vanellus armatus*

Common and widespread, in pairs (often sedentary) and nonbreeding-season flocks; at moist, short grass and mud at edges of pans, lakes, rivers, estuaries and artificial wetlands (CWAC records from many dams, ponds, sewage works, etc.); also dry ground near water, e.g. mown grass, crop and ploughed fields, airfields, etc. Breeds mainly July–November. No regular movements known; postbreeding dispersal occurs, and irregular movements in response to flooding and drying of habitats. Good body of CWAC data for this conspicuous wader shows preponderance of summer peaks in all regions, most consistently in Western Cape.

		Summer			Winter		
		Mean	Max.	N	Mean	Max.	N
2838S 1627E	Orange River Estuary, Alexander Bay, Northern Cape	34	34	1	459	459	1
3351S 1829E	Rietvlei, Milnerton, Western Cape	286	384	5	136	183	4
2818S 2712E	Allemanskraal Dam, Ventersburg, Free State	247	577	6	52	86	6
3247S 1812E	Berg River System, Velddrif, Western Cape	142	232	5	144	192	4
2834S 2650E	Erfenis Dam, Winburg, Free State	168	316	6	91	174	6
2804S 2433E	Spitskop Dam, Spitskop, Northern Cape	169	180	2	72	109	2
2741S 2540E	Bloemhof Dam, Bloemhof, Free State	121	287	6	113	303	6
2932S 2515E	Kalkfontein Dam, Koffiefontein, Free State	54	90	6	160	305	6
2635S 2535E	Barberspan, Delareyville, North West	68	122	4	134	138	2
3338S 1843E	Droëvlei, Klipheuwel, Western Cape	185	197	2	16	22	3
2553S 2918E	Witbank Dam, Witbank, Mpumalanga	121	153	4	73	147	5
2852S 2600E	Krugersdrift Dam, Bloemfontein, Free State	126	212	6	61	113	6
3318S 1845E	Radyn Dam, Malmesbury, Western Cape	167	220	5	19	36	4
2715S 2741E	Koppies Dam, Koppies, Free State	94	133	6	80	298	6
2629S 2828E	Blesbokspruit, Nigel, Gauteng	79	79	1	95	95	1

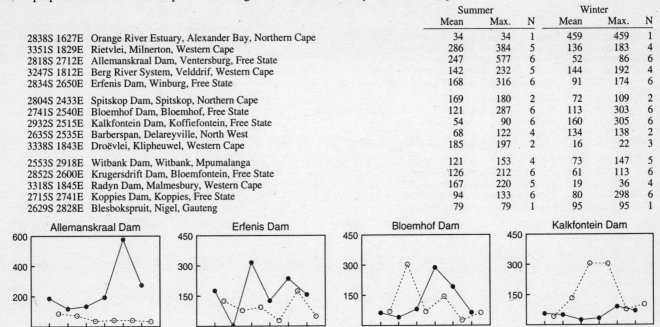

259 Whitecrowned Plover *Vanellus albiceps*

Occurs in the extreme northeast, on sandbanks and mudbanks of tropical rivers; resident. No CWAC records available.

260 Wattled Plover *Vanellus senegallus*

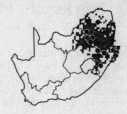

In RSA largely from central Northern Province south to KwaZulu-Natal. Usually in short wet grass at marshes, streams, rivers and pastures; also forages at dry open or burned sites near water. Breeds September–January; in small flocks when not breeding. Habitat changes may cause much movement in non-breeding season; CWAC data show fewer birds in winter at high altitude sites (reduced prey levels?), and at some sites where habitat may dry out. Seasonal movements may be local as sites with winter and summer peaks occur in the same areas. Winter and summer fluctuations at sites appear to be in step for extended periods (see figures).

		Summer			Winter		
		Mean	Max.	N	Mean	Max.	N
2557S 2800E	Diepsloot Nature Reserve, Johannesburg, Gauteng	23	50	4	43	65	5
2804S 3227E	Lake St Lucia, Hlabisa, KwaZulu–Natal	7	23	6	12	25	6
2629S 2828E	Blesbokspruit, Nigel, Gauteng	12	12	1	7	7	1
2740S 3226E	Tshanetshe Pan, Mbazwane, KwaZulu–Natal	7	18	5	6	15	6
2805S 3220E	Hluhluwe River Vlei & Floodplain, Hluhluwe, KwaZulu–Natal	4	7	2	9	9	1
2735S 2935E	Seekoeivlei, Memel, Free State	12	42	5	0	0	5
2351S 2927E	Pietersburg Bird Sanctuary, Pietersburg, Northern Province	12	12	1	0	0	1
2737S 3233E	Mfula Pan, Mbazwane, KwaZulu–Natal	6	15	5	6	13	6
2725S 3158E	Pongolapoort Dam, Mkuze, KwaZulu–Natal	10	42	6	2	3	6
2554S 2842E	Bronkhorstspruit Dam, Bronkhorstspruit, Gauteng	7	18	4	4	11	4
2915S 2941E	Hlatikulu Vlei, Hlatikulu, KwaZulu–Natal	9	11	2	2	2	1
2931S 3011E	Midmar Dam, Howick, KwaZulu–Natal	6	21	5	3	5	3
2611S 2818E	Korsman Bird Sanctuary, Benoni, Gauteng	5	13	3	3	9	3
2750S 3035E	Blood River Vlei, Vryheid, KwaZulu–Natal	3	3	1	5	5	1
2510S 2751E	Klipvoor Dam, Brits, North West	1	2	4	7	12	3

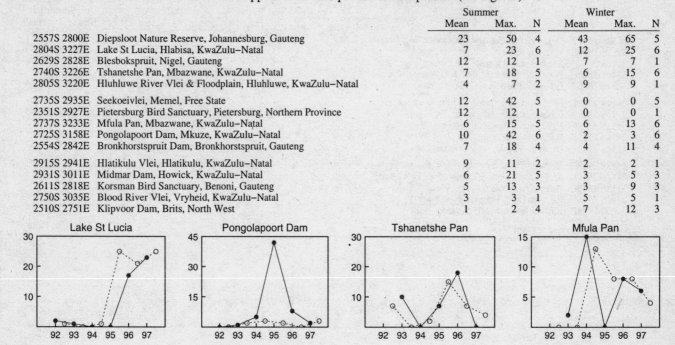

261 Longtoed Plover *Vanellus crassirostris*

Rare; occurs erratically in northern KwaZulu-Natal, where it has bred. Two CWAC records from Mfula Pan.

262 Turnstone *Arenaria interpres*

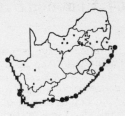

Palearctic migrant; primarily coastal, most numerous on sheltered rocky shores, mixed rocky and sandy shores, and shores with kelp wrack; sometimes on sandflats and mudflats; good numbers recorded by CWAC at some coastal saltpans. Small numbers occur inland, especially during southward passage. CWAC data confirm the continuing significance of Langebaan as the prime site for this species in Southern Africa; Swartkops estuary has also held globally significant numbers. Migrants arrive from August; CWAC data confirm that many birds remain at some coastal sites during the austral winter.

		Summer			Winter		
		Mean	Max.	N	Mean	Max.	N
3309S 1804E	Langebaan Lagoon, Langebaan, Western Cape	2433**	4587**	6	414**	796**	6
3352S 2538E	Swartkops River Estuary, Port Elizabeth, Eastern Cape	294*	376**	6	92	165	6
3351S 2535E	Chatty Saltpans, Port Elizabeth, Eastern Cape	29	43	2	23	70	3
3400S 2456E	Kabeljous River Estuary, Jeffreys Bay, Eastern Cape	13	25	2	0	0	3
2953S 3101E	Durban Bayhead, Durban, KwaZulu–Natal	10	26	5	1	6	5
2658S 3250E	Kosi Bay Nature Reserve, Manguzi, KwaZulu–Natal	10	43	5	1	5	6
3247S 1812E	Berg River System, Velddrif, Western Cape	1	3	5	8	19	4
2838S 1627E	Orange River Estuary, Alexander Bay, Northern Cape	0	0	1	4	4	1
3350S 2535E	Redhouse Saltpan, Port Elizabeth, Eastern Cape	2	7	4	1	4	4
2849S 3202E	Richards Bay, Richards Bay (town), KwaZulu–Natal	3	8	5	0	0	5
3329S 2707E	Great Fish River Estuary, Port Alfred, Eastern Cape	1	2	4	1	5	4
3402S 2324E	Keurbooms River Estuary, Plettenberg Bay, Western Cape	2	4	2	0	0	3
2658S 3253E	Maputaland Coast, Kwangwanase, KwaZulu–Natal	1	1	1	–	–	–
2804S 3227E	Lake St Lucia, Hlabisa, KwaZulu–Natal	0	2	6	1	3	6
3350S 2533E	Bar None Saltpans, Port Elizabeth, Eastern Cape	0	0	2	1	2	3

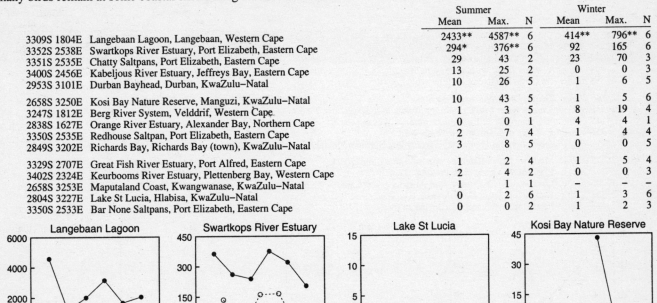

263 Terek Sandpiper *Xenus cinereus*

A Palearctic migrant, wintering mainly along the Indian Ocean coast; densities decrease southwards so that in RSA, large numbers are recorded only from three localities: Richards Bay, the Swartkops Estuary (numbers apparently increasing) and, on the Atlantic coast, Langebaan Lagoon. Rarely recorded inland, mostly on southward passage (no inland CWAC records during the survey period). Frequents coastal sandbars, muddy lagoons and estuaries, often occurring several kilometres upstream of river mouths. Many first-year birds spend the austral winter in Africa; CWAC shows winter occurrences at four coastal sites.

		Summer			Winter		
		Mean	Max.	N	Mean	Max.	N
3352S 2538E	Swartkops River Estuary, Port Elizabeth, Eastern Cape	161	260	6	8	21	6
2849S 3202E	Richards Bay, Richards Bay (town), KwaZulu–Natal	161	410	5	1	6	5
3309S 1804E	Langebaan Lagoon, Langebaan, Western Cape	94	251	6	14	58	6
2953S 3101E	Durban Bayhead, Durban, KwaZulu–Natal	18	35	5	0	1	5
3329S 2707E	Great Fish River Estuary, Port Alfred, Eastern Cape	3	5	4	0	0	4
2949S 3102E	Umgeni River Estuary, Durban, KwaZulu–Natal	2	4	5	0	0	5
3443S 2007E	De Mond Estuary, Bredasdorp, Western Cape	1	2	4	0	0	5
3247S 1812E	Berg River System, Velddrif, Western Cape	0	0	5	0	1	4
2804S 3227E	Lake St Lucia, Hlabisa, KwaZulu–Natal	0	1	6	0	0	6

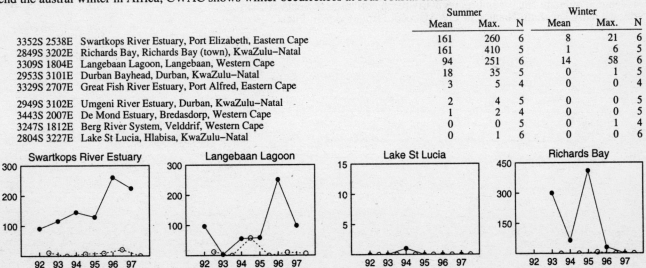

264 Common Sandpiper *Actitis hypoleucos*

Palearctic migrant, widespread and common at edges of almost every kind of flowing or standing water, e.g. sandy, rocky or wooded freshwater shorelines, ditches, road puddles, seashores, tidal creeks and estuaries, and wet ground in woodland or forest; few occur at saline pans. Solitary forager; in parties on migration and flocks at roosts: some large CWAC counts may be of roosts but others are totals of individuals along extensive shorelines. A few overwinter, especially inland; arrivals from late July. Large July counts presumably reflect concentrations of early arrivals at waters in largely dry areas.

		Summer			Winter		
		Mean	Max.	N	Mean	Max.	N
3421S 1906E	Botriviervlei, Kleinmond, Western Cape	158	578	4	0	0	5
3247S 1812E	Berg River System, Velddrif, Western Cape	2	5	5	54	204	4
2804S 3227E	Lake St Lucia, Hlabisa, KwaZulu–Natal	53	93	6	2	5	6
2553S 2918E	Witbank Dam, Witbank, Mpumalanga	44	149	4	1	• 2	5
2653S 3218E	Nyamithi Pan (Ndumo), Ingwavuma, KwaZulu–Natal	27	50	4	1	2	5
2834S 2650E	Erfenis Dam, Winburg, Free State	1	6	6	22	134	6
2923S 3121E	Umvoti River Estuary, Stanger, KwaZulu–Natal	18	39	3	2	6	5
3421S 1905E	Kleinmond River Estuary, Kleinmond, Western Cape	19	58	3	0	0	4
2635S 2535E	Barberspan, Delareyville, North West	5	13	4	15	29	2
2351S 2927E	Pietersburg Bird Sanctuary, Pietersburg, Northern Province	14	14	1	4	4	1
2857S 3146E	Mtunzini Prawn Hatchery, Mtunzini, KwaZulu–Natal	14	19	2	2	5	3
2534S 2814E	Rooiwal Sewage Works, Pretoria, Gauteng	15	31	4	0	1	5
3329S 2707E	Great Fish River Estuary, Port Alfred, Eastern Cape	13	21	4	0	1	4
2932S 2515E	Kalkfontein Dam, Koffiefontein, Free State	12	60	6	0	0	6
3341S 1858E	Paarl Bird Sanctuary, Paarl, Western Cape	11	33	5	0	0	5

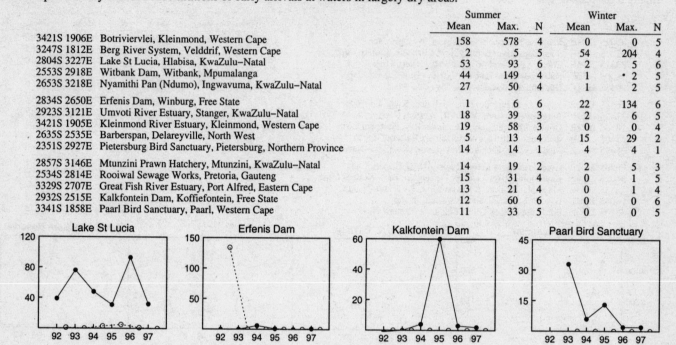

265 Green Sandpiper *Tringa ochropus*

Palearctic migrant; small numbers regularly reach northeastern South Africa, occasionally KwaZulu-Natal. One CWAC record from Lake St. Lucia.

266 Wood Sandpiper *Tringa glareola*

Palearctic migrant; widespread and locally fairly abundant, mainly at inland waters. Usually in small scattered parties, also in larger flocks. A few birds remain during the austral winter; first migrants return late July. Prefers freshwater swamp and marshland habitats with shallow water and mud or emergent/fringing vegetation, e.g. flooded grassland, irrigation, edges of lakes, dams and marshes, grassy pans, streams and muddy channels; sometimes walks on floating vegetation. Makes good use of artificially created wetlands, and largest CWAC concentrations recorded from sewage works, a very popular habitat.

		Summer Mean	Max.	N	Winter Mean	Max.	N
2948S 3100E	Northern Treatment Works, Durban, KwaZulu–Natal	87	272	5	0	1	5
2534S 2814E	Rooiwal Sewage Works, Pretoria, Gauteng	82	288	4	1	3	5
2351S 2927E	Pietersburg Bird Sanctuary, Pietersburg, Northern Province	45	45	1	0	0	1
2847S 3203E	Thulazihleka Pan, Richards Bay, KwaZulu–Natal	40	152	5	0	1	5
2915S 2941E	Hlatikulu Vlei, Hlatikulu, KwaZulu–Natal	35	54	2	0	0	1
2629S 2828E	Blesbokspruit, Nigel, Gauteng	30	30	1	2	2	1
2756S 2444E	Espagsdrift Vlei, Jan Kempdorp, Northern Cape	25	47	2	0	0	2
3401S 2323E	Bitou River, Plettenberg Bay, Western Cape	24	36	2	0	0	3
3338S 2634E	Ghio Pans, Kenton–on–Sea, Eastern Cape	23	38	4	0	0	4
2857S 3146E	Mtunzini Prawn Hatchery, Mtunzini, KwaZulu–Natal	22	34	2	1	3	3
3351S 1829E	Rietvlei, Milnerton, Western Cape	22	30	5	0	0	4
2619S 3015E	Lake Chrissie East Pan, Lake Chrissie, Mpumalanga	21	21	1	0	0	1
2840S 2446E	Kamfers Dam, Kimberley, Northern Cape	21	48	3	0	1	3
2849S 3202E	Richards Bay, Richards Bay (town), KwaZulu–Natal	20	57	5	0	0	5
2834S 2948E	Malandeni Sewage Works, Ladysmith, KwaZulu–Natal	18	24	5	0	1	5

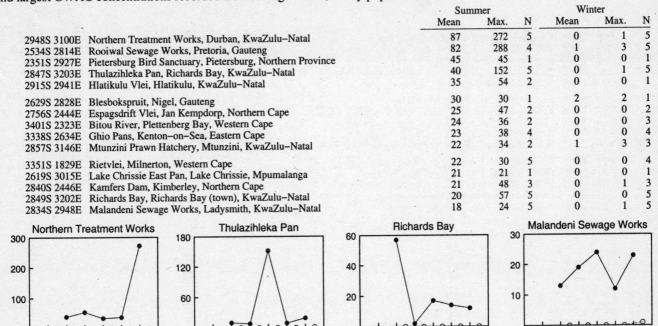

269 Marsh Sandpiper *Tringa stagnatilis*

Widespread and common Palearctic migrant; rarely in large concentrations. Compared to Greenshank, relatively few remain during austral winter. The only globally significant count (Koppiesdam, summer 1992, with a high count of Little Stint), was the only summer record for that site. Prefers to forage in shallow water over mud; often at marshy margins of open waters, even in sparse emergent vegetation; rarely feeds at coastal shorelines. Good counts from many wetland types, e.g. freshwater sites, saline pans, lagoons and estuaries; some artificial impoundments (e.g. dams and saltworks) hold good numbers.

		Summer Mean	Max.	N	Winter Mean	Max.	N
2839S 2437E	Platfontein Pans, Kimberley, Northern Cape	208	208	1	1	1	1
2715S 2741E	Koppies Dam, Koppies, Free State	142	850**	6	3	18	6
3247S 1812E	Berg River System, Velddrif, Western Cape	60	134	5	25	66	4
2840S 2446E	Kamfers Dam, Kimberley, Northern Cape	83	109	3	0	0	3
3400S 2245E	Wilderness Lakes – Swartvlei System, Sedgefield, Western Cape	79	87	2	0	0	3
3351S 1829E	Rietvlei, Milnerton, Western Cape	78	200	5	0	0	4
3351S 2535E	Chatty Saltpans, Port Elizabeth, Eastern Cape	63	105	2	0	1	3
3236S 1818E	Rocher Pan, Velddrif, Western Cape	54	120	5	0	0	6
3403S 2302E	Knysna Lagoon, Knysna, Western Cape	44	90	5	4	21	5
2804S 3227E	Lake St Lucia, Hlabisa, KwaZulu–Natal	38	91	6	9	19	6
2846S 2448E	Du Toit's Pan, Kimberley, Northern Cape	37	66	2	0	0	2
2653S 3218E	Nyamithi Pan (Ndumo), Ingwavuma, KwaZulu–Natal	32	102	4	0	1	5
2847S 3203E	Thulazihleka Pan, Richards Bay, KwaZulu–Natal	31	81	5	0	1	5
3350S 2535E	Redhouse Saltpan, Port Elizabeth, Eastern Cape	24	70	4	0	1	4
2755S 2446E	Ganspan Pans & Vlei, Jan Kempdorp, Northern Cape	21	38	2	0	0	2

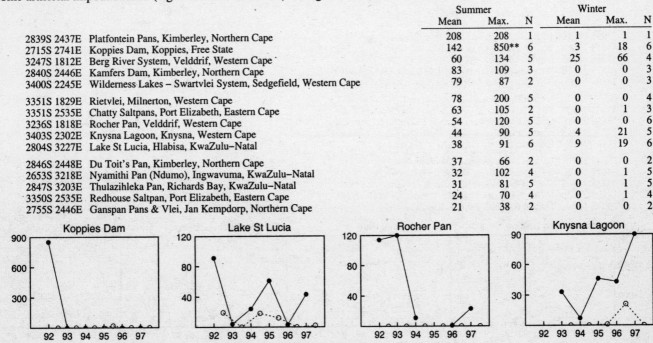

270 Greenshank *Tringa nebularia*

The most widespread *Tringa* sandpiper in RSA. Unlike Marsh Sandpiper, many occur at coastal sites, at which CWAC data show the largest concentrations, especially in the Cape (counts are increasing at the Swartkops estuary); inland waters seldom hold large numbers. Frequents a wide variety of habitats; needs shallow water for foraging. Normally solitary or in small parties but may roost in large flocks. Many birds spend the austral winter here; high winter counts at some sites. Winter counts may also be augmented by early-returning migrants; arrivals over the whole country regularly occur from late July.

		Summer			Winter		
		Mean	Max.	N	Mean	Max.	N
3309S 1804E	Langebaan Lagoon, Langebaan, Western Cape	578	992	6	200	320	6
3403S 2302E	Knysna Lagoon, Knysna, Western Cape	353	499	5	76	94	5
3247S 1812E	Berg River System, Velddrif, Western Cape	268	566	5	90	147	4
3352S 2538E	Swartkops River Estuary, Port Elizabeth, Eastern Cape	160	237	6	77	107	6
3416S 2149E	Voëlvlei, Mossel Bay, Western Cape	166	700	5	3	8	4
2804S 3227E	Lake St Lucia, Hlabisa, KwaZulu–Natal	58	133	6	63	250	6
3402S 2324E	Keurbooms River Estuary, Plettenberg Bay, Western Cape	92	108	2	26	35	3
2619S 3015E	Lake Chrissie East Pan, Lake Chrissie, Mpumalanga	76	76	1	0	0	1
3350S 2535E	Redhouse Saltpan, Port Elizabeth, Eastern Cape	48	122	4	14	41	4
3400S 2245E	Wilderness Lakes – Swartvlei System, Sedgefield, Western Cape	51	83	2	7	12	3
3329S 2707E	Great Fish River Estuary, Port Alfred, Eastern Cape	38	67	4	10	11	4
3351S 2535E	Chatty Saltpans, Port Elizabeth, Eastern Cape	42	57	2	2	4	3
3142S 1812E	Olifants River Mouth (South), Lutzville, Western Cape	37	72	2	2	2	1
2953S 3101E	Durban Bayhead, Durban, KwaZulu–Natal	30	53	5	5	12	5
3408S 1821E	Wildevoëlvlei, Kommetjie, Western Cape	30	71	6	0	0	6

271 Knot *Calidris canutus*

Palearctic migrant; occurs mainly on Western Cape coast; the most important site is Langebaan Lagoon, but smaller numbers also along southern and eastern coasts; good counts recorded at Botriviervlei and Droëvlei (Western Cape), and Kosi Bay (KwaZulu–Natal). Concentrations occur only at sheltered tidal estuaries and lagoons with extensive mudflats and sandflats. Inland records are rare, but 6 birds were at Korsman Bird Sanctuary, Gauteng, in winter 1993. Some first-year birds remain during the austral winter, as is shown by counts at five CWAC sites in the survey period. Migrants arrive September–October.

		Summer			Winter		
		Mean	Max.	N	Mean	Max.	N
3309S 1804E	Langebaan Lagoon, Langebaan, Western Cape	838	2171	6	21	90	6
3421S 1906E	Botriviervlei, Kleinmond, Western Cape	73	225	4	0	0	5
3338S 1843E	Droëvlei, Klipheuwel, Western Cape	37	74	2	0	0	3
2752S 3236E	Sodwana Bay to Cape Vidal, St Lucia, KwaZulu–Natal	23	23	1	0	0	2
2658S 3250E	Kosi Bay Nature Reserve, Manguzi, KwaZulu–Natal	20	100	5	0	0	6
2740S 3219E	Nsumu Pan, Mkuzi Game Reserve, KwaZulu–Natal	0	0	6	16	95	6
3400S 2456E	Kabeljous River Estuary, Jeffreys Bay, Eastern Cape	0	0	2	13	38	3
3352S 2538E	Swartkops River Estuary, Port Elizabeth, Eastern Cape	8	16	6	0	1	6
3402S 2324E	Keurbooms River Estuary, Plettenberg Bay, Western Cape	4	4	2	0	0	3
2611S 2818E	Korsman Bird Sanctuary, Benoni, Gauteng	0	0	3	2	6	3
2804S 3227E	Lake St Lucia, Hlabisa, KwaZulu–Natal	2	9	6	0	0	6
3247S 1812E	Berg River System, Velddrif, Western Cape	1	4	5	0	1	4
2923S 3121E	Umvoti River Estuary, Stanger, KwaZulu–Natal	1	3	3	0	0	5
2849S 3202E	Richards Bay, Richards Bay (town), KwaZulu–Natal	1	1	5	0	0	5
2953S 3101E	Durban Bayhead, Durban, KwaZulu–Natal	0	1	5	0	0	5

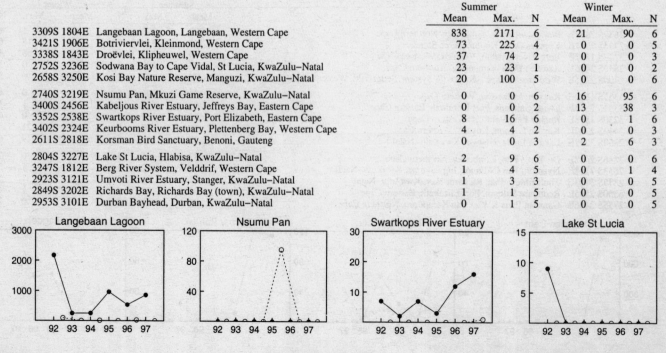

272 Curlew Sandpiper *Calidris ferruginea*

A common and widespread Palearctic migrant, often the most abundant wader at coastal and inland sites (compare with CWAC figures for other species). Langebaan holds globally significant numbers, and nationally significant counts were recorded at three coastal sites from the Western Cape to KwaZulu-Natal. It occurs mainly at tidal estuaries, and at inland waters with muddy edges and receding waterlines. Arrivals are from August. Some birds remain during the austral winter; in the survey period large winter counts were made at several coastal localities, and also at the ephemeral Platfontein Pans in winter 1997.

		Summer			Winter		
		Mean	Max.	N	Mean	Max.	N
3309S 1804E	Langebaan Lagoon, Langebaan, Western Cape	14564**	18495**	6	1272	2303	6
3247S 1812E	Berg River System, Velddrif, Western Cape	4062*	6818*	5	480	769	4
3403S 2302E	Knysna Lagoon, Knysna, Western Cape	2452	2817	5	25	99	5
2804S 3227E	Lake St Lucia, Hlabisa, KwaZulu-Natal	1562	4117*	6	193	923	6
3416S 2149E	Voëlvlei, Mossel Bay, Western Cape	1370	3000	5	10	40	4
3350S 2535E	Redhouse Saltpan, Port Elizabeth, Eastern Cape	1182	4187*	4	11	24	4
3352S 2538E	Swartkops River Estuary, Port Elizabeth, Eastern Cape	1010	2099	6	47	137	6
2838S 1627E	Orange River Estuary, Alexander Bay, Northern Cape	0	0	1	793	793	1
3400S 2456E	Kabeljous River Estuary, Jeffreys Bay, Eastern Cape	660	1320	2	14	42	3
2839S 2437E	Platfontein Pans, Kimberley, Northern Cape	372	372	1	283	283	1
3421S 1906E	Botriviervlei, Kleinmond, Western Cape	584	1000	4	0	0	5
3142S 1812E	Olifants River Mouth (South), Lutzville, Western Cape	406	663	2	0	0	1
2949S 3102E	Umgeni River Estuary, Durban, KwaZulu-Natal	401	631	5	0	0	5
3236S 1818E	Rocher Pan, Velddrif, Western Cape	400	1090	5	0	0	6
3351S 1829E	Rietvlei, Milnerton, Western Cape	387	1435	5	4	13	4

274 Little Stint *Calidris minuta*

Common and widespread Palearctic migrant, particularly numerous in highveld panveld. Usually in flocks, frequently with Curlew Sandpiper, at muddy wetland edges and on coasts at sheltered intertidal mudflats. It breeds when one year old, so occurrences during the austral winter are regarded as uncommon, but there are winter counts from 26 CWAC sites, usually of small numbers but including large numbers at one inland and two coastal sites (Erfenisdam, Mossel Bay and Lake St Lucia). As shown by CWAC data, it readily utilises artificial wetlands such as dams, sewage works and saltpans.

		Summer			Winter		
		Mean	Max.	N	Mean	Max.	N
3247S 1812E	Berg River System, Velddrif, Western Cape	1060	1575	5	29	72	4
2804S 3227E	Lake St Lucia, Hlabisa, KwaZulu-Natal	853	3721	6	90	478	6
3416S 2149E	Voëlvlei, Mossel Bay, Western Cape	906	2500	5	35	140	4
3351S 1829E	Rietvlei, Milnerton, Western Cape	792	1501	5	0	0	4
2932S 2515E	Kalkfontein Dam, Koffiefontein, Free State	688	1222	6	12	51	6
3405S 1831E	Strandfontein Sewage Works, Muizenberg, Western Cape	455	793	6	0	0	6
3309S 1804E	Langebaan Lagoon, Langebaan, Western Cape	406	721	6	6	19	6
3350S 2535E	Redhouse Saltpan, Port Elizabeth, Eastern Cape	410	1320	4	0	0	4
2840S 2446E	Kamfers Dam, Kimberley, Northern Cape	337	497	3	0	0	3
3350S 2533E	Bar None Saltpans, Port Elizabeth, Eastern Cape	288	304	2	0	1	3
2918S 2637E	Rusfontein Dam, Thaba Nchu, Free State	257	660	6	0	2	6
2839S 2437E	Platfontein Pans, Kimberley, Northern Cape	243	243	1	0	0	1
3236S 1818E	Rocher Pan, Velddrif, Western Cape	225	396	5	0	0	6
3400S 2456E	Kabeljous River Estuary, Jeffreys Bay, Eastern Cape	222	337	2	0	0	3
3443S 2007E	De Mond Estuary, Bredasdorp, Western Cape	221	291	4	0	0	5

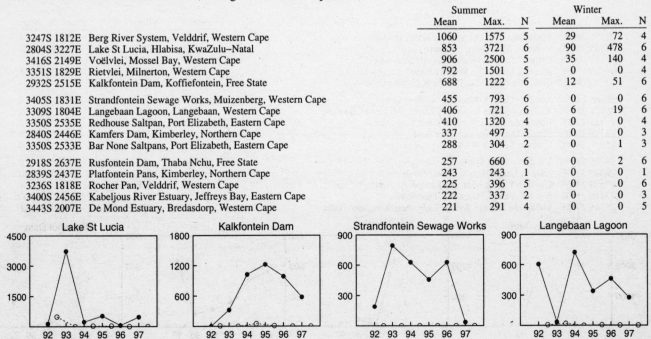

281 Sanderling *Calidris alba*

A common Palearctic migrant along most of the coast, at sand beaches, wave-cut platforms, shores with seaweed wrack, and sandbanks at inlets and estuaries. Isolated inland records are usually of birds on southward passage. Globally significant numbers occur at Langebaan. Migrants arrive mainly in October–December, and first-year birds commonly remain during the austral winter, when good numbers are recorded at several CWAC sites. Southern Africa holds a significant nonbreeding population of this species, but much of its habitat is used for human recreational activities; undisturbed refuges are needed for its conservation.

		Summer			Winter		
		Mean	Max.	N	Mean	Max.	N
3309S 1804E	Langebaan Lagoon, Langebaan, Western Cape	1387*	2260**	6	41	155	6
2857S 3147E	Mlalazi River Estuary, Mtunzini, KwaZulu–Natal	159	307	2	28	55	2
3352S 2538E	Swartkops River Estuary, Port Elizabeth, Eastern Cape	131	182	6	8	26	6
2658S 3253E	Maputaland Coast, Kwangwanase, KwaZulu–Natal	87	87	1	–	–	–
3421S 1905E	Kleinmond River Estuary, Kleinmond, Western Cape	53	160	3	0	0	4
3426S 2023E	De Hoop Vlei, Bredasdorp, Western Cape	51	235	5	0	0	4
3443S 2007E	De Mond Estuary, Bredasdorp, Western Cape	39	96	4	1	4	5
3329S 2707E	Great Fish River Estuary, Port Alfred, Eastern Cape	28	38	4	12	36	4
2752S 3236E	Sodwana Bay to Cape Vidal, St Lucia, KwaZulu–Natal	28	28	1	7	14	2
2635S 2535E	Barberspan, Delareyville, North West	32	129	4	0	0	2
2824S 3225E	Mfolozi Mouth Area, St Lucia, KwaZulu–Natal	–	–	–	30	30	1
2913S 3128E	Tugela River Mouth, Mandini, KwaZulu–Natal	19	42	3	–	–	–
2658S 3250E	Kosi Bay Nature Reserve, Manguzi, KwaZulu–Natal	19	93	5	0	0	6
3400S 2456E	Kabeljous River Estuary, Jeffreys Bay, Eastern Cape	17	24	2	0	0	3
3351S 1829E	Rietvlei, Milnerton, Western Cape	13	40	5	0	0	4

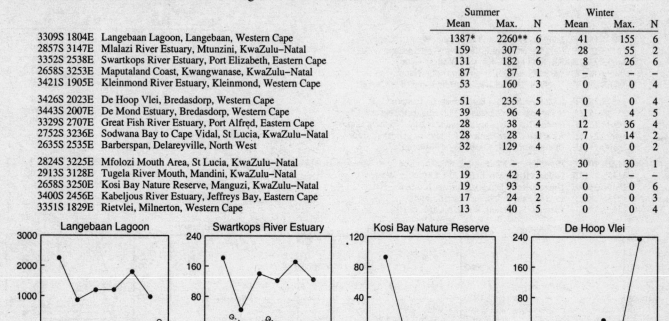

284 Ruff *Philomachus pugnax*

A Palearctic migrant; widespread and common throughout the country; main concentrations in the panveld of the central highveld. Prefers shallow water, mud and short emergent vegetation; occurs at freshwater, saline and alkaline wetlands, including vleis, pans, irrigation, flooded grass, sewage works and saltworks; less common in coastal intertidal habitats. Large flocks feed on seeds in pastures and wheat stubble. Arrives mainly from September. Small numbers sometimes remain during the austral winter, but there are few CWAC records of such occurrences; large count at Bloemhof Dam in winter 1992 is noteworthy.

		Summer			Winter		
		Mean	Max.	N	Mean	Max.	N
2839S 2437E	Platfontein Pans, Kimberley, Northern Cape	1531	1531	1	1	1	1
3416S 2149E	Voëlvlei, Mossel Bay, Western Cape	1160	3000	5	0	0	4
2715S 3007E	Clarens' Pan, Wakkerstroom, Mpumalanga	539	539	1	–	–	–
3351S 1829E	Rietvlei, Milnerton, Western Cape	496	1161	5	0	1	4
3351S 2535E	Chatty Saltpans, Port Elizabeth, Eastern Cape	443	572	2	0	0	3
2840S 2446E	Kamfers Dam, Kimberley, Northern Cape	423	612	3	0	0	3
2622S 2810E	Vlakplaas Water Treatment Works, Germiston, Gauteng	384	700	4	0	0	4
2932S 2515E	Kalkfontein Dam, Koffiefontein, Free State	356	2038	6	0	2	6
2834S 2650E	Erfenis Dam, Winburg, Free State	256	1295	6	0	0	6
2534S 2814E	Rooiwal Sewage Works, Pretoria, Gauteng	217	470	4	0	0	5
2807S 2455E	Vaalharts Weir, Warrenton, Northern Cape	206	407	2	0	0	2
2804S 3227E	Lake St Lucia, Hlabisa, KwaZulu–Natal	184	328	6	4	20	6
2755S 2446E	Ganspan Pans & Vlei, Jan Kempdorp, Northern Cape	170	318	2	1	1	2
2741S 2540E	Bloemhof Dam, Bloemhof, Free State	51	243	6	117	700	6
2834S 2948E	Malandeni Sewage Works, Ladysmith, KwaZulu–Natal	162	333	5	0	1	5

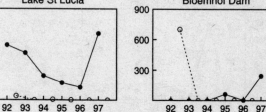

286 Ethiopian Snipe *Gallinago nigripennis*

Widespread in wetter regions; concentrations in Western Cape, interior of KwaZulu-Natal and highveld from eastern Free State to Mpumalanga and Northwest Province, whence come all large CWAC counts. Prefers wet areas with short grass and marsh vegetation interspersed with exposed mud; often feeds at cattle-trampled areas. Breeds mainly July–September. Often resident, but has extensive local movements associated with seasonal flooding and drying of habitat. CWAC data show no good patterns of seasonal occurrence: marked summer peaks at some Western Cape, Free State and KwaZulu-Natal sites, and winter peaks in Gauteng.

		Summer			Winter		
		Mean	Max.	N	Mean	Max.	N
2629S 2828E	Blesbokspruit, Nigel, Gauteng	34	34	1	65	65	1
3339S 1858E	Wellington Waste Water Works, Wellington, Western Cape	54	54	1	0	0	1
2621S 2830E	Marievale Bird Sanctuary, Nigel, Gauteng	7	17	5	24	81	5
2750S 3035E	Blood River Vlei, Vryheid, KwaZulu–Natal	26	26	1	3	3	1
2702S 3030E	Heyshope Dam, Piet Retief, Mpumalanga	–	–	–	24	24	1
2915S 2941E	Hlatikulu Vlei, Hlatikulu, KwaZulu–Natal	18	22	2	5	5	1
2613S 2828E	Springs Bird Sanctuary, Springs, Gauteng	7	16	5	13	31	5
2735S 2935E	Seekoeivlei, Memel, Free State	18	62	5	0	0	5
2715S 2741E	Koppies Dam, Koppies, Free State	13	75	6	0	2	6
2840S 2446E	Kamfers Dam, Kimberley, Northern Cape	4	7	3	6	15	3
2554S 2842E	Bronkhorstspruit Dam, Bronkhorstspruit, Gauteng	0	1	4	8	17	4
3351S 1829E	Rietvlei, Milnerton, Western Cape	7	14	5	1	3	4
3402S 1845E	Klavervlei, Somerset West, Western Cape	8	15	3	0	0	3
2553S 2918E	Witbank Dam, Witbank, Mpumalanga	6	23	4	1	4	5
2834S 2948E	Malandeni Sewage Works, Ladysmith, KwaZulu–Natal	2	8	5	4	11	5

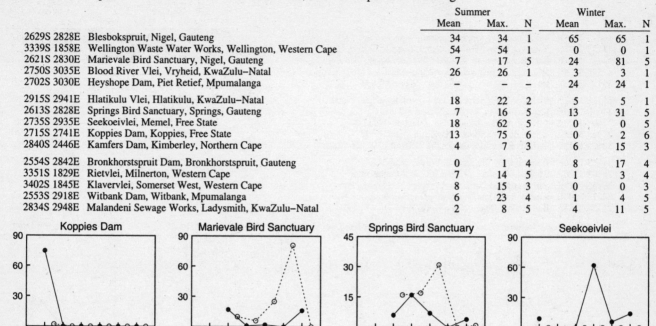

288 Bartailed Godwit *Limosa lapponica*

A Palearctic migrant, mostly of coastal occurrence, mainly frequenting sheltered inlets, estuaries and lagoons with extensive intertidal sand and mud; most CWAC sites fall into these habitat categories, but birds also recorded at Redhouse Saltpan, Eastern Cape. Inland records rare, mostly during southward passage; none at CWAC sites during survey period. Langebaan holds high numbers in summer and winter; many individuals remain during the austral winter and birds may overwinter twice in southern Africa before first breeding. Has expanded its wintering range into southern Africa during the 20th century.

		Summer			Winter		
		Mean	Max.	N	Mean	Max.	N
3309S 1804E	Langebaan Lagoon, Langebaan, Western Cape	427	620	6	60	211	6
3352S 2538E	Swartkops River Estuary, Port Elizabeth, Eastern Cape	50	92	6	14	32	6
3247S 1812E	Berg River System, Velddrif, Western Cape	19	41	5	6	19	4
3402S 2324E	Keurbooms River Estuary, Plettenberg Bay, Western Cape	4	5	2	0	1	3
3443S 2007E	De Mond Estuary, Bredasdorp, Western Cape	4	10	4	0	0	5
2849S 3202E	Richards Bay, Richards Bay (town), KwaZulu–Natal	3	10	5	0	0	5
3426S 2023E	De Hoop Vlei, Bredasdorp, Western Cape	3	10	5	0	1	4
3350S 2535E	Redhouse Saltpan, Port Elizabeth, Eastern Cape	2	8	4	1	2	4
3405S 1831E	Strandfontein Sewage Works, Muizenberg, Western Cape	0	2	6	0	0	6
3329S 2707E	Great Fish River Estuary, Port Alfred, Eastern Cape	0	1	4	0	0	4
3403S 2302E	Knysna Lagoon, Knysna, Western Cape	0	1	5	0	0	5

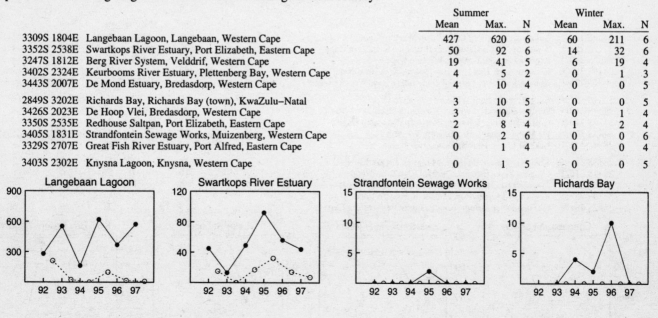

289 Curlew *Numenius arquata*

A Palearctic migrant, occurring mainly at coastal wetlands; distribution concentrated on coastline from Western to Eastern Cape. Counts often small, but high numbers at Langebaan. Relatively few inland records, but more regular inland than Whimbrel, as CWAC data show. Normally on intertidal sandbanks and mudflats at large, undisturbed estuaries, also salt-marshes; inland at muddy river banks and lakeshores. Arrives in August; many birds remain during the austral winter. Unusually high counts in winter 1994 at three freshwater pan/floodplain sites in KwaZulu-Natal: Neshe, Tshanetshe and Hlonhlela.

		Summer			Winter		
		Mean	Max.	N	Mean	Max.	N
3309S 1804E	Langebaan Lagoon, Langebaan, Western Cape	326	1373	6	82	362	6
3352S 2538E	Swartkops River Estuary, Port Elizabeth, Eastern Cape	62	85	6	18	27	6
3247S 1812E	Berg River System, Velddrif, Western Cape	12	22	5	7	13	4
2739S 3224E	Neshe Pan, Mbazwane, KwaZulu-Natal	0	0	5	18	108	6
3443S 2007E	De Mond Estuary, Bredasdorp, Western Cape	6	13	4	2	10	5
2849S 3202E	Richards Bay, Richards Bay (town), KwaZulu-Natal	7	13	5	1	4	5
3403S 2302E	Knysna Lagoon, Knysna, Western Cape	5	7	5	1	2	5
2740S 3226E	Tshanetshe Pan, Mbazwane, KwaZulu-Natal	0	0	5	5	29	6
2736S 3212E	Hlonhlela Pan, Mkuze, KwaZulu-Natal	0	0	5	4	20	5
3142S 1812E	Olifants River Mouth (South), Lutzville, Western Cape	3	4	2	0	0	1
3421S 1906E	Botriviervlei, Kleinmond, Western Cape	2	5	4	0	0	5
2620S 3020E	Blinkpan (Lothair), Lake Chrissie, Mpumalanga	1	2	2	0	0	2
2818S 2712E	Allemanskraal Dam, Ventersburg, Free State	1	3	6	0	0	6
2852S 2600E	Krugersdrift Dam, Bloemfontein, Free State	1	4	6	0	0	6
2635S 2535E	Barberspan, Delareyville, North West	1	2	4	0	0	2

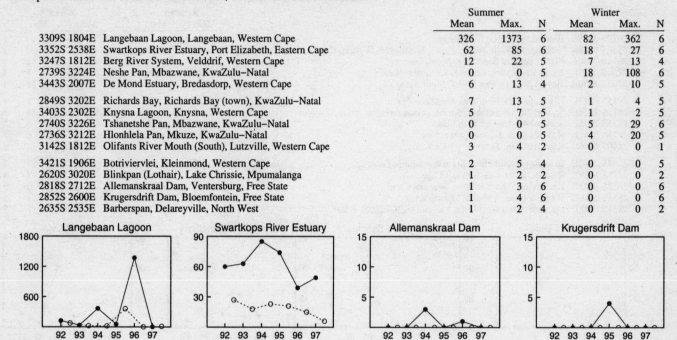

290 Whimbrel *Numenius phaeopus*

A Palearctic migrant to coastal habitats, where it is more widespread and numerous than the Curlew; occurs in a wider variety of habitats, from rather exposed sandy and rocky shores to sheltered muddy estuaries; largest CWAC counts at estuaries and lagoons; also recorded at saltpans. Very few inland records, most at large waterbodies such as dams and pans. Arrivals begin in August; many birds remain during the austral winter, when good counts recorded from several CWAC sites. Formerly less numerous than Curlew in southern Africa but numbers have increased this century and population now 6-7 times that of its congener.

		Summer			Winter		
		Mean	Max.	N	Mean	Max.	N
3309S 1804E	Langebaan Lagoon, Langebaan, Western Cape	825	1193	6	219	312	6
3352S 2538E	Swartkops River Estuary, Port Elizabeth, Eastern Cape	577	755	6	154	194	6
3403S 2302E	Knysna Lagoon, Knysna, Western Cape	319	387	5	31	56	5
2849S 3202E	Richards Bay, Richards Bay (town), KwaZulu-Natal	182	356	5	43	119	5
3402S 2324E	Keurbooms River Estuary, Plettenberg Bay, Western Cape	129	133	2	29	35	3
3247S 1812E	Berg River System, Velddrif, Western Cape	36	67	5	4	11	4
2953S 3101E	Durban Bayhead, Durban, KwaZulu-Natal	23	50	5	4	8	5
3329S 2707E	Great Fish River Estuary, Port Alfred, Eastern Cape	21	29	4	5	8	4
3443S 2007E	De Mond Estuary, Bredasdorp, Western Cape	12	14	4	2	6	5
2804S 3227E	Lake St Lucia, Hlabisa, KwaZulu-Natal	10	15	6	3	8	6
2658S 3250E	Kosi Bay Nature Reserve, Manguzi, KwaZulu-Natal	10	41	5	1	2	6
2949S 3102E	Umgeni River Estuary, Durban, KwaZulu-Natal	10	31	5	0	1	5
2658S 3253E	Maputaland Coast, Kwangwanase, KwaZulu-Natal	8	8	1	–	–	–
3350S 2535E	Redhouse Saltpan, Port Elizabeth, Eastern Cape	8	15	4	0	0	4
3142S 1812E	Olifants River Mouth (South), Lutzville, Western Cape	3	3	2	5	5	1

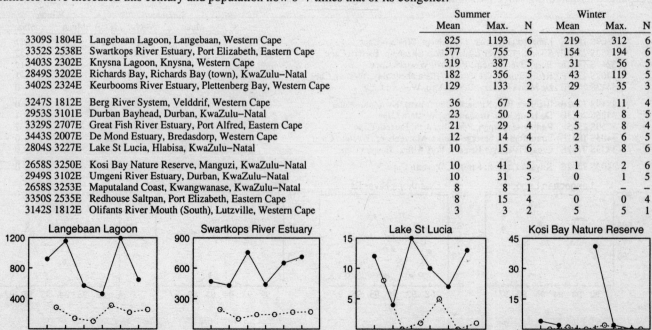

294 Avocet *Recurvirostra avosetta*

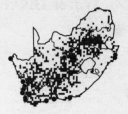

Typically at highly saline waters such as pans, saltworks, coastal lagoons and sewage evaporation ponds. Breeds opportunistically at ephemeral sites with receding waterlines; in winter-rainfall area most breed in spring; elsewhere peak tends towards late summer. Nomadic; movements complex, probably mainly in response to rains; many probably spend drought periods at the coast. CWAC data show more January peaks than July peaks in all regions. Some particularly good counts in Western Cape, summer 1993. Has benefited from construction of saltworks and sewage works which form drought refuges.

		Summer			Winter		
		Mean	Max.	N	Mean	Max.	N
2839S 2437E	Platfontein Pans, Kimberley, Northern Cape	530	530	1	57	57	1
2838S 1627E	Orange River Estuary, Alexander Bay, Northern Cape	0	0	1	510	510	1
3405S 1831E	Strandfontein Sewage Works, Muizenberg, Western Cape	441	649	6	60	130	6
3351S 2535E	Chatty Saltpans, Port Elizabeth, Eastern Cape	352	490	2	121	244	3
3247S 1812E	Berg River System, Velddrif, Western Cape	84	251	5	205	247	4
3416S 2149E	Voëlvlei, Mossel Bay, Western Cape	157	600	5	118	230	4
2804S 3227E	Lake St Lucia, Hlabisa, KwaZulu–Natal	69	254	6	180	300	6
2741S 2540E	Bloemhof Dam, Bloemhof, Free State	61	360	6	131	716*	6
3351S 1829E	Rietvlei, Milnerton, Western Cape	166	669*	5	0	0	4
3309S 1804E	Langebaan Lagoon, Langebaan, Western Cape	69	135	6	65	130	6
3142S 1812E	Olifants River Mouth (South), Lutzville, Western Cape	11	20	2	74	74	1
3220S 1825E	Verlorenvlei, Elandsbaai, Western Cape	78	452	6	3	16	5
3236S 1818E	Rocher Pan, Velddrif, Western Cape	78	145	5	0	0	6
3403S 2302E	Knysna Lagoon, Knysna, Western Cape	15	50	5	53	103	5
2824S 3225E	Mfolozi Mouth Area, St Lucia, KwaZulu–Natal	–	–	–	64	64	1

Strandfontein Sewage Works   **Lake St Lucia**   **Bloemhof Dam**   **Langebaan Lagoon**

295 Blackwinged Stilt *Himantopus himantopus*

Widespread but local, high SABAP reporting rates concentrated in Western Cape, Free State and North West. Inhabits shallow waters, often with some vegetation: marshes, rivers, lakes, floodplains, pans, mudflats, coastal lagoons, estuaries; distribution has expanded owing to artificial habitats, e.g. saltpans, sewage works, dams. Breeds opportunistically at edges of ephemeral wetlands; peaks winter to spring. Movements poorly known. CWAC data show winter peaks at KwaZulu-Natal sites (good breeding habitat?), summer peaks at Northern Cape sites (birds from north? – see SABAP), winter and summer peaks at Western Cape sites.

		Summer			Winter		
		Mean	Max.	N	Mean	Max.	N
2839S 2437E	Platfontein Pans, Kimberley, Northern Cape	774*	774*	1	258	258	1
3247S 1812E	Berg River System, Velddrif, Western Cape	159	239	5	511	751*	4
3416S 2149E	Voëlvlei, Mossel Bay, Western Cape	274	800*	5	159	210	4
3405S 1831E	Strandfontein Sewage Works, Muizenberg, Western Cape	280	407	6	104	190	6
2840S 2446E	Kamfers Dam, Kimberley, Northern Cape	162	229	3	58	85	3
3351S 2535E	Chatty Saltpans, Port Elizabeth, Eastern Cape	99	173	2	111	185	3
3341S 1858E	Paarl Bird Sanctuary, Paarl, Western Cape	77	141	5	131	240	5
2804S 3227E	Lake St Lucia, Hlabisa, KwaZulu–Natal	42	125	6	150	383	6
3403S 2302E	Knysna Lagoon, Knysna, Western Cape	54	85	5	101	184	5
3351S 1829E	Rietvlei, Milnerton, Western Cape	82	99	5	69	101	4
2741S 2540E	Bloemhof Dam, Bloemhof, Free State	42	169	6	90	355	6
2715S 3007E	Clarens' Pan, Wakkerstroom, Mpumalanga	122	122	1	–	–	–
3426S 2023E	De Hoop Vlei, Bredasdorp, Western Cape	75	226	5	46	83	4
3309S 1804E	Langebaan Lagoon, Langebaan, Western Cape	39	98	6	74	132	6
2804S 2433E	Spitskop Dam, Spitskop, Northern Cape	82	88	2	28	39	2

Strandfontein Sewage Works   **Lake St Lucia**   **Bloemhof Dam**   **Langebaan Lagoon**

298 Water Dikkop *Burhinus vermiculatus*

In RSA occurs in lowlands of extreme north, northeast and coast. Typically at sandbanks and shorelines of rivers, dams, lakes, mangrove swamps and estuaries; occasionally on open beaches. Fairly common; occurs in groups outside breeding season. Sedentary; makes very local movements in response to fluctuating water levels; e.g. moves to high ground when water rises. Breeds mainly August–January. No definite pattern to CWAC data: may be commoner summer or winter; counts fluctuate widely. Though it will occupy dams, it has not expanded its range into the dry interior with the creation of artificial impoundments.

		Summer			Winter		
		Mean	Max.	N	Mean	Max.	N
2804S 3227E	Lake St Lucia, Hlabisa, KwaZulu–Natal	9	15	6	7	19	6
2740S 3219E	Nsumu Pan, Mkuzi Game Reserve, KwaZulu–Natal	6	20	6	10	28	6
2653S 3218E	Nyamithi Pan (Ndumo), Ingwavuma, KwaZulu–Natal	8	14	4	6	22	5
2949S 3102E	Umgeni River Estuary, Durban, KwaZulu–Natal	2	4	5	9	18	5
3400S 2456E	Kabeljous River Estuary, Jeffreys Bay, Eastern Cape	3	5	2	7	11	3
3421S 1906E	Botriviervlei, Kleinmond, Western Cape	8	16	4	2	5	5
2653S 3213E	Shokwe Pan (Ndumo), Ingwavuma, KwaZulu–Natal	5	12	3	3	14	5
2611S 2819E	Homestead, Benoni & Middle Lakes, Benoni, Gauteng	7	13	2	2	3	2
2612S 2817E	Steward's Pan, Benoni, Gauteng	3	6	2	4	4	1
3443S 2007E	De Mond Estuary, Bredasdorp, Western Cape	1	4	4	6	8	5
3359S 2240E	Wilderness Lakes – Touw River System, Sedgefield, Western Cape	0	1	6	7	18	6
3408S 1821E	Wildevoëlvlei, Kommetjie, Western Cape	1	2	6	6	10	6
3405S 2454E	Seekoei River Estuary, Jeffreys Bay, Eastern Cape	1	2	2	6	15	3
3351S 1829E	Rietvlei, Milnerton, Western Cape	2	6	5	5	9	4
2611S 2818E	Korsman Bird Sanctuary, Benoni, Gauteng	4	12	3	2	7	3

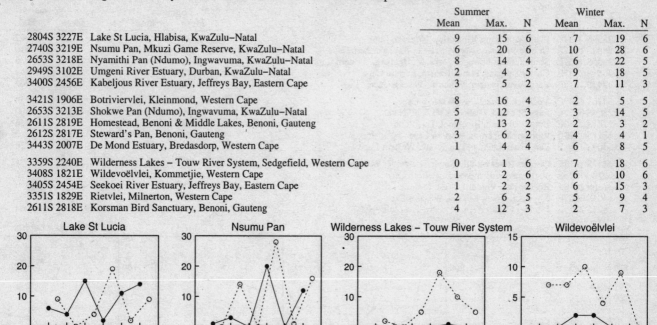

304 Redwinged Pratincole *Glareola pratincola*

In RSA largely confined to northern coastal KwaZulu-Natal; also occurs eastern Swaziland and extreme eastern Mpumalanga and Northern Province. Frequents sandbanks, mudflats, grassy floodplains, ploughed fields and other open areas, always near water. Breeds August–December. Nomadic; movements poorly understood; gregarious, and large flocks sometimes recorded (e.g. at Clarens' Pan, summer 1992). Largely absent from KwaZulu-Natal February–June, but this period not covered by CWAC. Counts show no overall pattern: occurrences erratic, and abundance may be greater in summer or winter.

		Summer			Winter		
		Mean	Max.	N	Mean	Max.	N
2715S 3007E	Clarens' Pan, Wakkerstroom, Mpumalanga	191	191	1	–	–	–
2804S 3227E	Lake St Lucia, Hlabisa, KwaZulu–Natal	7	22	6	66	165	6
2805S 3220E	Hluhluwe River Vlei & Floodplain, Hluhluwe, KwaZulu–Natal	16	32	2	33	33	1
2923S 3121E	Umvoti River Estuary, Stanger, KwaZulu–Natal	30	41	3	0	0	5
2805S 3218E	Bushlands Pan, Hluhluwe, KwaZulu–Natal	0	0	2	10	10	1
2742S 3237E	kuNdlebeni Pan, Mbazwane, KwaZulu–Natal	2	11	5	7	41	6
2847S 3203E	Thulazihleka Pan, Richards Bay, KwaZulu–Natal	0	1	5	4	18	5
2849S 3202E	Richards Bay, Richards Bay (town), KwaZulu–Natal	1	4	5	3	13	5
2739S 3224E	Neshe Pan, Mbazwane, KwaZulu–Natal	0	0	5	1	8	6
2721S 3240E	Lake Sibaya, Ubombo, KwaZulu–Natal	1	2	4	0	0	6
2737S 3233E	Mfula Pan, Mbazwane, KwaZulu–Natal	0	0	5	0	2	6
2913S 3128E	Tugela River Mouth, Mandini, KwaZulu–Natal	0	1	3	–	–	–
2653S 3218E	Nyamithi Pan (Ndumo), Ingwavuma, KwaZulu–Natal	0	1	4	0	0	5
2740S 3226E	Tshanetshe Pan, Mbazwane, KwaZulu–Natal	0	0	5	0	1	6

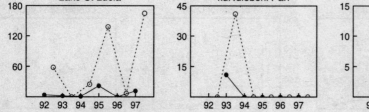

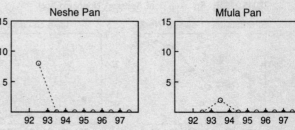

305 Blackwinged Pratincole *Glareola nordmanni*

A Palearctic migrant, in South Africa occurring mainly on the highveld in open grassland (often flooded), at pan edges, and on fields (especially mowed or ploughed). Recorded at only five CWAC sites in the Free State and adjacent Northern Cape, all within its normal range, although it occurs less regularly in these provinces than further north (former Transvaal), where it is annual. Nomadic; numbers fluctuate greatly; commonest in wet years; flocks of hundreds or thousands of birds occur, but all CWAC records are of single birds. Easily overlooked when flying or foraging high in the sky, even if in large flocks.

		Summer			Winter		
		Mean	Max.	N	Mean	Max.	N
2839S 2437E	Platfontein Pans, Kimberley, Northern Cape	1	1	1	0	0	1
2755S 2446E	Ganspan Pans & Vlei, Jan Kempdorp, Northern Cape	1	1	2	0	0	2
2807S 2455E	Vaalharts Weir, Warrenton, Northern Cape	1	1	2	0	0	2
2818S 2712E	Allemanskraal Dam, Ventersburg, Free State	0	1	6	0	0	6
2834S 2650E	Erfenis Dam, Winburg, Free State	0	1	6	0	0	6

312 Kelp Gull *Larus dominicanus*

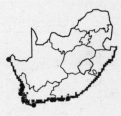

Most occur on west and south coasts; sparse on northern KwaZulu-Natal coast. Nests in marine and coastal habitats, September–January. Forages regularly inland only in Western Cape. In survey period, regular counts of good to high numbers recorded east to Port Elizabeth; in KwaZulu-Natal regular small numbers only from Durban Bayhead to Richards Bay; winter peaks support SABAP suggestion of eastward movements in winter. Postbreeding movements noted in Western Cape: many leave coastal breeding sites and numbers increase elsewhere; counts show summer and winter peaks in this region.

		Summer			Winter		
		Mean	Max.	N	Mean	Max.	N
3405S 1831E	Strandfontein Sewage Works, Muizenberg, Western Cape	768**	1067**	6	551**	1124**	6
3350S 2535E	Redhouse Saltpan, Port Elizabeth, Eastern Cape	651**	799**	4	362**	678**	4
3403S 2302E	Knysna Lagoon, Knysna, Western Cape	338**	437**	5	511**	580**	5
3309S 1804E	Langebaan Lagoon, Langebaan, Western Cape	479**	1106**	6	359**	611**	6
3352S 2538E	Swartkops River Estuary, Port Elizabeth, Eastern Cape	326**	417**	6	491**	682**	6
3402S 2324E	Keurbooms River Estuary, Plettenberg Bay, Western Cape	544**	628**	2	238*	385**	3
3247S 1812E	Berg River System, Velddrif, Western Cape	256*	411**	5	472**	596**	4
2838S 1627E	Orange River Estuary, Alexander Bay, Northern Cape	7	7	1	453**	453**	1
3351S 1829E	Rietvlei, Milnerton, Western Cape	69	160*	5	224*	420**	4
3410S 1854E	Steenbras Dam, Gordon's Bay, Western Cape	27	54	2	250*	350**	3
3421S 1906E	Botriviervlei, Kleinmond, Western Cape	116	150*	4	64	78	5
3236S 1818E	Rocher Pan, Velddrif, Western Cape	118	341**	5	33	114	6
3205S 1819E	Jakkalsvlei, Lambert's Bay, Western Cape	91	91	1	47	47	1
3220S 1825E	Verlorenvlei, Elandsbaai, Western Cape	102	235*	6	14	30	5
3443S 2007E	De Mond Estuary, Bredasdorp, Western Cape	36	61	4	53	119	5

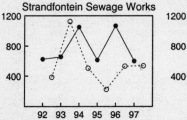
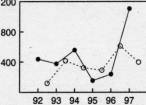
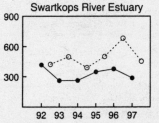
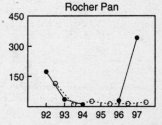

315 Greyheaded Gull *Larus cirrocephalus*

Widespread along coast and at inland sites, usually associated with shallow open water, especially at estuaries, harbours and large freshwater and alkaline lakes; often scavenges at rubbish tips, etc. Breeds in winter and spring, disperses widely thereafter; wanders freely to temporary sites in dry areas, where it may breed. Data from CWAC counts show expected winter peaks at breeding sites (e.g. Lake St Lucia, Stewards Pan, Rolfe's Pan) and summer peaks at many other inland and coastal sites including sewage works, saltpans, dams, estuaries, and permanent and ephemeral pans. Numbers have increased greatly in the 20th century.

		Summer			Winter		
		Mean	Max.	N	Mean	Max.	N
2804S 3227E	Lake St Lucia, Hlabisa, KwaZulu–Natal	158	273	6	803*	1332**	6
2949S 3102E	Umgeni River Estuary, Durban, KwaZulu–Natal	569*	831*	5	50	158	5
2612S 2817E	Steward's Pan, Benoni, Gauteng	151	300	2	301	301	1
2614S 2819E	Leeupan, Benoni, Gauteng	249	653*	5	149	461	6
2622S 2810E	Vlakplaas Water Treatment Works, Germiston, Gauteng	329	539*	4	4	12	4
3351S 2535E	Chatty Saltpans, Port Elizabeth, Eastern Cape	300	363	2	12	31	3
2804S 2433E	Spitskop Dam, Spitskop, Northern Cape	220	256	2	43	61	2
2839S 2437E	Platfontein Pans, Kimberley, Northern Cape	248	248	1	0	0	1
2611S 2818E	Korsman Bird Sanctuary, Benoni, Gauteng	135	300	3	107	174	3
2741S 2540E	Bloemhof Dam, Bloemhof, Free State	193	423	6	41	69	6
2932S 2515E	Kalkfontein Dam, Koffiefontein, Free State	136	175	6	62	90	6
2849S 3202E	Richards Bay, Richards Bay (town), KwaZulu–Natal	120	210	5	72	97	5
2610S 2813E	Rolfe's Pan, Kempton Park, Gauteng	10	16	3	112	265	5
2553S 2918E	Witbank Dam, Witbank, Mpumalanga	79	164	4	39	104	5
3341S 1858E	Paarl Bird Sanctuary, Paarl, Western Cape	23	40	5	83	272	5

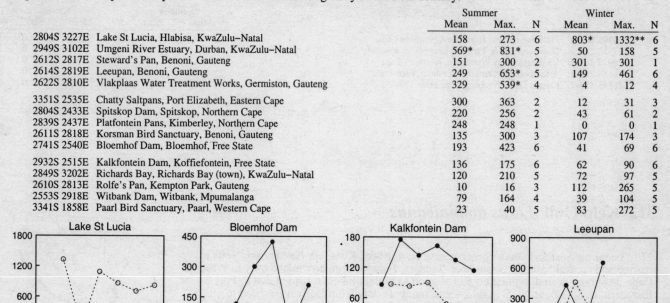

316 Hartlaub's Gull *Larus hartlaubii*

Endemic to coastal Namibia and RSA; population c. 25 000 birds. Breeds along west coast south to Dyer Island; also a small colony at Heuningnes River mouth, Bredasdorp. It occurs regularly east to Quoin Point (ASAB1); vagrant east to St Lucia. In survey period, CWAC records from 24 sites east to De Hoop Vlei; globally significant numbers at 7 sites. Occupies variety of natural and artificial habitats (well shown by CWAC sites); nests on offshore islands, along coast, and inland as far as Paarl Bird Sanctuary. Moves locally between breeding sites and when foraging; numbers at sites show no seasonal pattern (CWAC).

		Summer			Winter		
		Mean	Max.	N	Mean	Max.	N
3405S 1831E	Strandfontein Sewage Works, Muizenberg, Western Cape	1186**	1717**	6	386**	920**	6
3309S 1804E	Langebaan Lagoon, Langebaan, Western Cape	575**	1025**	6	882**	1550**	6
3351S 1829E	Rietvlei, Milnerton, Western Cape	722**	1331**	5	405**	899**	4
3341S 1858E	Paarl Bird Sanctuary, Paarl, Western Cape	234*	387**	5	620**	852**	5
3247S 1812E	Berg River System, Velddrif, Western Cape	327**	585**	5	419**	672**	4
2838S 1627E	Orange River Estuary, Alexander Bay, Northern Cape	0	0	1	397**	397**	1
3356S 1828E	Raapenberg Bird Sanctuary, Cape Town, Western Cape	160*	213*	2	34	34	1
3220S 1825E	Verlorenvlei, Elandsbaai, Western Cape	161*	377**	6	8	26	5
3236S 1818E	Rocher Pan, Velddrif, Western Cape	51	81	5	73	139*	6
3205S 1819E	Jakkalsvlei, Lambert's Bay, Western Cape	47	47	1	75	75	1
3421S 1906E	Botriviervlei, Kleinmond, Western Cape	93	121	4	25	48	5
3408S 1821E	Wildevoëlvlei, Kommetjie, Western Cape	47	75	6	56	85	6
3142S 1812E	Olifants River Mouth (South), Lutzville, Western Cape	11	21	2	57	57	1
3406S 1828E	Zandvlei, Muizenberg, Western Cape	24	47	5	25	28	5
3404S 1830E	Rondevlei, Cape Flats, Western Cape	25	54	4	19	45	4

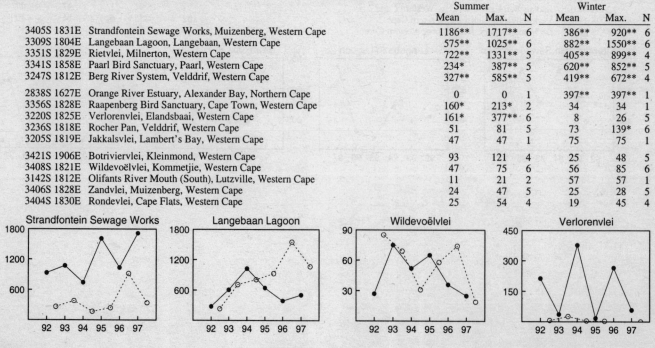

322 Caspian Tern *Hydroprogne caspia*

Widespread, mainly along coast, also at scattered inland waters. Feeds mainly at bays, estuaries, rivers, pans and dams. Breeds on islands, offshore or at waterbodies (including saltworks and sewage works), from September–March in west, January–August in Eastern Cape, March–September in east; in each region SABAP reporting rates highest in breeding season, but CWAC data show no such definite pattern. Resident at permanent waters but young wander widely. Migrants/vagrants occur widely inland; isolated CWAC occurrences in east mainly in winter. Globally significant counts at important St Lucia breeding site.

		Summer			Winter		
		Mean	Max.	N	Mean	Max.	N
2804S 3227E	Lake St Lucia, Hlabisa, KwaZulu–Natal	220*	372**	6	188*	476**	6
3350S 2535E	Redhouse Saltpan, Port Elizabeth, Eastern Cape	36	59	4	25	64	4
2932S 2515E	Kalkfontein Dam, Koffiefontein, Free State	49	152*	6	10	19	6
3247S 1812E	Berg River System, Velddrif, Western Cape	34	69	5	18	29	4
2715S 2741E	Koppies Dam, Koppies, Free State	6	30	6	34	110	6
3421S 1906E	Botriviervlei, Kleinmond, Western Cape	29	41	4	10	30	5
2804S 2433E	Spitskop Dam, Spitskop, Northern Cape	29	45	2	9	16	2
2849S 3202E	Richards Bay, Richards Bay (town), KwaZulu–Natal	19	30	5	18	32	5
3309S 1804E	Langebaan Lagoon, Langebaan, Western Cape	19	24	6	16	42	6
3352S 2538E	Swartkops River Estuary, Port Elizabeth, Eastern Cape	14	20	6	11	16	6
3405S 2454E	Seekoei River Estuary, Jeffreys Bay, Eastern Cape	8	11	2	15	30	3
2741S 2540E	Bloemhof Dam, Bloemhof, Free State	19	61	6	2	4	6
3350S 2533E	Bar None Saltpans, Port Elizabeth, Eastern Cape	1	1	2	16	21	3
3220S 1825E	Verlorenvlei, Elandsbaai, Western Cape	8	16	6	8	31	5
2805S 3220E	Hluhluwe River Vlei & Floodplain, Hluhluwe, KwaZulu–Natal	0	0	2	15	15	1

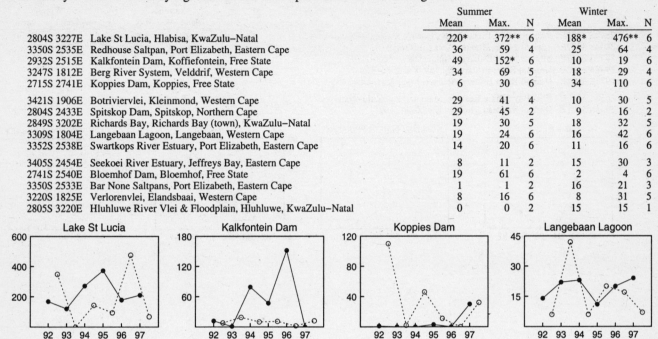

324 Swift Tern *Sterna bergii*

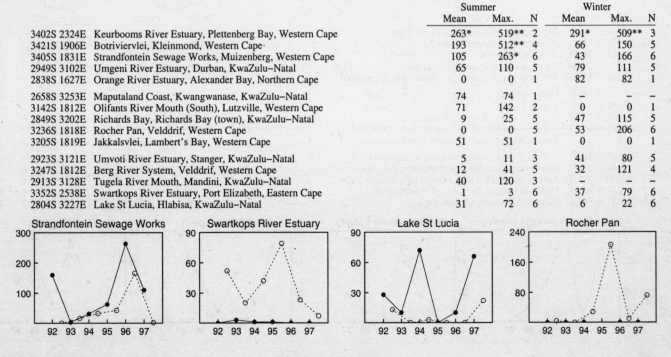

Distribution coastal; nominate race breeds from Swakopmund, Namibia, to Algoa Bay, Eastern Cape, (80% of population at islands from Saldanha Bay to Cape Town); nonbreeders occur east to Kosi Bay. Breeds Feb.–Oct., peak Feb.–March in Western Cape. Disperses widely after breeding; winter peaks at some Eastern Cape and KwaZulu-Natal sites consistent with SABAP view that Western Cape birds move east after breeding. CWAC data also show summer peaks at several Western Cape sites, just before breeding season, but numbers at Keurbooms estuary high all year. A few nonbreeders of eastern race *enigma* also occur south to Durban.

		Summer			Winter		
		Mean	Max.	N	Mean	Max.	N
3402S 2324E	Keurbooms River Estuary, Plettenberg Bay, Western Cape	263*	519**	2	291*	509**	3
3421S 1906E	Botriviervlei, Kleinmond, Western Cape	193	512**	4	66	150	5
3405S 1831E	Strandfontein Sewage Works, Muizenberg, Western Cape	105	263*	6	43	166	6
2949S 3102E	Umgeni River Estuary, Durban, KwaZulu–Natal	65	110	5	79	111	5
2838S 1627E	Orange River Estuary, Alexander Bay, Northern Cape	0	0	1	82	82	1
2658S 3253E	Maputaland Coast, Kwangwanase, KwaZulu–Natal	74	74	1	–	–	–
3142S 1812E	Olifants River Mouth (South), Lutzville, Western Cape	71	142	2	0	0	1
2849S 3202E	Richards Bay, Richards Bay (town), KwaZulu–Natal	9	25	5	47	115	5
3236S 1818E	Rocher Pan, Velddrif, Western Cape	0	0	5	53	206	6
3205S 1819E	Jakkalsvlei, Lambert's Bay, Western Cape	51	51	1	0	0	1
2923S 3121E	Umvoti River Estuary, Stanger, KwaZulu–Natal	5	11	3	41	80	5
3247S 1812E	Berg River System, Velddrif, Western Cape	12	41	5	32	121	4
2913S 3128E	Tugela River Mouth, Mandini, KwaZulu–Natal	40	120	3	–	–	–
3352S 2538E	Swartkops River Estuary, Port Elizabeth, Eastern Cape	1	3	6	37	79	6
2804S 3227E	Lake St Lucia, Hlabisa, KwaZulu–Natal	31	72	6	6	22	6

325 Lesser Crested Tern *Sterna bengalensis*

A nonbreeding migrant to the east coast of Africa, occurring fairly commonly along the KwaZulu–Natal coast, whence come CWAC records of small to moderate numbers at five sites south to the Umgeni River Estuary, Durban; there are also summer records of single birds from Kosi Bay and Durban Bayhead. Most records are during the summer (December–May), but some birds occur throughout the year and there was a good winter count at Lake St Lucia in 1992. This tern feeds inshore and normally roosts at river mouths and coastal wetlands, whence come the largest counts.

			Summer			Winter		
			Mean	Max.	N	Mean	Max.	N
2849S 3202E	Richards Bay, Richards Bay (town), KwaZulu–Natal		34	80	5	0	0	5
2804S 3227E	Lake St Lucia, Hlabisa, KwaZulu–Natal		12	24	6	8	45	6
2857S 3147E	Mlalazi River Estuary, Mtunzini, KwaZulu–Natal		3	5	2	0	0	2
2949S 3102E	Umgeni River Estuary, Durban, KwaZulu–Natal		1	4	5	0	0	5
2923S 3121E	Umvoti River Estuary, Stanger, KwaZulu–Natal		1	1	3	0	0	5
2658S 3250E	Kosi Bay Nature Reserve, Manguzi, KwaZulu–Natal		0	1	5	0	0	6
2953S 3101E	Durban Bayhead, Durban, KwaZulu–Natal		0	1	5	0	0	5

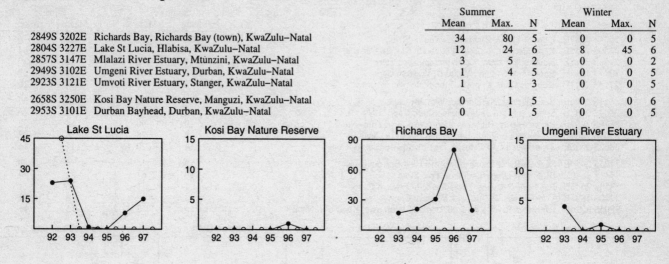

326 Sandwich Tern *Sterna sandvicensis*

A seasonally abundant nonbreeding visitor to all southern African coasts from its Palearctic breeding grounds. Almost exclusively marine, it comes to land only to roost when it may bathe and fish in estuaries and coastal lakes. CWAC counts record small to good numbers at sites along almost the entire coastline, with the largest concentrations in the Western Cape; counts at individual sites fluctuate widely from year to year. Arrivals are in September–October and departures in February–May. Small numbers, mainly juveniles, remain during the austral winter, as may be seen from CWAC data.

			Summer			Winter		
			Mean	Max.	N	Mean	Max.	N
3421S 1906E	Botriviervlei, Kleinmond, Western Cape		246	951*	4	5	25	5
3405S 1831E	Strandfontein Sewage Works, Muizenberg, Western Cape		235	586	6	0	0	6
3247S 1812E	Berg River System, Velddrif, Western Cape		70	120	5	0	0	4
3352S 2538E	Swartkops River Estuary, Port Elizabeth, Eastern Cape		55	123	6	4	21	6
2849S 3202E	Richards Bay, Richards Bay (town), KwaZulu–Natal		48	81	5	1	2	5
3309S 1804E	Langebaan Lagoon, Langebaan, Western Cape		31	57	6	1	6	6
2913S 3128E	Tugela River Mouth, Mandini, KwaZulu–Natal		31	80	3	–	–	–
3403S 2302E	Knysna Lagoon, Knysna, Western Cape		26	34	5	0	0	5
2838S 1627E	Orange River Estuary, Alexander Bay, Northern Cape		0	0	1	20	20	1
2923S 3121E	Umvoti River Estuary, Stanger, KwaZulu–Natal		16	31	3	0	0	5
2857S 3147E	Mlalazi River Estuary, Mtunzini, KwaZulu–Natal		15	30	2	0	0	2
3402S 2324E	Keurbooms River Estuary, Plettenberg Bay, Western Cape		15	16	2	0	0	3
3400S 2456E	Kabeljous River Estuary, Jeffreys Bay, Eastern Cape		13	13	2	0	0	3
3443S 2007E	De Mond Estuary, Bredasdorp, Western Cape		11	36	4	0	0	5
3351S 1829E	Rietvlei, Milnerton, Western Cape		8	17	5	1	3	4

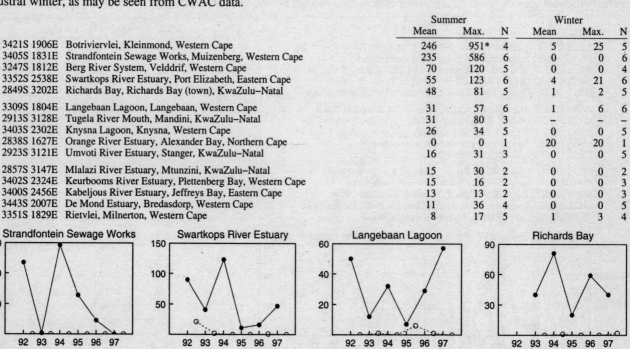

327 Common Tern *Sterna hirundo*

Abundant Palearctic migrant to coasts, river estuaries and coastal lakes (also good counts at Strandfontein Sewage Works in 1992 and 1994); few inland records. Roosts communally on coastal points, sandspits, estuaries, islands, etc., at which sites high counts are made. CWAC data show highest counts at sites in northern KwaZulu-Natal, Western Cape, and from Wilderness Lakes east to Port Alfred. Arrivals are in September–November and departures in March–April; many first-year birds remain through the austral winter, when small to moderate counts are reported from many coastal CWAC sites.

		Summer			Winter		
		Mean	Max.	N	Mean	Max.	N
2849S 3202E	Richards Bay, Richards Bay (town), KwaZulu–Natal	2866	13000**	5	3	8	5
2913S 3128E	Tugela River Mouth, Mandini, KwaZulu–Natal	2117	3000	3	–	–	–
2923S 3121E	Umvoti River Estuary, Stanger, KwaZulu–Natal	1188	1960	3	2	6	5
3309S 1804E	Langebaan Lagoon, Langebaan, Western Cape	1150	4078*	6	13	56	6
3352S 2538E	Swartkops River Estuary, Port Elizabeth, Eastern Cape	1033	1618	6	53	96	6
3400S 2456E	Kabeljous River Estuary, Jeffreys Bay, Eastern Cape	666	1330	2	1	2	3
3421S 1906E	Botriviervlei, Kleinmond, Western Cape	553	868	4	13	56	5
3247S 1812E	Berg River System, Velddrif, Western Cape	415	1561	5	1	3	4
2949S 3102E	Umgeni River Estuary, Durban, KwaZulu–Natal	388	650	5	3	16	5
3405S 1831E	Strandfontein Sewage Works, Muizenberg, Western Cape	245	1000	6	0	0	6
3329S 2707E	Great Fish River Estuary, Port Alfred, Eastern Cape	169	435	4	1	3	4
3403S 2302E	Knysna Lagoon, Knysna, Western Cape	106	151	5	45	123	5
2658S 3253E	Maputaland Coast, Kwangwanase, KwaZulu–Natal	129	129	1	–	–	–
3351S 1829E	Rietvlei, Milnerton, Western Cape	25	30	5	79	180	4
3405S 2454E	Seekoei River Estuary, Jeffreys Bay, Eastern Cape	52	103	2	11	24	3

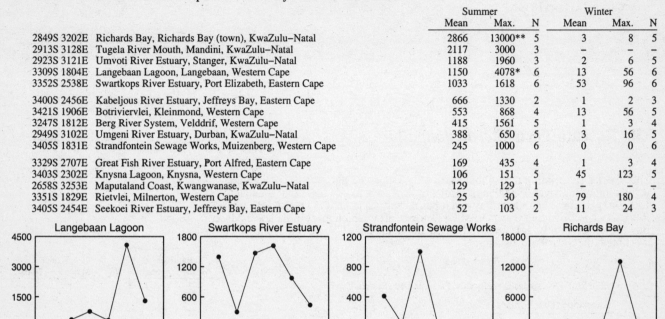

328 Arctic Tern *Sterna paradisaea*

Unique in being the only Palearctic breeding bird to have the status of a passage migrant in southern Africa. Peak passage occurs past southern Africa in October–December, when some birds come inshore and move along the coasts. Northward migration is across the mid-Atlantic, so few birds reach our coasts during this passage. Some birds occur along the coasts during the austral winter, when they are seldom reported owing to confusion with Common Tern. CWAC records are of small to moderate numbers from four localities in the Cape and one in KwaZulu-Natal, with a winter occurrence at Jeffreys Bay in 1997.

		Summer			Winter		
		Mean	Max.	N	Mean	Max.	N
3400S 2456E	Kabeljous River Estuary, Jeffreys Bay, Eastern Cape	59	108	2	0	0	3
3443S 2007E	De Mond Estuary, Bredasdorp, Western Cape	28	109	4	0	0	5
3405S 2454E	Seekoei River Estuary, Jeffreys Bay, Eastern Cape	2	2	2	7	20	3
2949S 3102E	Umgeni River Estuary, Durban, KwaZulu–Natal	6	30	5	0	0	5
3405S 1849E	Paardevlei Dam, Somerset West, Western Cape	2	10	5	0	0	5

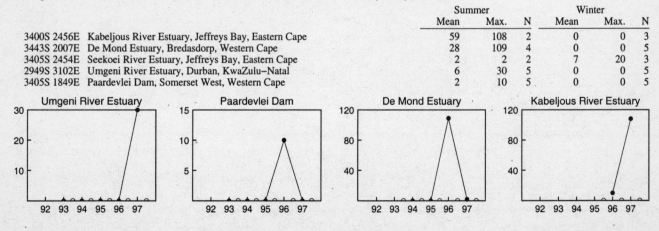

329 Antarctic Tern *Sterna vittata*

A regular nonbreeding winter visitor to the Western and Eastern Cape, between Lambert's Bay and East London, from its Antarctic Peninsula and Southern Ocean breeding grounds. South Africa supports c. 10% (over 15 000 birds) of the world population in winter; birds feed at sea but often roost on offshore islands and at safe coastal localities, sometimes occurring in large numbers on islands (flocks of up to 4500 birds recorded). It occurs between mid-April and October, with a few summer records. Under-recorded by CWAC mainly because it does not occur at the wetlands currently surveyed. Single CWAC record from Seekoei River.

330 Roseate Tern *Sterna dougallii*

This species is declining throughout much of its range and has an African breeding population of just over 38 000 individuals. In RSA, where it is regarded as endangered, 130–140 pairs breed in Algoa Bay and it has recently also bred at Dyer Island in the Western Cape. Breeding occurs in May–October, after which most birds leave Algoa Bay to wander widely. It is recorded irregularly at the only CWAC site from which it is noted, the Swartkops Estuary.

	Summer			Winter		
	Mean	Max.	N	Mean	Max.	N
3352S 2538E Swartkops River Estuary, Port Elizabeth, Eastern Cape	3	10	6	1	4	6

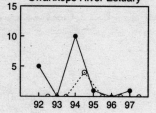

334 Damara Tern *Sterna balaenarum*

Globally near-threatened; an intra-African migrant known to breed only in South Africa and Namibia, with a total world population of c. 14450 individuals, of which c. 150 pairs breed (October–March) in South Africa. The only CWAC site, the De Mond State Forest/Heuningnes River estuary, holds 5-7 breeding pairs. Almost all birds migrate to West Africa (Cameroon to Ghana) after breeding. This species is threatened by habitat alteration, human disturbance, especially disturbance of nests and breeding habitat by offroad vehicles, and encroachment by alien vegetation.

		Summer			Winter		
		Mean	Max.	N	Mean	Max.	N
3443S 2007E	De Mond Estuary, Bredasdorp, Western Cape	3	10	4	0	1	5

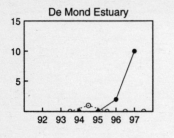

335 Little Tern *Sterna albifrons*

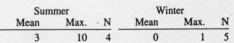

A Palearctic migrant to the coasts of southern Africa, being common only along the northern coast of KwaZulu-Natal, where it may occur in large numbers at roosts on sandbanks or islands; maximum counts of 650–800 birds were recorded from five sites in this region during the survey period. It is relatively sparse elsewhere along the southern and southwestern coasts of RSA and this is reflected in the small numbers recorded during the survey period (except at Port Elizabeth). Arrivals begin in August and departures in February; few birds remain in the austral winter.

		Summer			Winter		
		Mean	Max.	N	Mean	Max.	N
2658S 3253E	Maputaland Coast, Kwangwanase, KwaZulu–Natal	793*	793*	1	–	–	–
2849S 3202E	Richards Bay, Richards Bay (town), KwaZulu–Natal	335	700*	5	0	0	5
2923S 3121E	Umvoti River Estuary, Stanger, KwaZulu–Natal	293	650*	3	3	13	5
2913S 3128E	Tugela River Mouth, Mandini, KwaZulu–Natal	280	800*	3	–	–	–
2804S 3227E	Lake St Lucia, Hlabisa, KwaZulu–Natal	266	816*	6	7	35	6
3352S 2538E	Swartkops River Estuary, Port Elizabeth, Eastern Cape	94	123	6	0	0	6
2949S 3102E	Umgeni River Estuary, Durban, KwaZulu–Natal	58	270	5	0	0	5
2752S 3236E	Sodwana Bay to Cape Vidal, St Lucia, KwaZulu–Natal	46	46	1	0	0	2
3350S 2535E	Redhouse Saltpan, Port Elizabeth, Eastern Cape	28	50	4	0	0	4
2658S 3250E	Kosi Bay Nature Reserve, Manguzi, KwaZulu–Natal	20	100	5	0	0	6
3247S 1812E	Berg River System, Velddrif, Western Cape	15	67	5	0	1	4
2824S 3225E	Mfolozi Mouth Area, St Lucia, KwaZulu–Natal	–	–	–	8	8	1
3309S 1804E	Langebaan Lagoon, Langebaan, Western Cape	6	16	6	0	1	6
3443S 2007E	De Mond Estuary, Bredasdorp, Western Cape	6	21	4	0	0	5
2740S 3219E	Nsumu Pan, Mkuzi Game Reserve, KwaZulu–Natal	1	6	6	4	21	6

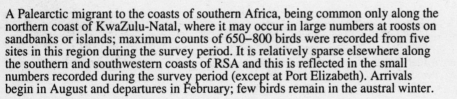

338 Whiskered Tern *Chlidonias hybridus*

Core of RSA distribution is highveld panveld; also northern KwaZulu-Natal, and southern and southwestern Cape. Occurs at a wide variety of inland wetlands; feeds over open water, marshes and reedbeds; breeding sites have much floating vegetation. Breeds in summer, except in winter-rainfall area where peak is October–November. Movements complex and poorly understood; as confirmed by CWAC data, in most regions birds apparently depart after breeding, but some remain all year in lowland KwaZulu-Natal; good numbers are still present in January at important Western Cape sites.

		Summer			Winter		
		Mean	Max.	N	Mean	Max.	N
2622S 2810E	Vlakplaas Water Treatment Works, Germiston, Gauteng	241	570*	4	0	0	4
3426S 2023E	De Hoop Vlei, Bredasdorp, Western Cape	166	427	5	0	0	4
3416S 2149E	Voëlvlei, Mossel Bay, Western Cape	156	280	5	3	12	4
2847S 3203E	Thulazihleka Pan, Richards Bay, KwaZulu–Natal	29	100	5	82	200	5
2553S 2918E	Witbank Dam, Witbank, Mpumalanga	86	217	4	1	3	5
2805S 3218E	Bushlands Pan, Hluhluwe, KwaZulu–Natal	65	130	2	0	0	1
2740S 3219E	Nsumu Pan, Mkuzi Game Reserve, KwaZulu–Natal	41	179	6	12	26	6
2804S 3227E	Lake St Lucia, Hlabisa, KwaZulu–Natal	40	172	6	7	16	6
2721S 3240E	Lake Sibaya, Ubombo, KwaZulu–Natal	30	76	4	7	43	6
2807S 2455E	Vaalharts Weir, Warrenton, Northern Cape	24	47	2	7	14	2
3408S 1821E	Wildevoëlvlei, Kommetjie, Western Cape	29	71	6	0	0	6
2618S 2812E	Rondebult Bird Sanctuary, Germiston, Gauteng	29	56	4	0	0	4
2948S 3100E	Northern Treatment Works, Durban, KwaZulu–Natal	28	140	5	0	0	5
2741S 2540E	Bloemhof Dam, Bloemhof, Free State	1	5	6	27	155	6
3401S 2323E	Bitou River, Plettenberg Bay, Western Cape	25	33	2	0	0	3

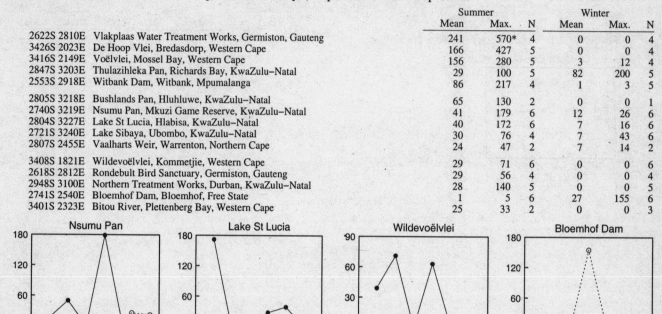

339 Whitewinged Tern *Chlidonias leucopterus*

A common Palearctic migrant, occurring at inland waterbodies and some coastal wetlands; CWAC data confirm that, in RSA, core of distribution is the northcentral panveld region, with good numbers also present in Western Cape and northeastern KwaZulu-Natal. As shown by CWAC data, artificial impoundments and sewage works often hold significant numbers. Some individuals remain during the austral winter, when small numbers are recorded from several sites; a winter 1997 count of 900 birds at Richards Bay is noteworthy. Arrivals are in August–October, departure mainly in April.

		Summer			Winter		
		Mean	Max.	N	Mean	Max.	N
3341S 1858E	Paarl Bird Sanctuary, Paarl, Western Cape	2903**	5101**	5	0	1	5
2847S 3203E	Thulazihleka Pan, Richards Bay, KwaZulu–Natal	1005*	2000**	5	230	900	5
3405S 1831E	Strandfontein Sewage Works, Muizenberg, Western Cape	1154*	1800*	6	0	1	6
2741S 2540E	Bloemhof Dam, Bloemhof, Free State	853	1420*	6	7	32	6
2932S 2515E	Kalkfontein Dam, Koffiefontein, Free State	727	1806*	6	4	17	6
2804S 2433E	Spitskop Dam, Spitskop, Northern Cape	587	1128*	2	0	0	2
3205S 1819E	Jakkalsvlei, Lambert's Bay, Western Cape	518	518	1	0	0	1
2839S 2437E	Platfontein Pans, Kimberley, Northern Cape	509	509	1	0	0	1
2629S 2828E	Blesbokspruit, Nigel, Gauteng	400	400	1	0	0	1
3351S 1829E	Rietvlei, Milnerton, Western Cape	372	804	5	1	2	4
2852S 2600E	Krugersdrift Dam, Bloemfontein, Free State	349	1182*	6	7	36	6
2624S 2828E	Stan Madden Bird Sanctuary, Nigel, Gauteng	291	600	5	0	2	5
2614S 2819E	Leeupan, Benoni, Gauteng	272	1300*	5	0	0	6
2834S 2650E	Erfenis Dam, Winburg, Free State	250	486	6	3	17	6
2534S 2814E	Rooiwal Sewage Works, Pretoria, Gauteng	227	467	4	0	1	5

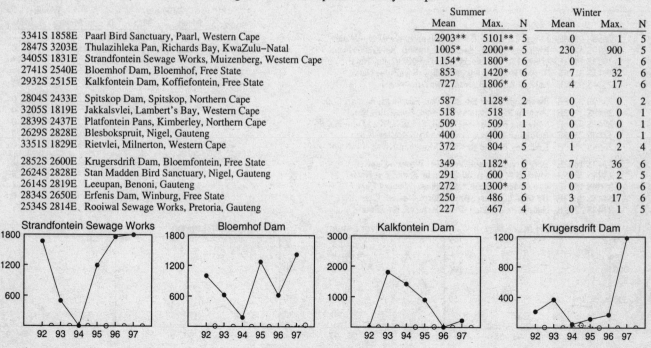

393 Grass Owl *Tyto capensis*

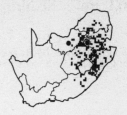

In South Africa confined to east, mainly through the highveld west to c. 26°E, and in KwaZulu-Natal and adjacent Eastern Cape; isolated population in coastal Western Cape (George – Knysna region and De Hoop Nature Reserve). Inhabits rank open grassland and marshes, also dense grass in light *Acacia* woodland; possibly has some local and nomadic movements. Apparently uncommon, but status uncertain as birds often difficult to find: almost entirely nocturnal, seen during day only if flushed. Very under-recorded by CWAC; records from only seven sites, five in Gauteng, one in Free State and one in North West.

		Summer			Winter		
		Mean	Max.	N	Mean	Max.	N
2612S 2817E	Steward's Pan, Benoni, Gauteng	0	0	2	7	7	1
2611S 2818E	Korsman Bird Sanctuary, Benoni, Gauteng	4	7	3	1	3	3
2629S 2828E	Blesbokspruit, Nigel, Gauteng	0	0	1	1	1	1
2735S 2935E	Seekoeivlei, Memel, Free State	1	2	5	0	2	5
2614S 2819E	Leeupan, Benoni, Gauteng	1	4	5	0	0	6
2635S 2535E	Barberspan, Delareyville, North West	0	1	4	0	0	2
2621S 2830E	Marievale Bird Sanctuary, Nigel, Gauteng	0	0	5	0	1	5

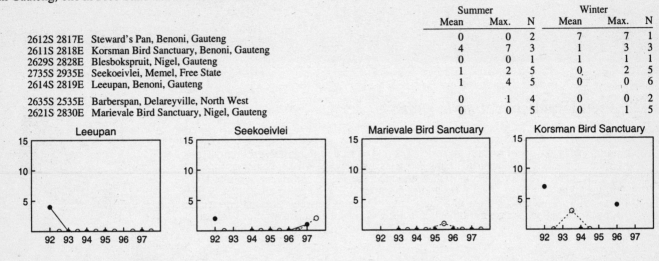

395 Marsh Owl *Asio capensis*

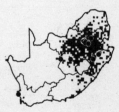

Locally common in eastern RSA in grasslands and marshes, principally Gauteng, Mpumalanga, eastern Free State and North West (total 19 CWAC sites), and interior KwaZulu-Natal (5 CWAC sites); also at scattered localities in Western and Eastern Cape (one CWAC site). Often recorded in groups; it roosts communally. Breeds mostly at end of rains and in dry season. Nomadic in response to prey and habitat availability. In eastern regions, SABAP shows much higher reporting rates in midwinter than in summer; CWAC data show no marked winter increase in numbers, but isolated occurrences are recorded more often in winter.

		Summer			Winter		
		Mean	Max.	N	Mean	Max.	N
2612S 2817E	Steward's Pan, Benoni, Gauteng	1	2	2	11	11	1
2611S 2819E	Homestead, Benoni & Middle Lakes, Benoni, Gauteng	6	9	2	5	9	2
2611S 2818E	Korsman Bird Sanctuary, Benoni, Gauteng	4	10	3	5	15	3
2620S 2817E	Rietspruit (Rooikraal), Boksburg, Gauteng	2	4	3	5	8	4
2629S 2828E	Blesbokspruit, Nigel, Gauteng	4	4	1	3	3	1
2635S 2857E	Leeuwpan, Secunda, Mpumalanga	2	2	3	2	4	4
2553S 2918E	Witbank Dam, Witbank, Mpumalanga	1	3	4	2	6	5
2621S 2830E	Marievale Bird Sanctuary, Nigel, Gauteng	0	1	5	1	4	5
2840S 2446E	Kamfers Dam, Kimberley, Northern Cape	1	2	3	0	0	3
2614S 2819E	Leeupan, Benoni, Gauteng	1	6	5	0	0	6
2618S 2812E	Rondebult Bird Sanctuary, Germiston, Gauteng	1	2	4	1	1	4
2755S 3035E	Klipspruit Dam Complex, Vryheid, KwaZulu–Natal	–	–	–	1	1	1
2834S 2948E	Malandeni Sewage Works, Ladysmith, KwaZulu–Natal	0	0	5	1	3	5
2840S 2618E	Rietpan, Brandfort, Free State	–	–	–	1	1	1
3309S 1804E	Langebaan Lagoon, Langebaan, Western Cape	0	0	6	1	5	6

403 Pel's Fishing Owl *Scotopelia peli*

Occurs in the extreme northeast; uncommon at rivers/swamps with large trees.
Single CWAC records from Kosi Bay and Hlonhlela.

428 Pied Kingfisher *Ceryle rudis*

A common and widespread species, recorded in small to moderate numbers at many types
of natural and man-made waters, including estuaries and sewage works; its occurrence is
entirely dependent on the presence of fish. Although normally sedentary, with no known
regular migrations, it moves when waterbodies dry up and it will appear at temporary pans.
At some sites, CWAC counts show no significant differences between summer and winter
means, but seasonal peaks occur at others; it is not clear whether such variations reflect
changes in site conditions, or local movements to and from seasonal waterbodies.

		Summer			Winter		
		Mean	Max.	N	Mean	Max.	N
2804S 3227E	Lake St Lucia, Hlabisa, KwaZulu–Natal	36	53	6	36	56	6
3247S 1812E	Berg River System, Velddrif, Western Cape	27	42	5	39	50	4
2721S 3240E	Lake Sibaya, Ubombo, KwaZulu–Natal	30	36	4	31	44	6
2838S 1627E	Orange River Estuary, Alexander Bay, Northern Cape	5	5	1	56	56	1
3421S 1906E	Botriviervlei, Kleinmond, Western Cape	25	48	4	15	29	5
3403S 2302E	Knysna Lagoon, Knysna, Western Cape	10	21	5	25	35	5
2658S 3250E	Kosi Bay Nature Reserve, Manguzi, KwaZulu–Natal	15	19	5	17	24	6
2841S 2929E	Spioenkop Dam, Winterton, KwaZulu–Natal	13	25	4	11	15	5
3220S 1825E	Verlorenvlei, Elandsbaai, Western Cape	13	20	6	12	14	5
2653S 3218E	Nyamithi Pan (Ndumo), Ingwavuma, KwaZulu–Natal	5	9	4	16	24	5
3359S 2240E	Wilderness Lakes – Touw River System, Sedgefield, Western Cape	6	13	6	11	16	6
3352S 2538E	Swartkops River Estuary, Port Elizabeth, Eastern Cape	4	12	6	11	17	6
2849S 3202E	Richards Bay, Richards Bay (town), KwaZulu–Natal	5	10	5	10	14	5
2520S 2728E	Vaalkop Dam, Brits, North West	6	8	4	9	16	5
2847S 3203E	Thulazihleka Pan, Richards Bay, KwaZulu–Natal	6	10	5	8	14	5

429 Giant Kingfisher *Megaceryle maxima*

A normally solitary species, pairs maintaining large territories on suitable stretches of perennial rivers; it also occurs at streams, estuaries, coastal lagoons, lakes and dams, and even at ornamental ponds. CWAC data reflect its fairly sparse distribution in these habitats, and its solitary nature. It is regarded as largely sedentary, but SABAP data show some seasonal variation in reporting rates in northeastern South Africa; CWAC data are too few to give any clear indication of consistent seasonal variation.

		Summer			Winter		
		Mean	Max.	N	Mean	Max.	N
3402S 1913E	Theewaterskloof Dam, Villiersdorp, Western Cape	4	7	5	2	3	5
2611S 2818E	Korsman Bird Sanctuary, Benoni, Gauteng	3	7	3	2	7	3
3356S 1828E	Raapenberg Bird Sanctuary, Cape Town, Western Cape	2	3	2	2	2	1
2658S 3250E	Kosi Bay Nature Reserve, Manguzi, KwaZulu–Natal	1	2	5	3	4	6
2507S 3028E	Lydenburg Fisheries, Lydenburg, Mpumalanga	3	3	1	0	0	1
2545S 2752E	Hartbeespoort Dam, Hartbeespoort, North West	3	3	1	–	–	–
2553S 2817E	Rietvlei Dam, Pretoria, Gauteng	0	0	1	3	3	1
2553S 2918E	Witbank Dam, Witbank, Mpumalanga	1	2	4	2	5	5
2612S 2817E	Steward's Pan, Benoni, Gauteng	0	0	2	3	3	1
2849S 3202E	Richards Bay, Richards Bay (town), KwaZulu–Natal	1	3	5	2	6	5
2923S 3121E	Umvoti River Estuary, Stanger, KwaZulu–Natal	1	3	3	1	3	5
2834S 2948E	Malandeni Sewage Works, Ladysmith, KwaZulu–Natal	2	3	5	1	2	5
3421S 1906E	Botriviervlei, Kleinmond, Western Cape	2	2	4	1	3	5
2804S 3227E	Lake St Lucia, Hlabisa, KwaZulu–Natal	1	3	6	1	2	6
3405S 2454E	Seekoei River Estuary, Jeffreys Bay, Eastern Cape	1	1	2	2	3	3

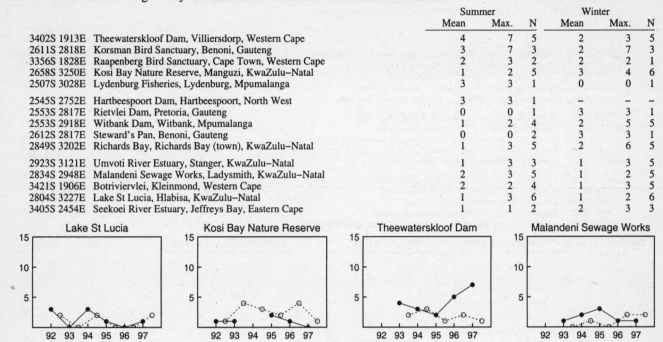

430 Halfcollared Kingfisher *Alcedo semitorquata*

Typically occurs along fast-flowing streams and rivers with clear water and well-wooded banks, often with emergent or fringing vegetation; in RSA it is most frequent in broken escarpment terrain. Because of these habitat preferences it is rarely recorded on CWAC counts at still waters, but it does sometimes occur along the vegetated shores of lakes, ponds, dams, coastal lagoons and estuaries. CWAC records come from eight sites, six of these along the south coast at estuaries, lagoons, lakes and rivers; in KwaZulu-Natal it is recorded at Kosi Bay and at Reichenau Mission farm dam near Underberg.

		Summer			Winter		
		Mean	Max.	N	Mean	Max.	N
3359S 2240E	Wilderness Lakes – Touw River System, Sedgefield, Western Cape	0	2	6	0	1	6
3400S 2245E	Wilderness Lakes – Swartvlei System, Sedgefield, Western Cape	0	0	2	1	1	3
2658S 3250E	Kosi Bay Nature Reserve, Manguzi, KwaZulu–Natal	1	3	5	0	0	6
3421S 1906E	Botriviervlei, Kleinmond, Western Cape	0	1	4	0	1	5
3403S 2302E	Knysna Lagoon, Knysna, Western Cape	0	0	5	0	1	5
3401S 2323E	Bitou River, Plettenberg Bay, Western Cape	0	0	2	0	1	3
2948S 2938E	Reichenau Mission Dam, Underberg, KwaZulu–Natal	0	1	5	0	0	5
3352S 2538E	Swartkops River Estuary, Port Elizabeth, Eastern Cape	0	0	6	0	1	6

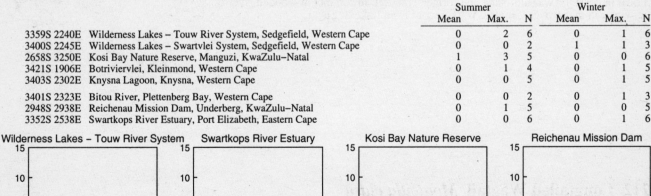

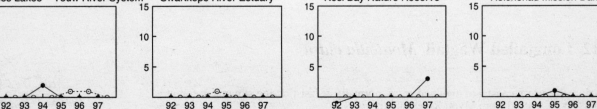

431 Malachite Kingfisher *Alcedo cristata*

In contrast to the preceding species, this is a common and widespread bird of many types of flowing and still waters in open country, including marshes, sewage ponds, farm dams, irrigation canals and ornamental ponds. Small numbers are widely recorded on CWAC counts, with few real indications of seasonal variations in numbers. Summer peaks at a few sites in the Western Cape, KwaZulu-Natal and Gauteng, and apparent small winter peaks at one site in each of the first two provinces, could reflect its well-known tendency to breed at seasonal waters and to wander to other sites thereafter.

		Summer			Winter		
		Mean	Max.	N	Mean	Max.	N
2834S 2948E	Malandeni Sewage Works, Ladysmith, KwaZulu–Natal	7	12	5	2	6	5
3341S 1858E	Paarl Bird Sanctuary, Paarl, Western Cape	5	13	5	3	9	5
2721S 3240E	Lake Sibaya, Ubombo, KwaZulu–Natal	4	12	4	4	10	6
2847S 3203E	Thulazihleka Pan, Richards Bay, KwaZulu–Natal	4	5	5	3	7	5
2948S 3100E	Northern Treatment Works, Durban, KwaZulu–Natal	2	3	5	3	7	5
2923S 3121E	Umvoti River Estuary, Stanger, KwaZulu–Natal	2	5	3	2	4	5
2507S 3028E	Lydenburg Fisheries, Lydenburg, Mpumalanga	3	3	1	1	1	1
3359S 2240E	Wilderness Lakes – Touw River System, Sedgefield, Western Cape	2	2	6	2	8	6
2553S 2918E	Witbank Dam, Witbank, Mpumalanga	1	3	4	2	5	5
3421S 1906E	Botriviervlei, Kleinmond, Western Cape	3	10	4	1	2	5
2841S 2929E	Spioenkop Dam, Winterton, KwaZulu–Natal	3	12	4	0	1	5
2611S 2818E	Korsman Bird Sanctuary, Benoni, Gauteng	3	9	3	0	0	3
3406S 1828E	Zandvlei, Muizenberg, Western Cape	2	3	5	1	2	5
2740S 3226E	Tshanetshe Pan, Mbazwane, KwaZulu–Natal	1	3	5	2	4	6
2805S 3220E	Hluhluwe River Vlei & Floodplain, Hluhluwe, KwaZulu–Natal	1	1	2	2	2	1

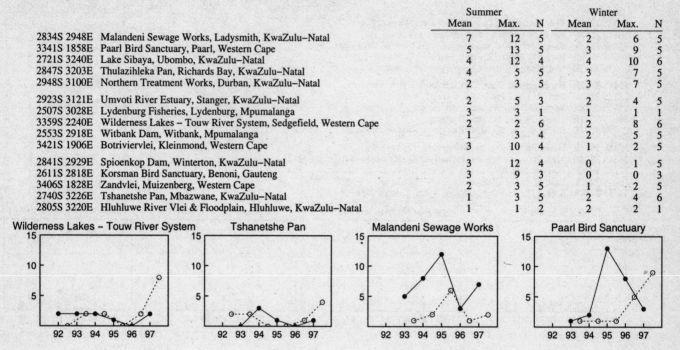

434 Mangrove Kingfisher *Halcyon senegaloides*

Local in coastal KwaZulu-Natal and former Transkei; in summer at wooded rivers, in winter in mangroves. Single CWAC record from Lake St Lucia.

712 Longtailed Wagtail *Motacilla clara*

Occurs in eastern coastal to highland areas, normally at fast-flowing streams in forest. One CWAC record from Mvoti River mouth.

711 African Pied Wagtail *Motacilla aguimp*

Distributed mainly along the southern and eastern coasts, and inland along major rivers. Recorded at 32 CWAC sites, predominantly in northern coastal KwaZulu-Natal, but also inland to the Free State and former Transvaal; also on the coast at Jeffreys Bay and Mossel Bay (the southern limit of its normal range), and at the Orange River Estuary. Small numbers usual; largest count was of 20 at Stanger, KwaZulu-Natal (winter 1997). Little evidence of large-scale seasonal movements, but SABAP reporting rates slightly higher in winter, and winter numbers tend to be higher at almost half the CWAC sites.

		Summer			Winter		
		Mean	Max.	N	Mean	Max.	N
3010S 2455E	Vanderkloof Dam, Vanderkloof, Northern Cape	11	11	1	17	17	1
2948S 3100E	Northern Treatment Works, Durban, KwaZulu–Natal	7	12	5	8	16	5
2653S 3218E	Nyamithi Pan (Ndumo), Ingwavuma, KwaZulu–Natal	6	9	4	8	11	5
2534S 2814E	Rooiwal Sewage Works, Pretoria, Gauteng	5	10	4	6	12	5
2740S 3219E	Nsumu Pan, Mkuzi Game Reserve, KwaZulu–Natal	5	8	6	2	4	6
2849S 3202E	Richards Bay, Richards Bay (town), KwaZulu–Natal	3	5	5	2	7	5
2917S 3117E	Mbozambo Waste Water Lagoon, Stanger, KwaZulu–Natal	0	1	3	5	20	5
2838S 1627E	Orange River Estuary, Alexander Bay, Northern Cape	3	3	1	2	2	1
2804S 3227E	Lake St Lucia, Hlabisa, KwaZulu–Natal	2	6	6	2	4	6
2926S 3024E	Albert Falls Dam, Pietermaritzburg, KwaZulu–Natal	2	7	4	1	2	4
2941S 3105E	Umhlanga Treatment Works, Umhlanga, KwaZulu–Natal	0	0	3	3	8	5
2652S 3217E	Banzi Pan (Ndumo), Ingwavuma, KwaZulu–Natal	1	5	4	2	4	5
3037S 2537E	Gariep Dam (West), Gariep Dam (town), Free State	1	4	6	1	4	6
2507S 3028E	Lydenburg Fisheries, Lydenburg, Mpumalanga	0	0	1	2	2	1
3405S 2454E	Seekoei River Estuary, Jeffreys Bay, Eastern Cape	2	4	2	0	0	3

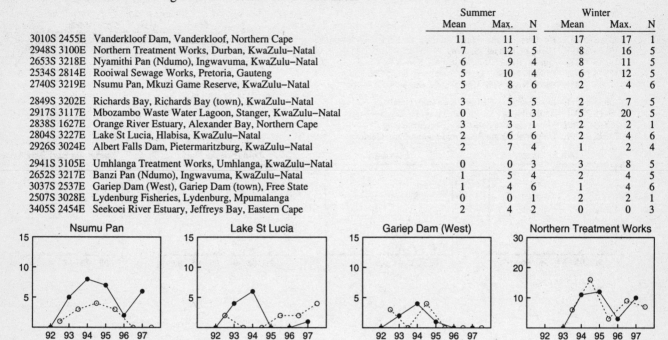

713 Cape Wagtail *Motacilla capensis*

Widespread and common throughout most of South Africa, normally in pairs and family groups; occurs in large flocks near waterbodies (including sewage works, where food is abundant) in the nonbreeding period, and roosts in reedbeds. Breeds all year, mostly spring and early summer. It is not consistently counted at all CWAC sites, so interpretation of the data is difficult. Results show large concentrations at dams and sewage works in both summer and winter, with more peaks in winter than in summer. It is a commensal of humans, uses parks, gardens and lawns, and has benefited from the construction of artificial wetlands.

		Summer			Winter		
		Mean	Max.	N	Mean	Max.	N
2838S 1627E	Orange River Estuary, Alexander Bay, Northern Cape	25	25	1	222	222	1
2553S 2918E	Witbank Dam, Witbank, Mpumalanga	26	47	4	187	325	5
2932S 2515E	Kalkfontein Dam, Koffiefontein, Free State	7	20	6	174	373	6
3247S 1812E	Berg River System, Velddrif, Western Cape	74	135	5	81	109	4
3309S 1804E	Langebaan Lagoon, Langebaan, Western Cape	91	128	6	63	114	6
3150S 2208E	Sakriviersspoort Wetlands, Loxton, Northern Cape	69	89	3	62	80	2
3351S 1829E	Rietvlei, Milnerton, Western Cape	69	121	5	60	81	4
2614S 2819E	Leeupan, Benoni, Gauteng	39	107	5	80	125	6
3341S 1858E	Paarl Bird Sanctuary, Paarl, Western Cape	76	85	5	39	63	5
3052S 2438E	Faugh A Ballagh Dam, Hanover, Northern Cape	3	3	1	108	124	2
3405S 1831E	Strandfontein Sewage Works, Muizenberg, Western Cape	71	149	6	38	66	6
2611S 2819E	Homestead, Benoni & Middle Lakes, Benoni, Gauteng	39	60	2	32	43	2
2915S 2941E	Hlatikulu Vlei, Hlatikulu, KwaZulu–Natal	22	30	2	48	48	1
2534S 2814E	Rooiwal Sewage Works, Pretoria, Gauteng	27	35	4	41	62	5
2818S 2712E	Allemanskraal Dam, Ventersburg, Free State	7	29	6	58	255	6

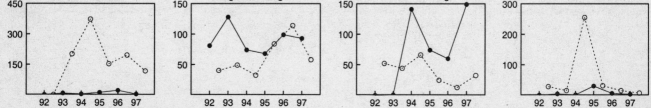

714 Yellow Wagtail *Motacilla flava*

In South Africa this Palearctic migrant occurs at widely scattered localities, usually in small numbers. Records come from nine CWAC sites, five in Gauteng and four in KwaZulu-Natal. At Rooiwal Sewage Works, Gauteng, good numbers (10–47 birds) were noted during all summer counts, and 20 birds were at Leeupàn (Benoni) in summer 1993. Occurrences in KwaZulu-Natal are of 1–7 birds, with records from three summers at Mvoti River mouth. It arrives November–December and departs March–April; a few remain in the austral winter, e.g. two at Marievale in 1997. It is often found at sewage works, especially on short grass.

		Summer			Winter		
		Mean	Max.	N	Mean	Max.	N
2534S 2814E	Rooiwal Sewage Works, Pretoria, Gauteng	25	47	4	0	0	5
2614S 2819E	Leeupan, Benoni, Gauteng	4	20	5	0	0	6
2923S 3121E	Umvoti River Estuary, Stanger, KwaZulu–Natal	2	4	3	0	0	5
2554S 2842E	Bronkhorstspruit Dam, Bronkhorstspruit, Gauteng	2	4	4	0	0	4
2750S 3035E	Blood River Vlei, Vryheid, KwaZulu–Natal	2	2	1	0	0	1
2804S 3227E	Lake St Lucia, Hlabisa, KwaZulu–Natal	1	7	6	0	0	6
2847S 3203E	Thulazihleka Pan, Richards Bay, KwaZulu–Natal	1	2	5	0	0	5
2621S 2830E	Marievale Bird Sanctuary, Nigel, Gauteng	0	0	5	0	2	5
2557S 2800E	Diepsloot Nature Reserve, Johannesburg, Gauteng	0	1	4	0	0	5

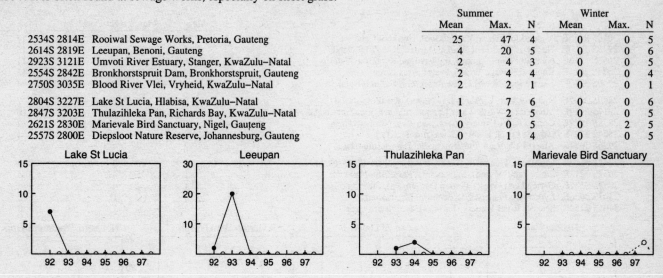

References

The abbreviation **ASAB** refers to **Harrison, J.A., Allan, D.G., Underhill, L.G., Herremans, M.** *et al.* (eds). 1997a. The atlas of southern African birds. Vols 1 & 2. Johannesburg: BirdLife South Africa.

Allan, D.G. 1988. Whiskered Terns *Chlidonius hybridus* breeding in the southeastern Transvaal highveld. Cormorant 16: 3–6.

Allan, D.G. 1990. Counting waterbirds – the Strandfontein example. Birding in Southern Africa 42: 9–12.

Allan, D.G. 1995. Observations on roosting Blue Cranes. Ostrich 66: 148–150.

Allan, D.G. 1996. Rietvlei – wetlands and cities can co-exist. Africa – Birds & Birding 1(2): 35–40.

Allan, D.G. 1999. Mega-developments and birds: the waterbirds impacted by the Lesotho Highlands Water Scheme as an example. In: Proceedings of the 22nd International Ornithological Congress, Durban. Adams, N.J. & Slotow, R.H. (eds). Johannesburg: BirdLife South Africa. pp. 1556–1578.

Allan, D.G. & Davies, G.B. 1999. The birds (Aves) of the middle Komati River valley. Durban Museum Novitates 24.

Allan, D.G. & Jenkins, A.R. 1993. A count of waterbirds along a section of the lower Orange River. Bontebok 8: 33–34.

Allan, D.G., Seaman, M.T. & Kalejta, K. 1995. The endorheic pans of South Africa. In: Wetlands of South Africa. Cowan, G.I. (ed.). Pretoria: Department of Environmental Affairs and Tourism. pp. 75–101.

Allan, D.G., Harrison, J.A., Herremans, M., Navarro, R.A. & Underhill, L.G. 1997. Southern African geography: its relevance to birds. In: Harrison, J.A., Allan, D.G., Underhill, L.G., Herremans, M. *et al.* (eds). The atlas of southern African birds. Vol. 1: Non-passerines. Johannesburg: BirdLife South Africa. pp. lxv–ci.

Allan, D.G., Sinclair, J.C. & Rossouw, J. 1999. The waterbirds (Aves) of Durban Bay: current status and historical trends. Durban Museum Novitates 24.

Arkell, G.B.F. 1979. Aspects of the feeding and breeding biology of the Giant Kingfisher. Ostrich 50: 176–181.

Ball, I.J., Frost, P.G.H., Siegfried, W.R. & McKinney, F. 1978. Territories and local movements of African Black Ducks. Wildfowl 29: 61–79.

Barnes, K.N. (ed.) 1998. The Important Bird Areas of southern Africa. Johannesburg: BirdLife South Africa.

Barnes, K.N. (ed.) 1999. Threatened birds of South Africa, Lesotho and Swaziland – 1999. Johannesburg: BirdLife South Africa.

Begg, G. 1978. The estuaries of Natal. Natal Town and Regional Planning Report 41. Pietermaritzburg: Natal Town and Regional Planning Commisssion.

Begg, G. 1988. The wetlands of Natal (Part 2). The distribution, extent, and status of wetlands in the Mfolozi catchment. Natal Town and Regional Planning Report 71. Pietermaritzburg: Natal Town and Regional Planning Commisssion.

Begg, G. 1989. The wetlands of Natal (Part 3). The location, status and function of the priority wetlands of Natal. Natal Town and Regional Planning Report 73. Pietermaritzburg: Natal Town and Regional Planning Commisssion.

Berruti, A. 1980a. Status and review of waterbirds breeding at Lake St Lucia. Lammergeyer 28: 1–19.

Berruti, A. 1980b. Birds of Lake St. Lucia. Southern Birds 8: 1–60.

Berruti, A. 1983. The biomass, energy consumption and breeding of waterbirds relative to hydrological conditions at Lake St Lucia. Ostrich 54: 65–82.

Boshoff, A.F. & Palmer, N.G. 1983. Aspects of the biology and ecology of the Osprey in the Cape Province. Ostrich 54: 189–204.

Boshoff, A.F., Palmer, N.G. & Piper, S.E. 1991a. Spatial and temporal abundance patterns of waterbirds in the southern Cape Province. Part 1: diving and surface predators. Ostrich 62: 156–177.

Boshoff, A.F., Palmer, N.G. & Piper, S.E. 1991b. Spatial and temporal abundance patterns of waterbirds in the southern Cape Province. Part 2: Waterfowl. Ostrich 62: 178–196.

Boshoff, A.F., Palmer, N.G. & Piper, S.E. 1991c. Spatial and temporal abundance patterns of waterbirds in the southern Cape Province. Part 3: Wading birds. Ostrich 62: 197–214.

Breen, C.M. & Begg, G.W. 1989. Conservation status of southern African wetlands. In: Biotic diversity in southern Africa: concepts of conservation. Huntley, B.J. (ed.). Cape Town: Oxford University Press.

Breen, C. M., Quinn, N. W. & Mander, J. J. 1997. Wetlands conservation and management in southern Africa: challenges and opportunities. Harare, Zimbabwe: IUCN/ROSA.pp. 254–263.

Broekhuysen, G.J. & Taylor, J.S. 1942. Some birds observed at Lake Mentz. Ostrich 13: 157–160.

Brooke, R.K. 1960. Waterfowl on the Free State goldfields. Ostrich 31: 27–79.

Brooke, R.K. 1984. South African Red Data book – birds. South African National Scientific Programmes Report 97. Pretoria: CSIR.

Brooke, R.K. 1992. The bird community of *Tamarix*-clad drainages, northwestern Karoo, Cape Province. Ostrich 63: 42–43.

Brown, A.C. & Jarman, N. 1978. Coastal marine habitats. In: Biogeography and ecology of southern Africa, Vol. 2. Werger, M.J.A. (ed.). The Hague: W. Junk. pp. 1239–1277.

Claassen, J. & Claassen, R. 1991. Voëls van Beaufort-Wes rioolwerke. Birding in Southern Africa 43: 85–86.

Collar, N.J., Crosby, M.J. & Stattersfield, A.J. 1994. Birds to watch 2. The world list of threatened birds. BirdLife Conservation Series 4. Cambridge: BirdLife International.

Connor, M.A. 1980. Development of energy and mineral resources and its effect on bird conservation in southern Africa. In: Proceedings of the Fourth Pan-African Ornithological Congress. pp. 389–406.

Cooper, J., Brooke, R.K., Cyrus, D.P., Martin, A.P., Taylor, R.H. & Williams, A.J. 1992. Distribution, population size and conservation of the Caspian Tern *Sterna caspia* in southern Africa. Ostrich 63: 58–67.

Cowan, G.I. 1995. South Africa and the Ramsar Convention. In: Wetlands of South Africa. Cowan, G.I. (ed.). Pretoria: Department of Environmental Affairs and Tourism.

Cowan, G.I. & van Riet, W. 1998. A directory of South African wetlands. Pretoria: Department of Environmental Affairs and Tourism. pp. 1–20.

Cramp, S., Simmons, K.E.L., Ferguson-Lees, I.J., Gillmor, R. *et al.* (eds). 1977. Handbook of the birds of Europe, the Middle East, and North Africa: the birds of the Western Palearctic. Vol. 1: Ostrich to ducks. Oxford: Oxford University Press.

Cramp, S., Simmons, K.E.L., Gillmor, R., Hollom, P.A. *et al.* (eds) 1980. Handbook of the birds of Europe, the Middle East, and North Africa: the birds of the Western Palearctic. Vol. 2: Hawks to bustards. Oxford: Oxford University Press.

Cramp, S., Simmons, K.E.L., Brooks, D.J., Collar, N.J. *et al.* (eds) 1983. Handbook of the birds of Europe, the Middle East, and North Africa: the birds of the Western Palearctic. Vol. 3: Waders to gulls. Oxford: Oxford University Press.

Cramp, S., Brooks, D.J., Dunn, E., Gillmor, R. *et al.* (eds). 1985. Handbook of the birds of Europe, the Middle East, and North Africa: the birds of the Western Palearctic. Vol. 4: Terns to woodpeckers. Oxford: Oxford University Press.

Davies, B.[R]. & Day, J.[N.] 1998. Vanishing waters. Rondebosch: University of Cape Town Press.

Davies, B.R., O'Keeffe, J.H. & Snaddon, C.D. 1993. A synthesis of the ecological functioning, conservation and management of South African river ecosystems. Water Research Commission Report TT 62/93.

Day, J.H. 1981. Summaries of current knowledge of 43 estuaries in southern Africa. In: Estuarine ecology with particular reference to southern Africa. Day, J.H. (ed.). Cape Town: A.A. Balkema. pp. 251–329.

Del Hoyo, J., Elliott, A., & Sargatal, J. (eds) 1992. Handbook of the birds of the world. Vol. 1: Ostrich to ducks. Barcelona: Lynx Edicions.

Del Hoyo, J., Elliott, A., & Sargatal, J. (eds) 1994. Handbook of the birds of the world. Vol. 2: New World vultures to guineafowl. Barcelona: Lynx Edicions.

Del Hoyo, J., Elliott, A., & Sargatal, J. (eds) 1996. Handbook of the birds of the world. Vol. 3: Hotazin to auks. Barcelona: Lynx Edicions.

Department of Water Affairs. 1986. Management of the water resources of the Republic of South Africa. Pretoria: Government Printer.

Dodman, T. 1997. A preliminary waterbird monitoring strategy for Africa: introduction and strategy. In: A preliminary waterbird monitoring strategy for Africa. Dodman, T. (ed.). Wetlands International Publication 43. Wageningen: Wetlands International. pp. 1–14.

Dodman, T. & Rose, P. 1997. Application of the African Waterfowl Census in estimating the distribution and abundance of African waterfowl. In: A preliminary waterbird monitoring strategy for Africa. Dodman, T. (ed.). Wetlands International Publication 43. Wageningen: Wetlands International. pp. 23–39.

Dodman, T. & Taylor, V. 1996. African waterfowl census 1996. Wageningen, the Netherlands: Wetlands International.

Eekhout, S., King, J.M. & Wackernagel, A. 1997. Classification of South African rivers. Vol. 1. Pretoria: Department of Environmental Affairs and Tourism.

Farkas, T. 1981. Bird communities of the False Upper Karoo. Memoirs of the National Museum (Bloemfontein) 16: 1–160.

Fishpool, L.D.C. (comp.) 1997. Important Bird Areas in Africa: IBA criteria: categories, species lists and population thresholds. Cambridge: BirdLife International.

Fry, C.H., Keith, S. & Urban, E.K. 1988. The birds of Africa. Vol. 3. London: Academic Press.

Geldenhuys, J.N. 1975. Waterfowl (Anatidae) on irrigation lakes on the Orange Free State. Ostrich 46: 219–235.

Geldenhuys, J.N. 1976. Breeding status of waterfowl at large lakes in the Orange Free State. Ostrich 47: 137–139.

Geldenhuys, J.N. 1980. Breeding ecology of the South African Shelduck in the southern Orange Free State. South African Journal of Wildlife Research 10: 94–111.

Geldenhuys, J.N. 1981. Moults and moult localities of the South African Shelduck. Ostrich 52: 129–134.

Geldenhuys, J.N. 1982. Classification of pans in the western Orange Free State according to vegetation structure, with reference to avifaunal communities. South African Journal of Wildlife Research 12: 55–62.

Geldenhuys, J.N. 1984. Status of Fish Eagle and Goliath Heron in the Orange Free State, South Africa. In: Proceedings of the Fifth Pan-African Ornithological Congress. Johannesburg: SAOS. pp. 577–587.

Guillet, A. & Crowe, T.M. 1987. Monthly and seasonal changes in the aquatic avifauna at Rondevlei Bird Sanctuary (Cape Province, South Africa). Avocetta 11: 1–16.

Harrison, J.A., Allan, D.G., Underhill, L.G., Herremans, M. et al. (eds). 1997a. The atlas of southern African birds. Vol. 1: Non-passerines. Johannesburg: BirdLife South Africa.

Harrison, J.A., Allan, D.G., Underhill, L.G., Herremans, M. et al. (eds). 1997b. The atlas of southern African birds. Vol. 2: Passerines. Johannesburg: BirdLife South Africa.

Hart, R.C. 1995. South African coastal lakes. In: Wetlands of South Africa. Cowan, G.I. (ed.). Pretoria: Department of Environmental Affairs and Tourism. pp. 103–130.

Heydorn, A.E.F. 1989. The conservation status of southern African estuaries. In: Biotic diversity in southern Africa – concepts and conservation. Huntley, B.J. (ed.). Cape Town: Oxford University Press. pp. 290–297.

Heydorn, A.E.F. & Tinley, K.L. 1980. Estuaries of the Cape. Part 1. Synopsis of the Cape Coast: natural features, dynamics and utilization. Stellenbosch: Council for Scientific and Industrial Research.

Heyl, C.W. 1988. Waterbird numbers from Rocherpan, south-western Cape. South African National Scientific Programmes Report 157. Pretoria: CSIR. pp. 158–162.

Heyl, C.W. & Currie, M.H. 1985. Variations in the use of the Bot River estuary by waterbirds. Transactions of the Royal Society of South Africa 45: 397–417.

Higgins, S.I., Coetzee, M.A.S., Marneweck, G.C. & Rogers, K.H. 1996. The Nyl river floodplain, South Africa, as a functional unit of the landscape: a review of current information. African Journal of Ecology 34: 131–145.

Hockey, P.A.R. & Douie, C. 1995. Waders of southern Africa. Cape Town: Struik Wincester.

Hockey, P.A.R., Siegfried, W.R., Crowe, A.A. & Cooper, J. 1983. Ecological structure and energy requirements of the sandy beach avifauna of southern Africa. In: Sandy beaches as ecosystems. McLachlan, A. & Erasmus, T. (eds). The Hague: Dr W. Junk. pp. 507–521.

Hockey, P.A.R., Brooke, R.K., Cooper, J., Sinclair, J.C. & Tree, A.J. 1986. Rare and vagrant scolacipid waders in southern Africa. Ostrich 57: 37–55.

Hockey, P.A.R., Underhill, L.G., Neatherway, M. & Ryan, P.R. 1989. Atlas of the birds of the southwestern Cape. Cape Town: Cape Bird Club.

Johnson, D.N. 1992. The status of cranes in Natal in 1992. In: Proceedings of the First Southern African Crane Conference. Porter, D.J. et al. (eds). Durban: Southern African Crane Foundation. pp. 20–28.

Junor, F.J.R. & Marshall, B.E. 1987. Factors influencing the abundance of piscivorous birds on Lake Kyle, Zimbabwe. Ostrich 58: 168–175.

Kalejta-Summers, B., Allan, D.G. & Longrigg, T.D. in press a. Long-term trends, seasonal abundance and energy consumption of waterbirds at Rietvlei, Western Cape, South Africa, 1953–1993. Ostrich.

Kalejta-Summers, B., McCarthy, M. & Underhill, L.G. in press b. Long-term trends, seasonal abundance and energy consumption of waterbirds at Strandfontein, Western Cape, South Africa. Ostrich.

Keith, S., Urban, E.K. & Fry, C.H. 1992. The birds of Africa. Vol. 4. London: Academic Press.

Kok, O.B. & Roos, Z.N. 1979. Die avifauna van Seekoeivlei, Memel. Southern Birds 7: 1–28.

Kotze, D.C. & Breen, C.M. 1994. Agricultural land-use impacts on wetland functional values. Water Research Commission Report 501/3/94. Pietermaritzburg: Department of Grassland Science, University of Natal.

Kotze, D.C., Breen, C.M. & Quinn, N. 1995. Wetland losses in South Africa. In: Wetlands of South Africa. Cowan, G.I. (ed.). Pretoria: Department of Environmental Affairs and Tourism. pp. 263–272.

Liversidge, R. 1958. The bird population of the dams of the Orange Free State Goldfields. Ostrich 29: 107–109.

Liversidge, R. 1962. Further notes on the wildfowl of the O.F.S. Goldfields. Ostrich 33: 29–32.

Maclean, G.L. 1993. Roberts' birds of southern Africa. Cape Town: The Trustees of the John Voelcker Bird Book Fund.

Macdonald, I.A.W. 1989. Man's role in changing the face of southern Africa. In: Biotic diversity in southern Africa: concepts and conservation. Huntley, B.J. (ed.). Cape Town: Oxford University Press. pp. 51–77.

Martin, A.P. & Baird, D. 1987. Seasonal abundance and distribution of birds on the Swartkops estuary, Port Elizabeth. Ostrich 58: 122–134.

Martin, A.P. & Randall, R.M. 1987. Numbers of birds at a commercial saltpan, and suggestions for management. South African Journal of Wildlife Research 17: 75–81.

McLachlan, A., Wooldridge, K., Schramm, M. & Kuhn, M. 1980. Seasonal abundance, biomass and feeding of shore birds on the sandy beaches in the eastern Cape, South Africa. Ostrich 51: 44–52.

Meine, C.D. & Archibald, G.W. (eds) 1996. The cranes – status survey and conservation action plan. Gland, Switzerland and Cambridge, United Kingdom: IUCN.

Monadjem, A. 1996. Habitat associations of birds along the Sabie River, South Africa. African Journal of Ecology 34: 75–78.

Milstein, P. le S. 1975. The biology of Barberspan, with special reference to the avifauna. Ostrich Supplement 12: 1–74.

Mulder, H., Breytenbach, N., Lotter, L., Louw, E. et al. 1993. Watervoëls van die O.P.M. Prozesky-Voëlreservaat. Birding in

Southern Africa 45: 60–61.

Mundy, P., Butchart, D., Ledger, J. & Piper, S. 1992. The vultures of Africa. Randburg and Halfway House: Acorn Books and Russel Friedman Books.

Noble, R.G. & Hemens, J. 1978. Inland water ecosystems in South Africa – a review of research needs. South African National Scientific Programmes Report 34. Pretoria: CSIR.

O'Keeffe, J.H. (ed.) undated. The conservation status of South African rivers. Mowbray, Cape Town: The Chief Directorate of Surveys and Mapping.

O'Keeffe, J.H., Davies, B.R., King, J.M. & Skelton, P.H. 1989. The conservation status of southern African rivers. In: Biotic diversity in southern Africa: concepts and conservation. Huntley, B.J. (ed.). Cape Town: Oxford University Press. pp. 266–289.

Parris, R. 1984. Pans, rivers and artificial waterholes in the protected areas of the southwestern Kalahari. Koedoe Supplement: 63–82.

Pringle, J.S. & Cooper, J. 1977. Wader populations (Charadrii) on the marine littoral of the Cape Peninsula, South Africa. Ostrich 48: 98–105.

Rogers, K.H. 1995. Riparian wetlands. In: Wetlands of South Africa, Cowan, G.I. (ed.). Pretoria: Department of Environmental Affairs and Tourism. pp. 41–52.

Rose, P. 1997. Uses of the African Waterfowl Census. In: A preliminary waterbird monitoring strategy for Africa, T. Dodman (ed.). Wetlands International Publication 43. Wageningen, the Netherlands: Wetlands International. pp. 19–22.

Ryan, P.G. & Cooper, J. 1985. Waders (Charadrii) and other coastal birds of the northwestern Cape Province, South Africa. Bontebok 4: 1–18,

Ryan, P.G., Cooper, J., Hockey, P.A.R. & Berruti, A. 1986. Waders (Charadrii) and other water birds on the coast and adjacent wetlands of Natal, 1980–81. Lammergeyer 36: 1–33.

Ryan, P.G., Underhill, L.G., Cooper, J. & Waltner, M. 1988. Waders (Charadrii) and other waterbirds on the coast, adjacent wetlands and offshore islands of the southwestern Cape Province, South Africa. Bontebok 6: 1–19.

Schwabe, C.A. 1995. Alpine mires in the eastern highlands of Lesotho. In: Wetlands of South Africa. Cowan, G.I. (ed.). Pretoria: Department of Environmental Affairs and Tourism. pp. 33–40.

Shewell, E.L. 1950. Birds of the Gamtoos estuary. Ostrich 21: 97–102.

Siegfried, W.R. 1967. Trapping and ringing of Egyptian Geese and African Shelduck at Vogelvlei, Cape. Ostrich 38: 173–178.

Siegfried, W.R. 1970. Wildfowl distribution, conservation and research in southern Africa. Wildfowl 21: 89–98.

Siegfried, W.R. 1981. The estuarine avifauna of southern Africa. In: Estuarine ecology with particular reference to southern Africa, Day, J.H. (ed.). Cape Town: A.A. Balkema. pp. 223–250.

Spearpoint, J.A., Every, B. & Underhill, L.G. 1988. Waders (Charadrii) and other shorebirds at Cape Recife, Algoa Bay, South Africa: seasonality, trends, conservation, and reliability of surveys. Ostrich 59: 166–177.

Steinke, T.D. 1995. A general review of the mangroves of South Africa. In: Wetlands of South Africa, Cowan, G.I. (ed.). Pretoria: Department of Environmental Affairs and Tourism. pp. 53–73.

Summers, R.W. 1977. Distribution, abundance and energy relationships of waders (Aves: Charadrii) at Langebaan Lagoon. Proceedings of the Royal Society of South Africa. 42: 483–495.

Summers, R.W., Pringle, J.S. & Cooper, J. 1976. The status of coastal waders in the south-western Cape, South Africa. Cape Town: Western Cape Wader Study Group.

Summers, R.W., Cooper, J. & Pringle, J.S. 1977. Distribution and numbers of coastal waders (Charadrii) in the southwestern Cape, South Africa, summer 1975/76. Ostrich 48: 85–97.

Summers, R.W., Underhill, L.G., Pearson, D.J. & Scott, D.A. 1987. Wader migration systems in southern and eastern Africa and western Asia. Wader Study Group Bulletin 49, Supplement/IWRB Special Publication 7: 15–34.

Summers, R.W., Underhill, L.G. & Prys-Jones, R.P. 1995. Why do young waders in southern Africa delay their first return migration to the breeding grounds? Ardea 83: 351–357.

Tarboton, W.R. 1977. The status of communal herons, ibis and cormorants on the Witwatersrand. South African Journal of Wildlife Research 7: 19–25.

Tarboton, W.R. 1987. The Nyl floodplain: its significance, phenology and conservation status. In: Ecology and conservation of wetlands in South Africa. Walmsley, R.D. & Botten, M.L. (eds). Occasional Report Series 28: 101–104. Pretoria: FRD, CSIR.

Tarboton, W.R. 1992. The population status of the Crowned Crane in the Transvaal. In: Proceedings of the First Southern African Crane Conference. Porter, D.J. et al. (eds). Durban: Southern African Crane Foundation. pp. 10–19.

Tarboton, W.R. & Allan, D.G. 1984. The status and conservation of birds of prey in the Transvaal. Transvaal Museum Monographs 3.

Tarboton, W.R., Kemp, M.I. & Kemp, A.C. 1987a. Birds of the Transvaal. Pretoria: Transvaal Museum.

Tarboton, W.R., Barnes, P.R. & Johnson, D.J. 1987b. The Wattled Crane in South Africa during 1978–82. In: Proceedings of the 1983 International Crane Workshop. Archibald, G.W. & Pasquier, R.F. (eds). Baraboo, Wisconsin: International Crane Foundation. pp. 353–361.

Taylor, J.S. 1945. Lake Mentz revisited. Ostrich 16: 217–218.

Taylor, J.S. 1947. Further notes on the birds of Lake Mentz. Ostrich 18: 51–53.

Taylor, P.B. 1994. The biology, ecology and conservation of four flufftail species, Sarothrura (Aves: Rallidae). Unpubl. PhD thesis. University of Natal, Pietermaritzburg.

Taylor, P.B. 1997a. The status and conservation of Rallids in South Africa: results of a wetland survey in 1995/96. ADU Research Report 23. Cape Town: Avian Demography Unit, University of Cape Town.

Taylor, P.B. 1997b. South African palustrine wetlands: the results of a survey in summer 1995/96. ADU Research Report 24. Cape Town: Avian Demography Unit, University of Cape Town.

Turpie, J.K. 1995. Prioritizing South African estuaries for conservation: a practical example using waterbirds. Biological Conservation 74: 175–185.

Underhill, L.G. 1987. Waders (Charadrii) and other waterbirds at Langebaan Lagoon, South Africa. Ostrich 58: 145–155.

Underhill, L.G. 1995. Migratory birds. In: Wetlands of South Africa. Cowan, G.I. (ed.). Pretoria: Department of Environmental Affairs and Tourism. pp. 163–177.

Underhill, L.G. & Cooper, J. 1984a. Counts of waterbirds at coastal wetlands in southern Africa. Unpubl. report, Western Cape Wader Study Group, Cape Town.

Underhill, L.G. & Cooper, J. 1984b. Counts of waterbirds on the coastline of southern Africa. Unpubl. report, Western Cape Wader Study Group, Cape Town.

Underhill, L.G., Cooper, J. & Waltner, M. 1980. The status of waders (Charadrii) and other birds in the coastal region of the southern and eastern Cape, summer 1978/79. Cape Town: Western Cape Wader Study Group.

Urban, E.K., Fry, C.H. & Keith, S. 1986. The birds of Africa. Vol. 2. London: Academic Press.

Van Zyl, B.J. 1991. The lower Orange River. Madoqua 17: 155–157.

Velásquez, C.R., Kalejta, B. & Hockey, P.A.R. 1991. Seasonal abundance, habitat selection and energy consumption of waterbirds at the Berg River estuary, South Africa. Ostrich 62: 109–123.

Weiss, Y. 1997. Rough diamond – Paarl Bird Sanctuary. Africa – Birds & Birding 1(5): 60–63.

Whitfield, A.K. & Blaber, S.J.M. 1978. Feeding ecology of piscivorous birds at Lake St Lucia. Part 1: Diving birds. Ostrich 49: 185–198.

Whitfield, A.K. & Blaber, S.J.M. 1979a. Feeding ecology of piscivorous birds at Lake St Lucia. Part 2: Wading birds. Ostrich 50: 1–9.

Whitfield, A.K. & Blaber, S.J.M. 1979b. Feeding ecology of piscivorous birds at Lake St Lucia. Part 3: Diving birds. Ostrich 49: 10–20.

Williams, A.J. 1986. Wetland birds at the Orange River mouth and their conservation significance. Bontebok 5: 17–23.

Williams, A.J. & Randall, R.M. 1995. Pelecaniform birds in South African wetlands. In: Wetlands in South Africa. Cowan, G.I. (ed.). Pretoria: Department of Environmental Affairs and Tourism. pp. 147–161.

Winterbottom, J.M. 1972. The ecological distribution of birds in southern Africa. Cape Town: Percy FitzPatrick Institute of African Ornithology.